PRINTING
AND
THE MIND
OF MAN

PRINTING AND
THE MIND OF MAN

———

LONDON
CASSELL AND COMPANY

NEW YORK
HOLT, RINEHART AND WINSTON

PRINTING
AND
THE MIND
OF MAN

A DESCRIPTIVE CATALOGUE ILLUSTRATING THE IMPACT OF PRINT ON THE EVOLUTION OF WESTERN CIVILIZATION DURING FIVE CENTURIES

COMPILED AND EDITED BY
JOHN CARTER & PERCY H. MUIR
ASSISTED BY NICOLAS BARKER
H. A. FEISENBERGER, HOWARD NIXON
AND S. H. STEINBERG

WITH AN
INTRODUCTORY ESSAY BY
DENYS HAY

PREFACE

A brief account of the evolution of this book is necessary to the reader's understanding, dutiful to historical record, and obligatory upon editors gratefully conscious of their many debts. It is divided into three sections: (I) the original exhibition, (II) the development into a book, with some notes on editorial method and formula, (III) acknowledgements.

I. THE IPEX EXHIBITION OF 1963

Printing and the Mind of Man, as it was in due course entitled, originated in a suggestion made about the turn of the year 1961/2 by Mr Stanley Morison. Preparations were then in train for the eleventh International Printing Machinery and Allied Trades Exhibition, due to be held in London in July 1963; and it was Mr Morison's notion that what promised to be (and was) the largest industrial and technical display of its kind ever mounted even under two roofs (IPEX '63 filled both Earls Court and Olympia) presented an opportunity, not to be missed, of illustrating to the printing industry its own historical evolution and of reminding the general public what western civilization owes to print.

This imaginative, doubly educative, and admittedly ambitious project called for a threefold approach. The invention of printing with movable types, by Johann Gutenberg of Mainz in the fifth decade of the fifteenth century, was crucial to the whole evolution of western civilization during the ensuing five hundred years; for the printing press furnished the means of repeatable precision of text and the capacity for mass circulation of ideas. It was our aspiration to illustrate, for the first time in a coherent display,[1] the internal development of the invention, in the technical progress of printing as a craft; its external development, in the significant achievements of printing (and illustration) as an applied art; and, beyond these limits, the impact of printing on the mind of man, with consequent effect on his history. In the early memoranda these three sectors were denominated *technique*, *aesthetic* and *impact*; but while it was obvious that each would require a corps of specialists for effective deployment, we were determined that they should as nearly as possible form a single front.

[1] A partial attempt had, indeed, been made in the Gutenberg Quincentenary exhibition at Cambridge in 1940. This was a suggestive forerunner for several sections in our display, and its invigorating catalogue was a constant friend.

The structure of such a projected historical annexe to IPEX '63 was now taking shape. But it was still no more than a project. *Why*, it might be asked (and was asked), should an association of shrewd and powerful industrialists, engaged on a very expensive, toughly competitive international trade exhibition, waste time and space, let alone money, on a 'cultural' sideshow dreamed up by a couple of visionary antiquarians? The keys to the answer—why *not*?—proved to be two: first, the mesmeric authority of Stanley Morison as an acknowledged mentor of the printing trade; second, the personality of Jack Matson of the Monotype Corporation, then President of the Association. Mr Matson's full-blooded yet thoroughly hard-headed enthusiasm for *Printing and the Mind of Man* communicated itself so effectively to his colleagues that the Association promptly offered us, with the cordial support of IPEX '63's organizers, Messrs F. W. Bridges & Co., not only 12,000 square feet of prime space at Earls Court but also the entire cost of preparation, assembly, insurance[1] and installation of the exhibition, and of the production of the catalogue. All this on our note of hand alone.

The initial vision and enthusiasm of our sponsors, their confident generosity, their steady administrative support during the succeeding fifteen months of hard work, with its normal quota of executive and financial crises, deserved, and was accorded, the unstinted gratitude not only of its immediate beneficiaries, the committees later charged with preparing the tripartite exhibition, but also of the interested public, lay as well as professional, of at least two continents. In a perceptive critique of the show Mr James M. Wells, of the Newberry Library, Chicago, saluted 'the enormous sense of public service displayed by the Association...in so handsomely underwriting a cultural undertaking which could not possibly return any cash profit'. Echoes of this salute have come from thousands of appreciative readers of the 200-page catalogue, which was published at an almost nominal price. And the editors of the present volume take this opportunity of contributing, *fortissimo*, to the still-reverberating chorus.

The projectors to whom these joint sponsors were confiding the responsibility for realizing *Printing and the Mind of Man* by now included Sir Frank Francis, Director and Principal Librarian of the British Museum. This was an accession of special weight; and not merely for Sir Frank's personal energy and resource, nor even for the prestige of his high office and the umbrella of respectability which the connexion would throw over an enterprise that must involve borrowing precious objects from dutifully cautious owners or custodians. (The British Museum sounds much more reassuring, whether at Windsor or Wolfenbüttel, than Earls Court.) For the obvious place for the aesthetic section of the exhibition, and the only place in England where most (though not, as it turned out, all) of the books needed for it could be found under one roof, was, of course, Bloomsbury; and here Sir Frank turned the third key. The Trustees not only responded cordially to a project involving the entire exhibition space in the King's Library: they also accepted responsibility for housing in transit,

---

[1] The British Museum does not insure. But the total for the printed books, only, at Earls Court ran well over a million pounds.

under Mr Howard Nixon's experienced direction, loans from the many institutional libraries and private collectors, at home and abroad, to the Earls Court exhibition.[1]

In March 1962, then, a Supervisory Committee of five was formally constituted, with Mr Matson in the chair, Robert Boardman representing Messrs Bridges, the organizers, and Francis Reed as executive secretary. In the course of the first meeting, and increasingly during its score of successors, the three projectors learned how fortunate they were in their colleagues. Mr Reed was a model of understanding efficiency, ever patient with the quiddities of the specialists who shortly gathered with us. No organizational or financial problem could ruffle the urbanity or defeat the ingenuity of Mr Boardman. And when, at Dr Robert Birley's inaugural lecture on *Printing and Democracy*,[2] Mr Matson was saluted as the best committee chairman since the late Lord Waverley, there were those who could have spared even that exalted qualification.

The Supervisory Committee's first task, after general strategy had been agreed, was to enlist executives and expert staff for the technical and historical sub-committees: the aesthetic section was to be entrusted to a team of members of the Department of Printed Books at the British Museum, designated and directed by Sir Frank. Now, therefore, Charles Batey, formerly Printer to the University of Oxford and a member of the Council of the Institute of Printing, was officially gazetted to the command of the technical committee, with Harry Carter, of the University Press, Oxford, as his adjutant; and Percy Muir, bibliographer and antiquarian bookseller, to the historical. We were further fortunate in recruiting to these two committees the groups of distinguished experts whose names are emblazoned on p. ix. Liaison between the three executive sub-committees was effected by the presence on each of the two concerned with Earls Court of a senior member of the British Museum staff, and by the attachment to the aesthetic sub-committee of John Dreyfus, typographical adviser to the Monotype Corporation and to the Cambridge University Press, who also acted, when the time came, as chairman of the editorial sub-committee responsible for the production of the catalogues by the Oxford University Press.

Once a month the chairmen reported to the Supervisory Committee, where work in progress was closely and stringently discussed and many a kite flown only to bite the dust. As D-Day drew near we were commonly joined by our designer, John Lansdell, whose imaginative eye and skilled hand were to give so lively a visual presentation to much inherently intractable material. The 1817 Columbian Press, with its cast-iron eagle acting as an adjustable counter-weight, or Harry Carter in his smock engraving a punch, the brilliant

---

[1] Headed by Her Majesty the Queen, the roster of lenders to the exhibition—often of fragile as well as precious objects necessary to our purpose—numbered over a hundred and sixty. It ranged from Austin, Texas, to Zürich, from Insch, Fife, to Uppsala, from Morristown, New Jersey, to Wolverhampton. Four preponderant contributors require special mention: the late Ian Fleming, King's College, Cambridge (mostly from the Maynard Keynes collections), the Lilly Library of Indiana University, and the Oxford University Press. And this is the proper place to record two special debts: to Dr A. N. L. Munby, Fellow and Librarian of King's, not only for the College's generosity but also for much sage advice in the early stages; and to Professor David Randall, Lilly Librarian, who became in effect a corresponding member of the historical sub-committee and acted as our recruiting agent for a majority of the American loans to the exhibition.

[2] Given in connexion with the exhibition at the Royal Institution and later printed for the Monotype Corporation.

patterns of the *editio princeps* of Euclid or the regal splendour of the Mainz *Psalter*—these spoke unassisted to the eye of the visitor. But the original printing of Bracton on the common law or Stevin on the decimal system, of Harvey on the circulation of the blood or Milton on the freedom of the press, of Beccaria on crime and punishment or the Declaration of Independence, of Clausewitz on war or Einstein on relativity, of *Hansard* or Kierkegaard's *Either/Or* or *The Communist Manifesto*: these and a hundred like them called for some ingenuity of presentation if the eye was to be held while the mind began to absorb their significance.

The discussion, selection, re-discussion, approval, location, borrowing and (last but not least) annotation of all this material involved more than a year's hard and expert work by the sub-committees, in and out of session. And no paragraph of the Supervisory Committee's preface to the exhibition catalogue came more directly from the heart than the last. 'Finally', it read, 'we wish to record our grateful admiration for the arduous and unremitting labours of the members of the executive sub-committees. . . They have somehow found time in the midst of busy professional lives to fulfil every demand imposed upon them by their indefatigable chairmen at the behest of an exacting "general staff".'

That *Printing and the Mind of Man* was a success with the general public is by now a matter of history. Especially gratifying to those responsible for it was the evidence that it had succeeded also in our hope of drawing the attention of members of the industry itself to the illustrious heritage of their craft. Not only squads of apprentices and printing-school students but, as the all-too-short ten days went by, increasing numbers from the thousands of specialist staff on duty at the exhibition stands at Earls Court and Olympia could be found in enthralled contemplation of the Caxton *Indulgence* of 1476 or the first edition of Newton's *Principia*, the copper plates for the ornaments in Clarendon's *History of the Rebellion*, 1702, or Marconi's original patent for wireless telegraphy.

II. EXPANSION

So much for *Printing and the Mind of Man* as an exhibition annexed to IPEX '63.

Now, it had been the projectors' intention from the first, as the original manifesto bears witness, that the exhibition catalogue (truly remarkable instrument as it proved to be) should be followed in due course by an ampler exposition of its content than was possible in an octavo guidebook. Accordingly, at the penultimate meeting of the Supervisory Committee in September 1963 preliminary plans to this end were searchingly discussed. It was agreed that the catalogue of the British Museum section[1] was in no need of textual amplification: 'with its bridge-passages making a running commentary to the often substantial entry-descriptions' it struck one reviewer, despite some weaknesses in the nineteenth-century section, as 'an extraordinarily good short history of the development of typography and book illustration in the western world'. It could, indeed, have been more fully illustrated, in a larger format; but there are plenty of historical albums of typographical examples available,

[1] Still (1967) obtainable from the British Museum's Publication Department.

ADMINISTRATION OF THE PRINTING AND THE MIND OF MAN EXHIBITION AT IPEX 1963

SUPERVISORY COMMITTEE

R. W. BOARDMAN; JOHN CARTER, C.B.E.
SIR FRANK FRANCIS, K.C.B.; J. MATSON, C.B.E.
STANLEY MORISON

Executive Secretary: F. E. G. REED

BRITISH MUSEUM COMMITTEE

SIR FRANK FRANCIS, K.C.B., *Director and Principal Librarian*
R. A. WILSON, *Principal Keeper, Department of Printed Books*
DAVID FOXON; HOWARD NIXON; GEORGE D. PAINTER
JULIAN ROBERTS; D. E. RHODES; MARGARET SCHEELE
JOHN DREYFUS

HISTORICAL COMMITTEE

PERCY H. MUIR
H. A. FEISENBERGER; S. H. STEINBERG; NICOLAS BARKER
HOWARD NIXON *of the British Museum*

TECHNICAL COMMITTEE

CHARLES BATEY, O.B.E., J.P.
HARRY CARTER, O.B.E.; MISS P. M. HANDOVER; ELLIC HOWE
JAMES MORAN; JAMES MOSLEY; MRS BEATRICE WARDE
DAVID FOXON *of the British Museum*

EDITORIAL COMMITTEE

JOHN DREYFUS
NICOLAS BARKER; CHARLES BATEY, O.B.E., J.P.

and we all concurred in Bloomsbury's view that since the meat here was in the text it would be useless ostentation to produce yet another.

The technical and historical sections had been interwoven at Earl's Court. Thus the visitor could follow in a single perambulation both the technical course which runs from Gutenberg and the first movable type, through Blaeu, Stanhope, Koenig, Mergenthaler, Lanston, to George Westover and the other pioneers of filmsetting without the use of any type at all; and also a selection, to the number of more than 400 entries, of those printed works, from Thomas Aquinas and Copernicus to Rutherford and Einstein, which might be called the decisive battles against ignorance and darkness in the history of mankind. The catalogue of necessity followed the same pattern. But we were agreed that in any proposed amplification the two sections must be treated separately. The difficulty of effective expansion of the technical entries, even with their series of introductions, when divorced from the actual exhibits, would not escape any attentive reader of the catalogue. It was made forcibly clear to us by the responsible experts: and the various possibilities which emerged in discussion were remanded for further consideration.

No such editorial dilemma inhibited our resolution in respect of the historical section. This had been arranged, and should remain, in chronological order. What was now required was a sufficient expansion of the descriptive formula, a suitable increase in the number of illustrations, and a substantial enlargement of the annotation. This last had been restricted in the catalogue to 80/100 words for each entry; and, brilliant examples of succinct exposition as these notes were generally acclaimed to be, the now projected book demanded much fuller treatment throughout. Yet if the objective was clear, the means to achieve it had still to be organized; and the Supervisory Committee decided to entrust this task to the present writers as joint editors. We were in no doubt of the team we wanted: the same scholarly quartet who had been our colleagues on the historical sub-committee. But, deservedly flushed as they might be with the success of the exhibition and its catalogue, could these gentlemen be induced, after very little respite, to sign on for another year and more's hard labour? The fact that, despite the expectation (amply fulfilled) that the labour would be even harder and its term even longer, every one of them re-enlisted is, surely, a striking testimony to the loyalty and devotion which *Printing and the Mind of Man* had somehow, from its very inception, inspired in the large and widely various collection of professionals who were in one capacity or another connected with it.

In December 1963 the imminently disbanding Supervisory Committee confirmed, and in due course the Association and Messrs Bridges, as sponsors of our exhibition and its catalogue, formally ratified, the delegation to the joint editors of the honourable responsibility for producing the promised book on the impact of print. And here, more than three years later, it is.

Printing and the Mind of Man was, and this book is, directly concerned only with the western world, even though western ideas have taken fertile root in every continent. The selection of printed works here discussed is therefore deliberately confined (with few exceptions) to Greek and Latin, the foundation tongues of western civilization, and the languages of Europe, of which in this context the British Isles may be considered to form a part, and the Western Hemisphere an extension. One probably general criticism we must forestall. Creative literature has elevated and inspired the *spirit* of man. But examples here have been restricted, again with a few exceptions, to the propagation of ideas (e.g. *Candide*, *Alice in Wonderland*) or characters (e.g. Hamlet or Faust) which have sensibly affected his *thinking* and thence his actions. Our task has necessarily been that of exclusion rather than inclusion, and no doubt each reader will make his own list of deplorable omissions.

Within these limitations, imposed or self-imposed, it had been the aim of the original historical sub-committee to achieve a representative conspectus. Candidates for inclusion in the canon had to be justified by their proposer (and thus potential expositor) to the whole committee; and the stringency of this screening may be judged by the fact that the eventually agreed list, as ratified by the Supervisory Committee, was the sixteenth of the series. Before transfer from the exhibition catalogue to this book the list was again reviewed, in the light not only of our own later thoughts but also of criticisms and suggestions from outside. It was decided that there should be no extrusions. But in certain cases (e.g. 168, 189, 390) we have substituted as the main entry a more representative publication by the author included or an edition more significant for our purpose than the one exhibited; in others (e.g. 155, 278, 307) we have combined two entries under one heading; in a number of cases (e.g. 232, 302, 316) we have added, as sub-entries, publications by other authors, for the fuller exposition of the subject; and there are twelve additional entries, which are indicated by an asterisk.

This readjusted framework had now to be clothed. The catalogue notes were notes and no more: our duty here, as we saw it, was to supply, in as full measure as seemed appropriate to each case, background and perspective as well as analysis and exposition; that is to say, to expand a carefully considered list of landmarks, furnished with annotation sufficient to explain why we had chosen them, into a book which could be not merely consulted but read. Thus, while each of the 424 entries has been written by a specialist and scrutinized by one or more other specialists (some have been rewritten as many as four times), each was also scrutinized in draft by the other members of the team—experts maybe in other fields but not in the one concerned—each of whom maintained throughout, and ruthlessly, the posture of the uninstructed layman seeking instruction in plainly intelligible terms.

That the facts should be accurate, the commentary reliable, and the judgements balanced has been, of course, the editors' prime concern; and our indebtedness in this respect to outside experts is acknowledged on a later page. But while we hope (probably vainly) to satisfy the specialists, this book is intended for the edification of those general readers who are, or can be, interested in the history of ideas, the advance of science and technology, the evolution of philosophy, theology, politics, economics, sociology, jurisprudence, education, historiography, linguistics, and the rest, *as conveyed in print*.

Accordingly, the descriptive formula is designed for the accurate identification of the entry, and no more. This is not a bibliographical reference book; and we have aimed at precision without pedantry. Authors' names are given in their most easily recognizable form, without square brackets for the pseudonymous and anonymous; titles are abbreviated; imprints are generally of printers for earlier, of publishers for later entries. Translations of titles from languages other than English are set, in the commentary, within quotation marks. In transcribing titles we have retained (in defiance of Dr Steinberg and the expectable disapprobation of other professional scholars and bibliographers) the traditional capitalization of the important words: e.g. *De Motu Cordis*, not *De motu cordis*, *The Pilgrim's Progress*, not *The pilgrim's progress*. The names of the more familiar European cities are given (at risk of the accusation of insularity) in the form commonly used in English, the language in which this book is written: e.g. Venice, not Venezia; Brussels, not Bruxelles; Nuremberg, not Nürnberg; Basle, not Basel or Bâle. Bibliographical references are given where, but only where, they seemed strictly necessary.

The entries are, as in the exhibition, chronologically arranged. They have of necessity (since the exhibition catalogue included technical material) been renumbered. Entries of the same year are listed alphabetically by author unless priority within the year is evident. Cross-references are normally given by a bracketed entry-number.

In selecting the illustrations (from about 400 photostats) we aimed, not at highlighting the most important entries—a hopeless rather than merely a presumptuous notion—but at variety, unfamiliarity, and the visual diversification of the otherwise rather severe double-columned pages. The photographs for the line-blocks all came from the British Museum except those for 32 (New York Public Library), 46, 79, 178 and 308 (University Library, Cambridge), 159 (Royal College of Surgeons), 271 (King's College, Cambridge), 323 and 398 (London University) and 356 (Burndy Library, Norwalk, Conn.); and they are reproduced by courtesy of the appropriate authorities.

III. ACKNOWLEDGEMENTS

The editors, and those formally associated with them in the preparation of this book, are much indebted for expert assistance with a number of the more specialized entries to Professor A. Rupert Hall and Dr G. J. Whitrow of the Imperial College of Science and Technology, Professor Denys Hay of Edinburgh University, Mr D. M. Knight of the University of Durham, Dr F. N. L. Poynter, Director of the Wellcome Historical Medical Library, Mr A. Hyatt King of the British Museum, Mr C. Harvard Gibbs-Smith of the Victoria and Albert Museum, Mr Robert Race, Mr G. Allen Hutt, Mr G. N. Sharp, Mr Ryland Davis, Professor David Randall and Mr W. R. Cagle of Indiana University, the last of whom contributed many of the American entries.

The preparation of the index, a task as formidable as it was indispensable to a book of this kind, was entrusted to Mrs Howard Nixon. Mr M. R. Perkin of the University of London Library was responsible for checking the titles and imprints. Mr R. H. Read maintained a steady rhythm for the outgoing and incoming drafts which have for more than two years been circulating through the operational headquarters at Takeley; and he was a meticulous scrutineer of the proofs. Mr John Dreyfus, a veteran of the Earls Court catalogue, has been equally invaluable, and twice as ingenious, in planning the layout and production details of its enlarged successor. Mr Reynolds Stone's incomparable graver was enlisted for the majestic title-pages.

To all these the editors offer their hearty thanks. To Professor Hay we are especially grateful for his provision of the introductory essay. This was not intended to be an 'introduction' in the sense that its writer was expected to approve either the selection of entries here presented or the details of their exposition (however fruitful his comments on the latter). It is, rather, a discourse preparatory to, and elucidatory of, the book's general theme: the impact of printing on the mind of man.

As for our learned colleagues, Messrs Barker, Feisenberger, Nixon and Steinberg, we can but echo, with increased resonance, the sentiments earlier expressed by the Supervisory Committee for the exhibition from which this book derives. If their exertions in its preparation were—and indeed they were—even more arduous in compilation, even more unremitting in revision, subject to even more insistent perfectionist exigence from the editors, our grateful admiration for their prowess (and their endurance) is proportionately the more fervent.

Finally, we and our associates, together with all those who saw the 1963 exhibition and all who read this book, owe a profound debt to Mr Stanley Morison. The originator of the project, he was the supercharger, the conscience and the mentor (often a very intransigent mentor) of the Supervisory Committee for the exhibition. His determination that a substantial book must come out of it fortified the original proposals therefor: 'it ought to be a folio', he would say with a commanding glint from behind the spectacles. And his faith in our capacity to produce it was not expressed in exhortation only. If this was the sort of book that admitted of a dedication, the reader will know by now whose name, in the largest available capitals, would have a page to itself. Mr Morison will prefer that we say, on behalf of everyone on the title-page, that we have done our best to deserve his confidence.

JOHN CARTER
PERCY H. MUIR

NOTE: Mr John Carter, Mr Percy H. Muir, Mr Stanley Morison, Dr S. H. Steinberg and Mr James M. Wells have all been good enough to read and comment on a draft of this essay. In addition I have had the benefit of several stimulating conversations with Mr Morison.

FIAT LUX

BY DENYS HAY

I

In principio creavit Deus caelum et terram. These are the first words of the text of the first book to be printed with movable metal type, the great 42-line Bible that came out at Mainz about 1455. In Genesis that beginning was followed by others. Immediately after heaven and earth came light. 'And God said: Let there be light.' On the sixth day God created man in his own image: 'male and female created he them'.

The earliest men and women communicated with each other (it must be supposed) by making noises. Grunts and screams, ejaculations prompted by pain, fear, hunger and desire, the smoother tones of momentary comfort and warmth, these were intelligible in a given situation when eked out by gesture and mime. Groups of men were small and their material equipment was scanty. The family and the tribe responded instinctively to the rhythmical demands of the seasons and met the slow changes in climate and geography with a dogged love of life which made them move their hunting grounds in the face of ice or drought. One can capture still this inarticulate but expressive atmosphere in moments of panic, in grief and in laughter and in the obscure but telling sounds made by babies and lovers.

Yet the passing millennia brought words, and this command of language was probably the most important single instrument which primitive peoples were able to use in the complicated game of survival. Particular noises became attached to particular actions and objects. It became possible to describe absent things and to construct future relationships. The tribe could debate its problems and plan concerted action. The powerful could exert their wills in relatively distant places by servants carrying messages; and one way of winning and consolidating power was the exercise of oratory, the construction of arguments, the pronouncement of effective verbal threats and promises. The leader of men, though tongue-tied himself, might yet have fluent spokesmen and such men were at hand in the priests. With words came the magic of words, the power to identify gods and to offer them prayer and praise. And with words came poetry. The bard who recited the deeds of the heroes of the tribe and the dynasty passed on his talents and his stories to other bards, as the priests trained other priests to recite the hallowed incantations. Memories were acute and tradition strong, for the lines spoken by bard and priest, like the commands borne by the courier of a king, had to be exactly reproduced. Curiously enough it is more difficult for people living in advanced societies to recapture this phase of speech than the earlier phase of sounds and signs. The glimpses one can get of it suggest languages (there were many of them) of repetitious formulae. For those members of society for whom words had public importance it must have been like the game 'I packed my bag and in it I put'; if one forgot one's sequences one was out of the game, perhaps painfully or utterly out of the game. In a world of speech words could become shackles.

II

The bondage of words was broken by writing them down. This stage seems to have been first reached in Mesopotamia between about 4000 and 3000 B.C. From a large number of conventional pictorial signs marked on clay tablets, symbols for things and numerals, writing arrived at a point where abstractions could be conveyed. It could further use the symbols to represent not only things and the actions or abstractions associated with them, but also phonetic qualities—a step towards the transcription of actual speech which the Sumerians had evidently reached at the time the earliest surviving examples of their cuneiform script were made. A little later writing roughly similar in accomplishment was evolved in the so-called hieroglyphics of Egypt and the 'characters' of Chinese. Sumerian cuneiform and Egyptian hieroglyphics perished in the course of time; Chinese has survived, a living fossil, so to speak, among the great scripts of the world.

Almost as important as the achievement of pictorial abstractions was the invention of a purely phonetic alphabet. This is known to have existed in Syria from at least the sixteenth or fifteenth century B.C. and there is now strong evidence of an alphabetical script being used in Canaan one or two centuries earlier than that. 'Of all the areas of the Near East', writes David Diringer, 'the region of Palestine and Syria provides the most likely source for the invention of the Alphabet.' The antecedents of 'Northern-Semitic' may be obscure. It can however be shown that from Canaanite, through Greek, were to descend the European alphabets, destined to overrun most of the world.

Writing and literature developed in every part of the globe. They were to have the greatest extension in Europe because there writing was practised in an alphabet composed of a very small number of letters. Latin, which had originally only twenty-one characters (derived from Etruscan and Greek) and the alphabets derived from it (such as modern English with its twenty-six), should be compared with the enormous numbers of characters of Chinese; some 5,000 to 6,000 are regularly used. Moreover the materials used for writing in Europe also changed. From carvings or incisions on wood, stone and clay, and marks on bark, leather and cloth, scribes adopted first of all papyrus and then prepared skins marked with ink. Papyrus, fibre from a marsh plant found in the Nile valley and in the East Mediterranean area, was formed into sheets which could be used separately or glued together lengthways to make a continuous writing surface which was rolled up for storage. In the fourth century A.D. these rolls of papyrus came to be replaced by books made from sheets of vellum or parchment, in which the material was folded and sewn, in much the same manner as a modern book. Papyrus books are found, but the material was less robust and did not lend itself to this format. The paged book made of skins was also easier to handle than a roll on which the columns of writing succeeded each other continuously, and the surface of parchment lent itself to more rapid cursive writing.

The availability of the written word conditioned the whole development of civilization. A new dimension was given to the mind of man: he could afford to forget since he could store his information outside himself. The priest could list his temple-dues, assemble the canon of his scriptures and preserve the details of the liturgy. The prince could have his rights listed and transmit his orders with a new precision and authority. In both religion and politics the written word encouraged larger unities. In place of the fugitive contacts of speech the written word remained: *littera scripta manet*. The seeds of an advanced civilization could thus scatter themselves and the dominant position in the Mediterranean area and the southern half of Europe acquired successively by Greek and then by Latin culture was due principally to writing. These seeds could, moreover, lie dormant for centuries and yet spring to life, as did the literature and learning of the Greeks and Romans in the European Middle Ages and Renaissance.

The literature of the written word was not only religious and political. The bard gave way to the poet and in its turn imaginative prose found a place beside older epic and newer lyric. Men could and did play with their pens, and more subtly than they could play with their tongues: the crude pun and spoonerism could be matched by complicated acrostic and anagram, meaningless until seen in black and white. The simple arithmetic of addition and subtraction could give rise to the abstractions of pure mathematics. Language and literature acquired norms preserved in the certainties of grammar and orthography. The scriptures of religion could have secular parallels, 'classics' as they were later to be called, to which the grammarians turned as models of style.

These changes occurred in all regions where writing developed. They were probably carried furthest and fastest in Christian Europe. The 'third portion of the inhabited world', peopled by the sons of Japhet, inherited the simplified alphabet of the Graeco-Roman Mediterranean tradition and acquired a religion based on written scriptures, old and new. Christianity was thus pledged to the promotion of reading and writing. Its Bible or book bred other books. Its priests were committed to an educational programme which in the end was to make so many men clerkly that the demand for the written word could not be met by conventional methods. The pressures thus built up in Europe resulted in the invention of printing.

The growth of literacy in the Middle Ages is imperfectly documented. Broadly speaking the education of priests was the main aim of formal instruction until the thirteenth century, and the curriculum was geared to the acquisition of a mastery of Latin, both written and spoken. The grammar school and the university remained throughout the period coloured by this original purpose; but by the later Middle Ages large numbers of laymen were attending both types of institution with no intention of following either a career in the Church or in one of the professions (law and medicine) for which the universities also catered. Secondary schools began to multiply in all European countries in the fourteenth and fifteenth centuries. They were most common in the bigger towns but gradually the gentry also sent their sons to be educated. Laymen in public positions in the tenth or eleventh centuries were usually illiterate. By the fifteenth century a nobleman and his steward could read and write, so could many of the ladies in the landed classes, and so of course could the merchants and shopkeepers in the towns. Doubtless by 1400 the illiterate still formed the large majority of the population; but it is certain that by then the clergy formed a minority of those who could read and write.

This transformation of society was accompanied by a transformation in the character of the book. In the so-called Dark Ages a book was a rarity. Produced in a sheltered corner of culture, a monastery in Ireland or Italy, it was usually connected with the Church and was treated with the reverence accorded to sacred things. With the spread of parishes over Christendom and the rising number of monasteries (in England convents increased from about sixty in the early eleventh century to just over 1,000 at the beginning of the fourteenth century) books ceased to be so precious. They were needed as Bibles and service books, they were needed as grammars to instruct clergy, they were needed for the religious who were transcribing old commentaries and works of devotion and composing new works of their own. Education by the twelfth century was entirely dependent on books. At school and even more at the university 'authors', prescribed and approved, were read and glossed and considerable numbers of texts were required.

By this time the monasteries, which had earlier been the main centres of book-production in western Europe, could not meet the demand and their monks were, in any case, not particularly involved in the education of the secular community or even of the clergy, except their own monks. Hence the market was supplied by professional scriveners, men who made a career as book-producers. In Barbarian Europe author and scribe were often the same person. By the thirteenth century there began to be a difference between them. In and after the thirteenth century one could rely on there being a bookshop in a university town. Furthermore a big step had been taken to increase production of books, and lower the costs of producing them, by the use of paper. Parchment, it is true, had by the end of the Middle Ages become very fine and light and until the mid-fifteenth century there seems to have been enough of it. But by then the use of paper was widespread. Paper had first entered Europe from China by way of Muslim countries in the twelfth century. By the early fourteenth century rag paper was manufactured on a considerable scale both in Spain and in Italy and from Italy its manufacture spread north of the Alps. This does not mean that by about 1400, with an important manufacture of books (many made of paper), in all essentials the situation as we know it today had been reached. There were big differences and to appreciate the influence of printing one must look carefully at the manuscript book in the last two centuries before Gutenberg's invention.

The handwritten book was a separate unit unlike any other. This is true not only of original works, written *ab initio*. It is almost as true of books of which very large numbers of copies were made, works like the Bible itself, or the dozens of approved authors read by students at school or university. The very greatest care was certainly taken to secure authentic texts.

Rules for copyists in the *scriptoria* of monasteries were strict and universities laid down the most stringent regulations for the *stationarii* who supplied texts. Yet the transcribers each wrote a distinct hand, conforming certainly with the accepted style of their time and place but permitting themselves endless variations in the formation of letters and in methods of abbreviating words or shortening them by other conventions, such as suspension of final syllables. Even when a work was copied quire by quire with gatherings of parchment or paper of the same length as the gatherings of the *exemplar* (the *pecia* system), the resulting manuscript was still distinguishable from its exemplar by infinite if subtle or minor variations. If the text of no two books was exactly alike, it can be imagined how much greater differences there were in apparatus—contents, index, glosses. The index in particular tended to be a highly particularized exercise and when found was the work of an owner rather than of a copyist. In such a situation the identification of books was frequently less by the general description afforded by a title, and more often by the precise indications afforded by their opening words (*incipits*) and concluding words (*explicits*) together with the number of the first and last folio. This is how books were usually catalogued in the public libraries which were beginning to be found in universities at the end of the Middle Ages, as in the collections formed earlier by great monasteries and cathedrals.

When books were made by hand errors were thus bound to occur and they naturally had a cumulative effect. In the case of fundamental texts like the Bible repeated efforts at emendment were made and a general correctness was maintained. In service books knowledge of the liturgy secured correct copies. But in a wide range of writing a manuscript book tended to become less authentic the more it was copied. This deterioration was intensified when the main source of supply was no longer the clergy, especially the regular clergy, but lay scriveners. Writing often under great pressure, for a steady and known market, the professional scribe was often careless and incompetent. At the same time the handwriting itself became poorer in quality. Though there were splendid manuscripts produced by proud calligraphers in fifteenth-century Italy, and even some noble volumes made in the north of Europe, the average manuscript book of the later Middle Ages was slovenly, unattractive to look at and difficult to read when compared with similar works of the eleventh and twelfth centuries. Writing and reading were, as has been observed already, much commoner by the later date, and familiarity bred contempt.

The book trade existed. It was, however, essentially dealing in well-known works, and it did not have much if any influence on the composition of new books, which entered the dealer's regular stock only when there was a large and certain demand. An author as such (as in the days of Greece and Rome) thus needed to support himself by means other than his pen; he was a monk, a beneficed clerk, a university professor or the familiar protégé of a prince or great man, occasionally an official in the employment of a city. His writing could redound to the honour and prestige of his patron, and occasionally he might be rewarded by some extraneous Maecenas to whom he dedicated a work; but he was in no sense paid for writing. Above all he had no right in his book, no copyright. If it proved popular and began to figure regularly on the stalls of Paris or Cologne, he had no royalties.

In these circumstances publication was effected in one of two ways. The writer could deliberately send a fair copy of his completed manuscript to a friend or patron, usually with a letter of dedication. Or he might lend his work, perhaps in an unfinished state, to a colleague and find later that copies of it were circulating without his prior agreement. Further, the author often dedicated the same work to different patrons, perhaps revising the text to suit them; in this way arose the four main recensions of Froissart's *Chronicle*. Or he might keep the original manuscript beside him, constantly tinkering with it but allowing portions of it or the whole of it to be transcribed from time to time; this explains the complicated textual history of Thomas à Kempis's *De imitatione Christi*. Here again a vast range of variables distinguishes copies of the same work. Which is the 'true' text of Froissart or the *Imitation of Christ*?

If publication was erratic, suppression of manuscript books could be much more systematic. Nothing offers better evidence of the rapid spread of books than the repeated attempts made to stifle the use of some of them. From the early thirteenth century (and there are cases even before that) works by theologians and philosophers were from time to time proscribed by other, more powerfully placed theologians and philosophers. Sometimes such attempts were in vain, as was the hierarchy's condemnation of Aristotle in the schools of Paris in the early thirteenth century; in the next generation a new race of Aristotelians had secured acceptance for his doctrines. Marsilio of Padua and William of Occam encountered papal censure; they and their works survived unscathed. A more concerted attack, in which the popes concerned had the support of most responsible theologians, was made on the teaching of Wycliffe, though he was burned as a heretic only many years after his death. John Huss's writings brought him to the pyre at Constance in 1415. The condemnation of a man carried with it the condemnation of his books and they too were destroyed. Clearly it was easier for bishops and inquisitors to obliterate heretical works when they had just been written and before they had attained a wide circulation, and this in fact happened: many a minor heretic's writings have survived only in the indictment of his crimes. Yet the circulation of books was such that not only did Wycliffe's theology easily move from Oxford to Prague, but the writings of Wycliffe and Huss (wrongly accused of being a disciple of Wycliffe) in large measure survived the official holocaust.

An author might not be able to control the publication of his book or ensure in all cases that it survived unmutilated or at all, and he could not derive an income from it even if it was successful. But by the later Middle Ages he had readers beyond his own immediate circle and, if the work was non-technical and in the vernacular, he had a public in the modern sense of the term. Dante's *Divine Comedy*, Petrarch's lyrics, the *Decameron* of Boccaccio and Chaucer's *Canterbury Tales* were written not to entertain one man or even a court or a coterie but to be enjoyed by all who had the ability to read. The fourteenth or fifteenth-century author had linguistic difficulties. There was no one French or English or Italian. Significant creative writing in the vernacular did, however, promote the emergence of dominant literary languages as the works of Dante, Petrarch and Boccaccio stimulated the later importance of what might be called 'courtly Tuscan'.

The rising literacy of the fifteenth century was to make many more readers, so many more that the printing press was invented. At that critical moment, what was the intellectual stock of Europe? What books existed for the early printers to print? The list is formidably long. It contains the main writers of classical antiquity, including by 1450 all the main Roman writers save Tacitus, and (in Latin translation as well as in the original) most of Aristotle and some Plato, as well as Homer. From these works there had already stemmed a vast literature of commentary and creation as Roman and Greek ideas mingled with and challenged the most revolutionary corpus of writing inherited from the past—the Hebrew Scriptures and the Christian New Testament. With these Greek, Roman and Hebrew ingredients were mixed the scholarship and science of the Arab world—Rhases, Averroes and the rest. Like their Hellenistic predecessors, medieval scholars and men of letters often channelled their vast reservoirs of ideas into digests, anthologies and *florilegia*. They had developed to a fine art, again repeating the pattern of an older day, the habit of glossing and expounding a text, aided by the conviction that dialectic was a way of approaching the truth and that the written word of an *auctor*, an authority, was at any rate the beginning of wisdom.

The plenitude of ideas generated by medieval books defies simple analysis. One finds in the millennium between the fall of Rome in 410 and the fall of Constantinople in 1453 the expression of practically every imaginable opinion. There are monarchists, republicans, and communists. There are philosophers who bound man and the created world in a net of rational causation and others who denied this legalism in favour of a subjective approach to the mysteries and a pragmatic attitude to the language of metaphysics. There are cynics and mystics, and many who are a bit of both. There are chroniclers and memorialists, and scholars whose computations of chronology formed the basis for such narrators. There are tellers of stories, of lives of the saints and of great men, and there are even a few introspective writers (like Petrarch) who display their souls with pen and ink. And there are poets. The poets in Latin sometimes aped the classical writers they had learned at school—with happy results in a few cases. But they had a better chance when they let their fancy wander, even in Latin, to the rhythmical and rhymed verse of the vernacular as in the goliardic songs, full of a casual gusto and sometimes of a carnal pathos which should have been foreign to the 'clergy' who wrote them.

One important distinction must be made. With few exceptions, writing on serious subjects was in Latin and the vernaculars were the vehicles of written compositions only in what at the time were regarded as frivolous and secular fields. Dante's scholarship, like Petrarch's and Boccaccio's, was in Latin: like theirs his Italian writings were reserved for more popular themes. Latin was the language of cultivated men, understood universally and taught in every part of Christendom. It was the only language which was regularly taught beyond the elementary stage. Italian did not exist: there were a dozen Italians; and so it was with French, German, English and the languages of Spain. In France and England the court and the capital were giving one particular kind of French and English a predominance over the others. By the early fifteenth century there was no similar incipient unity in other parts of Europe save what was being imposed (as observed earlier) by the great vernacular writers themselves.

Yet even in the dialects, as the regional languages would later become, there was a remarkable sharing of cultural trends. Arthurian romance penetrated everywhere, and so did many of the Latin classics, translated into North German or Catalan. The really literate were still the clerks and the men (often laymen now) who had acquired some Latin at a grammar school or university primarily designed for clerks. But for those who were not able to read Latin there was also much to hand. Among the works generally available in a vernacular version by the end of the Middle Ages was the Vulgate Bible.

III

At the entrance to the 1963 Exhibition, of which this volume is an outcome, there was an enlarged reproduction of the first page of Gutenberg's Bible, on which a spotlight picked out the words *fiat lux*; 'Let there be light'. The vast increase in the accessibility of books which resulted from printing may suitably be illustrated by the example of the Bible itself. The Latin Vulgate had been printed ninety-four times by 1500; vernacular translations were in print for virtually every European language by 1600. By the latter date a press was to be found in nearly every town of any size. Some inventions (the water mill, for example) have taken centuries to be widely adopted and even more have taken several generations. Printing was an exception. It spread at a phenomenal speed from Mainz and by the 1490s each of the major states had one important publishing centre and some had several.

The world of books had been transformed and it is impossible to exaggerate the rapidity of the transformation. It is all too easy to exaggerate the consequences and to credit printing as such with occasioning as rapid a change in the mind of man. When Bacon listed the printing press along with gunpowder and the compass as ushering in the modern world he sadly oversimplified the realities. A closer examination of the first age of printing, from Gutenberg in the 1450s to the early nineteenth century, reveals many and profound continuities with the old manuscript-bound Middle Ages.

The early printed book physically resembled the manuscript book. The latter had been made up of gatherings of parchment or paper, sewn and bound between covers. On a shelf a row of medieval manuscripts does not look different from a row of early printed books. Nor does a manuscript look different from an early printed book when taken off the shelf and opened. The printer aimed his wares at the existing book-buying public and he did his best to provide an article with which his customers were familiar. In the Rhineland Gutenberg had used type designed to look like the best local book hands. In the Low Countries a 'bastard' hand was imitated and this Caxton used for the first works for the English market. In Italy 'humanist' hands, to settle down as 'Italic' and 'Roman', were being used, especially for the copying of texts in the humanities. These were the models followed by the printers of Rome, Venice, Milan, Naples and Florence; printers were at work at all of these places by the early 1470s. Nor did the first printers venture often to display their capacity for large-scale production. Editions seldom consisted of more than 1,000 copies and 200 seems to have been a common figure. There were technical and financial reasons for this, and not least the difficulty of raising capital to be tied up in large stocks of paper, metal and finished books. Yet the main explanation lay in the dependence of the printer-publisher on a market which was not unlimited. He could rely on a steady sale only of established works like the Bible, Donatus's grammar, prayer books and so on. The bulk of the works printed in the first century of printing were the old works, familiar to the region where the printer was at work. Fairly soon a degree of specialization developed and the volumes produced by some printers established themselves as articles of long-distance commerce and formed the staple of special markets or book fairs, such as the celebrated ones at Frankfurt and Leipzig.

Nor was there any change in the position of the author, who was not paid for the sales of his work on any pro rata basis. Many new books, perhaps most, were printed at the cost of the author or his patron. If the author was becoming well known the printer might share the costs. If the author was famous—Erasmus or Luther, for example—the printer might bear the entire cost and even allow the author some copies to give away. But nothing prevented a popular book being reprinted dozens of times and in dozens of places without the knowledge of the author. Men like Erasmus and Luther could thus make a fortune for a printer; the reverse was not true. It was only in the course of the seventeenth century that authors began to be paid in cash and not until the early eighteenth that they were given big sums of money. Finally, beginning with England, the state gave copyright to the author. By 1800 the process had been more or less completed. Authors could, if successful, live directly from their pens and not indirectly through a proliferation of dedications to rich and powerful men or by enjoying sinecures in Church or State. One of the fundamental characteristics of the first three centuries of printing is that the creative writer, the man of ideas and inspiration, wrote his books because he wished to express himself and not to make money. Erasmus with his well-placed friends was comfortably off, but his enormous output of best sellers, the *Praise of Folly*, the *Adagia*, the *Colloquies*, the long series of volumes of educational and moral works, the massive erudition of his classical and patristic editions, were the product of a man who re-searched and wrote compulsively and not for cash. Milton did not write *Paradise Lost* for the £5 paid for the manuscript by his publisher (or the further £5 which was to follow if a reprint was needed).

In many respects books and authors were thus not materially affected by printing, save that larger numbers of a work could now be rapidly made. Yet this multiplication of books was itself a very remarkable change. Coinciding, as the invention and spread of printing did, with the further development of the rising literacy which had provoked it, the increasing con-sumption of books undeniably meant that more persons wanted to read, just as it facilitated their acquiring the ability: a *virtuous* circle had been set up. In the sixteeenth and later centuries it became almost impossible for a man to attain positions of wealth or influence if he was illiterate. The well-to-do in every European country knew that to survive here below, and even to spend their money in fashionable ways, education was necessary; the ambitious knew that education opened a well-paved road to success. All gentlemen's sons and the sons of most of the urban bourgeoisie went to grammar school, *lycée* or *gymnasium*. The crofter's son in Scotland who sought his M.A. to become a minister or a dominie, the sons of *contadini* in the Romagna and the Abruzzi who entered religious orders, caused (in the seventeenth and early eighteenth centuries) what would be termed, in the jargon of the modern economist, 'a crisis of overproduction'. The curriculum of secondary education was remarkably similar in all European countries. Roman and Teuton, Roman Catholic and Protestant, were given a lot of Latin grammar and a little Greek. The texts they read furnished their masters with moral aphorisms and the subjects pursued were those which could be illustrated by the ancient classics: the history of antiquity, rhetoric, poetry—in a word, the humanities. Education was literary and mathematics had small part in it. At a level below this children could learn their letters and some arithmetic in the sporadic schools run by a parson or his clerk or by a literate 'dame', and the craftsman and the merchant picked up their skills, including the ability to read and write, mainly through apprenticeship or its equivalent. The grammar school was, however, the main regular source of education for those who could afford it and it covered the gentry and upper bourgeoisie of Europe with a patina of Latin-based culture.

The books used by the schoolmaster and his pupils, and those written and read by the handful of *literati* and scholars, were also technically improved compared with those of the later Middle Ages. When a volume was printed instead of being copied by hand it became worth while to take pains, infinite pains, to get the text right. In the manuscript accuracy was highly desirable but in practice hardly attainable; in print, with careful composition, with careful proof-reading, with the *corrigenda* published at once and then incorporated in later reprints, something like perfection seemed in sight and was certainly aimed at by the great printers of the sixteenth century (Aldus, Froben, the Estiennes and others) and by their successors. Further, when there were more books than before it became necessary to identify them precisely and quickly. The title of a book, obscurely found (if at all) in the colophons of manuscripts and early incunables, came to figure prominently at the beginning of the printed work and soon occupied a full preliminary page—an advertisement for the work which followed. The clumsy gloss gradually gave way to the footnote, permitting author and reader to avoid tiresome interruptions of the text by learned references or lengthy asides. The index was perfected and the alphabet took a further big step forward as an instrument of enlightenment and erudition.

Libraries became more plentiful and much bigger. The library of the Sorbonne in the early fourteenth century numbered fewer than 2,000 volumes and at Cambridge in the fifteenth century there were only 500 or so books in the University collection. By the seventeenth century the picture had altered. Princely patrons and great men were competing to establish great public libraries, such as that formed by Cardinal Mazarin with its 40,000 volumes. England lagged behind as far as noble or princely patronage was concerned, but the Bodleian Library at Oxford at this time became a national institution and led the way with its printed catalogues, as the Library of the British Museum, founded in the mid-eighteenth century, still does in the mid-twentieth. More significant, perhaps, was the spread of private libraries. In the course of the sixteenth century the main purchasers of books ceased to be the clergy: between 1557 and 1600 surviving inventories of books in France show that for every collection made by an ecclesiastic (prelate, priest or don) there were more than three made by lawyers and administrators, the lay 'aristocracy' of the *gens de robe*. 'In 1500' (Mr Sears Jayne tells us in his *Library Catalogues of the English Renaissance*) 'the principal owners of books in England were ecclesiastical institutions...By 1640...both Universities boasted many fine libraries of thousands of volumes each, there were several private collections of more than a thousand volumes, and there was not a single important ecclesiastical library in the country.' By the early eighteenth century a gentleman's house of any size had a room called the library. With this development went a new system in library management and in bibliographical expertise. Lists of books on a subject basis begin almost with printing. Johann Tritheim, who became abbot of Spanheim (not far from Mainz), published a *Liber de scriptoribus ecclesiasticis* in 1494. In 1545 the Swiss physician and naturalist Conrad Gesner published his *Bibliotheca Universalis* 'or complete catalogue of all writers in Latin, Greek and Hebrew, surviving and perished, old and modern up to the present...A new work necessary not only for the formation of public and private libraries but for all students...'. The science of bibliography had been established. By the mid-seventeenth century it was relatively easy to find out what books had been published on any topic. The purchaser was already able to turn to catalogues produced regularly by the biggest printing houses. The annual lists of the Frankfurt book fair began in 1564. More or less full lists of books published in France were issued from 1648 to 1654; a similar English catalogue appeared first in 1657. Even more important for the dissemination of information about new books and the ideas in them was the review-journal. This started with the French *Journal des Savants* (1665) which was followed by the *Philosophical Transactions* of the Royal Society of London (1675). By the early eighteenth century this process had been internationalized by translations of such periodicals and by the group of scholars, of whom Pierre Bayle was the most important, who diffused the intellectual novelties circulating in Europe from their asylum in the United Provinces where they published *Nouvelles de la République des lettres* and similar reviews.

One other list of publications was also published from time to time, but with the object of warning readers against the books it named. This was the *Index Librorum Prohibitorum*, issued under papal authority from 1559. The papal inquisitor or, in areas where there was no papal Inquisition (England was one), the local bishop had been responsible in the later Middle Ages for the suppression of heretical and erroneous writings. The printing press made such supervision of books of even greater concern not only to the prelates or the pope, but also to governments. Two generations after Gutenberg Luther roused Germany and a horrified orthodoxy tried to identify the sources of Lutheran doctrine and prevent such influences continuing to be effective; not only were earlier prohibitions of the books of Wycliffe and Huss repeated, but at the same time Erasmus's writings were attacked and condemned. Equally the hierarchy and its theologians attempted to suppress Luther's writings and those of his disciples. At first the attempts at censorship were localized, as described below at p. 49. The centralization of Roman Catholic censorship in the Roman *Index* was effected after the Council of Trent. Frequently issued in revised editions, the *Index* undoubtedly impeded the free circulation of books in countries where there was a vigilant bishop or inquisitor, and it continued to do so for centuries, though signs of increasing tolerance became apparent in the year of grace 1966. But it entirely failed to prevent the books which it condemned from penetrating even areas obedient to Rome. Elsewhere, among Protestants or (later) among *libres penseurs* or 'progressives', the knowledge that a book was in the *Index* constituted a positive reason for reading it. Nor were princes and town magistrates much more successful in suppressing books which they judged to be seditious or immoral; it should be remembered here that with printing came pornography. There were many attempts at state supervision of unwelcome works. The wary, ingenious and covetous printer defeated them all, though not without occasional danger to himself and not without leaving behind some bibliographical puzzles. It had not been easy to burke a manuscript book. It was impossible to stifle print. In Milton's *Areopagitica* the doctrine of freedom of publication was given canonical form.

The printed book thus differed from the manuscript book by appearing in numbers so large that suppression was in practice impossible, by presenting in general a more reliable text (supported when appropriate by footnotes, indices and other apparatus), by lending itself easily to collection in public and private libraries and to access through bibliographies and periodical reviews. In all these ways printing made book-learning, and book-pleasures of other kinds, much more accessible. It also promoted changes in style and presentation which caused the printed book to become inherently more attractive, more attractive as a physical object, than earlier manuscripts. It is, of course, true that all through the Middle Ages beautiful books were made by hand, from the glorious manuscripts made in Charlemagne's day down to the glorious manuscripts collected by Guidobaldo Montefeltre at Urbino in the fifteenth century; it was said that he would not tolerate a printed volume in his library. But the general level of ordinary manuscript books, the workaday tools of teacher or researcher, were unpleasant to look at by the fourteenth and fifteenth centuries. Bibles could be made sufficiently neat and small, but at the price of writing them in a hand so minute as to be almost indecipherable. Early printing, aimed at a mass market, at first copied locally prevailing book hands. This however changed as printers and typographers accustomed themselves to the new medium. Everywhere the trend was away from heavy black pages towards lighter pages, which gave an overall impression of grey. This was achieved mainly by adopting a lettering which was lighter, finer, better spaced and arranged. In this steady transition Italian printers provided in their italic and roman faces a model which was generally followed in Europe, save in Germany and in Slavonic lands. The victory of Italian typography was the last, but by no means the least, stage in the conquest of the rest of Europe by the values and methods evolved in the peninsula during the Renaissance. Associated at first with the texts of Latin classics and the humanists of Italy, these agreeable and economical founts acquired general prestige by being used by the Venetian printer Aldus Manutius. That they were steadily adopted all over Europe is a tribute to the key position of the grammar-school master and his high-born and influential pupils. Even in Germany roman type was used for classical or humanist texts. At the same time books began to be smaller. Great folios still abounded in the seventeenth and eighteenth centuries, but there were more quartos, octavos and duodecimos.

It has been observed earlier that the advent of printing had no immediate effect on the material circumstances of the author. As the printed book slowly evolved and perfected itself, consequences for authorship nevertheless slowly followed.

It is impossible to believe that the writers of the sixteenth and seventeenth centuries did not feel sensuous pleasure at the sight of their work in print, as their twentieth-century successors do. The smell of the paper, the ink and the glue have not (thank heavens) been distilled and bottled in Paris or New York and one can still discriminate between the scent of a woman and the perfume of a new book: yet the ensuing sensations can be of the same invading wholeness. The authors of an earlier day would, it is true, have titivated their noses with vellum and leather, odours which can nowadays only be savoured among the aromatic shelves of a great library where the gold and the calf exude incense, even if it is only saddle-soap and insecticide. They too would view a dozen crisp copies of one of their books with astonished pride: not everyone can father such multiplicity, nor send into the unknown so many heralds and hawkers.

Composition of a book which was to be 'published' in manuscript meant that the writer knew who would read it, at any rate initially. With a printed work publication meant something different. Automatically it was offered to a number, perhaps a very large number, of purchasers and readers with whose background and tastes the author could not be familiar. In the case of some specialized works, for instance in medicine and law, a professional audience could be anticipated. But in more general fields, history, literary criticism, philosophy, natural philosophy and even theology, as well of course as imaginative prose and verse, there was no telling in advance who precisely would be attracted. It is true that the medieval writer was aware that he could often expect ultimately to have unknown readers, but the degree of anonymity in his public to which an author was committed by printing was of a different order. New inducements existed to make one's writing intelligible and its presentation agreeable. Where appropriate, the author must now avoid plunging *in medias res*; he must rather set the scene and provide an introductory summary, explaining himself and his subject. (Compare the preliminary pages of the fourteenth-century Florentine *Chronicle* of Giovanni Villani with the beginning of Machiavelli's *Istorie Fiorentine*, which was designed for publication though it appeared after the author's death.) Moreover an attractively written book was much more likely to be published, for—from the mid-sixteenth century onwards—it was booksellers rather than printers who put up the capital for a new work and they knew, or thought they knew, what the public wanted.

From the sixteenth century there arose one basic change in the public for books which conditioned authorship: Latin gradually ceased to be the only or even the main vehicle for serious writing. It has already been pointed out that the vernaculars were used in the Middle Ages, broadly speaking, only for ephemeral works, even if a later age was to regard the *Romance of the Rose* and the *Divine Comedy* as immortal. This attitude persisted in the first century of printing, but gradually the vernaculars (under the pervasive influence of Latin) acquired a maturity which enabled English, French and the others to carry with confidence and efficiency the most sophisticated thoughts. Prudent and far-sighted men might question whether professional knowledge (in medicine, physical science or theology) should thus be made available on the market-place; certainly there were meaner experts who resented their *arcana* being exposed to the light of common day. But the process was irreversible. Latin scholarship in all subjects was turned into English and French and Castilian, and in the same languages scholars now began to compose. By the end of the seventeenth century Latin was no longer indispensable to the learned *writer*, even though as a *scholar* he still found it indispensable. At the Frankfurt book fair the proportion of Latin to German books was two to one in the decades between 1560 and 1630; by the 1680s more books were for sale in German than in Latin.

In English the appearance of Richard Hooker's *Of the Laws of Ecclesiastical Polity* (1594–7) marks the emancipation of English as an autonomous medium. Fifty years earlier such a book would have been written in Latin or else would have appeared in the clumsy obscurity of what C. S. Lewis called 'drab'. Yet Hooker paid a penalty for his achievement. His remarkable theological work remained virtually unknown to continental scholars. Isaak Walton in his life of Hooker (1664) described how he had been told 'more than forty years past' that the attention of Pope Clement VIII was drawn to the book by 'either Cardinal Allen, or learned Dr Stapleton'. The pope was informed that 'though he [the pope] had lately said he never met with an English book whose writer deserved the name of an author; yet there now appeared a wonder to them, and it would be to his Holiness, if it were in Latin; for a poor obscure English priest had writ four such books of Laws and Church-Polity, and in a style that expressed such a grave and so humble a majesty, with such clear demonstration of reason, that in all their readings they had not met with any that exceeded him'. With this view Clement concurred when Dr Stapleton read him the first part in an extempore Latin translation.

Across the linguistic frontiers of Europe scholars continued to communicate in Latin even when they ceased to publish in it. One must remember that many original Latin works were being printed until well on in the eighteenth century, and that many writers (Galileo, Descartes and scores more) published works with equal fluency in Latin and a vernacular. Latin remained the normal language for international correspondence between scholars in different countries, only slowly being replaced by Italian and then by French. Translation was also able to diffuse knowledge originally available only in vernacular writing and was undertaken with an increasing care for accuracy. Latin translations were even published of periodicals such as the French *Journal des Savants* and the English *Philosophical Transactions*. Translation was, moreover, facilitated by the nature of vernacular prose and poetry down to the end of the eighteenth century. Heavily influenced everywhere by Latin grammar and syntax, vernacular writers shared a common attitude to style. They had also been brought up on a classical pabulum which ensured that their allusions and points of reference were readily understood everywhere. There was nevertheless now a choice before an educated author, whether to address himself first or mainly to an international audience in Latin or to a national audience in his mother-tongue.

The choice of such a writer was often determined by his purposes. The moralist and above all the church reformer naturally sought to address large numbers. This was not a new situation. Huss preaching in Czech, Bernardino in Italian, were doing what Luther and others were to do in print—going to the masses. Indeed the sermon-hungry audiences of the fifteenth century often represented the whole population of a town, whereas the printed word immediately reached only those who could read, though they in turn might speak out the message. But the vast quantities of pamphlets issued in Germany (630 have been listed from the years 1520 to 1530) leave no doubt that without the printing press the course of the German Reformation might have been different. Luther's own writings constitute a third of the German books printed in the first four decades of the sixteenth century; his address *To the Christian Nobility of the German Nation* (August 1520) was reprinted thirteen times in two years; *Concerning Christian Liberty* (September 1520) came out eighteen times before 1526; as for his translation of the Bible, Dr Steinberg summarizes the complicated bibliographical story thus—'All in all, 430 editions of the whole Bible or parts of it appeared during Luther's lifetime'. Polemical literature was also naturally put to the service of governments. Here again the propagandist had predecessors, as can be seen in the chauvinist pamphleteering provoked by Anglo-French hostilities during the Hundred Years War or by the respect accorded by other courts in Italy to the Florentine scholar-chancellors from Salutati onwards. But the government which sponsored manuscript warfare was trying merely to influence other chanceries and the councillors of princes. Printed polemics were designed to interest large and influential sections of public opinion. Hence the retained men who wrote for kings and ministers from the days of Henry VIII, Francis I and Charles V down to the hacks operating official journalism in the eighteenth century. Hence the 'historiographers royal' who spread from the French court to other countries in the seventeenth century. Hence, too, the counter-government publications of critics and rebels, the object of censorship and persecution, which reached behind the police to the man in the study, if not the man in the street.

Much, perhaps most, of what was printed in the centuries which followed the invention was to be of no lasting interest, save when digested statistically: the mounting number of royal proclamations, the emergence and diffusion of the periodical press, the very numbers of books published themselves. What is of interest is the growing enlargement of the human spirit which is recalled in the pages of this book. By 1600 the whole range of ancient thought was available to the curious, and much of it was accessible in vernacular versions. The main philosophers, scientists and historians of the Middle Ages had been printed, though as yet without the critical care that was beginning to be lavished on the writings of antiquity. And to this inherited knowledge and reflexion the Renaissance added its own contributions, which germinated rapidly and which thus could rival the influence of the works by those established *auctores* of the ancient and medieval periods. The pace of intellectual change quickened and the notion of *auctoritas* was challenged by novelty. The excitement of the new began to act as a leaven. There are no medieval Utopias. From More onwards the world has never been without them, and it was by printed books that moralists, scientists, philosophers and critics of art and literature mapped out fresh paths.

Prior to the French Revolution the audience for serious writing was composed of all educated men and women and learning was, at any rate in principle, undivided. The rigid academic distinctions which were later to impose themselves were absent. Galileo regarded himself not only as a scientist but as a philosopher and a man of letters and he did in fact write good Latin and good Italian. The cultivated public was able to understand, even if it disapproved of, the current advances in natural philosophy and technology, let alone the more familiar subjects of ethics and theology. Difficult some of the ideas were, but good writing and the device of correspondence or dialogue facilitated attractive exposition; when a physicist like Newton was too austere to do this for himself a writer like Fontenelle was available to undertake the necessary *haute vulgarisation*. Even reference books could be idiosyncratic, witty and stylish, as Bayle and Johnson showed. The existence of a wide reading public turned publication itself into a gesture of some significance and the writer, even if unrewarded as such until the eighteenth century, had emerged as a distinct species. And some writers had *genius* 'as opposed' (says the dictionary) 'to *talent*'. Genius in this sense apparently comes into English in 1759.

Printers were responsible not only for issuing books and pamphlets of temporary significance and for works of genius or at least talent. They also published an increasing number of books which, by adding to the conveniences of the scholar and man of affairs, saved his time for more important things. Dictionaries are the most obvious instance of this and the student who had a printed *Thesaurus* should be compared with the medieval scholar who had to make his own or depend on a tatty copy of the *Catholicon*. The published tables of logarithms and other tabulated mathematical and astronomical material not only speeded up scientific calculation but put reliable instruments into the hands of ships' navigators.

Besides the utilities the press encouraged the graces of life. The printing of music disseminated the latest songs and compositions among the gentry who were often still themselves performers. Hand-copied music depended on skills which the amateur could scarcely be expected to possess; the engraved music of the printer provided the equivalent in accurate, legible and convenient form. Engraving also speeded up the knowledge of the pictorial art of distant centres. Long before the young painter or architect had visited Italy he could study the masters in albums and absorb the principles of Palladio. His patron came back from the Grand Tour provided, if he could afford it, with some original canvases but certainly with engravings by Piranesi.

With music and the fine arts the function of printing was, so to say, ancillary. With imaginative literature it had by the seventeenth century become an essential part of composition. Though the bard lingered on in the Balkans and Finland until the twentieth century, though ballads were composed in industrial Britain and in America during the nineteenth, oral literature was in effect displaced by print, and the poetry of the later Renaissance has a quality it could not otherwise have possessed; it was meant to be read, not recited. Read aloud it often was, and so were the prose romances and the elegant essays (of indescribable dullness for the most part), on wet days when hunting was impossible, or by the ladies after dinner while the men sobered up. But it was designed by the writer for the reader. Both saw it silently on a printed page.

IV

With the nineteenth century the pace of communication speeded up, at first with books themselves and later with the invention of other devices. The more rapid production of books was made possible by the perfection of various technical improvements—stereotyping, then mechanical type-setting and machine binding—which enabled steam and other forms of power to be applied to printing so that what had remained for centuries a craft was steadily transformed into an industrial enterprise. Publishers, who had by the end of the eighteenth century become largely separated from the printers who made books and the shopkeepers who sold them, were often now large companies of influential businessmen, keen to supply the widening market for print.

That market increased rapidly. The men who came to power in Europe in the generation after the French Revolution can be described, in a phrase which came to be generally adopted at the time, as middle class. At one end of the spectrum they were promoters of industrialization, of international commerce and banking, and at the other they were middlemen and retailers. Their prescription for the world's woes was the diffusion of their own values as the wealth of the community increased. Those of their critics who deplored the passing of the golden age of an educated *élite* were powerless to resist the march of bourgeois egalitarianism. Their other adversaries, who challenged capitalism and foretold its doom, shared to the full the optimism of the age. Both capitalists and socialists advocated universal literacy to be achieved by compulsory education. They were pushing at an open door. A predominantly agrarian community can dispense with reading and writing: the farmer's education is (or perhaps was) provided through an apprenticeship with nature. The industrial revolution brought in its wake the necessity for a lettered population. In the world of nineteenth-century machinery the illiterate not only went to the wall; they could be dangerous in a big factory and were useless as shop assistants in a big store.

The Revolution in France had led to the enunciation of the principles of free and compulsory education at the primary level, and this was incorporated in the constitution of 1791. On the Continent the early nineteenth century saw the general adoption of state schools for all. In Britain progress was, as usual, much slower, save in Scotland where effective parish schools were already in existence. Yet even in Britain the provision of public schools (as opposed to Public Schools) came hesitantly in the mid-century although, before that, there was an amazing degree of self-improvement: Mechanics' Institutes, the *Penny Cyclopaedia*, and so forth. Nor was self-improvement restricted to the working class. In the early decades of the nineteenth century a big town usually acquired an institution—the one at Newcastle upon Tyne is called the Literary and Philosophical Society—which organized lectures and maintained a library of serious books. At the same time the intelligent reader could now turn to an intelligent journalism, of which the *Edinburgh Review* was the first great example.

The idealization of literacy and the remarkably quick progress which literacy made, at any rate in Western Europe and North America, were further encouraged by more rapid transport. The isolated parts of great countries were penetrated by better roads, by canals and, even more important, by railway lines, which drove first from one big centre to another and then curved through tunnels and over viaducts into mountain and moor. One could now travel through the Apennines, the Massif Central and the Scottish Highlands in hours instead of days. Pockets of traditional life were eliminated. The language (and the books and ideas) of Paris and London began to erode ever more quickly the frontiers, already in retreat, of Catalan, Provençal and Breton, of Welsh and Gaelic. The schoolmasters in highland areas had been trained in the big towns and their pupils were brought up to feel that culture went with capital cities. The demand for books was stimulated by these enlargements of the market. Railways also affected publisher and author by providing tranquil hours of dis-occupation. The railway bookstall supplied the necessary distraction. The yellowbacks of early Victorian England, the sophisticated publications of Tauchnitz (designed for the English-speaking visitor to the Continent) and serious magazines like *Blackwood's*, *The Atlantic Monthly* and so on, were direct results of the new world of steam.

'World' is the right word. Just as the railway made for rapid and certain travel on land, so did the steamboat at sea. Here, too, there were *longueurs* to be sweetened by print and here too there were markets to be exploited. The English publisher now had vast English-speaking areas overseas at his disposal—North America, where the population was quickly augmented by immigrants from all over the world, Australia, India and a wide network of smaller colonies where literacy was largely confined to the white administrators, the settlers and missionaries, who did their best to spread a reading knowledge of the Word.

Until the early twentieth century the overseas conquests of English might have been paralleled, though not equalled, by German, French and Spanish. In the event, although Spanish has still a huge currency in South and Central America, English is now unrivalled as a world language, and it is surely not fanciful to foresee the day when it will be universally known. This is a factor which weighs heavily with contemporary publishers and authors and which will undoubtedly weigh much more heavily in years to come.

The scholarship and the science of nineteenth-century Europe were, however, far from being determined by the British. The leadership in letters, the arts and academic subjects had moved at the Renaissance from France to Italy. In the nineteenth century a much more complicated *translatio litterarum* came about. Cultural primacy was shared by Germany and France, and to some extent the division was one between the 'two cultures' about which so much has been written in recent years. The German university recovered first from the dol-drums in which higher education had been becalmed and it was in the German university that a new science and a new scholarship emerged in the post-Napoleonic period to set their seal on advanced teaching elsewhere in Europe and in North America. The German pro-fessor, with his disciples in a seminar or laboratory, was interested in furthering the know-ledge of his subject, not in turning out gentlemen or even men of affairs. France, on the other hand, with romantic literature and later with realism, with the impressionists and the post-impressionists, acted as a magnet for poets, novelists and painters. There were, of course, great French scientists; Darwin was an Englishman educated in Scotland. But the pacemaking in nineteenth century history, philology, physics and chemistry was by Germans and there is no British Stendhal or Flaubert, no Spanish or Italian Cézanne. The decision to exclude from the 1963 Exhibition works of imaginative literature (though some squeezed themselves in) means that this French monopoly is not reflected in this book. But it is noticeable that, of the scholarly works described below which were published in the century and a half after 1800, a third are from German-speaking Europe, mostly from Germany itself.

As for the attitudes to books themselves which developed by 1900, one finds a curious contradiction. On the one hand old books are cherished with care, and on the other new books are generally regarded as expendable. The collecting of books, which had originally been restricted to incunables and editions of celebrated authors, has been enlarged in the last two generations to cover every variety of printing and every type of writer. Bibliographical expertise has increased and a tender concern watches for minute variants. This, reflected in sale-room prices, has led to the amassing of collections by men who regard books as an investment rather than as reading matter, and among the connoisseurs and the Ph.D. students it has given enormous prestige to libraries lucky enough to possess or acquire numbers of rarities. The days are over when the Bodleian Library could eject its first folio of Shakespeare when the third edition was printed in 1664.

At the same time the paperback, starting slowly in the early decades of this century, has now taken over much of the market in books. The strident display at a shop like Brentano's Basement in New York is totally different from the quiet of even the pre-Second World War bookshops and this brittle assertiveness seems to be the pattern for the future. Who does not see his local bookshop being slowly engulfed by the lava from the paperback volcanoes? The issue of a serious work in paper covers apparently for many readers confers on it the hallmark of the classical. Such books do not last physically; they are as flesh, all too easily assimilated to the lascivious-seeming works of fiction which are sold beside them. The reader buys the solid product as an instrument of entertainment or ambitious self-improvement. My own shelves are clogged with the detritus of thirty years of casual buying of paperbacks on all sorts of subjects, kept because I am an old-fashioned book-keeper and these belong to the genus *book*; but not kept in my study. Yet there, too, I have paperbacks—some of them, it is true, are in French and Italian (for publishers of serious and even expensive books in continental countries still tend to assume that their readers will have them bound) but some of them are editions of important works of scholarship in English which one might hunt for too long in a bound edition.

The multiplication of books in our own day is only one aspect of the changes which have recently occurred in communications. Far more important has been the advance of radio—first sound and then television. Like printing, radio is a technical innovation which has spread with extraordinary rapidity. And it represents a further stage not only in the diffusion of news and knowledge, but in the scope of political and cultural organization. Writing, it will be remembered, enabled government to increase in range and efficiency, and printing furthered the process. With radio the reach of political power is in principle almost boundless in our small universe. If the nineteenth century experienced a quickening pace in the penetration of more isolated areas by the central culture of bigger countries, radio is in a fair way to obliterating entirely the locally rooted community and the values that went with it.

It is, of course, conceivable that radio might replace the world of books. If this were to happen man might find himself back again in square two—not square one, that environment of gesture and emotive sound, but the next stage, the use of speech without writing. The invulnerability of the book must certainly not be taken for granted. Man has been reading now for something like six thousand years, a short enough space in the whole span of his development. He has been speaking for a far longer period than that and even before he spoke he had developed those activities of feeding and fighting and making love which still give him his deepest satisfactions. Reading and writing are relatively recent accomplishments and for that reason may suffer: 'last in, first out', as they say. There are, indeed, forces within scholarship itself which militate against the book. Advances in some of the sciences mean that a book on the subject is out of date almost as soon as it is printed. The biologist, the physicist and the medical researcher depend on periodical literature to keep in touch with their fields of interest. Even that is less satisfactory to them than direct contact and so they turn to the spoken word at congresses, conferences and colloquies. In the old humanist arts' subjects, where tradition might seem most deeply entrenched, the language laboratory is making otiose the familiar grammars and texts. Will radio, the acceleration of scientific discovery and new techniques of instruction mean that the book as we have known it will pass away?

Littera scripta manet: let us give the adage in its entirety—*Vox audita perit, littera scripta manet.* 'The spoken word passes away, the written word remains.' It is appropriate that the tag seems to have appeared first in one of the earliest printed books, Caxton's *Mirrour of the World* (1481). It is surely inconceivable that the impresarios of the future will succeed entirely in persuading the creators, the makers, to consign their inspiration to the ether, to be bounced about between the earth and the Heaviside Layer until the waves peter out in inaudible murmurs. Authors are not like children, content to see their beautiful pebbles flung into the pool of eternity. The student and the scholar, at any rate in many fields of human learning, will also want a measure of continuity. They will want shoulders to stand on as they peer at the past and future, and will not want to revert to the age when memory counted for everything. Equally the endless varieties of individual research and enjoyment could never be adequately reflected in the choices broadcast by Public Authority or Private Enterprise, however enlightened. Perhaps some day it may be possible to devise ways of recapturing the flying words and images of the past. Until that happens there will be no substitute for print and the book will remain the only way by which one age can speak to another.

This essay is entitled 'Let there be light'. This may seem a paradoxical way of describing printer's ink and the art of putting it on paper which was discovered by Gutenberg five hundred years ago: it is the dark letters we look at, not the white paper. But it may be justified. The printed page illuminates the mind of man and defies, in so far as anything sublunary can, the corrosive hand of Time.

THE CATALOGUE

PRINTING AND THE MIND OF MAN

I

'IN THE BEGINNING WAS THE WORD'

BIBLE, in Latin. [*Mainz: Johann Gutenberg, Johann Fust & Peter Schoeffer, c. 1455*]

The first substantial book to be printed from movable types in the western world was, appropriately, the most influential of all books—the Bible. The text used was the Latin version known as the Vulgate, which is still the standard text of the Roman Catholic Church. It is based largely on translations from the original tongues made by St Jerome (*c.* 340–420), but it embodies some of the work of earlier translators, and has undergone some modifications in later times.

The first printed Bible is most commonly known as the Gutenberg Bible, but bibliographers call it the 42-line Bible (in reference to the number of lines in a normal column) in order to distinguish it from a rival edition, probably printed at Bamberg, *c.* 1458–9, with 36 lines to the column. In earlier days it was also sometimes referred to as the Mazarin Bible, since the first copy to attract attention was that in the library of Cardinal Mazarin.

The Bible has no colophon, but there is general agreement that it was printed at Mainz, and that Johann Gutenberg, Johann Fust and Peter Schoeffer were concerned in the printing. The copy in the Bibliothèque Nationale, Paris, contains a manuscript note by its rubricator and binder, Heinrich Cremer, Vicar of St Stephen's at Mainz, stating that he completed his work on 24 August 1456. The printing of so large a book—it runs to 641 leaves and is normally bound in two volumes—must have taken more than a year; it must therefore have been begun at least several months before the partnership of Gutenberg, the inventor, and Fust, his financial backer, was dissolved by a lawsuit decided on 6 November 1455. Fust and Schoeffer in partnership printed the Mainz *Psalter*, dated 14 August 1457, and the type of the 42-line Bible reappears in a *Donatus* of *c.*1470, signed by Schoeffer. It is therefore thought that Gutenberg began the printing with Schoeffer as his assistant and Fust as his backer; that Fust, realizing that success in their venture was in sight, seized a legal opportunity to dissolve his partnership with Gutenberg and secure for himself the major share of the profits; and that Schoeffer sided with Fust, and probably completed the printing of the Bible.

Forty-eight copies of this Bible are known (if some seriously imperfect examples are counted), of which thirty-six are printed on paper and twelve on vellum; and thirty-one in all are perfect. Its printers were competing in the market hitherto supplied by the producers of high-class manuscripts. The design of the type and the layout of the book were therefore based on the book-hand and manuscript design of the day, and a very high standard of press-work was required—and obtained—to enable the new mechanical product to compete successfully with its hand-produced rivals. Standards were set in quality of paper and blackness of ink, in design and professional skill, which the printers of later generations have found difficult to maintain; it is only in legibility of type that they have been able to improve on this, the first and in many ways the greatest of all printed books.

BIBLIOGRAPHY: T. H. Darlow & H. F. Moule, *Historical Catalogue of the Printed Editions of Holy Scripture in the Library of the British and Foreign Bible Society*, 2 vols. (London, 1903–11; reprint 1965), no. 6076; Seymour de Ricci, *Catalogue raisonné des premières impressions de Mayence, 1445–67* (Mainz, 1911).

2

THE BIBLE IN THE VERNACULAR

BIBLE, in German. [*Strasbourg: Johann Mentelin, 1466*]

Within ten years of the completion of the first edition of the Bible in Latin (1), another German printer was at work on a Bible in the German language, and this was the first publication of the Scriptures in any vernacular tongue. Like the Gutenberg Bible, this first German version has no title-page, and no indication of the printer's name or the place and date of printing occurs in the book. A manuscript note by the rubricator in a copy at Strasbourg, however, records that the printing of the volume was completed in that city in 1466 by Johann Mentelin, and a similar note in the Munich copy states that it was bought unbound on 27 June of that year for 12 gulden.

The text is based on the Latin Vulgate, but the name of the translator is not known with certainty. It has been ascribed to a certain Rudigerus, who may be the Andreas (or Stephen) Rüdiger, known to have been Professor of Theology and Rector of the University of Leipzig in 1451. It has been suggested that it was influenced by the beliefs of the Waldenses, a sect which had renounced the doctrines, usages and traditions of the Roman Church in the twelfth century and continued to base its faith on the authority of the Bible alone. But this German version was certainly not regarded as heretical, and between 1466 and the publication in 1522 of Luther's translation of the New Testament (51) fourteen editions of the Bible in High German and four in Low German were printed, as well as over twenty vernacular editions of the Psalter alone.

Nor was it only in Germany that the Bible was allowed to circulate in the vulgar tongue before the Reformation.

Niccolo Malermi's translation into Italian was first printed by Wendelin of Speier at Venice in 1471 and at least ten Italian editions appeared before the end of the fifteenth century. Versions of both the Old and New Testaments in French came from the press of Guillaume Le Roy of Lyons at the end of the 1470s; but the French translations were not complete, being based on the paraphrases of Petrus Comestor and others which had circulated in the Middle Ages. The Old Testament without the Psalter was printed in Dutch at Delft in 1477; the Liturgical Epistles and Gospels were issued at Gouda in the same year; and the Psalter was printed at Delft in 1480. The complete New Testament was not, however, printed in Dutch until 1522. A Czech version of the New Testament was in print as early as 1475, and the complete Czech Bible appeared in Prague in 1488. A Catalan Bible was printed at Valencia in 1478.

BIBLIOGRAPHY: Darlow & Moule, no. 1466.

3

GOD'S GOVERNMENT ON EARTH

SAINT AUGUSTINE (354–430). De Civitate Dei. [*Subiaco: Conrad Sweynheym & Arnold Pannartz*], 1467

Aurelius Augustinus, Bishop of Hippo in North Africa, was one of the four great Fathers of the Latin Church. In his *Confessiones* (7) he described the influence of God's action on the individual. In 'The City of God' theology is shown in relation to the history of mankind and God's action in the world is explained.

In August 410 a Christian Gothic army under Alaric conquered and sacked Rome—its first capture by a foreign army for eight hundred years and an event which deeply disturbed the whole world. Two years later St Augustine received a letter from a Christian official, Marcellinus, pointing out that the Empire was now in decline; that it was being governed by rulers who had given up the old pagan deities in favour of the new Christian religion; and that the fall of Rome surely must be attributed to this change of religion. From his answer to this letter St Augustine was eventually led to write 'The City of God'. Its immediate purpose was, therefore, an apologia; the fall of Rome cannot be attributed to the abolition of pagan worship—a view of history which was revived by Gibbon (222); the happiness of mankind in this and the next world can only be assured by the Christian religion; and St Augustine explains the Christian Church as an organization which would fill the vacuum caused by the break-up of the secular state. There is no opposition between State and Church; the State is not necessarily evil; if it is pervaded by Christian ideals and the God-fearing life, then it approaches true justice and thereby the City of God.

The first five books deal with the polytheism of Rome, the second five with Greek philosophy, particularly Platonism and Neo-Platonism (which are seen as leading inevitably to Christianity in which their problems are finally resolved), and the last twelve books with the history of time and eternity as set out in the Bible. History is conceived as the struggle between two communities—the *Civitas coelestis* of those inspired by the love of God, leading to contempt of self, and the *Civitas terrena* or *diaboli* of those living according to man, which may lead to contempt of God. This struggle of the two conceptions of life had dominated Augustine's personal life (see the *Confessiones*) and is here transferred to the wider field of world history. Both these powers fighting for the allegiance of the human soul are inextricably intermingled in society's earthly institutions; but history is understood as a continuous evolution of the divine purpose and all forces work towards redemption of man by

De ſtimulis qbus ad mimim actū homo
impellit dea Stimula noietur. Strennua
dea ſit ſtrennuum faciendo. Numeria quę
nŭmerare doceat. Camena quę canet. Ipſe
ſit & deus Conſul prębēdo cōſilia: et dea
Sentia ſentētias inſpirando. Ipſe dea Iu-
uētas quę p9prętextatā excipiat iuuēilis
ętatis exordia. Ipſe ſit Fortuna barbata
quę adultos barba induit: quos honorar
uoluerit: ut hoc qualecūcq; numen ſaltem
maſculum deū: uľa barba Barbatū ſicut
a nodis Nodotū. uel certe nō Fortunam:
ſed qa barbas barbatū habet Fortunium
noiarent. Ipſe in Iugatino deo comiuges
iungat: et cū uirgini uxori zona ſoluitur
ipſe inuocet ſiue ūtutes ei9: et dea uirgi-
nenſis uocet. Ipſe ſit Motumus uel Tutu-
mus: q̄ ē apđ gręcos Priap9 ſi nō pudet.
Hęc oia quę dixi & quęcūcq; nō dixi: non
eni oia dicēda arbitratus ſum: hi oēs dii

God's grace, the central feature of St Augustine's theology. It is for this reason that he is considered as the founder of a new science, to which Voltaire (202) assigned the name 'philosophy of history'. For the first time a comprehensive survey of human history is presented. History, he maintained, has a goal. Salvation by God's grace is not just a cyclical, haphazard occurrence of events. In Augustine's view the victory of faith is historically inevitable.

In economics Augustine praised labour as a means towards moral perfection; interest charges on money were not allowed under his system, but trade could be carried on, if selling was done honestly and a 'just price' was charged and paid. Many of the medieval regulations about commerce and prices were derived from these ideas, and his contrasting description of a just ruler (imbued with piety, humility, fairness) and the tyrant or Antichrist (impiety, craving for glory) powerfully influenced Renaissance thought.

'The City of God' pervaded the whole Middle Ages— Einhard tells us that it was one of Charlemagne's favourite books—and in the struggle between Pope and Emperor both sides drew arguments from it. The Holy Roman Empire was conceived as a Catholic Commonwealth with the two swords in all executive departments, the secular and the spiritual. It had an essentially religious character and as such it had affinities with St Augustine's great Church State. The book remained authoritative until the seventeenth and eighteenth centuries, when Bossuet (157) was the last 'Augustinian' historian; and Vico (184) was much indebted to him, though, of course, where Augustine is chiefly concerned with the Church and salvation, Vico is concerned with the world and the manifestations of human nature. The idea of international law was partly derived from the book; Grotius (125) cites St Augustine. Both Luther (49) and Calvin (65) took Augustine as the foundation of Protestantism next to the Bible itself. More than four thousand quotations from Augustine have been traced in the writings of Calvin alone.

In our own day Lionel Curtis, Jacques Maritain, Reinhold Niebuhr, Paul Tillich and other thinkers have drawn inspiration from this great work.

The first edition of 1467 is the third book to be printed in Italy and the last of three printed at Subiaco before the printers removed their press to Rome.

4

ROMAN LAW

FLAVIUS PETRUS SABBATIUS JUSTINIANUS (483–565). Institutiones. *Mainz: Peter Schoeffer, 1468*

No single authority has had greater influence in shaping the existing legal codes of all nations than the Roman Law; obvious in those which, like the *Code Napoléon*, sought to impose a theoretic standpoint, it may be felt even in fundamentally empiric bodies of law like the English Common Law.

The credit for the survival of this authority can be ascribed in a very large degree to the work undertaken by Justinian I, Roman Emperor of the East from 527 to 565. When he came to the throne, the law was in a chaotic state: it was divided into the statutes, decrees of the Senate and writings of the old jurists, known as the *jus vetus*, and the imperial *constitutiones* and later juristic writings which formed the *jus novum*. Not even the public libraries contained a complete set of all this literature; it was confused, disorganized and sometimes self-contradictory. On the other hand, it contained much valuable precedent and the writings of such eminent jurists as Papinian, Ulpian and Gaius, the last of whom

exercised great influence on the work which Justinian produced.

By 533 the task was complete. A commission headed by Tribonian, the Emperor's principal adviser, first collated and ordered all the imperial edicts, and the *Codex Constitutionum* was made law in 529 by a consolidating statute repealing all that had gone before. Then came the much more difficult task of removing the inconsistencies and organizing the older law incorporated in the writings of the jurists; the extracts thus made were enacted in 533 under the name of *Digests* (or *Pandects*). Finally, while these tasks were in progress, the Emperor directed Tribonian to prepare an introduction to the main work, and the elementary treatise thus produced, the 'Institutes of Justinian', has been for students ever since the introduction to the Roman Law.

The code of Justinian persisted through later Byzantine additions and successfully absorbed the impact of the local customary laws of invading tribes in the West during the Dark Ages. The famous legal school of Bologna popularized it from the eleventh century on. One of the first demands to be made on the printing press was to disseminate it further, and the classical research first of Politian (32) and later of Alciati and Cujas in the sixteenth century established it as the starting point for legal speculation and the core of existing codes. When people speak of the Roman Law today, what they mean is Justinian.

5

ALL THE KNOWLEDGE
OF THE ANCIENTS

GAIUS PLINIUS SECUNDUS (A.D. 23–79). Historia Naturalis. *Venice: Johannes de Spira, 1469*

The 'Natural History' of Pliny the Elder is more than a natural history: it is an encyclopaedia of all the knowledge of the ancient world. The famous story of Pliny's death while trying to observe the eruption of Vesuvius at closer quarters than was prudent is often, and justly, cited as an example of the devoted curiosity on which the furthering of knowledge depends, and to the Romans his writing on the natural sciences was pioneer work (held in small esteem, as he modestly says, by his countrymen).

He was a compiler rather than an original thinker, and the importance of this book depends more on his exhaustive reading (he quotes over four hundred authorities, Greek and Latin) than on his original work. All the spare time allowed him by a busy administrative career was devoted to reading; he began long before daybreak, his nephew the younger Pliny recorded, and grudged every minute not spent in study; no book was so bad, he used to say, as not to contain something of value. When he died the 'Natural History' (the sole extant work out of one hundred and two volumes from his pen) was still incomplete. It comprises thirty-seven books dealing with mathematics and physics, geography and astronomy, medicine and zoology, anthropology and physiology, philosophy and history, agriculture and mineralogy, the arts and letters. He is scrupulous in his acknowledgement of his sources (you must, he wrote, with honest humility, declare those from whom you have profited), and the whole of the first book is devoted to the tables of contents and authorities which bear witness to his method.

The *Historia* soon became a standard book of reference: abstracts and abridgements appeared by the third century. Bede (17) owned a copy, Alcuin sent the early books to Charlemagne, and Dicuil, the Irish geographer, quotes him in the ninth century. It was the basis of Isidore's *Etymologiae* (9) and such medieval encyclopaedias as the *Speculum Majus* of Vincent of Beauvais and the *Catholicon* of Balbus. One of the earliest books to be printed at Venice, the centre from which so much of classical literature was first dispensed, it was later translated into English by Philemon Holland in 1601, and twice reprinted (a notable achievement for so vast a text).

More recently, scholars as various as Humboldt (301) and Grimm (281) have praised and acknowledged their debt to it. Over and over again it will be found that the source of some ancient piece of knowledge is Pliny.

6
THE EPIC OF ROME

PUBLIUS VERGILIUS MARO (70–19 B.C.). Opera. (*a*) *Rome: Sweynheym & Pannartz [1469]. (b) Venice: Aldus Manutius, 1501*

Virgil was born in Mantua, achieved fame in Rome in the early years of the Emperor Augustus, and died at Naples. The land of Italy which he knew so well is the underlying theme of all his surviving work, in the *Aeneid* as well as more directly in the pastoral *Eclogues* and the nominally didactic *Georgics*. The tale of Aeneas, the legendary founder of Rome, how he fled from the sack of Troy, found refuge with Dido at Carthage, and eventually came to conquer and settle in Rome, is ostensibly a panegyric of the family of Augustus and the great destiny of Rome in the history of the world—*Tantae molis erat Romanam condere gentem.*

Despite the magnificent statement of the honour and duties of imperial status—*Parcere subjectis et debellare superbos*—Virgil was too great an artist to be confined to a formal theme. His sympathies lie rather with what his hero stands for—pious obedience, resolute purpose, and order—than with the hero himself. Indeed, of his characters, it is those who suffered from the triumph of Aeneas, Dido and Turnus, who engage the author's feelings most. When he returns to describe and muse on his own country he seems to move in a higher and more serene sphere than this world, and it is this which gave the *Aeneid* its impact on Virgil's contemporaries; an impact which has persisted to this day. Never before had the sense of nobility, in human affairs and institutions and in nature, the imaginative spell of natural beauty, of the past, and of the unseen world, been so compellingly expressed. The veneration accorded to Virgil throughout the Dark Ages is a notable tribute to the impression he had made.

He was even brought within the ambit of the Christian Church as a foreteller of the Messiah, a belief to which he owes his position as Dante's guide and mentor (8); and medieval fancy converted him into a famous sorcerer.

A hundred separate editions of the whole or part of the Virgilian corpus were printed before the end of the fifteenth century. The first is an early and beautiful work of the first printers in Rome. Later editions were often accompanied by the fourth-century commentary of Servius, an invaluable source of information. But perhaps the most important of all editions was that produced in the first year of the new century by Aldus: the first pocket book to be printed and the ancestor of the millions of cheap editions and paperbacks not represented in these pages but as a whole perhaps the most significant of all testimonies to the impact of the printing press. Aldus's edition, and the series of pocket classics that followed, was a vast success. The italic type which he had cut for it endorsed the victory of the Roman renaissance letter over the north European black letter. The triumph of Aldus was also the triumph of his choice of author. As the revival of learning brought greater knowledge of the influence of Rome, Virgil came to be recognized as the greatest of Latin poets; and his majestic lines and noble sentiments have become a part of the European heritage.

7
THE FIRST GREAT AUTOBIOGRAPHY

SAINT AUGUSTINE (354–430). Confessiones. [*Strasbourg: Johann Mentelin, not after 1470*]

This is the first great autobiography in which personal confessions and revelations are linked with the spirit of Christian piety and devotion.

The 'Confessions' were written about 400, five years after Augustine had become Bishop of Hippo in North Africa. The first nine books contain a general sketch of his life up to his conversion and baptism and the death of his mother in 387; book 10 is a psychological study in which he considers the implications of authorship of the book by a bishop; books 11–13 contain a commentary on the first chapter of Genesis.

Aurelius Augustinus, though educated as a Christian, became a follower of Manichaeism when studying at Carthage, but after passing through a period of scepticism and studying Neo-Platonism he was converted by Bishop Ambrosius of Milan and baptised in 387.

The 'Confessions' were something quite new in literary composition. Their frank description of both emotional and intellectual problems, their acute psychological observations and the analysis of complex sentiments, and at the same time their obvious sincerity and humility, account for their immediate and lasting influence. But this autobiography of a man's soul is made a vehicle for a revelation of God's goodness, guidance and protection of man; it is the doctrine of grace, one of the central ideas of Augustine's teachings. He himself described it in his 'Retractions', written about 428: 'The

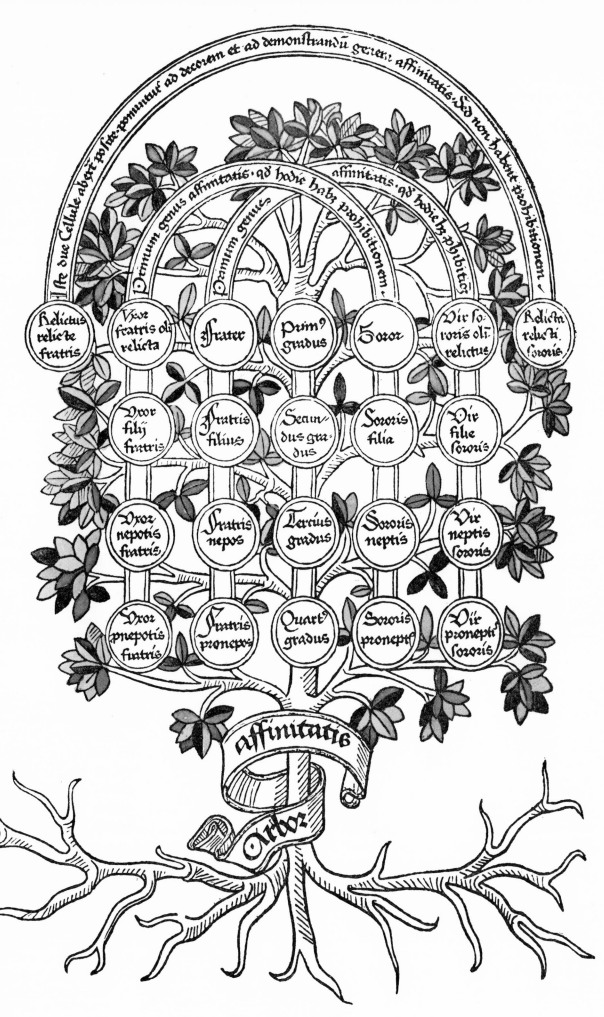

NO. 9, ISIDORE

thirteen books of my Confessions, both of my sins and my good deeds, do praise God who is both just and good and do excite both the affection and understanding of man towards Him.'

None of St Augustine's other writings except 'The City of God' (3) has been more universally read or admired. It is a book which both in its strength of thought and confession of weakness has been a constant companion to many Christians, and Rousseau's and other notable autobiographies are greatly indebted to it.

8

THE DIVINE COMEDY

DANTE ALIGHIERI (1265–1321). La Commedia. (a) Foligno: Johann Neumeister & Evangelista Angelini, 1472. (b) Florence: Nicolaus Laurentii, Alemanus, 1481

'The Divine Comedy' of Dante could have been written at no other time than at the beginning of the fourteenth century. It was essentially an age of freedom and daring in thought and speech, which it was natural to express in verse. To this Dante added a deep knowledge of the learning of his time, and he was himself a profound and original political thinker whose ideals outran the strifes and feuds which divided Italy, to which, however, we owe his best work. For it was the total downfall of his political hopes on 27 January 1302 that condemned Dante to perpetual exile and turned him to the writing of the epic which begins with the vision of himself lost in a forest, his way barred by a wolf, a lion and a leopard on the Thursday before Easter, 1300.

Dante's theme, the greatest yet attempted in poetry, was to explain and justify the Christian cosmos through the allegory of a pilgrimage. To him comes Virgil (6), the symbol of philosophy, to guide him through the two lower realms of the next world, which are divided according to the classifications of the 'Ethics' of Aristotle (38). Hell is seen as an inverted cone with its point where lies Lucifer fixed in ice at the centre of the world, and the pilgrimage from it a climb to the foot of and then up the Purgatorial Mountain. Along the way Dante passes Popes, Kings and Emperors, poets, warriors and citizens of Florence, expiating the sins of their life on earth. On the summit is the Earthly Paradise where Beatrice meets them and Virgil departs. Dante is now led through the various spheres of heaven, and the poem ends with a vision of the Deity. The audacity of his theme, the success of its treatment, the beauty and majesty of his verse, have ensured that his poem never lost its reputation. The picture of divine justice is entirely unclouded by Dante's own political prejudices, and his language never falls short of what he describes.

The Commedia was printed and reprinted from 1472 onwards when Johann Neumeister printed the first edition at Foligno. The 1481 edition is famous for the remarkable series of engravings by Baldini from drawings made by Botticelli for a manuscript of the work probably commissioned by Lorenzo de' Medici; it also contains the famous commentary of Christoforo Landino.

The epithet 'Divina' was not added till 1555, when it appears on the title-page of Lodovico Dolce's edition.

9

THE MEDIEVAL ENCYCLOPAEDIA

ISIDORE OF SEVILLE (died 636). Etymologiae. [Augsburg]: Günther Zainer, 1472

From the year 1460, when Gutenberg printed the Catholicon of the thirteenth-century friar, Johannes Balbus of Genoa, encyclopaedias have remained one of the most popular productions of the printing press: profitable to printers, publishers and booksellers and desired by the reading public wishing for comprehensive information on the range of human knowledge available at any given time.

Before 1500, in addition to the Catholicon (of which six editions were published in Venice alone between 1483 and 1506), at least three other encyclopaedias appeared in print, and the fact that their first editions were brought out virtually simultaneously by three different printers shows the widespread interest in this kind of book as well as the fierce spirit of competition within the printing trade. In 1472 the unknown Cologne printer, in whose shop William Caxton learned printing, published De Proprietatibus Rerum by the thirteenth-century English Franciscan, Bartholomaeus de Glanville. After two and a half centuries this encyclopaedia was still a standard work used at all cisalpine universities, as is shown by its frequent reissue (Nuremberg, Anton Koberger, 1483; Haarlem, Bellaert, 1485; Westminster, Wynkyn de Worde, 1495).

Older and of infinitely greater importance than these three encyclopaedias is the work of the Spanish bishop Isidore, which is now known under the title of 'Etymologies, or the Origins of Words'. An industrious and uncritical compiler, he supplied factual as well as fantastic information culled from all the ancient authors available to him (and incidentally preserved much material that has since been lost). Isidore thus became the chief authority of the Middle Ages, and the presence of his book in every monastic, cathedral and college library was a main factor in perpetuating the state of knowledge and the modes of thought of the late-Roman world.

Johannes Balbus, Bartholomaeus Anglicus and a host of other writers were deeply indebted to Isidore. In his homeland, Spain, his reputation outlasted the Middle Ages far into the seventeenth century; Calderón was still grounded in the Etymologiae. To our age, Isidore has remained a primary source of the ancient world-picture as conceived in the Middle Ages.

10

THE EARLIEST TECHNICAL ILLUSTRATIONS

ROBERTUS VALTURIUS (1413–84). De Re Militari. [*Verona*]: *Johannes Nicolai de Verona, 1472*

Roberto Valturio, a native of Rimini, after having been Apostolic Secretary in Rome, became technical adviser and engineer to Sigismondo Malatesta, Lord of Rimini. He composed his book 'On Military Matters' about 1460. After wide circulation in manuscript, it was printed in 1472. Written when gunpowder's powerful influence on military technique was already a century old, yet ancient methods of siege-warfare were still practised, the text of the book is on the whole rather backward-looking and contains no revolutionary military principles. Some of its most novel-seeming ideas had been described in the fourteenth century, for Valturio followed a long tradition of military engineering.

The historical importance of the *De Re Militari* lies in the fact that it is the first book printed with illustrations of a technical or scientific character depicting the progressive engineering ideas of the author's own time. The eighty-two woodcuts illustrate the equipment necessary for the military and naval engineer; they include revolving gun turrets, platforms and ladders for sieges, paddle-wheels, a diver's suit, a lifebelt, something resembling a tank, pontoon and other bridges, a completely closed boat that could be half submerged, etc.

The book was the second printed at Verona and the illustrations are the first true Italian book illustrations, probably after designs by Matteo de Pasti, the medallist and pupil of Alberti (28). They were preceded in Italy only by a blockbook and the 1467 Rome edition of Torquemada, which contains a series of rather crude woodcuts probably designed under German influence. The illustrations were not printed together with the letterpress as in later books; they were added in thinner ink after the text was printed, either by the printer or possibly by the illuminator. They were used again (copies from the same blocks but in reverse) in the German edition of Vegetius's *De Re Militari* (Augsburg, 1476), the first technical book published in Germany, and had a considerable vogue throughout the sixteenth century. The Verona Valturius and its reprints were the handbooks of the military leaders of the Renaissance, and Leonardo da Vinci, when acting as chief engineer to Cesare Borgia, possessed a copy and borrowed some of its designs.

BIBLIOGRAPHY: Leo S. Olschki, 'La Prima Edizione di Valturio'. In: *Bibliofilia*, I (Florence, 1899).

11
ARABIC MEDICINE

AVICENNA (980–1037). Canon Medicinae. [*Strasbourg: Adolf Rusch (the R printer), before 1473*]

Avicenna, an Arabian philosopher, physician, poet, courtier and politician, had perhaps a wider influence in the eastern and western hemispheres than any other Islamic thinker. He lived mainly in Persia but wrote mostly in Arabic, though a few of his works were written in Persian. He is reputed to have produced more than one hundred and sixty books, most of which are now lost. At the age of sixteen he read medicine—'not one of the difficult sciences', he said—and became physician to the Emir of Bokhara, where he had access to a great library and continued his studies in philosophy and other branches of learning.

The *Canon*, written in Arabic and here translated into Latin by Gerardus of Cremona, is a compendium of Greek and Muslim medical knowledge of Avicenna's time, co-ordinating the teachings of Galen (33), Hippocrates (55) and Aristotle (38). It superseded all previous works—even the great medical encyclopaedia of Rhazes—and in its Latin translation became the authoritative book in all universities. It was still being printed in the seventeenth century, though by that time its influence had been superseded by Galen and then by the new medical school represented by Sydenham (159) and others. It is, however, still in use in parts of the Arab world today.

The last book, containing his own records of cases, is lost, but the *Canon* still contains many original observations. Avicenna recognized the distribution of diseases by water and soil. He describes many nervous ailments, skin diseases, etc. In the section *Materia Medica* he records seven hundred and sixty drugs and, for the first time, the preparation and properties of alcohol. By treating surgery as a separate and inferior part of medicine, he was un-fortunately responsible for a setback in the development of this department of medical science.

Avicenna's philosophical works, attempting a recon-ciliation of Plato, Aristotle and oriental thought and religion, became one of the fundamental sources for scholasticism and probably influenced such thinkers as Aquinas (30), Duns Scotus and Roger Bacon. His work on psychiatry and psychology derived from Aristotle and acquired a wide following. Body and soul were con-ceived as separate entities; the soul emanates from God, enters the body after generation and is immortal. This conception is similar to that of St Augustine (3) and leads directly to the *cogito, ergo sum* of Descartes (129). Avicenna wrote on mathematics (translating Euclid, see 25), optics and physics. His work on the 'origin of mountains' is a remarkable early survey of geology and the main source for the thirteenth-century encyclo-paedists. His opposition to alchemy was a unique phenomenon for his time.

The *Canon* was translated into Hebrew (1491), the first Arabic printing appeared in 1593, and there were many editions of, and commentaries on, the Latin trans-lation by Gerardus of Cremona (1114–87). Through these printings Avicenna's work transmitted to the West the ideas of the great Greek writers and also introduced ideas of his own which in some respects superseded them.

12
RENAISSANCE BAEDEKER

MIRABILIA ROMAE. [*Rome: Adam Rot, 1473?*]

'The Wonders of Rome', the earliest printed guide book, developed out of the lists of Roman remains and temples which had existed since late classical times. When, during the twelfth century, there was a revival of the idea of the greatness of Rome, an enthusiast compiled this work in about 1140–50 as a guide for the pilgrims to the city. His identity was unknown until recent times, but he is now believed to have been Benedict, Canon of St Peter's, who also compiled a manual of the administration of the Curia. During the following centuries its form under-went some changes, but essentially it remained the same.

It opens with a short history of Rome down to the time of Constantine, after which follows a description of the remains of ancient Rome and suggestions for a perambu-lation of the city with references to its churches—in later editions about eighty of these were cited. There are comments on their religious significance, their relics, special feast days, etc., but an increasing amount of in-formation on their art treasures is included. This illustrates a new awareness of the significance of ancient Roman remains and was instrumental in preserving some of them.

The *Mirabilia* is a valuable source for our knowledge of what remained and attracted notice in medieval Rome. One of its pleasant side-effects was the beginning of measures for the 'protection of ancient monuments'—such as Trajan's column—as the Roman authorities realized their importance for tourism. Petrarch and Dante both appear to have known the book.

The edition cited is believed to be the earliest of several undated editions of the early 1470s. The first with a date was published in 1475, and from then onwards innumer-able editions were published, many in Germany—in-cluding a remarkable blockbook in about 1474–5—but principally in Italy; and there were Italian, English, German and Spanish translations. More than thirty editions were printed in the sixteenth century, with in-creasing details about the artistic treasures of Rome, over forty in the seventeenth, but only seven in the eighteenth century. By that time this prototype had been superseded by the large number of Italian guide books—not only on Rome, but on other important artistic centres—which began to appear from the seventeenth century onwards, until their role in turn was taken over in modern times by the publication of Baedeker (302).

BIBLIOGRAPHY: Chr. Hülsen, *Mirabilia Romae* (Berlin, 1925).

13
THE IMITATION OF CHRIST

THOMAS À KEMPIS (1379 or 1380–1471). De Imitatione Christi. [*Augsburg*]: *Günther Zainer* [*1473*]

'The Imitation of Christ' is a book of mystical thought which throughout history has appealed to Roman Catholics and Protestants alike. It has been the most widely read devotional manual apart from the Bible, perhaps even surpassing the influence of such books as *Pilgrim's Progress* (156) and St Augustine's *Confessiones* (7).

This is the more surprising as in the first place it was addressed to monks and recluses. An expression of the German–Dutch mystical school of the fifteenth century, its message stressed the humble Christian virtues as they were preached in the Sermon on the Mount. Self-renunciation and the study of the life of Christ are the central points of its instruction. The criticism has in fact been made that its piety is hostile to learning, stresses the passive qualities, and takes little account of human activity as a whole in relation to the struggle for existence. Its universal appeal remains undeniable, however, and this is at least partly due to the great simplicity of its style and its freedom from intellectualism or theological dogmatism.

The book is written partly in verse. Its title is derived from that of the first of its four books 'De imitatione Christe et contemptu vanitatum mundi' (of the imitation of Christ and the contempt of all worldly vanities). Its authorship has been the subject of dispute—sometimes violent: the rival to the accepted author being Johannes Gerson, though claims have been made for others—among them Walter Hilton, the English divine. However, Thomas à Kempis is now definitely recognized as its author. Born at Kempen in the Diocese of Cologne, he was educated by the Congregation of the Brothers of the Common Life, lately founded at Deventer by Gerard Groot and Florentius Radewyn. Their aim was to revive the zeal and fervour of the early Christians of Jerusalem and Antioch. The community took no vows, but lived according to the monastic principles of poverty, obedience and chastity; all earnings were put into a common fund and the devotees spent their lives in teaching and transcribing books—about 1475 they established the first printing press in Brussels.

In 1399, having completed his studies at Deventer, Thomas sought out his brother John, who was the Prior at the reformed monastery of the Augustinian Canons Regular at Mount Saint Agnes, near Zwolle. Some time elapsed before the question of his vocation was decided, for it was not until 1408 that he took his vows and became a full member of the Congregation. He was ordained priest in 1413 and became Sub-Prior in 1429. He lived there all his life. He wrote a history of Agnetenberg and the lives of Groot and Radewyn, and transcribed a number of manuscripts, among them the works of St Bernard and a large Bible which is still extant at Darmstadt.

The masterly edition of Thomas's holograph manuscript produced by L. M. J. Delaissé (Brussels, 1956) shows conclusively that the 'Imitation', as we are accustomed to read it, consists of four disparate mystical writings, of which manuscripts exist dated 1427. These began to circulate from about 1431, and a codex signed by Thomas himself and dated 1441 survives in the Royal Library at Brussels. The title *Liber de Imitatione Christi* began to be used for the collection in the second half of the fifteenth century.

The 'Imitation' was first printed in 1473. Since then there have been thousands of editions and translations into fifty languages, a record rivalled only by the Bible itself. The first English translation by William Atkinson and Margaret, Duchess of Beaufort, mother of Henry VII, was published in 1503. It influenced the most diverse personalities such as Wesley, de Quincey, Milman, George Eliot and General Gordon, who carried a copy with him on the battlefield.

14*
FAITH AND REASON

MOSES BEN MAIMON, known as MAIMONIDES (1135–1204). Moreh Nebukim. *Rome: printer unknown, c. 1473–5*

During the centuries before printing the ideas of Aristotle (38) had been propagated largely through the works of others; such as Albertus Magnus (17) and Avicenna (11). It was in the twelfth and thirteenth centuries that philosophers essayed to harmonize them with the tenets of the three principal religious faiths of the West; Aquinas (30) for Catholics, Averroes (24) for Muslims, and Maimonides—like Averroes a native of Cordova in Spain and like him a doctor as well as a philosopher, educated by Arabic masters—for the Jews. His 'Guide for the Perplexed', taking Aristotelianism as a basis, insists that reason is limited and must be supplemented by revelation.

When Cordova fell to the Arab invaders in 1148 the position of the Jews became intolerable. Maimonides, after ten years of wandering, settled in Fez; moving five years later to Cairo, where he was soon recognized as the greatest rabbinical scholar of his time. He married a lady of the Court and was appointed physician to Saladin.

The 'Guide', written in Arabic and completed about 1190, was shortly translated into Hebrew under the title *Moreh Nebukim*. Its influence was soon felt not only by Jewish but also by Christian and Muslim religious philosophers: both Albertus Magnus and Thomas Aquinas quoted extensively from the Latin translation which was made at some time during the thirteenth century.

Moreh Nebukim was first printed, in the Hebrew text, in Rome in the 1470s, by a printer still not identified. A Latin translation, under the title *Dux seu Director Dubitantium aut Perplexorum*, was published in Paris in 1520. The standard edition (3 vols., Paris, 1856–66) appeared in an English translation by M. Friedlander in 1881–5, later reissued in one volume.

Maimonides's other works included a commentary on the *Mishnah*, first published in Hebrew at Naples in 1492, the *Mishnah Torah*, *Kitab al-Fara'id* (in Hebrew, Lisbon, 1497), *Responsa*, and treatises on logic and on poisons.

15
AESOP'S FABLES

AESOP (*c.* 610–*c.* 560 B.C.). (*a*) Vita et Fabulae. *Milan: Antonius Zarotus, 1474.* (*b*) With Italian translation. *Naples: Francesco del Tuppo, 1485 (see cut)*

Whether or not Aesop was the author of the 'Fables' to which his name is attached, whether indeed—as has sometimes been doubted—he ever existed at all, hardly matters. The fact that the text which survives, and was first printed (with a biography of Aesop) in the Latin translation of Rinucius, is a collection made by Maximus Planudes in the fourteenth century (with some oriental additions) from a translation by Andreopoulos of a Syriac version by Syntipas of the Greek text as turned into choliambics by Babrius in the earlier part of the third century, is equally immaterial. Something of the fables which, according to Plato, Socrates while in prison turned into verse, has come down to us, and from it all the popular fables of modern Europe are derived.

'Moralized', illustrated, quoted, copied, parodied and reprinted, they have been diffused over the whole western world and—who knows?—some of the oriental 'originals' may themselves be copied from still earlier lost Greek sources. Innumerable imitators, from La Fontaine to Thurber, have given new life to the form.

16
THE VENERABLE BEDE

BEDE (or BAEDA) (673–735). Historia Ecclesiastica Gentis Anglorum. [*Strasbourg: Heinrich Eggesteyn, c. 1475*]

Bede, who in the century after his death became known as the Venerable Bede, was the greatest English historian

and one of the greatest European historians of the Middle Ages. It is therefore not surprising that his most important work—and certainly the one with the strongest appeal to laymen—should have been one of the first historical books to be printed. The 'Ecclesiastical History of the English People', which is in fact a comprehensive history of the Anglo-Saxon tribes, was completed in 731 and its fame soon spread far and wide. The English scholars and missionaries who worked in the Frankish empire in the eighth and ninth centuries—men such as Boniface and Alcuin—were well acquainted with Bede's writings, and manuscripts of the *Historia Ecclesiastica* were in many monasteries of the Rhine and Moselle regions.

The appearance in Strasbourg of the *editio princeps* of the *Historia Ecclesiastica* is less puzzling than might appear at first sight. The publisher, Heinrich Eggesteyn, like all his Strasbourg fellow-printers, specialized in publications for the laity; and the fact that he produced the earliest surviving advertisement sheet (1466) shows that he had a shrewd eye for the market. Moreover, the Rhenish printers—besides those of Strasbourg, especially those of Cologne—were obviously interested in the English market: one Cologne printer, Johann Schilling, in 1472–3 issued four books by English authors, including Richard de Bury's *Philobiblon.* Thus Eggesteyn no doubt reckoned that Bede's masterpiece would sell among the educated public on the continent as well as in England. He was not mistaken: the *Historia Ecclesiastica* had to be reprinted in 1500 in Strasbourg, and, by Heinrich Gran of Hagenau in Alsace, in 1506 and 1514.

Though Bede's treatise *De Temporum Ratione* (on chronology) is nowadays known only to a handful of scholars, his influence nevertheless affects our daily life. For this book helped to establish the custom of counting years from the birth of Christ. When we say that Queen Elizabeth II was born in 1926 (not 'in the 16th year of the reign of George V', or 'in the year 2678 after the foundation of Rome', or in the '2nd year of the 481st Olympiad'), we are indebted to the Venerable Bede.

BIBLIOGRAPHY: *Beda-Bibliographie,* ed. Preussische Staatsbibliothek (Berlin, 1939).

17
THE UNIVERSAL DOCTOR

ALBERTUS MAGNUS (1193–1280). (*a*) De Mineralibus. [*Padua: Petrus Maufer for Antonius de Albricis, 1476*]. (*b*) De Animalibus (edited by Fernandus Cordubensis). *Rome: Simon Chardella, 1478*

Albertus Magnus was the most learned scholar of his age, the 'Doctor Universalis' of the Middle Ages and the only one to whom the epithet 'The Great' was applied. A German nobleman (Count of Bollstädt), he became a Dominican. He taught in Germany and Paris, became Provincial of his Order in Germany and Bishop of Regensburg, and eventually retired to the Dominican house at Cologne. He was considered a saint from the fourteenth century, beatified in 1622, canonized and proclaimed a Doctor of the Church in 1931.

Albertus was active in practically all departments of learning—theological, philosophical, scientific—and his influence in all these directions was immense. He combined elements of Aristotelianism, Neo-Platonism, Christian theology and Muslim and Jewish philosophy, which he formed into one great system; but his chief aim as a philosopher remained the reconciliation of Aristotelianism with Christian teaching. His system became one of the bases of scholasticism all over Europe. Thomas Aquinas (30) attended his lectures and Dante (8) placed both master and pupil among the *Spiriti Sapienti* in the heaven of the sun.

Since Albertus's system was essentially a compilation, his standing in philosophy and theology may be challenged by others: but he was the most important observer of nature that the Middle Ages had yet produced, the greatest naturalist since Pliny (5). He wrote in the form of paraphrases of Aristotle, into which he interpolated his personal observations of natural and scientific phenomena, and he had at least a conception of the importance of experimentalism. His most valuable studies are perhaps his botanical and zoological works, as he had personally observed many plants and animals on his travels. His book on minerals contains descriptions of such chemical substances as alum, arsenic and vitriol, details of ninety-five precious stones or minerals, and many other particulars collected on his visits to alchemical laboratories. The *De Mineralibus* went into seven editions by 1569 and was translated into Italian.

Albertus's collected works appeared in 1651 in twenty-one folio volumes, edited by Pierre Jammy, and again in thirty-eight volumes in Paris, 1890-9, edited by A. and E. Borgnet, which latter edition includes a bibliography.

18*

THE PTOLEMAIC UNIVERSE

Claudius Ptolemæus (d. after A.D. 161). Cosmographia. *Bologna: Dominicus de Lapis, '1462'* [1477]

Ptolemy was born in Egypt and lived during the second half of the second century in Alexandria, where he raised two pillars with his astronomical discoveries engraved upon them. He wrote in Greek.

The Ptolemaic conception of the universe dominated the thinking of western man from the second to the sixteenth and even continued into the eighteenth century. Ptolemy's influence can be compared only with that of Aristotle. It derives from his two great books: the *Almagest* (see 40) and his 'Geography' or 'Cosmography'. Ptolemy also compiled a catalogue of 1,028 stars which

remained the only one until the fifteenth century, and wrote two other important works, on optics and on the theory of music.

In his 'Geography' he showed the earth to be a perfect sphere, with land and water intermingled, gave a table of longitudes and latitudes of 8,000 places in the world and first made technical use of the terms *parallel* and *meridian*. Many of his ideas were derived from Hipparchus and Marinus of Tyre, but Ptolemy corrected their findings and adapted them to practical purposes. Of course, his system had many errors. His mistaken estimate of the extent of the Asiatic continent induced Columbus (35) to travel westwards, and his statement that the Indian Ocean was largely surrounded by the great southern continent was only disproved by the voyages of Captain Cook (223). It must be remembered, however, that Ptolemy's texts reached the West via Byzantine and Arabic scholars —the fifteenth-century editions were all Latin translations of the Greek original—and we cannot tell how far the maps represent his own designs or have been altered in transmission. Even after the voyages of Columbus and Magellan (see 57), his influence persisted on many maps of the seventeenth and eighteenth centuries and for the interior of Africa until the nineteenth.

But it was the general Ptolemaic conception of the universe which prevailed in the western world for centuries. It placed the earth and man in the centre of the world, it arranged the planets in orderly orbits and systems round it, and it connected each planet with a certain class of people. This was an idea which strongly appealed to the Church, which similarly conceived the world as a great hierarchical system, from God through man downwards to the lowest form of animal life. Society was equally divided politically into three feudal states—nobility, clergy and the common man, each with his particular function. These systems formed an orderly world picture which survived the shattering discovery of Copernicus (70) that the universe was not centred round the earth.

Dante (8) and Milton both organized their works round Ptolemy's cosmic system; it occurs frequently in Chaucer; it dominated the Elizabethan world—see Spenser's *Faerie Queene*—and even Pope in his *Essay on Man* still speaks of the 'vast chain of being' as essential to an orderly universe. Nevertheless, the Reformation and the scientific revolution which followed it eventually shattered this great universal and unifying system of cosmography and thought.

The first edition of Ptolemy in the Latin translation of Jacobus Angelus de Scarparia was published in Vicenza in 1475 without maps; the Bologna edition is the first to be illustrated with maps. The original Greek text was not published until 1533 (Basle, edited by Erasmus).

BIBLIOGRAPHY: Wilberforce Eames, *A List of Editions of Ptolemy's Geography* (New York, 1886); Henry N. Stevens, *Ptolemy's Geography* (1908).

19

THE FIRST BILINGUAL DICTIONARY

VOCABOLARIO ITALIANO-TEUTONICO. *Venice: Adam von Rottweil, 1477*

It is not surprising that Venice, the economic metropolis of the Mediterranean, should have been the predestined place for the publication of the first dictionary of two living languages. Venice had a large German colony of businessmen, centred on the Fondaco dei Tedeschi, and there can be little doubt that the 'Italian–German Vocabulary' was chiefly meant for their use. It is not a work of philological scholarship but the ancestor of our modern conversational pocket dictionaries.

The printer, Adam von Rottweil, may have gone to Italy to join Sweynheym and Pannartz in Rome during the years 1471–4. He worked in Venice from 1476 to 1481, in Aquila from 1481 to 1486, and later appears and disappears in Naples.

The production of a simple phrase-book promised obvious rewards to a publisher residing in a commercial centre. William Caxton, the first English printer, took up the idea and brought out an English–French vocabulary in London about 1480. Like Adam von Rottweil's book, only a few tattered copies have survived the fate common to books of this type—old schoolbooks, of course, being among the *rarissima*.

20

MEDICAL BOTANY

DIOSCORIDES (first century A.D.). De Materia Medica. *Colle: Johannes de Medemblick, 1478*

This was the first authoritative work of antiquity on the *Materia Medica*, that branch of science which treats of remedial substances. Very little is known about its author, Dioscorides, except that he was a Cilician Greek who lived in the time of Claudius and Nero, and that he travelled widely in the Middle East, probably as a physician in the Roman army. His predecessor Theophrastus was the first scientific botanist, but Dioscorides was the first to write on medical botany and thus his book was of more immediate practical use and the more influential of the two. It was first in circulation in Greek in about A.D. 78, and in its four parts treats of aromatic, oily, gummy or resinous plant products, animals and animal products of medicinal use, cereals, garden herbs and a large number of other medicinal plants.

In his classification the author recognized natural families long before Bauhinus (121) or Linné (192), and the book also contains some important material on early chemistry and descriptions of chemical substances. Six hundred plants with their medical properties are described —one hundred more than by Theophrastus—of which ninety are still in use today.

It is no exaggeration to say that from its publication until well into the seventeenth century—even after the appearance of the *Pinax* of Bauhinus in 1623—all botanical studies were based on this book, and the greater part of any new botanical matter published during the sixteenth and seventeenth centuries was in the form of a commentary on Dioscorides. Dodonaeus, Matthiolus, Caesalpinus (97), Columna, Brunfels, Bock, Fuchs (69) were largely commentators on Dioscorides, and it is only with the rise of modern scientific botany in the eighteenth century that his influence began to wane.

From the sixth century onwards there are many manuscripts of this text, and their frequent illustrations are our most important source for the history of botanical illustration. The first edition was published in a medieval Latin version in 1478, and the first in the original Greek in 1499. Only five Greek editions were published in the sixteenth century; and it was the numerous Latin editions which had the greater impact.

BIBLIOGRAPHY: R. T. Gunther, *The Greek Herbal of Dioscorides* (Oxford, 1934; reprinted, New York, 1959).

21

THE BIRTH OF MODERN SURGERY

GUY DE CHAULIAC (1300–68). Chirurgia (in the French version of Nicolaus Panis). *Lyons: [Nicolaus Philippi & Marcus Reinhart for] Barthelemy Buyer, 1478*

With Guy de Chauliac modern surgery begins; his treatise, entitled simply 'Surgery', was the standard textbook for centuries. The son of a peasant, he took holy orders and studied at Montpellier, Toulouse, Paris and Bologna, eventually settling at Avignon where he became physician to three successive Popes. Unlike his fellow physicians he stayed in the town during the Black Death in 1348, looked after his patients and described the disease; he realized the value of isolation and ordered the Pope to remain inside his palace. He caught the disease himself but recovered.

Chauliac separated surgery from general medicine and attempted to raise its status. His descriptions of surgical procedure are so valuable and modern that some of them are applicable today. He advocated excising certain abnormal growths at an early stage, he operated for hernia and cataract—an operation which had hitherto been left to itinerant quacks—but not for stone. In fractures he used the best of the classical methods, which are still in use today: suspended bandages, continuous traction with pulley and lead weights, deep sutures, drainage and light compression bandages. He introduced the overhead rope for bed patients and described a narcotic or soporific inhalation, the medieval substitute for anaesthesia. He was a great vascular surgeon and has excellent sections on eye injuries and materia medica. He included a medical history, the first since Celsus and unsurpassed until the time of Haller.

Some writers have claimed that by using plasters and salves and plugging wounds incessantly instead of leaving the healing to nature, he retarded the progress of medicine. However that may be, there is no doubt that he founded the great French school of surgery and prepared the way for Paré, its most distinguished representative in the sixteenth century.

The book was composed about 1363 in Latin—Guy de Chauliac wrote other works but most of them are lost—and was first printed in French at Lyons in 1478, the earliest important medical book in French to be printed, and of great rarity. The Latin text was first printed in 1498 at Venice; sixty-eight editions were published between 1478 and 1683, mostly in Latin.

BIBLIOGRAPHY: Guy de Chauliac, *La Grand Chirurgie*, edited by E. Niçaise (Paris, 1890).

England—thought wrongly by some to be Robert of Normandy, the Conqueror's son—and was memorized by generations of doctors. Its sayings became popular maxims of hygiene and some have survived to our own day.

The texts were probably first written down about 1160 (the 'Breslau Codex') and consisted then of 362 verses. It was subjected to many interpolations, and one much later edition contains no less than 3,520 verses. By our standards it is not a scientific book, but a collection of popular, didactic verse, and as such it had an immense vogue for centuries. It was translated into English, German, French, Irish, Provençal and Bohemian, and about three hundred editions have been published.

BIBLIOGRAPHY: Salvatore de Renzi, *Collectio Salernitana*, 5 vols. (Naples, 1852–9).

22

THE EARLIEST MEDICAL SCHOOL

REGIMEN SANITATIS SALERNITANUM. [*Cologne: Conrad Winters, 1480?*]

This popular work on diet and hygiene was a product of the medical school at Salerno which flourished from the eleventh to the fourteenth century. Salerno is an ancient seaport not far from Naples and was an early health resort. The surviving Greek medical tradition in Southern Italy became fused with Latin, Jewish and Muslim influences and thus the first great western medical school came into existence here. Salerno was in fact the earliest university in Europe and despite the presence of a bishop it remained a completely secular institution where medicine was first treated as a separate science.

The first known literary products of the school are of the eleventh century and its heyday was in the twelfth. After the rise of Venice and the subsequent northward trend of trade and culture Salerno eventually survived only as a source of bogus degrees until Napoleon closed it in 1811.

Salerno produced a corpus of books covering most aspects of medicine and including important medieval medical texts in several branches of the science. A famous book on gynaecology, *De Passionibus Mulierum*, was long attributed to a woman professor called Trotula—her name survives in children's literature as Dame Trot—but she has been found to be a myth; the book was composed by a Salernitan doctor Trottus—a mere man.

The *Regimen Sanitatis* was perhaps the most popular of all these texts. It contains rules on diet and hygiene and recommends simple drugs as a basis for treatment. It comprises much earlier knowledge and was already an established book when edited for the first printed edition by Arnaldus de Villanova (1248–1314) to whom the authorship has sometimes been wrongly attributed. It may go back to a pseudo-Aristotelian 'Epistle to Alexander the Great' which was Latinized by John of Toledo, a baptized Jew, about 1130.

Written in doggerel Latin verse 'The Salernitan Regimen of Health' was addressed to a mythical king of

23

ENGLISH LAW

SIR THOMAS LITTLETON (*c.* 1407–81). Tenores Novelli. *London: John Lettou & William de Machlinia*, [*1481*]

Littleton was a successful lawyer and judge of whom little is known save the dates of his preferments in his profession. His 'Treatise on Tenures' was probably written after he became a judge in 1466 and was no doubt called forth by the confused state of the branch of law of which it treats. The English law of property had grown up through the administration, by regular courts since the Conquest, of a legal system based on partly Saxon and partly Norman customs. Precedent was the essential guide: principle was unknown. Attempts to organize the material of precedents were made in the Registers of Original Writs, which by Littleton's time were four times the size of the earliest compilations of the time of Edward I, and the equally enlarged Yearbooks. To this confusion Littleton brought a gift for organization and the original mind which it so much needed.

His first break with tradition was to write his book in the Anglo–French which was the language of the courts, as opposed to the Latin of previous textbooks such as Bracton (89) and Glanville. With the Latin language, Littleton also rejected the Roman law and its commentators. The 'Treatise' deals only with the English law. In his systemization, however, the influence of the method of the Roman law can be seen. Where before there had been only collections of reports of actual cases in no special order, Littleton divided his subject by classifying the different kinds of property rights, each of which was expressed in a succinct definition; and he then proceeded to illustrate them, either with a report of an actual decision or more commonly—and here he follows the practice of the Roman law—with hypothetical cases. Liberated from the need to refer to precedent, he could achieve a breadth and method hitherto impossible.

For the next century and more 'Littleton's Tenures' remained the basic English lawbook and when Coke came to publish his commentary upon it (126) he called it 'the most perfect and absolute work that ever was written in any human science'. 'Coke upon Littleton' went on being published until the nineteenth century, and thus the work of an obscure fifteenth-century judge became the basis of the essential rights of property in all English-speaking countries.

BIBLIOGRAPHY: W. H. Winters, 'A Bibliographical Essay on the First Printed Book of English Law, London, circa 1481. (Littleton's Tenures)'. In: *New York Law Institute. Report of the Librarian. Appendix A* (New York, 1916).

24

ARISTOTLE INTERPRETED

MUHAMMAD IBN AHMAD, called AVERROES (1126-98). Colliget. *Ferrara: Laurentius de Rubeis, 1482*

Averroes was the outstanding Arab philosopher and physician of his time in Spain. He lived in Cordova, Seville, and later in Marrakesh. He is memorable chiefly for his interpretation of Aristotle (38) which developed into the complete philosophical system now called Averroism. The central feature of this was a theory that the world is eternal, not a creation *ex nihilo*, but actuated by a creative power continuously at work: a view not far removed from the idea of evolution.

Other features of the system were a belief in psychological determinism—incompatible with the doctrine of moral responsibility—and the theory of the two truths: one for the philosophers and another more literal one for the masses ('teach the people what they can understand'). Averroism was essentially an attempt to reconcile reason and philosophy with faith and religion. Averroes was not unique in this, but he expressed it perhaps more intelligently and forcefully than others. Nevertheless, the orthodox philosophers and theologians largely misunderstood him and disapproved of his ideas. Aquinas (30) made an effort at reconciliation; but the Holy See in 1270 and 1277 forbade the reading of Averroes, and his theories were condemned by the orthodox Muslims in Spain as well as by the bishops in Paris and Canterbury and some authorities at Oxford. In spite of this, Averroism deeply influenced both Christian and Jewish thought (it had curiously little impact on Muslim philosophy) and initiated the Schoolmen into the knowledge of Aristotle.

The earliest editions of Aristotle, 1472–4, were published with Averroes's commentaries (both text and commentary were Latin translations, the latter partly direct from the Arabic, partly from Hebrew versions) in which, and in various tracts, Averroism was adumbrated. He is represented here by his most substantial printed book, 'Observations on Medicine'. The best early collected edition of Averroes's works, in Latin, was published in Venice by the Giuntas in 1552.

25

THE ELEMENTS OF GEOMETRY

EUCLID (fl. *c.* 300 B.C.). Elementa Geometriae. *Venice: Erhard Ratdolt, 1482*

Euclid's 'Elements of Geometry' is the oldest mathematical textbook in the world still in common use today. Its author was a Greek mathematician living about 300 B.C. who founded a mathematical school in Alexandria in the reign of Ptolemy I.

The 'Elements' is a compilation of all earlier Greek mathematical knowledge since Pythagoras, organized into a consistent system so that each theorem follows logically from its predecessor; and in this simplicity lies the secret of its success. Of the thirteen books into which it is divided, nos. 1 to 4 are on plane geometry; 5 and 6 on the theory of proportion due to Eudoxus and its application; 7 to 9 on the properties of numbers; 10 on irrational quantities; 11 to 13 on solid geometry culminating in the proof that there are only five regular solids; books 14 and 15 were added later but are not by Euclid. He wrote several other treatises, some of which have come down to us, notably on optics, the elements of music, astronomy and spherical geometry.

The 'Elements' remained the common school textbook of geometry for hundreds of years and about one thousand editions and translations have been published. In the latter part of the nineteenth century an attempt was made to replace it by rival textbooks. (The Mathematical Association is in fact a continuation of the Society for the Improvement of Geometrical Teaching which was founded with this object.) Lobatchewsky's book on non-Euclidean geometry, published in 1829 (293), challenged the supremacy of the Euclidean system, a process which has been continued in our time by Einstein's work (408) and by modern developments in astronomy and mathematics.

The first edition of Euclid's 'Elements' is an outstandingly fine piece of printing, and the care and intelligence with which diagrams are combined with the text made it a model for subsequent mathematical books. It was the first substantial book to be printed with geometrical figures.

BIBLIOGRAPHY: Sir C. Thomas-Stanford, *Early Editions of Euclid's Elements* (London, 1926); Sir T. L. Heath, *The 13 Books of Euclid's Elements*, 3 vols. (Cambridge, 1926) with a bibliography in the introduction to vol. 1.

26

CLASSICAL ARCHITECTURE

MARCUS VITRUVIUS POLLIO (fl. 27 B.C.). De Architectura. [*Rome: Eucharius Silber, 1483–90*]

This handbook on classical architecture is the only Roman work inspired by Greek architecture that has come down to us. It is therefore important as our prime source of many lost Greek writings on the subject and as a guide to

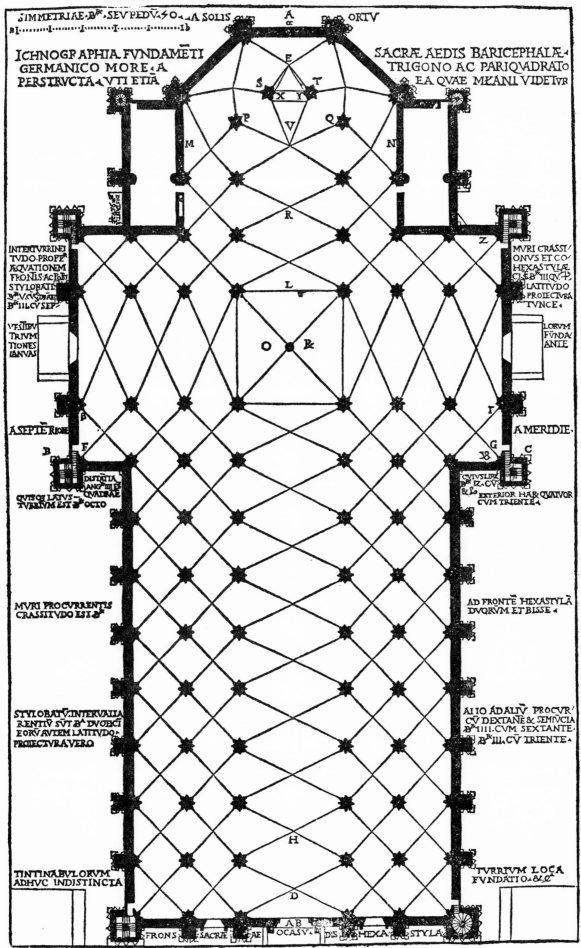

archaeological research in Italy and Greece. By exemplifying the principles of classical architecture it became the fundamental architectural textbook for centuries. Vitruvius, who lived during the time of Julius Caesar and Augustus, and probably composed his book prior to 27 B.C., was basically a theoretical rather than a practising architect and his only known work is the Basilica at Fano.

The ten books of 'On Architecture' deal with principles of building in general, building materials, designs of theatres, temples and other public buildings, town and country houses, baths, interior decoration and wall paintings, clocks and dials, astronomy, mechanical and military engineering. There are many ingenious devices for dealing with the echo in theatres and ideas on acoustic principles generally; on methods of sanitation—Vitruvius is believed to have been responsible for the new plumbing system introduced when Augustus rebuilt Rome; on correct proportions, proper location of building, town planning and much on ballistic and hydraulic problems. The classical tradition of building, with its regular proportion and symmetry and the three orders—Doric, Ionic and Corinthian—derives from this book. In recent times Vitruvius's considerable importance in the history of science has also been recognized, as he made some valuable contributions to astronomy, geometry and engineering.

Although his influence on practical architecture during the Middle Ages was obviously small, at least fifty-five manuscripts of the *De Architectura* are known, from the ninth century onwards, many now in the Vatican. The earliest surviving is in the British Museum; written in the ninth century at Jarrow in Northumberland and based on Italian examples brought thither by Coelfrid in the seventh century.

It was with the Renaissance that his influence began. Alberti (28), Bramante, Ghiberti, Michelangelo, Vignola, Palladio (92) and many others were directly inspired by Vitruvius. The first printed edition appeared in Rome (*c.* 1483–90), the first illustrated one in Venice, 1511, and French, German, Italian and Spanish translations soon followed. The first English edition is the magnificent folio of W. Newton's translation, in two volumes, 1771–91. The Como edition of 1521 is the first in Italian—by Cesare Cesariano, a pupil of Bramante. It has splendid new illustrations, some of which are now attributed to Leonardo da Vinci, and is the most beautiful of all the early editions.

cording to human nature, developed by education, which represents the authority of the State, fitted in as well with the philosophical, religious and political thought of western Europe in the fifteenth century, striving to free itself from the shackles of scholasticism, as it did with those of the Byzantine Greeks, by whom Plato was re-popularized in the western world. His master Socrates had laid the foundation of scientific method in asking the essential question 'What is. . . ?' rather than improvising theories, and this passionate belief in the answerableness of questions and the certainty that good came from knowledge was developed and idealized in the writings of Plato. Amidst a great diversity, both of subject and treatment, the dialogues are pervaded by two dominant impulses: a love of truth and a passion for human improvement. While nowhere is a definite system laid down, it has been truly said that the germs of all ideas can be found in Plato.

The systematic co-ordination of Plato's ideas came from Aristotle (38), and subsequent philosophers have often owed more than they have known to the most fertile of philosophic writers. Nor has the influence ever disappeared: Zeno, Epicurus, Plutarch all depended on him; Clement and Origen brought him within the scope of the Christian religion; Plotinus and John the Scot, in different ways, gave him new life. One of the effects of the Council of Florence in 1439 was the reintroduction of his philosophy through the lectures of Gemistus Pletho, among whose pupils were Cardinal Bessarion and Marsilio Ficino; the latter a central figure in the humanistic movement and translator of the edition here cited (the first edition of the Greek text did not appear till 1513). By fifteenth-century standards, his Plato was a best-seller; it is a fame which succeeding ages have not diminished.

28

RENAISSANCE ARCHITECTURE

LEON BATTISTA ALBERTI (1404–72). De Re Aedificatoria. *Florence: Nicolaus Laurentii, 1485*

Alberti was both a true humanist of great learning and a practising architect. Philosophy, religion, education and manners all came within his scope; he also wrote some poetry and fables. But his most enduring books are those on the theory of art. They constitute the first literary formulation of the aesthetic and scientific theories of the Renaissance on architecture, painting and sculpture.

The *De Re Aedificatoria* ('On Building'), the first original Renaissance treatise on the art, may have been finished as early as 1450—before Alberti himself became a practising architect of importance—but was published posthumously by Bernardo Alberti in 1485; it was translated into French, Italian, and Spanish. The treatise on painting, *De Pictura*, was completed in 1435 and first printed at Basle in 1540; and the book on sculpture, *Della Statua*, was written probably before 1464 and first published in 1651.

His work on architecture is largely based on classical

27

THE IDEAL UNIVERSE

PLATO (428–347 B.C.). Opera. *Florence: Laurentius (Francisci) de Alopa, Venetus,* [1484 or 1485]

That Plato should be the first of all the ancient philosophers to be translated and broadcast by the printing press was inevitable. Plato's central conception of a universe of ideas, Perfect Types, of which material objects are imperfect forms, and his ethical code based on action ac-

principles as expressed in Vitruvius (26). Like Vitruvius's own book Alberti's is divided into ten books treating of general principles of design and ornament, churches, palaces in town and country, and the planning of towns, gardens, canals, locks, etc.

In accordance with classical principles, the principal elements of architecture are defined as beauty and ornament. Beauty is essentially harmony, the correct proportion of the parts. This, according to Alberti—and he dwells on this subject also in his treatise on painting—is not a conception of the artist's fancy but can be reasonably calculated on mathematical principles. It is related to Pythagoras's system of musical harmonies. Beauty is a quality not recognized purely by individual taste, but by a rational faculty common to all men.

Alberti considers architecture not only for ecclesiastical purposes or private patrons, but for the first time particularly as a civic activity. His book includes a scheme for building a whole new town, the earliest printed example of town planning. To Alberti the architect is purely an artist, educated in the liberal arts and working on scientific principles. He is the designer and planner: the technical execution should be left to a practical builder. Nevertheless, he was responsible for some of the most famous buildings of his time, such as the façade of S. Maria Novella and the Rucellai Palace in Florence, S. Sebastiano and S. Andrea at Mantua.

In his book on painting Alberti lays stress on realism and the imitation of nature; to obtain these results the painter must be familiar with the science of perspective to which the first two books of the work are devoted. The painting also must be beautiful in the sense alluded to above, and Alberti considers historical and subject painting as more important than figure painting, because they show the activities of men in their own lives and will therefore move the spectator. The contemporary influence of this work was rather small, except in the case of Paolo Uccello and Piero della Francesca whose pictures could not have been produced without a knowledge of Alberti. Leonardo's *Trattato della Pittura* is greatly indebted to Alberti, and it was partly through Leonardo's *Paragme*, not published until the seventeenth century, that Alberti exercised so powerful an influence on the classical and academic styles of painting of the seventeenth and eighteenth centuries.

29

THE ENGLISH EPIC

SIR THOMAS MALORY (fl. 1470). Thys Noble and Joyous book entytled le Morte Darthur, Nothwythstondyng it treateth of the Byrth, Lyf, and Actes of the sayd Kyng Arthur. *Westminster: William Caxton, 1485*

The *Morte d'Arthur* is the most famous version and the first in English prose of all the legends which have collected about King Arthur. It is the only true English epic; its matter is 'the Matter of England'. The matchless style, the humour, the magnificence, the magic that takes away the breath, combine in a masterpiece of legendary narrative. Each century has produced its own version of the Arthurian tapestry, but Malory's will never be forgotten.

Beyond the fact that he was alive in 1470, when he finished this book, practically nothing is known of the life and origins of its author. (Bale says he was a Welshman, but *D.N.B.* finds no evidence for it.) If he wrote anything else, it has not survived.

Malory himself implies, and Caxton in his preface flatly states, that the *Morte d'Arthur* is a translation of a French original; but scholars have traced its 'mosaic of adaptations' through a bewildering variety of originals, not by any means all of them French. No originals have been found for important sections of the book—parts of Merlin and Tristram, for example—and these may be virtually, if not entirely, the work of Malory's own imagination.

It was Caxton (publisher in this case as well as printer) who divided Malory's text into twenty-one books, subdivided into chapters. Of the first edition only one perfect copy (Pierpont Morgan Library) and one incomplete (John Rylands Library) survive.

30

THE SUM OF THE KNOWLEDGE OF GOD

THOMAS AQUINAS (c. 1227–74). Summa Theologiae. *Basle: [Michael Wenssler], 1485*

Thomas of Aquino, always known as Thomas Aquinas, was the greatest of medieval philosophers and theologians. Like his master Albertus Magnus (17) under whom he studied at Cologne and Paris, he was a Dominican, and throughout his life he was actively engaged in the service of his Order, travelling, lecturing, advising successive Popes in affairs of state; he rejected the preferments that were offered him and ended his days as a professor at Naples.

In the midst of all this activity he found time to write an astonishing number of books, of which the *Summa* is the last and greatest. The combination of theology and philosophy which was the basis of scholasticism found its finest expression in his writings. Aquinas held that knowledge came from two sources: the truths of Christian faith and the truths of human reason. Each is a distinct source, but the revelation which comes from faith is the greater of the two, and its chief characteristic is that it consists of mysteries to be believed rather than understood. Reason is the source of natural truth, which the heathen philosophers Plato and Aristotle (especially the latter) have systematized, and which if correctly analysed can be seen manifest in the appearing world.

Aquinas prepared himself for the exposition of his philosophy by a series of commentaries on Holy Scripture and the Fathers, and a study of Plato and his followers, notably the work of the pseudo-Dionysius; and above all of Aristotle (38), in whose writings he saw the highest point to which natural reason had yet attained. The *Summa* is divided into three parts, the first of which treats of the nature, attributes and relations of God, including the physical universe; the subject of the second being man and the chief end of man, in which a definitive code of Christian ethics is laid down; the third part, which was completed according to Aquinas's plan after his death, dealt with Christ, God and man. Even in this attenuated summary, the systematizing influence of Aristotle can be seen operating on 'all the learning of the Fathers', and it is this system which led Leo XIII in his Encyclical of 1879 to declare it the indisputable basis of Catholic theology; equally, it underlies much subsequent theological, political and social inquiry into the nature and position of man in the state or in the universe.

31
THE HOMERIC AGE

HOMER. Opera. *Florence: Bernardus Nerlius, Nerius Nerlius & Demetrius Damilas, [1488/9]*

The *Iliad* and the *Odyssey* are the first perfect poetry of the western world. They spring fully grown, their predecessors lost, and their magic has persisted ever since. The legends of the siege of Troy and the return of Odysseus are the common heritage of all. The beauty of Helen, the courage of Hector, the grief of Achilles for Patroclus, the meeting of Nausicaa and Odysseus, the magic of Circe, all these are now a part of the mythology of Europe. It matters not whether they were first written or handed down orally, whether both are by the same poet, whether the poet was Homer—all these and many other unanswered questions are secondary to the perennial appeal of the narrative and the poetry. The form, the action and the words have had incalculable influence on the form, action and words of poetry ever since; the composition of the *Aeneid*, the *Divine Comedy*, *Paradise Lost*, and many others, has been determined by the *Iliad* and the *Odyssey*.

Their popularity never diminishes: translations into more and more languages abound; more than a million copies of a recent version of the *Odyssey* (that by E. V. Rieu for the Penguin Classics) have been printed.

32
THE APEX OF HUMANISM

ANGELO AMBROGINI POLIZIANO (1454–94). Miscellaneorum Centuria Prima. *Florence: Antonio Miscomini, 1489*

Politian, in his short lifetime, saw the climax of the movement of humanistic scholarship, which on the one hand brought about a new and vital interest in the classical past, and yet, by classicizing the vernacular, ousted Latin as the language of the literary world, and thus, paradoxi-

cally, caused the present decline of classical learning. Born at the same time as the art of printing, he stands at the beginning of one era and the end of another. At the age of ten his parents, political refugees, brought him to Florence, where he studied Latin and Greek under Landino and Argyropoulos and philosophy under Marsilio Ficino. Lorenzo de' Medici appointed him tutor to his sons Piero and Giovanni (later Pope Leo X).

Before he was twenty he had made his name with a translation of the *Iliad* into Latin hexameters, essays on Greek versification, and his letters, and within a decade his lectures at the University of Florence had achieved a reputation unequalled even in that city of scholars. Among the pupils who carried his fame abroad were the German Reuchlin and the Englishmen Grocyn and Linacre. In addition to his lectures, Politian also published a number of translations.

The 'Century of Miscellanies', a distillation of all this scholarship, was the most popular of his learned works, and set a standard of erudition and readability which lasted well into the eighteenth century. His vernacular works were written in response to the demand of his patron, Lorenzo de' Medici, for literature which would ensure for the Tuscan dialect the primacy it had attained through Boccaccio and Dante. His love lyrics (*Stanze per la Giostra*) and the pastoral idyll *Orfeo* paved the way for the triumph of the language of Tasso and Ariosto throughout Europe, a triumph the greater when one reflects that it might have been the language of *Paradise Lost*.

Not all the surviving works, let alone a single one of them, can bring to life the genius of this many-sided man. At a time when learning and the pursuit of knowledge were flourishing as never before, he was pre-eminent in every category; yet perhaps it is not so much Politian's achievement as his personality, the central figure of a movement which included so many famous scholars and writers, that has ensured his immortality.

33
THE 'BIBLE' OF CLASSICAL MEDICINE

GALEN (c. A.D. 130–201). Opera (in the Latin translation by Diomedes Bonardi). *Venice: Philippus Pincius, 1490*

Galen, a Greek, was the most voluminous of all ancient medical writers and left a vast medical encyclopaedia. His works fill twenty-two volumes in the standard edition by Kühn, Leipzig, 1821–33.

For nearly fifteen hundred years his authority was unassailable and every medical question was automatically referred to him: there was no appeal. Galen was a good observer and investigator, and some of his works in physiology and anatomy—he left a brilliant study of the brain—in neurology and diagnosis are of especially high quality. However, his assumption that the blood passed between the two ventricles of the heart by invisible pores inhibited all research into the circulation until Harvey's discovery (127). He developed a system of pathology in which the humoral ideas of Hippocrates were combined with the Pythagorean theory of the four elements, and all his experiments had to be related to this or some other dogma. Hippocrates (55) had taught the value of observation and experiment, but Galen replaced this empirical attitude with a teleological system: everything in nature was considered as being designed beforehand, and from this it followed that the theories of atomism and evolution were erroneous, a view which greatly endeared him to orthodox Christian theologians.

His disciples throughout the centuries disregarded his work as an experimentalist, but admired him as a philosopher and regarded his works as infallible dogma. In consequence, his influence retarded in many ways the progress of medicine in more modern times. The first effective break with Galenism came with Vesalius (71) and Paracelsus (110); yet Galen's influence on medical practice remained powerful even into the nineteenth century. He wrote in Greek, but his works were early translated into Arabic, thence into Hebrew and Latin and thus reached the West. Although this is the first considerable printed collection of his works, some of them had appeared in the assemblage of medical texts known as *Articella* as early as *c.* 1476. The first Greek edition of Galen was published by Aldus in Venice in 1525.

34

THE THEORY OF MUSIC

BOETHIUS (*c.* 480–524?). Opera. *Venice: Johannes & Gregorius de Gregoriis, de Forlivio, 1492–*

Although there are allusions to music in several of his philosophical works, the core of Boethius's musical thought is found in his *De Institutione Musica*. There is no early separate edition of this treatise, but it is included in both the first (1492) and the second (1499) edition of his collected works.

The importance of Boethius is twofold. This, though basically a synthesis, was the first work of musical theory written in the Christian West, and as such widely influenced musical thought right through the Middle Ages. It was the moral basis of his ideas which gave them their novelty and their appeal.

Boethius's approach to what was, even in the sixth century, a widely developed art, is curiously limited. He says nothing of church music, rhythm, or melody, and alludes only very briefly to instrumental music. He is concerned with acoustics and harmony. The treatise is in five books, of which the contents may be summarized as follows: I. Elementary acoustics. II and III. A philosophical introduction leads to an exposition of the two principal schools of antiquity—the Pythagorean—where musical scales and intervals were treasured for their numerical ratios—and the Aristotelian—where music was regarded as part of the educational system, and especially for its influence on morals. IV. The monochord and the important types of consonance. V. Ptolemaic harmony as the divisions of the tetrachord.

Boethius mentions as some of his own sources: Plato, Aristotle, Nicomachos, Ptolemy, and Albinus. In the second section of his treatise, his own admitted preference between the two rival systems was for the Pythagorean.

A statesman as well as a philosopher, Boethius was appointed Consul in Rome under Theodoric the Ostrogoth in 510. He was, however, accused of treason and his most famous work, the *De Consolatione Philosophiae*, was written while he was in prison at Pavia before being put to death. It was highly esteemed throughout the Middle Ages. Alfred the Great translated it into Anglo-Saxon and Chaucer turned it into English, while before the end of the eighteenth century versions had appeared in French, Italian, Spanish, German and Greek.

35

THE COLUMBUS LETTER

CHRISTOPHER COLUMBUS (1451–1506). Epistola de Insulis nuper inventis. [*Barcelona: Pedro Posa, 1493*]

The four small folio pages of this report on 'newly discovered islands', cited above under its familiar Latin title, announced the discovery of the New World.

Christopher Columbus, born in Genoa, came to Spain in 1484 after having served as a navigator with the

Portuguese. It took him seven years to persuade the Spanish authorities to support his project for an expedition *westwards* in search of the Indies. Between 1492 and 1504 he made four different voyages, reaching the West Indies, Haiti, Cuba and the Gulf of Mexico. To the end of his life he did not realize that he had discovered a new continent; he believed he had reached outlying islands of the Indies.

Columbus personified the age of transition in which he lived; his faith in the scriptural authority for his voyage was medieval, but his adventurous spirit and his desire for honours and gold was modern. He was a brilliant seaman, and though the variation of the compass needle was probably known to the Portuguese before him, he was certainly the first to mention it.

The idea of sailing westward to reach the Indies was first proposed by the Florentine cosmographer Paolo Toscanelli. He relied on Marco Polo (39), according to whom the Asiatic land mass extended even farther eastward than Ptolemy (18*) had supposed. Columbus followed this suggestion; he studied Ptolemy and was further misled by his erroneous measurement of the circumference of the earth (eighteen thousand miles). It seemed to him, therefore, a logical idea to cross the Atlantic by as direct a route as possible and so to reach Asia.

Columbus's dispatch for his patrons, King Ferdinand and Queen Isabella of Spain, was written in Spanish and printed in Barcelona in 1493; today only one copy of that edition survives (discovered in Spain, 1889; Maisonneuve, Paris; Quaritch, London, 1890; bought by the Lenox Library, New York, 1892—James Lenox himself had died in 1880; now in the New York Public Library). Nine separate editions were printed before 1500: one in Spanish (the second edition, also known in one copy only), six in Latin, the earliest being the Rome edition of Stephen Plannck, 1493, and one in German. It is ironic that the continent was eventually named not after Columbus but after Amerigo Vespucci, who had travelled to South America in 1499 and 1501. Waldseemüller in his *Cosmographiae Introductio* (St Dié, 1501) named part of South America after him, and in 1538 the name America was applied to the whole continent by Mercator (100).

The 'Columbus Letter', as it is commonly called, described at first hand what is undoubtedly the most momentous of all voyages of discovery. (The Norsemen had been there long before, but the rest of Europe was unaware of it.) The existence of an American continent was now made common knowledge and history was reorientated. An immense impetus was given to the rise of capitalism, both by the exploitation of the riches of America and by providing a new outlet for European trade. The centre of political and economic power was shifted from the Mediterranean to the Atlantic seaboard, resulting in the great westward migration from the old world to the new.

36

DISSECTION ILLUSTRATED

JOHANNES DE KETHAM (fl. *c.* 1460). Fasciculo di Medicina. *Venice: Johannes & Gregorius de Gregoriis, de Forlivio, 1493/4*

This 'Medical Miscellany' is not a work of original research but a compilation of medical texts, some medieval, all hallowed by long practice. Manuscript versions of it were widespread, some as early as the thirteenth century. It was from such a manuscript that the printed book was produced and in all probability attributed by the Italian printers to its former owner, Johannes von Kirchheim, corrupted by them to 'Ketham'. Johannes von Kirchheim, born in Swabia, was a professor of medicine in Vienna in about the year 1460.

The book includes sections on surgery, epidemiology, uroscopy, pregnancy and the diseases of women, herbal and other remedies, etc. It was first published in Latin in 1491 as *Fasciculus Medicinae*; but as reissued in an Italian translation by Sebastian Manilius in 1493 it underwent changes sufficiently significant to make it into what Dr Singer has called the first modern medical book imbued with the humanist spirit—perhaps a rather ambitious statement.

The 1493 edition contains additional illustrations and text; notably the 'Anatomy' of Mundinus, which had been a popular book since the middle 1470s. Mundinus's work, completed in 1316, though still largely based on Galen (33) and the Arabic writers, shows some first-hand acquaintance with the structures described and its conciseness and systematic arrangement made it the most popular anatomy before Vesalius (71).

The typography and artistic qualities of this edition of the *Fasciculus* make it of interest far beyond the world of medicine. It was the first printed medical book to be illustrated with a series of realistic figures: these include a Zodiac man, bloodletting man, planet man, an urinoscopic consultation, a pregnant woman and notably a dissection scene which is one of the first and finest representations of this operation to appear in any book and, furthermore, is one of the first three known examples of colour printing, four colours having been laid on by means of stencils.

Most of these figures have medieval prototypes, but they are here designed by an artist of the first rank. His identity has never been discovered; it has been suggested —wrongly—that he was the Polifilo master; but he was certainly an artist close to the Bellini school.

Between 1491 and 1523 fourteen editions were published, but the influence of the book, particularly through its illustrations, long outlived them.

BIBLIOGRAPHY: Charles Singer, *The Fasciculo di Medicina*, 2 vols. (Milan, 1925).

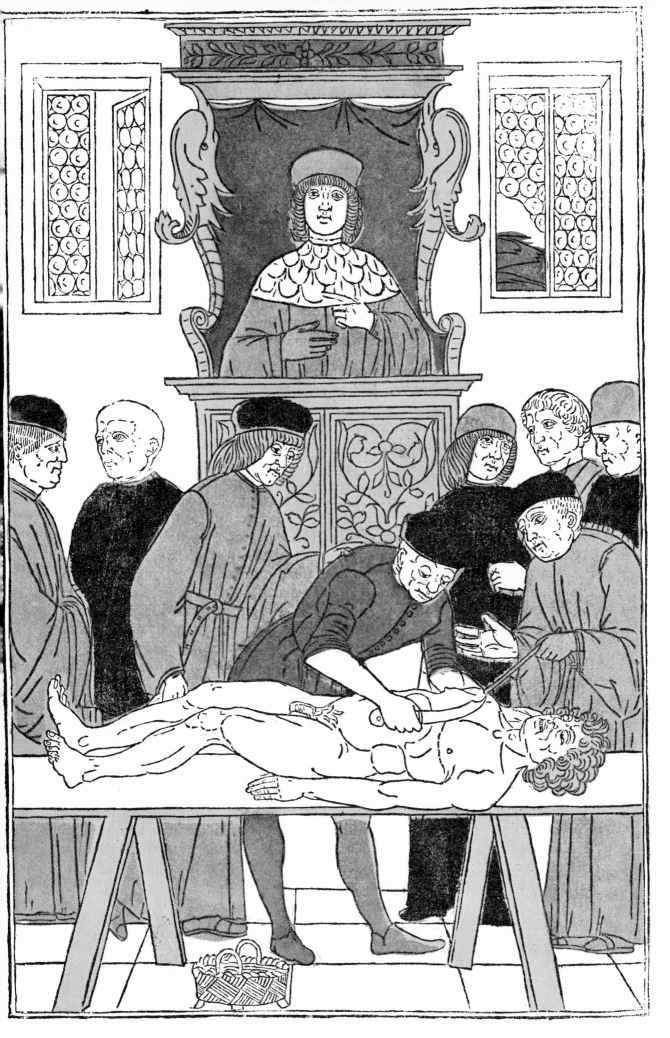

NO. 36 KETHAM

37

THE SHIP OF FOOLS

SEBASTIAN BRANT (1457–1521). Das Narrenschiff.
Basle: Johann Bergmann, 1494

Sebastian Brant was born in Strasbourg. After studying,
and later teaching, law in Basle, he returned to become
syndic of his native city and Imperial Councillor under
Maximilian I. 'The Ship of Fools' is the most important
of a long line of moralizing works in which the weaknesses and vices of mankind are satirized as follies. The
tradition goes back to early medieval times both in
England and on the Continent (e.g. Lydgate's *Order of
Fools* and Wireker's *Speculum Stultorum*).

In a ship laden with one hundred fools, steered by fools
to the fools' paradise of Narragonia, Brant satirizes all
the weaknesses, follies and vices of his time. Composed
in popular humorous verse and illustrated by a remarkable series of woodcuts—of which seventy-five are now
attributed to the young Dürer—the book was an immediate success. Brant's purpose was a moral one: he
wanted to improve the life of his contemporaries and to
help in the regeneration of the Holy Roman Empire and
the Church. The follies of the clergy did not escape his
censure.

Brant was a humanist—the book is full of classical
allusions—but he was undoubtedly conservative in his
wish to strengthen the existing order. Nevertheless, there
is much criticism and a strong feeling that man, in striving for his salvation, deals directly with God and not
necessarily through the Church: a foretaste of the movement for reform. Incidentally, the book also contains the
earliest literary reference to the discovery of America;
the Columbus Letter had been published by the same
printer the year previously (35).

The influence of 'The Ship of Fools' was extensive and
prolonged: thirty-six editions were published between
1494 and 1513, though there were none between 1670
and 1839 when the first modern edition appeared. There
were twelve translations in about forty different editions.
Its most immediate imitators were Geiler von Kaisersberg,
Thomas Murner, Hans Sachs and Johannes Fischart in
Germany, where the 'Narr' as a type has lived until
today. Erasmus's *Moriae Encomium* (43) was directly
inspired by it.

'The Ship of Fools' was the first original work by a
German which passed into world literature. Its influence
is demonstrated in France by the translations of Rivière
and Drouyon and the works of Robert de Balsac—
probably known to Rabelais—Pierre Gringore, Jean
Bouchet and others; in England by the translations of
Alexander Barclay and Henry Watson, both published
in 1509, and the works of John Skelton, Robert Copland
and Richard Tarlton. Thus Brant's book played an
important part in European literature, and helped to
blaze the trail that leads from medieval allegory to
modern satire, drama and the novel of character.

BIBLIOGRAPHY: Friedrich Zarncke, *Sebastian Brant's
Narrenschiff* (Leipzig, 1854), includes a bibliography.

38

THE MASTER OF THOSE WHO KNOW

ARISTOTLE (384–322 B.C.). Opera Omnia (in Greek).
5 vols. *Venice: Aldus, 1495–8*

Aristotle is not only one of the great classical philosophers,
the master of every branch of ancient knowledge: his
method still underlies all modern thinking. His works
include the six logical treatises that make up the *Organon*,
a score on scientific subjects, the 'Metaphysics', 'Ethics'
and 'Politics', works on rhetoric and poetry, and the
tract 'On the Constitution of Athens' (the only one of
one hundred and fifty or more on different constitutions
which has survived). Most of his writings show signs of
being worked over more than once, and some were
clearly written over a period of time (such as the 'Politics',
begun about 357). But is is possible to distinguish the
early period when he produced dialogues in the manner of
Plato (27), whose disciple he was; the middle period from
which derive some of the works which have come down
to us as unfinished drafts; and the later finished works,
such as the 'Metaphysics' and the 'Nicomachean Ethics'.
Most of Aristotle's ideas were originally delivered in the
form of lectures, and the texts we have are probably the
lecture-notes of his pupils, which he may or may not
have edited.

In all of these lectures there is a connexion and unity of
thought which make up the fundamental position of
Aristotelianism. All things are substances (not, as Plato
held, ideas), separate though related; some things are
attributes having existence only as being some substance
affected in some way; without substances there is nothing,
and nothing is universal apart from individual substances.
It is a philosophy of substantial things, which comes between the Platonic philosophy of ideas, according to
which visual objects are shadows and only the supernatural forms are real, and the modern philosophy of the
mind. To Aristotle the answer is that all things are substances, not all supernatural, not all in the mind; some are
natural substances, and these, and the relations between
them, form the subject matter of all Aristotle's works.

Unlike other classical writers Aristotle retained his
fame throughout the Middle Ages, largely through the
works of Thomas Aquinas (30), Albertus Magnus (17)
and Averroes (24); the last of whom provided the Latin
translation and the extensive commentary to his works as
published in Padua in the 1470s. But the great Aldine
editio princeps, issued in five folio volumes between 1495
and 1498, was the first major Greek prose text to be reintroduced in the original to the western world by the
intervention of the printing press.

39

THE FAR EAST

MARCO POLO (1254?–1324). Delle Meravegliose Cose
del Mondo. *Venice: Johannes Baptista Sessa, 1496*

Marco Polo was a member of a prosperous Venetian
family engaged in commerce. He set out with his father

and uncle in 1271 on a journey to the East. Starting from Acre the party travelled through Persia and the upper Oxus to the Pamir plateau, and then through Mongolia and the Gobi desert to the extreme north-west of China, reaching Shantung in 1275. Here they sojourned at the Court of Kublai Khan until 1292, finally arriving back in Venice, after travelling through south-east Asia and southern India, in 1295. During his stay in China Marco Polo took an active part in the administration of the country and travelled widely in the Great Khan's service. He saw—or obtained knowledge of—large parts of China, northern Burma, Tibet, Japan, south-east Asia, the East Indies, Ceylon, southern India, Abyssinia, Zanzibar and Madagascar, Siberia and the Arctic.

Marco Polo himself wrote down no account of his travels; but in 1298–9, while a prisoner after the victory of the Genoese over the Venetians in Curzola Bay, he dictated his story to a fellow-prisoner, one Rusticiano (or Rustichiello) of Pisa, a literary hack. The text of 'The Wonders of the World', apparently written originally in French, circulated widely; 138 manuscripts have survived. In printed form it appeared first in German—*Buch des edlen Ritters und Landfahrers Marco Polo*, Nuremberg, Friedrich Creussner, 1477 (translator unknown). This edition, however, seems to have had little impact, and, despite the obvious importance of the Latin edition of [1483–5] (see below) it is probable that the Italian text was the most widely read by the Mediterranean navigators and traders whose adventurousness so greatly extended our knowledge of the globe. Marco Polo was the first to give anything approaching a correct and detailed account of China and the Far East, and the accuracy of his geographical knowledge is indicated in the correct placing of Far Eastern countries in the fourteenth-century Portolani (manuscript charts), which are clearly based on his book.

Fra Mauro's wall map of 1459, now in the Marciana Library, Venice, and the Catalan Atlas (drawn up by

Abraham Cresques, a Jew of Majorca, in 1375, now in the Bibliothèque Nationale, Paris), which give us the most complete picture of geographical knowledge in the later Middle Ages, and other cartographers and geographers, all owe much to Marco Polo in their attempts at a true representation of the known world, disregarding theories and fables. Prince Pedro, elder brother of Prince Henry the Navigator, on his visit to Venice in 1426, was given a copy of this book, which thus influenced the Portuguese navigators. Toscanelli's map of the eastern world, which he sent to Columbus in 1474, was indebted largely to Marco Polo, and Columbus himself owned a copy of the undated Gouda Latin edition of Marco Polo which he annotated and which is still preserved in the Columbian Library at Seville. This influence prevailed until the seventeenth century when the maps of Martini, the visits of the Jesuits and the work of de l'Isle and d'Anville superseded his accounts.

As a story of adventure, an account of the experiences of one of the greatest travellers who ever lived, the book has remained alive. Editions in all languages are innumerable, and the Everyman Library keeps the book in print for the popular market in English to this day.

BIBLIOGRAPHY: *The Book of Ser Marco Polo*, translated and edited by Sir H. Yule, 2 vols., London, 1903 (with supplement by H. Cordier, 1920).

40

PTOLEMY EXPOUNDED

JOHANNES MÜLLER, called REGIOMONTANUS (1436–76). Epytoma in Almagestum Ptolemaei. *Venice: Johannes Hamman, 1496*

The importance of this book lies in the fact that it enshrines, within the editor's commentary, the first appearance in print, in a Latin translation from the Greek, of the monumental compendium of Claudius Ptolemaeus of Alexandria (18*) known as the *Almagest* (an Arabic portmanteau word derived from the Greek for 'the great astronomer'). Its editor, Johannes Müller of Königsberg (Franconia), called after his birthplace Regiomontanus, had studied in Vienna under the astronomer Peuerbach, who had begun this translation of an abbreviated version of the *Almagest*. After Peuerbach's death Regiomontanus visited Italy where he became attached to Cardinal Bessarion. He studied Greek and after finding another, more accurate, manuscript of the text he finished the edition of Ptolemy's great work and had it published in Venice.

The *Almagest* is an encyclopaedia of astronomical knowledge—much of it derived from Hipparchus, whose original texts are lost—which established astronomy as a mathematical discipline. It contains an elaborate theory of the planets, the discovery of the second inequality of the moon's motion (known as evection), the determination of the distance of the moon, an exposition of spherical and plane trigonometry and an account of the construction and use of astronomical instruments.

After a stay at the Court of the Emperor Matthew Corvinus at Budapest, Regiomontanus finally settled at

Nuremberg. With his patron Bernhard Walther he established the first European observatory and constructed many scientific instruments, such as astrolabes, surveying instruments, sundials and celestial globes. He founded his own printing press from which he issued his famous *Ephemerides* for 1474-1506. These contained calculations for the daily phases and constellations of the moon and the planets. They became a model for such tables and were widely used by the early navigators, notably Columbus (35). Regiomontanus corrected certain errors in the Alphonsine tables (composed in the thirteenth century and first published in Venice, 1483) which had been used hitherto; and it has even been suggested that his commentary on Ptolemy adumbrates a belief that the sun is in the centre of the universe and that the earth moves.

Regiomontanus also published calendars and assisted Pope Sixtus IV in the reform of the Calendar. His most original contribution to science was his book on trigonometry, *De Triangulis*, written in 1464 but not published until 1533, with the earliest modern exposition of plane and spherical trigonometry by which for many generations the movements of the planets, comets and eclipses were calculated.

Regiomontanus's influence was felt in both western and eastern Europe and his publication of the *Almagest* helped to re-introduce Greek astronomy into the western world. The first complete edition of the *Almagest* was published in Greek in 1533.

41

THE FATHER OF HISTORY

HERODOTUS (*c.* 484–*c.* 424 B.C.). Historiae. *Venice: Aldus, 1502*

Herodotus is the earliest historian; his predecessors were by contrast chroniclers. He was the first to collect his materials systematically, to test their accuracy as far as he could, and to arrange his story so as to appeal to, as well as inform, his readers.

His subject, too, was a definite one: the history of the great Persian invasion of Greece between 490 and 479 B.C. The first four books—two thirds of the whole work—are devoted to the earlier history of the two protagonists. And, as he traces the growth of Persia from subject state to empire, he also takes in the history of the adjacent countries such as Lydia, Assyria, Egypt and even Scythia, and describes them and their peoples, giving what we should now call the geographical data in full. Likewise, in describing the parallel development of Greece, he tells of the migrations, the colonies, the commerce, monuments, revolutions, religious beliefs and so on, of the peoples and cities. By contrast, Thucydides (102), equally concerned with a single war, longer but more limited, concentrated his introduction in a single book.

If Thucydides wrote a tragedy, Herodotus's work is undoubtedly an epic. To him the major objective was a vivid and picturesque narrative, the lively depiction of places and human actions, not the subtle analysis of character and underlying motives. He is a romantic, with all the faults and virtues of the romantic. If he is inclined to be credulous or to strain the facts to create dramatic effect, it is generally when dealing with the distant past or far-off countries, and his extensive travels and endless curiosity gave him a far greater knowledge than his less well-informed contemporaries credited him with. Certainly for the war itself his authority forms the basis of all modern histories; and, more than that, it is the stuff of legends. Herodotus is far more than a valuable source: always readable, his work has been quoted and translated ever since.

42

THE ROUTE TO THE INDIES

MONTALBODDO FRACAN (or FRACANZANO). Paesi Novamente Retrovati. *Vicenza: Henricus Vicentinus, 1507*

Apart from the little *Libretto*, 1504, this account of 'The New Found Lands' is the earliest printed collection of voyages and discoveries. It includes the voyages of the following explorers:

(1) Alvise Cadamos, who on two voyages in 1455 and 1456 made extensive explorations of the West African coast, visiting Madeira, Senegal, Gambia and discovering the Cape Verde Islands. He was the first navigator to make stellar observations using the Southern Cross and, though others visited the same region, his account is the most interesting one we have of West Africa at that period.

(2) Pedro Cabral, who, having left Portugal in 1499 for Africa, went off course accidentally and discovered the Brazilian, Guianaian and Venezuelan coast. His successors brought back some dye wood (resembling the Asian brasile wood, known in the Mediterranean) after which Brazil was named.

(3) Vincente Yanez Pinzon, who in 1500 discovered another section of the Brazilian coast and explored the Amazon delta. Cabral arrived in February, Pinzon in April.

(4) The first three voyages of Columbus, 1492–1500 (35) and the third voyage of Vespucci, 1501–2, to Brazil.

(5) Two letters of Girolamo Sernigi, an Italian merchant of Lisbon, with the earliest printed account of the voyage of Vasco da Gama.

Columbus, Magellan (see 57), and Vasco da Gama accomplished the three greatest feats of navigation in history. Vasco da Gama's was an even more remarkable performance than that of Columbus, who covered 2,600 miles in five weeks from Gomera to the Bahamas compared with the 3,800 miles in three months travelled by Vasco da Gama, from the Cape Verdes to the same point, crossing almost completely the South Atlantic. Leaving Lisbon on 8 July 1497, he sailed via St Helena (8 August) to the Cape of Good Hope, up the East African coast to the Bay of Lourenço Marques, Mozambique, Mombasa to Calcutta, where he arrived on 20 May 1498. He returned to Lisbon in September 1499.

This voyage in the eastern hemisphere is comparable in importance to Columbus's in the western. It opened the way for the maritime invasion of the east by Europe. Hitherto Moslem merchants had dominated the eastern trade which was then channelled through the Italian merchants into Europe. Thanks to Vasco da Gama and his successors the Portuguese and later other western European nations were able to trade direct with the east, to make permanent settlements and eventually to control the administration of the surrounding countries. Like the discovery of America, this great navigational achievement helped to shift the centre of power away from the Mediterranean to the countries with Atlantic seaboards.

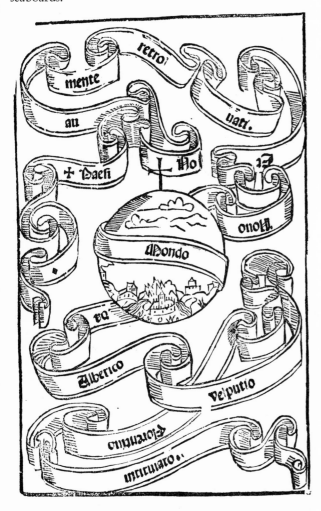

Six Italian, six French, two German editions and many others in the version edited by Grynaeus of 'The New Found Lands' were published during the sixteenth century. It was the most important vehicle for the dissemination throughout Renaissance Europe of the news of the great discoveries both in the east and the west.

43

SATIRE ON TYRANNY

DESIDERIUS ERASMUS (1466?–1536). Moriae Encomium. Erasmi Roterodami Declamatio. [*Paris*]: *Gilles de Gourmont*, [*1511*]

'The Praise of Folly' was written when Erasmus (see also 46, 53) was staying in the house of Thomas More (47) in the winter of 1509–10. Its title is a delicate and complimentary play on the name of his host: its subject-matter is a brilliant, biting satire on the folly to be found in all walks of life. The book stemmed from the decision which Erasmus had taken when he left Rome to come to England, that no form of preferment could be obtained at the sacrifice of his freedom to read, think and write what he liked. In it Kings and Popes, Princes of the Church and temporal rulers are alike shown to be ruled by Folly, and it seems almost inconceivable that an age of absolute authority should have allowed him to remain unscathed. The work was first secretly printed in Paris, and, as in other cases, its immediate success safeguarded him from the consequences of his audacity. Posterity took the revenge his contemporaries could not exact: Erasmus figures in the *Index Expurgatorius* of 1559 (82) in Category A, which lists authors whose complete work was condemned.

Whenever tyranny or absolute power threatened, 'The Praise of Folly' was re-read and reprinted. It is a sign of what was in the air that Milton found it in every hand at Cambridge in 1628. His inherent scepticism has led people to call Erasmus the father of eighteenth-century rationalism, but his rationalist attitude is that of perfect common sense, to which tyranny and fanaticism were alike abhorrent.

44

RENAISSANCE CHEMISTRY

HIERONYMUS BRUNSCHWIG (*c.* 1430–1512/13). Das Buch der Wahren Kunst zu Distillieren. *Strasbourg*: [*J. Grüniger*], *1512*

Hieronymus Brunschwig of Strasbourg was a travelling surgeon and apothecary. He wrote two books on pharmacology, one on simple remedies, the 'small distilling book' (first published in 1500) and the present work, the 'great distilling book', on composite ones.

'The True Art of Distilling' describes the technique of distilling medicines, mostly from plants and roots, but also from other substances. Other sections are devoted to medical remedies, the treatment of wounds, therapeutics and pathology, the description of installations in a distilling laboratory and an apothecary's shop. The last section lists many inexpensive and easily obtainable remedies.

Brunschwig describes many new plants and the method of distilling medicaments from them, which signalized a major extension of the use of chemical preparation in pharmacy. Distilling was a new trade and so was chemical pharmacy; and Brunschwig's book, with its wealth of woodcut illustrations of chemical apparatus and medicinal plants, brought this knowledge to a wider public, whereas hitherto the knowledge of pharmacology had been limited to a few experts, mainly in the monasteries. 'The True Art of Distilling' was issued in many forms and editions throughout the sixteenth century and set a prototype for this class of book.

Brunschwig left two other works, an important book on surgery and a book on the plague.

45

FORERUNNER OF
THE ENLIGHTENMENT

NICOLAUS CUSANUS (1401–64). Opera. 3 vols. *Paris: Badius Ascensius, 1514*

Nicolas of Cusa was born the son of a fisherman at Cues on the Moselle. He studied Hebrew and Greek, philosophy, theology and mathematics. At the age of thirty, as Archdeacon of Liège, he was a stout defender of papal infallibility at the Council of Basle. After a series of papal missions he was made a Cardinal by Nicholas V in 1448, and at the end of a busy and generally successful life he founded in his native town a hostel for thirty-three poor persons, to which he bequeathed his library, and which now bears his name.

Cusanus, as he is generally known, did much to strengthen the unity of the Church, in particular travelling to Constantinople to try and bring about the union of east and west against the threat of the Turks. He also went on a mission to check ecclesiastical abuses and reform monastic discipline in Germany and the Netherlands, a task which he executed gently but firmly, but which was unfinished at his death.

As in this respect he was the forerunner of the sixteenth-century reformers, so in his philosophical writings he broke with the scholasticism which was still the orthodox system. He maintained that all human knowledge was conjecture, and that wisdom lay in recognizing our essential ignorance. To avoid the charge of scepticism (made in his lifetime) which this implies, he took the view that God can be apprehended by intuition, in which, as in mysticism, all limitations disappear. This doctrine was taken up a century later by Giordano Bruno, who called him 'divus Cusanus', and through Bruno his views came to influence Spinoza (153), Leibniz (177) and Hegel (283). Cusanus indulged in many theologico-physical speculations concerning the form of the universe and the possibility of its infinity, speculations which continued to fascinate some minds for centuries. The view that he anticipated Copernicus (70) is hardly justified by these vague and general speculations, but the stimulus which he provided to cosmological thought lasted long after his death.

46

THE NEW TESTAMENT
IN THE ORIGINAL GREEK

NEW TESTAMENT, in Greek and Latin. Novum Instrumentum omne, diligenter ab Erasmo Roterodamo recognitum & emendatum. *Basle: Johannes Froben, 1516*

Nearly one hundred Latin Bibles were printed in the fifteenth century and translations of the Vulgate into all the principal European languages, except English, were also made before 1500. There was, however, a long delay in the production of a printed New Testament in the original Greek, since this necessarily involved a challenge to the official Latin Bible of the Church. Any scholar acquainted with both languages would be in a position to criticize and correct Jerome's Vulgate.

As early as 1440 Lorenzo Valla, the greatest Latin philologist of the fifteenth century, had composed a series of notes on the New Testament based on three Greek manuscripts. It was the discovery of a manuscript of this work at Louvain in 1504 which first aroused Erasmus's interest in New Testament translation and he published Valla's *Adnotationes* from this manuscript in Paris in the following year. While he was in England in 1505–6 he made a new Latin version of the Greek Testament, but the main work on the notes which were to accompany his first critical edition was carried out in Cambridge between 1511 and 1514. The New Testament volume of the Complutensian Polyglot (52) was already in print—its colophon is dated 10 January 1514—but not yet published when Erasmus arranged with the Basle printer Froben to issue his text. Printing began in September 1515 under the supervision of Johannes Œcolampadius (Johann Hausschein) and the book appeared in March 1516.

Evidence of this haste, due no doubt to the wish to forestall Cardinal Ximenes, is not difficult to find, and Erasmus's editorial methods, in the absence of any palaeographical knowledge at that time, were primitive by modern standards. There had been no elaborate comparison of Greek texts, and although he had made use of four manuscripts in Cambridge and five in Basle few contained the whole New Testament. Thus Erasmus seldom had more than two authorities for any one part of the text; he had to confess in his annotations that in some passages in Revelations the Greek was his own re-translation of the Vulgate. He failed to make use of the best manuscript at Basle, under the mistaken impression that it was later than the others, and all his sources depended on the Byzantine and Constantinopolitan text, which was much further from the truth of the apostolic autographs than the Old Latin version on which the Vulgate was based, or the Greek manuscripts which St Jerome had used to correct the Old Latin.

The resulting Greek text was unquestionably inferior to that produced by Stunica and the other scholars who had worked on the Complutensian Polyglot for some fifteen years. But that Bible was not to be published until 1522 and meanwhile the success of Erasmus's version among scholars was immediate. It was the first in the field, and this fact, combined with the reputation of the editor, its relative cheapness and convenience and its wider distribution, kept it in possession of the field for the next two and a half centuries. It formed the basis of the New Testament translations of both Luther (51) and Tyndale (58) and hence had a profound influence on later Protestant versions of the Bible.

BIBLIOGRAPHY: Darlow & Moule, no. 4591; C. H. Turner, *The Early Printed Editions of the Greek Testament* (Oxford, 1924).

NO VVM IN

strumentū omne, diligenter ab ERASMO ROTERODAMO
recognitum & emendatum, nō solum ad græcam ueritatem, ue-
rumetiam ad multorum utriusꝗ linguæ codicum, eorumꝗ ue-
terum simul & emendatorum fidem, postremo ad pro-
batissimorum autorum citationem, emendationem
& interpretationem, præcipue, Origenis, Chry
sostomi, Cyrilli, Vulgarij, Hieronymi, Cy-
priani, Ambrosij, Hilarij, Augusti-
ni, una cū Annotationibus, quæ
lectorem doceant, quid qua
ratione mutatum sit.
Quisquis igitur
amas ue-
ram
Theolo-
giam, lege, cogno
sce, ac deinde iudica.
Neꝗ statim offendere, si
quid mutatum offenderis, sed
expende, num in melius mutatum sit.

APVD INCLYTAM
GERMANIAE BASILAEAM.

CVM PRIVILEGIO
MAXIMILIANI CAESARIS AVGVSTI,
NE QVIS ALIVS IN SACRA ROMA-
NI IMPERII DITIONE, INTRA QVATV
OR ANNOS EXCVDAT, AVT ALIBI
EXCVSVM IMPORTET.

47
UTOPIA

THOMAS MORE (1477/8–1535). Libellus...de Optimo Reipublicae Statu, deque Nova Insula Utopia. [*Louvain*]: *Theodoric Martin*, [*1516*]

Utopia was published in the great year of Erasmian reform, when the new enlightenment seemed about to carry all before it. In the spring Erasmus had published his editions of the Greek New Testament (46) and Jerome, and the passionate plea for peace and reason in politics of the 'Institute of the Christian Prince'; in November More dated the introductory letter of the *Utopia*. It was written, like *Gulliver's Travels* (185★), as a tract for the times, to rub in the lesson of Erasmus; it inveighs against the new statesmanship of all-powerful autocracy and the new economics of large enclosures and the destruction of the old common-field agriculture, just as it pleads for religious tolerance and universal education. In this it is a work of reaction rather than progress: indeed, just as *Rasselas* might almost be a critique of *Candide* (204), so *Utopia* might seem an advocacy of the old virtues against the new totalitarianism of *Il Principe* (63). Here is the difference between Erasmus and More. More had been born and brought up in the law, the most traditional and the most English of all professions: to him, human institutes were not a matter for radical, theoretical reform, but were organic things to which change came slowly. In *Utopia* More is concerned to show that the old, medieval institutes, if freed from abuse, are the best; not the new theoretic reforms, which he justly feared.

Like Swift, More makes his point through satire-by-contrast. As the Houhynhnms were better than men, though horses, so Utopia, though pagan, is better than the vices of modern Europe. Utopia is not, as often imagined, More's ideal state: it exemplifies only the virtues of wisdom, fortitude, temperance and justice. It reflects the moral poverty of the states which More knew, whose Christian rulers should possess also the Christian virtues of Faith, Hope and Charity. But an ideal state is what it has come to mean: already before the end of the sixteenth century Robert Cecil could reject Tyrone's conditions of peace with a single contemptuous word—'Yewtopia'. Beyond all this, *Utopia* (like *Gulliver's Travels* again) has become a fairy-tale. More had all Swift's gift for utterly convincing romance: the beginning, when Rafael Hythlodaye recounts his voyages, has a vividness which draws the reader on into the political theory.

More, who was knighted in 1521, was later Speaker of the House of Commons, High Steward of Cambridge University, and Lord Chancellor. In 1535 he was executed for high treason. He is a saint to the Catholic, and a predecessor of Marx to the Communist. His manifesto is and will be required reading for both, and for all shades of opinion between.

BIBLIOGRAPHY: R. W. Gibson, *St Thomas More: A Preliminary Bibliography* (New Haven and London, 1961); R. W. Chambers, *Thomas More* (London and Toronto, 1935, reprinted London, 1945).

48
PLUTARCH'S LIVES

PLUTARCH (*c.* A.D. 46–120). Vitae Romanorum et Graecorum. *Florence: Philip Giunta, 1517*

During Plutarch's lifetime eleven Roman emperors came and went. The vicissitudes of the great must have suggested his peculiar moralistic method of comparing similar lives, a method which gave this work a scope greater than that of a mere collection of biographical facts. Educated in philosophy at Athens, Plutarch came to lecture at Rome, and is believed to have been appointed tutor to the young Hadrian by Trajan. He had therefore the opportunity to describe with equal authority the similarities and differences between the two civilizations through the means of 'parallel lives'—a system which must have appealed to his philosophic mind. In each pair of biographies—Theseus and Romulus, Alexander and Caesar —a Greek warrior, statesman, orator or legislator is set beside a famous Roman with the same characteristics, and conclusions are drawn both as regards the differences between the men and their countries, and about the moral lessons to be derived from their careers.

The 'Lives' are works of great learning and research, and Plutarch is careful to quote his authorities, whose number indicates a formidable amount of reading. Some of the biographies are more sketchy than others, notably of the Romans, to which Plutarch came only late in life; but his diligence as a historian is remarkable if his accuracy is less so. Their chief drawback to the historian is the predominance of the ethical motive, but it is this which has insured their survival and attracted the many readers whose interest is not only historical. Early translated, by Amyot into French and by North into English, the influence of Plutarch's method has been constantly manifest in the biographies of the modern great and in the authors who have been inspired by it.

Shakespeare (122) relied almost exclusively on Plutarch for the historical background of ancient Rome, and it is a very fair compliment to the genius of Plutarch that such magic as the departure of Antony from Alexandria can be wrought from it.

49
THE REFORMATION

MARTIN LUTHER (1483–1546). An den Christlichen Adel Deutscher Nation; von des Christlichen Standes Besserung. [*Wittenberg: Melchior Lotter, 1520*]

With this battlecry, 'To the Christian Nobility of the German Nation concerning the reformation of the Christian Commonwealth', Martin Luther (see also 51) opened his campaign of 1520 with the first of three great tracts—the manifesto of the Reformation.

After Luther's dialectic defeat in his bitter disputation in 1519 with Johannes Eck at Leipzig on the supremacy of the Pope, these three tracts made his position clear to himself and to the world at large. Religion was now seen to be on the side of a movement for liberty and the German humanists stood united behind Luther. The three tracts summed up all the grievances of the reformer and set forth all his proposals for reform. He claimed that spiritual power resided in the whole body of true believers, not in the ecclesiastical body alone; that Holy Scripture may be interpreted by all true Christians, not by the Pope alone; and that the clergy are not a separate fraternity distinguished by some mystical ordination but are accountable to the worldly power. Luther advocated the complete abolition of the supremacy of the Pope over the State, attacking the theory of the two Estates (spiritual and worldly) and the two swords (Pope and Emperor)—the Pope claimed both. He called for the creation of a national German Church with a national ecclesiastical council. Celibacy of the clergy should be abolished; the number of cardinals, of monasteries, of pilgrimages and of holidays should be reduced; interdicts and sales of indulgences should cease and schools and universities should be reformed.

This was Luther's answer to the Bull of Excommunication published in Rome in June 1520 and it had a powerful effect on all classes of society. With Luther the reformer almost unwittingly starting a social revolution, religious agitation became political rebellion with profound immediate effects on the history of Europe, and later of much of the rest of the world. It led to movements of nationalism and to social reforms not all of which Luther himself would have approved.

'To the Christian Nobility' was published in the middle of August 1520 and by the eighteenth of the month four thousand copies were sold; seventeen further editions were published in the sixteenth century. It was shortly followed by the two other revolutionary tracts: 'Concerning Christian Liberty' (on justification by faith alone) and 'On the Babylonian Captivity of the Church' (criticizing the sacramental system of the Church).

BIBLIOGRAPHY: A. Kuczynski, *Verzeichnis einer Sammlung von nahezu 3000 Flugschriften Luthers und seiner Zeitgenossen* (Leipzig, 1870); Dr Gustav Kawerau, *Luther's Schriften nach der Reihenfolge der Jahre verzeichnet* (2nd ed. Leipzig, 1929) (Schriften des Vereins der Reformationsgeschichte, Jahrgang 47, Heft 2); J. Benzing, *Lutherbibliographie* (Baden-Baden, in progress).

50

'DEFENDER OF THE FAITH'

HENRY VIII (1491–1547). Assertio Septem Sacramentorum. *London: Richard Pynson, 1521*

It was perhaps as early as 1516 that Cardinal Wolsey, anxious to distract him from more worldly preoccupations, first encouraged Henry VIII to embark on a serious rejoinder to Luther (49). In so doing Wolsey wrought his own downfall, and this was perhaps the least of the consequences of 'The Assertion of the Seven Sacraments',

one of the most fateful books in the history of western civilisation.

Despite his unfeigned zeal to extirpate heresy, it was not until Henry began to take a serious interest in foreign affairs that he realised the practical value which such a work might have, if dedicated to the Pope. It is difficult now to estimate the spiritual influence of the papacy at a time when the vast majority of Christendom saw it as a not specially powerful temporal state; but it was none the less felt. How much Henry's anxiety to complete the book (between May and July 1521) was activated by a real if romantic desire to become the champion of the papacy, it is hard to say. This point of view may be supported by Henry's statement to a startled and incredulous

Thomas More (47) that 'from that See we received our crown imperial'. More could see the dangers of so firm a commitment to the temporal, if not to the spiritual, power of the papacy, and his misgivings were soon to be justified a hundredfold.

Henry gained the recognition he sought from Leo X, the title of *Fidei Defensor*. But had he not made so absolute an admission of papal authority, it is unlikely that he would have felt so personally slighted by the Pope's refusal to give him his way in his 'great matter'—the divorce from Catherine of Aragon; unlikely that he would have turned with such vehemence on almost all the advisers, More among them, who had made his reign so successful hitherto; unlikely that he would have claimed the royal supremacy in the Church; unlikely—but there speculation must stop. Suffice it to say that the publication of the *Assertio* must be considered to mark a critical moment in the history of the English Reformation.

51

THE REFORMATION BIBLE

DAS NEWE TESTAMENT DEUTZSCH. *Wittenberg:* [*Melchior Lotter, 1522*]

This translation of the Bible into German by Martin Luther was of vital importance to the progress of the Reformation, giving a new impetus to the study of the scriptures in the vernacular all over Europe. It also was to have as profound an influence on the development of the German language as the King James Bible (114) later had on English.

In 1520 Luther, having already rendered some of the Psalms and parts of the Gospels and Epistles into German for the edification of the unlearned, seems to have planned a complete translation of the Bible to replace existing German versions. He began with the New Testament, translating from the second edition of Erasmus's Greek text (46), and this was ready for publication by September 1522—hence its earlier name, *Septemberbibel*. The text was accompanied by notes, some of which had a marked reforming bias, and the full-page woodcuts by Cranach included illustrations of dragons and the Woman of Babylon adorned with papal triple crowns. In 1523 and 1524 Luther published three volumes of his translation of the Old Testament, covering the books from Genesis to the Song of Solomon, but the Prophets did not appear until 1532 and the Apocrypha had to wait for the first edition of the complete Bible by Hans Lufft at Wittenberg in 1534. In translating the Old Testament, Luther made use of a much wider number of sources, using the Hebrew version printed at Brescia in 1494 as his basic text, but consulting the Septuagint, the Vulgate and the Latin translations and glosses. The Apocrypha was partly translated from the Vulgate and partly from the Greek of Aldus's recension of 1518.

The popularity of Luther's vernacular text was immediate and immense. By the time publication was completed in 1534 it has been estimated that over eighty editions of his New Testament had appeared. It was also the basis of translations into many other languages such as Dutch, in which the New Testament appeared in 1523 and the complete Bible in 1532. The Swedish Bible of 1540 and 1541, the Danish Bible of 1550, and the Icelandic New Testament of 1540 are all, also, founded on the Luther translation, and William Tyndale made use of it in his translation of the New Testament into English (58).

Linguistically its influence was equally striking. At first the editions which appeared at Augsburg, Nuremberg and elsewhere in South Germany needed many dialect alterations or explanations of words. So widely was it read, however, that by the middle of the seventeenth century Luther's High German had triumphed and was the dominant literary language of all modern Germany.

BIBLIOGRAPHY: Darlow & Moule, no. 4188.

52

THE FIRST OF THE POLYGLOTS

BIBLE, Polyglot. 6 vols. *Alcalá de Henares: Arnald Guillen de Brocar, 1514–17* [*1522*]

This great Bible—'The Old Testament in several tongues now first printed; The New Testament in Greek and Latin newly printed'—has the text of the Old Testament in Hebrew, Aramaic, Greek and Latin. It was edited and printed at Alcalá de Henares (near Madrid), the Latin name for which is Complutum, and so is usually referred to as the Complutensian Polyglot.

The first great work of co-operative biblical scholarship to be printed, it was instigated by, and produced at the expense of, Cardinal Francisco Ximenes de Cisneros (1436–1517), famous both as a statesman and patron of learning and founder of the University of Alcalá. There, under the leadership of Diego Lopez de Zuñiga (Stunica), a group of scholars spent over fifteen years editing the texts, beginning in 1502 and completing their task only a few months before the Cardinal's death. Unlike Erasmus (46) they made use of a considerable number of manuscripts, some—now preserved at Madrid—having been acquired by Ximenes, and others borrowed from various sources, including several from the Vatican.

The New Testament was finished by 10 January 1514, and was therefore printed (although not published) before Erasmus's first edition of 1516. The Appendix was completed in 1515, and the four volumes of the Old Testament were printed last, the final one in 1517. Publication was delayed, however, for over five years and the book does not seem to have been on sale before 1522. The most probable reason for this delay is the exclusive imperial privilege granted to Erasmus for four years in 1516. It meant that the Complutensian text of the New Testament was not available to Luther (51) when he made his translation, so that most Protestant versions have been based on Erasmus's less scholarly text. Full use was made of it, however, in the 1550 edition of the Greek New Testament published by Robert Estienne in Paris, which became known as the 'textus receptus' and dominated New Testament criticism for three centuries.

The Complutensian Polyglot was the first, and the most beautiful, of a series of great polyglot Bibles produced in the sixteenth and seventeenth centuries. Next came Plantin's edition, printed at Antwerp between 1568 and 1573 under the patronage of Philip II of Spain. In 1642 came the Paris Polyglot printed in eight volumes at the Imprimerie Royale under Sebastien Cramoisy; and finally, between 1653 and 1657, Bishop Walton's, printed at London by Thomas Roycroft.

Aldus Manutius had proposed to print a Bible in Hebrew, Greek and Latin before the close of the fifteenth century, but the project was never carried out and only a proof of one page survives in the Bibliothèque Nationale in Paris.

BIBLIOGRAPHY: Darlow & Moule, no. 1412; C. H. Turner, *The Early Printed Editions of the Greek Testament* (Oxford, 1924).

53
RENAISSANCE DIALOGUES

DESIDERIUS ERASMUS (1466?–1536). *Colloquia. Basle: Johann Froben, 1524*

If a single figure had to be chosen to typify the spirit of the northern Renaissance, there are few who would deny the claim of Erasmus. Born in poverty and out of wedlock, orphaned at an early age, he had all his way to make in the world. A reluctant religious, his energy was consumed in incessant reading of the Greek and Latin classics and the Fathers, and when his restless spirit chafed at the monastic life, he embarked on the travels which took him to Paris, London, Venice and Rome, where the fame of his learning and works brought him friends and honour.

About 1510 Erasmus began his long connexion with the famous Basle printer, Johann Froben, who published the extraordinary number of original works and editions which made him famous throughout Europe. Erasmus rejected the offers of Popes, Kings and friends and in 1521 he settled permanently with Froben as general editor and literary adviser. Here it was that his famous Greek New Testament appeared in 1516 (46) and here that the circle of friends and pupils, the Amerbachs, Glareanus and Œcolampadius among them, gathered round him. After Froben's death in 1527 he removed to Freiberg, but had returned to Basle when he died in 1536.

Perhaps the most lasting memorial of all this activity is the letters, of which over three thousand survive, the most vivid correspondence of the sixteenth century (superbly edited in 1906–7 by P. S. Allen and his collaborators). An equally lively picture of the author and his time comes from the even more popular *Colloquia*, or 'Conversations'. Originally written in his early days at Paris as dialogues illustrating the art of polite conversation, they were afterwards expanded into conversation pieces in which all the topics of the day are discussed with a freedom which ensured their popularity. Later in the century and up to the eighteenth century they were a set book in schools, and there are lines in Shakespeare (122) which directly recall Erasmus's words.

54
PERSPECTIVE

ALBRECHT DÜRER (1471–1528). *Underweysung der Messung. Nuremberg: [H. Andreas Formschneider], 1525*

This book—'A Course in the Art of Measurement'—was the first of the theoretical writings on art which Albrecht Dürer composed towards the end of his life. Its immediate object was to explain the application of practical geometry to drawing and painting and to teach the principles of perspective. These methods were to be applied to architecture, painting, lettering (Dürer designed both Roman and Gothic letters) and ornamental forms in general, and his book is therefore addressed not only to artists but also to sculptors, architects, goldsmiths, stonemasons and other craftsmen.

The work is divided into four books dealing with the problems of linear geometry, the two-dimensional figures, the construction of regular polygons, and the application of geometry in a practical manner to architecture, engineering, typography, etc.; and it ends with a discussion of three-dimensional bodies, stereometry and perspective. Dürer illustrated his book with woodcuts, some of which show the apparatus he constructed in order to produce correct drawing by mechanical rather than mathematical means. Perspective was supposed to be derived from Euclid's Optics and Vitruvius (26) but in fact neither of these ancient writers had a full conception

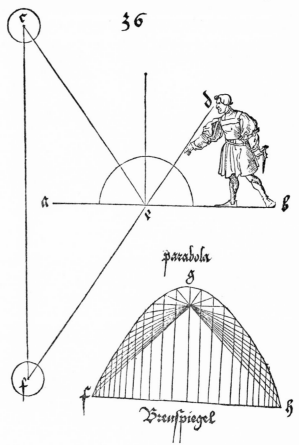

of its principles. Euclid wrote only on vision and Vitruvius gave only instructions on sketching buildings: they had no system of centralized projection. The first to use this was probably Brunelleschi (1379–1446). Alberti (28) wrote on it, but the first full account was given by Piero della Francesca between 1470 and 1490, in the *De Prospectiva Pingendi* (not published until 1899). Leonardo, Bellini and Mantegna were all concerned with the problem of perspective, but north of the Alps there was little knowledge of these mathematical aspects of art.

Dürer's work first presented to northern Europe the completely new attitude to artistic creation which had crystallized in Italy during the Renaissance. During the Middle Ages painting and sculpture were not conceived in their relation to natural objects and their imitation but as the projection of an idea existing in the artist's mind or an imitation of another work of art which served as a pattern or 'exemplar'. The Renaissance established a completely different aesthetic theory: the work of art as a representation of a natural object. The connexion of the beautiful with the natural, of the work of art with what is correct (i.e. mathematical) was a typical concept of the Renaissance. In the illustration of these principles lies the great historical importance of Dürer's theoretical writings (he supplemented the *Underweysung* with two more books, on human proportion and on the building of fortifications and towns). They were the foundation of accepted aesthetic dogma until the nineteenth century.

55
THE FATHER OF MEDICINE

HIPPOCRATES (460?–377? B.C.). Opera. *Rome: Franciscus Minitius Calvus, 1525*

This is the first complete Latin edition of the works of the greatest of clinical physicians. Little is known of the life of Hippocrates, a Greek doctor, except that he travelled extensively in the eastern Mediterranean and lived for a time on the island of Cos where there was a famous medical school.

What is now known as 'the Hippocratic collection' is a large corpus of works—the number varies between fifty-nine and a hundred—which was probably in existence in Alexandria by about 300 B.C. The present edition contains eighty works. They include contributions by various authors and schools but all are inspired by Hippocratic ideals. Indeed, we do not really know whether Hippocrates wrote any of the books himself, but the Hippocratic tradition has been recognized for many centuries.

Hippocrates first established an empirical system of medicine based on a combination of bedside experience and a collation of the many individual data which then formed the basis of clinical teaching. He freed medicine from superstition and the influence of priestcraft and derived his system from the accumulated empirical knowledge of Egypt, Cnidos and Cos. The clinical descriptions of fevers, phthisis, puerperal convulsions, epilepsy and other disorders have remained classics and no such records were kept again for over a thousand years.

The treatise on surgery includes treatment of dislocations and fractures, trephining the skull, descriptions of surgical instruments, rules on public health and diagnosis, a famous work on the brain, on the theory of the four humours, and many others. Laënnec (280) specifically acknowledges his debt to the Hippocratic writings in relation to his invention of the stethoscope. The most celebrated section of all is probably the 'Aphorisms', a collection of brief clinical observations many of which have become commonplaces or proverbs, such as the first one: 'Art is long, life is short.'

The ideal of the humane and learned physician originates with Hippocrates and the 'Hippocratic Oath' still remains the classic expression of the duties, ethics and moral standards of the medical profession. When in 1948 the World Health Association issued a declaration defining the duties of the physician it was no more than a modified re-statement of the Hippocratic Oath.

Hippocratic methods were employed by the Greeks for centuries, but suffered an eclipse during the Middle Ages when a combination of magic and scholastic theories—the latter largely based on Galen (33)—prevailed. The Renaissance and the classical revival brought the Hippocratic writings again to the forefront and they have remained an inspiration to medical research and ethics ever since.

The first Greek edition was published by Aldus in 1526 and the number of editions and translations since is countless. The standard editions are those of Emile Littré in ten volumes, Paris, 1839–61, and of Richard Kapferer and Georg Sticker, 25 vols. Leipzig, 1934, etc.

56
REFORMER'S MANIFESTO

ULRICH ZWINGLI (1484–1531). Commentarius de Vera et Falsa Religione. *Zürich: Christopher Froschauer, 1525*

The 'Commentary on True and False Religion' is one of the most characteristic pronouncements by Ulrich Zwingli, the Swiss humanist who was one of the three great leaders of the Reformation.

During his early life at Basle and Berne and as a parish priest at Glarus and Einsiedeln, Zwingli became deeply involved in the humanist movement. He studied Greek and Latin, read the Bible in its several versions, the Church Fathers and other early writings, and also Pico della Mirandola whose critical works contributed to his alienation from the Church of Rome. His most powerful religious and political influence was exercised as priest at the Gross-Münster at Zürich from 1519 until his death.

Theological and political ideas of reform were inextricably mixed in Zwingli, who was an ardent Swiss patriot and wanted to unite Switzerland and free it from French, Roman Catholic and other foreign influences. Indeed Zwingli personified the considerable degree to which the Reformation was a political as well as, if not more than, a religious movement. He saw clearly that if the political autonomy of a state was to be secured, religious no less than secular bodies must come under its control; and under his influence the civic authorities of Zürich took over much of the church government. At the instigation of the town council the religious houses were suppressed, the Mass was abolished in April 1525, images were removed and a new communion service established.

Nevertheless the State must be run on Christian lines and Zwingli suggested a return to the principles of primitive Christianity with the Bible as the supreme authority. Both his social and his religious theories, therefore, called for the elimination of the Pope. This caused a deep cleavage of opinion in Switzerland and on 8 April 1524 the Cantons of Lucerne, Uri, Schwyz, Unterwalden and Zug—the 'Forest Cantons'—met at Beckenried and formed a league to fight all the teachings of Luther (49),

Zwingli and Huss. After the new measures taken in Zürich civil war broke out. Zwingli himself led the Evangelical Cantons against those faithful to Rome. At Kappel in October 1531 he fell in battle and his corpse was subjected to terrible indignities by the Catholics.

Zwingli brought about by his teachings a division of the reform movement into the Lutheran and Reformed Churches. He broke even more radically than Luther with the Church of Rome and introduced a completely new form of liturgy and worship. 'Preaching the Gospel' was his main theme. He went much further than Luther, who was essentially a conservative, and who wished in the first place only to reform the Church within its existing structure, by eliminating what he regarded as uncanonical accretions.

An important difference arose over the nature of communion, which came to a head in the historic conference of the two leaders at Marburg on 1 October 1529. Both rejected the doctrine of transubstantiation; but whereas to Zwingli the nature of communion was purely symbolic, a commemoration of Christ's death, Luther adhered to the doctrine of the real presence. This fundamental disagreement was never resolved and was at the root of the separation of the two movements. Zwingli disagreed also with Calvin (65) over the doctrine of original sin. He regarded sin simply as a moral defect, not as punishable guilt.

Zwingli's mission failed in many respects: politically, since Swiss unity was postponed, and doctrinally because his views were eventually overshadowed by those of Calvin and Luther. Nevertheless, it was to Zwingli rather than to Luther that Calvin turned and the Reformed Church in most European countries has followed his lead, while the thoroughgoing independence of modern Switzerland accords with his political ideas.

57

ROUND THE WORLD

FRANCESCO ANTONIO PIGAFETTA (1491?–1534?). Le Voyage et Navigation faict par les Espaignolz es Isles de Mollucques. *Paris: Simon de Colines, [c. 1525]*

Columbus (35) had travelled westward in the hope of reaching the Indies, but instead discovered America. Fernando Magellan (1480–1521) was his rational successor and brought the enterprise to a successful conclusion by accomplishing the first voyage round the world. 'The Voyage and Navigation of the Spaniards to the Molucca Islands', written by Pigafetta, an Italian who sailed with the expedition as a volunteer, is its most authoritative account.

What is known as the Magellan Strait appears already on early maps, in particular the Johann Schöner globe of 1520, but this was wishful thinking rather than known fact. The Brazilian coast had been discovered by Cabral in 1500 (see 42) and the Pacific had first been seen by European eyes when Balboa in 1513 crossed the Isthmus of Darien. But this knowledge remained fragmentary until Magellan's great circumnavigation of the globe put it in proper perspective.

Magellan had first served in the Portuguese navy, cruising round Malacca and exploring the Spice Islands (Moluccas) between 1505 and 1508. Later he served his country in Morocco where he was wounded and lamed for life. Finding no recognition by King Manuel I after his return, he left Portugal for Spain. Here he persuaded Charles V that the Spice Islands were within the hemisphere assigned to Spain in the 1494 treaty between Portugual and Spain by which the world was divided

Le voyage et na-
uigation/faict par les Espaignolz es
Jsles de Mollucques.des isles quilz
ont trouue audict voyage/ des Roys
dicelles/de leur gouuernement & ma-
niere de viure/auec plusieurs aultres
choses.

Cum priuilegio.

¶ On les vend a Paris en la maison de
Simon de Colines/ libraire iure de lu
niuersite de Paris/demourãt en la rue
sainct Jehan de Beauluais/a lensei-
gne du Soleil Dor.

according to their respective spheres of influence. Magellan offered to prove his contention by undertaking a journey westward on which he hoped to discover a strait at the southern end of South America, and eventually the Spanish authorities agreed to the expedition.

Magellan set out on 10 August 1519 from San Lucar at the mouth of the Guadalquivir river with five ships. Sailing south, he discovered (and named) Patagonia, quelled a mutiny among his crews, found the eastern end of the Strait which now bears his name, christened Terra del Fuego, penetrated to the further ocean, which he called the Pacific for its calm waters and mild winds, survived the scurvy, and finally reached the Philippines, where he was killed by the natives in April 1521. The command of the expedition—only three ships by now—devolved on Sebastiano del Cano, a Basque; and by the end of the year it was only the 85-ton *Vittoria* which crossed the Indian Ocean, rounded the Cape, and cast anchor at Seville, almost three years after Magellan had set sail, with her complement reduced to eighteen hands.

Rightly (if inaccurately) is she depicted on the front cover of the Hakluyt Society's publications. For Magellan's achievement is probably the greatest feat of seamanship the world has ever known. It must be remembered that he had no charts, could calculate the latitude only by the sun, and the longitude not at all. All he had was the compass, hour-glass and astrolabe. Magellan's achievement is as important as Columbus's and had an equally potent effect on the fate of the world. He linked east Asia with Europe by the westward route, established the linear circumference of the earth and the length of a degree of latitude, and proved the loss of a calendar day in circling the globe westward. He fully explored the South American coast and discovered Chile, which recently renamed some of her southern regions 'Magellan's Land'.

There are several early accounts of Magellan's voyage, but Pigafetta's (surviving in several early manuscripts, mostly in French) is by far the best and the most detailed. It includes, incidentally, lists of words in the language of the Patagonians, Brazilians, Indians and natives of the Moluccas and Philippines, which was the first knowledge of these primitive languages to reach Europe.

BIBLIOGRAPHY: James Alexander Robertson, *Magellan's Voyage round the World, by Antonio Pigafetta*, 3 vols. (Cleveland, Ohio, 1906). Vol. 2 contains the bibliography.

58

TYNDALE'S NEW TESTAMENT

THE NEW TESTAMENT. Translated into English by William Tyndale. [*Worms: Peter Schoeffer, 1525 or 1526*]

William Tyndale's (?1494–1536) translation of the New Testament was the first to be printed in the English language. In Westcott's words 'He established a standard of Biblical translation which others followed. It is even of less moment that by far the greater part of his translation remains intact in our present Bibles, than that his spirit animates the whole...His influence decided that our Bible should be popular and not literary, speaking in a simple dialect, and that so by its simplicity it should be endowed with permanence'.

After taking his M.A. at Oxford in 1515 and further study at Cambridge, Tyndale was tutoring and preaching in Gloucestershire in 1522; but his advocacy of the new learning and his reforming zeal caused him to fall foul of the local clergy. He moved to London in 1523, having already determined to translate the New Testament, spurred on by the desire to 'cause a boy that driveth the plough to know more of the Scripture' than did most of the clergy of the day. Finding the atmosphere in London hostile, he left for Hamburg in 1524 and never returned to his native land.

Tyndale completed his New Testament translation in the following year, and printing began at Cologne of a quarto edition with notes. Before it was completed, however, he was forced to flee to Worms, where printing began afresh, this time of an octavo edition without notes, at Schoeffer's press. Some sheets of the Cologne quarto have survived in the Grenville Library at the British Museum, but the octavo Worms edition was probably the first to be published. Several other editions followed and were smuggled into England. The translation was, however, bitterly opposed by the ecclesiastical authorities and many copies were burned. It was almost entirely Tyndale's unaided work, being based on the Greek text of Erasmus (46), while he also made use of the Vulgate and the German New Testament of Luther (51) whom he visited in Wittenberg. He seems to have made no use of earlier Wycliffite or succeeding translations.

He subsequently translated the Pentateuch, and the publication of this by J. Hoochstraten at Antwerp—the imprint reads Marburg—in January 1531 marked the first appearance in print of any portion of the Old Testament in English. His version of Jonah followed at Antwerp, probably in the same year, and when he was martyred at Vilvorde in the Netherlands in 1536 he left in manuscript a translation of the historical books of Joshua to 2 Chronicles which was published in Matthew's Bible of 1537. Before his death, a change of government policy had permitted the circulation in England of the Bible of his disciple, Miles Coverdale, printed abroad in 1535, and a year later the second edition of that Bible was printed in England with royal permission. Coverdale made very full use of Tyndale's text and it influenced later English Bibles so strongly that it has been asserted that almost nine-tenths of the words in the Authorized Version of 1611 (114) are Tyndale's.

BIBLIOGRAPHY: Darlow & Moule, no. 2.

59

THE GENTLEMAN

BALDASSARE CASTIGLIONE (1478–1529). Il Cortegiano. *Venice: Aldus, 1528*

'The Courtier' depicts the ideal aristocrat, and it has remained the perfect definition of a gentleman ever since. It is an epitome of the highest moral and social ideas of the Italian Renaissance, many of them inspired by classical examples.

Castiglione, after serving the Sforzas at Milan and the Gonzagas at Mantua, came to the Court of Urbino in 1504. Here Guidobaldo de Montefeltre and his consort Elizabetta Gonzaga were the centre of the most brilliant court in Italy, which counted among its members Bembo, Cardinal Bibbiena, Giuliano de' Medici and many other eminent men. His book is based on his experience of life among these dazzling figures.

It is written in the form of a discussion between members of the court, such discussions being the most popular literary form of the Renaissance. The virtues and the qualities which the courtier should cultivate form the main content of the book. The fundamental idea that a man should perfect himself by developing all his faculties goes back to Aristotle's *Ethics* (38) and many of the Aristotelian virtues reappear—honesty, magnanimity and good manners. The ideal man should also be proficient in arms and games, be a scholar and connoisseur of art; he should avoid all affectation, develop graceful speech and cherish a sense of honour. The relations between the courtier and his prince are discussed and also forms of government. Another section provides similar rules for the conduct of a lady and the book ends with the celebrated pronouncement on platonic love by Bembo.

This Renaissance ideal of the free development of individual faculties and its rules of civilized behaviour formed a new conception of personal rights and obligations in Europe and each nation produced its own version of the ideal figure: the *caballero* in Spain, the *honnête homme* in France and the gentleman in England. Castiglione's 'The Courtier' became the prototype of the genus 'courtesy book' published in various forms during the following century, in which rules of behaviour were formulated.

The book was translated into most European languages and between 1528 and 1616 no less than one hundred and eight editions were published. It had great influence in Spain, where traces of it can be found in *Don Quixote* (111), and in France where Corneille's conception of character was largely derived from it. But its most potent influence was probably in England. In 1561 Sir Thomas Hoby published an English translation which became one of the most popular books of the Elizabethan age. Its influence can be seen frequently in Shakespeare (122) —particularly Polonius—Spenser, Ben Jonson, Sir Philip Sidney and Robert Burton (120), and later in Shelley's *Hymn to Intellectual Beauty*. Its conversational form had a great impact on the development of English drama and comedy and in the seventeenth century two famous books on the gentleman appeared, that by Peacham intended for the Cavaliers and that by Brathwaite intended for the Puritans. In spite of the changes in the character of courts during the eighteenth century and the great attack launched on the conception of the 'courtier' by the French Revolution, the ideal of the 'gentleman' still fortunately survives.

60

SCHOLARSHIP IN FRANCE

GUILLAUME BUDÉ (1467–1540). Commentarii Linguae Graecae. [*Paris*]: *Jodocus Badius, 1529*

Budé was the most influential of the French humanistic scholars at the beginning of the sixteenth century. He made his mark with a treatise on ancient coinage and measures, which was a major authority for years to come, and he corresponded with most of the learned men of his time, amongst them Erasmus (43, 46, 53), who had the highest opinion of his talents, and Thomas More (47). He was held in the highest esteem by Francis I, who did

so much to further the cause of humanism in France. With Jean du Bellay, Budé persuaded him to found the Collegium Trilingue, which afterwards became the Collège de France, and the library at Fontainebleau, famous for its Greek manuscripts, which afterwards formed the nucleus of the Bibliothèque Nationale. He also induced the King not to enforce the interdiction on printing which had been suggested by the Sorbonne in 1533.

The 'Commentaries on the Greek Language' were a collection of lexicographical, philological and historical notes, which formed the basis for the study of the Greek language in France. A monument of the new learning, it was several times reprinted, and gave Budé the reputation which is now commemorated in the modern series of parallel texts of Greek, Latin and Byzantine authors which bears his name.

61

EDUCATION FOR GOVERNMENT

SIR THOMAS ELYOT (c. 1490–1546). The Boke named the Governour. *London: Thomas Berthelet, 1531*

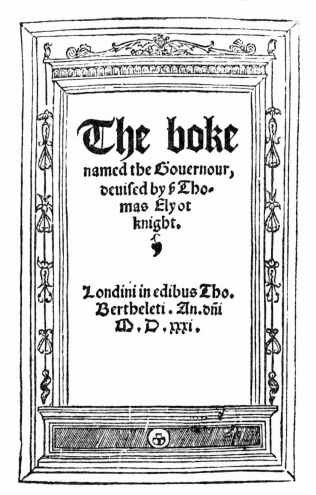

Sir Thomas Elyot, the son of a distinguished lawyer, was clerk of the Privy Council and was twice sent as ambassador to the Emperor Charles V. He was a friend of Sir Thomas More (47) and through this and a certain lukewarmness in carrying out the more arbitrary tasks required of him, he never obtained the full reward for his services. His books, however, were much valued. His Latin–English dictionary (for which Henry VIII lent him books) was a pioneer effort. He published a notable work of popular medicine, *The Castell of Helth*, and a number of translations from Pico della Mirandola and Plutarch.

His most famous book, however, was *The Boke named the Governour*, which went through edition after edition all through the sixteenth century. It achieved this fame for many reasons. It is the first work in recognizably modern English prose, to which Elyot added many new words. It provided influential advocacy for the study of the classics, from which he quotes extensively. The principal cause of its popularity was the current vogue for its subject—it is a treatise on moral philosophy, laying down the lines on which the education of those destined to govern should be directed, and inculcating the high moral principles which should rule them in the performance of their duties. There was nothing very original or revolutionary in the thoughts expressed: Elyot acknowledges his debt to the *Institutio Principis Christiani* of Erasmus and Castiglione's *Il Cortegiano* (59), though not that to Francesco Patrizzi, Bishop of Gaeta at the end of the fifteenth century, whose *De Regno et Regis Institutione* was certainly the model for *The Governour*. Nevertheless it remained a textbook for behaviour for generations and had a lasting effect on the writing of English.

62

LEXICOGRAPHY

ROBERT (I) ESTIENNE (1503 or 1504–59). (*a*) Dictionarium seu Latinae Linguae Thesaurus. *Paris: Robert Estienne, 1531* (*b*) Dictionarium Latino–Gallicum. *Ibidem, 1538*

The series of dictionaries edited and published by the Estienne or Stephanus family is perhaps the most significant, though by no means the sole achievement of the most renowned family of scholar-printers in history. Robert I, son of Henri I (died 1520), the founder of this intellectual dynasty, was the greatest of them all, with his son Henri II (1528–98) as a good second. Robert's fame rests on his activities as a typographer of Roman, Greek and Hebrew characters, as an accomplished editor of Latin authors and Latin, Greek and Hebrew Bibles, as a philologist and grammarian in these languages as well as his native French, and, above all, as the first scientific lexicographer of both ancient and modern languages.

The *Thesaurus* grew out of the demand for a reissue of the then standard Latin dictionary, the *Dictionarium* of Calepinus. Estienne considered the book too bad to merit a reprint; his appeal to a number of scholars to revise it was refused because of the tremendous labour involved—so, in the end, he undertook the work himself. His main innovations were threefold: contrary to the practice of his predecessors, he based his vocabulary exclusively on classical authors of whom he distilled some thirty; he clarified the meaning of the words by citing reputable

authorities, including his friend Budé (60); and he illustrated the correct usage of words and phrases by ample quotations from classical sources. The second edition (1536) was enlarged by the addition of proper names; the definitive edition, in three volumes, came out in 1543. As the *Thesaurus* of five German academies, begun in 1894, has, after seventy years, completed only the first half of the alphabet, Estienne's work is still unsurpassed as a whole. The *Thesaurus Linguae Romanae et Britannicae* by Thomas Cooper (London, Henry Wykes, 1565; reprinted 1573, 1578, 1584, 1587) was, in its Latin part, based on Estienne's *Thesaurus*, as the compiler acknowledged; Cooper's dictionary was, without any acknowledgement, copied and plagiarized by Thomas Thomas (Cambridge, 1587; 14th edition, 1644).

The *Dictionarium Latino–Gallicum* ('Latin–French Dictionary') of 1538 was inspired by the success of the *Thesaurus* and was based on the latter's second edition. It received, understandably, an even greater acclaim, was reprinted in 1543 and 1546, and served as the acknowledged model of Latin–German (Zürich, 1568) and Latin–Flemish (Antwerp, Plantin, 1573) dictionaries. The *Dictionnaire François–Latin* (1539) was mainly an improved inversion of the Latin–French book, but its second edition (1549) was greatly enlarged by the inclusion of many legal, medical, botanical and technical terms. Moreover it established, as it were, a standard French by basing its vocabulary on 'bon autheurs françois'—a principle later adopted by the *Dictionnaire de l'Académie* (1694).

In addition to these stately folios Robert also provided Latin and French school dictionaries such as the *Dictionariolum Puerorum* (1550) which were frequently reprinted and soon imitated. An English version, by John Vernon, with special reference to the *Dictionariolum*, appeared as early as 1552 (London, Thomas Wolfe).

Finally, in the mid-1550s, Robert Estienne turned to a Greek companion piece of the *Thesaurus*. His chief collaborator was his son Henri, who, after his father's death, eventually brought it out under his own imprint as *Thesaurus Linguae Graecae* (Geneva, 1572). Even more than with the *Thesaurus Latinus*, there has to this day been no substitute for the *Thesaurus Graecus*.

63

THE PRINCE

NICCOLO MACHIAVELLI (1469–1527). Il Principe. *Rome: Antonio Blado, 1532*

Between the years 1498 and 1512 Machiavelli served in the Chancery of the Florentine Republic. This afforded him unrivalled opportunities to investigate and consider the political systems and governments of half Europe. From the age of twenty-five onwards he was engaged on public duties for the republic, and in many diplomatic missions to the neighbouring Italian states, and as far as France and Germany. In 1502 came a decisive event in his career: the embassy to Cesare Borgia, then engaged in a complicated intrigue to strengthen his

IL PRINCIPE DI NICCHOLO MACHIA
VELLO AL MAGNIFICO LOREN.
ZO DI PIERO DE MEDICI.

LA VITA DI CASTRVCCIO CASTRA.
CANI DA LVCCA A ZANOBI BVON
DELMONTI ET A LVIGI ALEMAN.
NI DESCRITTA PER IL
MEDESIMÓ.

IL MODO CHE TENNE IL DVCA VA.
LENTINO PER AMMAZAR VITEL
LOZO, OLIVEROTTO DA FER.
MO IL.S.PAOLO ET IL DV
CA DI GRAVINA ORSI
NI IN SENIGAGLIA,
DESCRITTA PFR
IL MEDESIMO.

Con Gratie , & Priuilegi di . N.S. Clemente
VII.& altri Principi,che intra il termino di.X.
Anni non ſi ſtampino, ne ſtampati ſi uendino:
ſotto le pene, che in eſsi ſi contengono.
M. D. X X X II.

army by the removal of its disaffected captains. As he watched, Machiavelli developed a strong degree of admiration for the mixture of audacity and prudence, cruelty and fraud, self-reliance and distrust of others, which the prince displayed. The decline of the government of Piero Soderini and his own disgrace when it fell gave him the unwelcome leisure to put into words the reflexions perhaps originally prompted by his visit to Cesare.

'The Prince' is far more than a book of directions to any one of the many Italian princelings. Machiavelli had profited by his journeys to France and Germany to make the most able analyses (in his reports to his government) of a national government, and he now wrote for the guidance of the ruler by whom alone Italy, desperately divided, could be restored to political health. Hitherto political speculation had tended to be a rhetorical exercise based on the implicit assumption of Church or Empire. Machiavelli founded the science of modern politics on the study of mankind—it should be remembered that a parallel work to 'The Prince' was his historical essay on the first ten books of Livy. Politics was a science to be divorced entirely from ethics, and nothing must stand in the way of its machinery. Many of the remedies he proposed for the rescue of Italy were eventually applied. His concept of the qualities demanded from a ruler and the absolute need of a national militia came to fruition in the monarchies of the seventeenth century and their national armies.

What Machiavelli forgot is that man is not only a political animal, and that any attempt to govern without reconciling the other sides of his nature is bound to fail. Nevertheless, he wrote as a patriot and a political scientist, and he better deserves to be remembered as such than as the Borgia-like figure which his name now connotes. Paradoxically, it was the very people who practised his ruthless precepts to the letter—the Society of Jesus, the Spanish Hapsburgs, the French Bourbons—who first used 'machiavellists' as a term of abuse, by which they meant their opponents (when successful). Shakespeare (122) ironically acknowledges the fact when Hamlet says 'I'll put the murderous Machiavel to school'. More balanced modern judgement acknowledges his patriotism and studies his political thought, but the term 'machiavellian' retains its sinister meaning.

64

CICERO AND LATINITY

MARCUS TULLIUS CICERO (100–43 B.C.). Opera Omnia, cum Castigationibus Petri Victorii. 4 vols. *Venice: Giunta, 1534–7*

Throughout the hundreds of years when Latin was the *lingua franca* of thought and communication in Europe the works of Cicero were the most extensively read of all the Latin classics. Thus, while primarily giving a vivid picture of ancient Rome, Cicero's speeches and letters, as well as the philosophical works whose content formed the basis of so many medieval treatises, have had a deeper influence, if indirectly, on the means of expression than the works of any other writer. When Latin was superseded by the vernacular tongues, this influence was transmitted into the new languages.

Cicero's astonishing energy can be seen in everything that he wrote, a body of work unparalleled among those that have come down to us from classical antiquity. The forensic speeches which made him the foremost lawyer of his time show him principally as an able advocate for the defence. His prosecution speeches, notably that against Verres, the corrupt governor of Sicily, are equally effective, and they rise to an unequalled height in the famous 'Philippics'—those onslaughts on Mark Antony, modelled on the speeches of Demosthenes against Philip of Macedon, which Antony never forgave and which brought Cicero to his death. His political and philosophic works have been accused of lack of originality, to which Cicero would have been the first to confess: there were few philosophic works in Latin, except for the Epicurean work of Lucretius (87) which Cicero, a Stoic, opposed. His moral treatises and dialogues are thus largely works of translation and adaptation, but none the less influential for that.

MVSIS DICATVM

M.TVLLII
CICERONIS OPERA,
OMNIVM QVÆ HAC
TENVS EXCVSA
SVNT, CASTIGATIS
SIMA NVNC PRI,
MVM IN LVCEM
EDITA.

VENETIIS IN OFFICINA LV,
CÆANTONII IVNTÆ.

M. D. XXXVII.

NC REVIVIS

NV   CO

Perhaps the most valuable of Cicero's surviving works are the letters, such a vivid commentary on the last years of the Roman Republic as we have of no other period of ancient times. Here alone, devoid of formality, the character of Cicero and his contemporaries can be seen; and a picture appears of life two thousand years ago, what sort of people these were, how they travelled, what their houses were like, their troubles with servants—all the domestic detail which is elsewhere lacking. Its immediacy, too, reveals historical facts that would otherwise have been lost or deliberately concealed.

The editor of this collected edition (Cicero had been in print since the 1460s) was Pietro Vettori, or as he is better known, Victorius (1499–1585), the foremost Latin scholar of his day in Italy. His recension and his commentary on the text fully revealed his capacity; the feeling for meaning, and the sureness of his emendations opened a new era in textual criticism. As a later editor put it, Cicero owes more to him than all the other editors put together. It was moreover this edition, and Vettori's philological notes attached to it, which made Cicero's Latin the universal model for style, to which schoolboys still strive to attain in their Latin prose composition. The old eclectic styles of latinity died hard, and not without diatribes against the new 'Ciceronianism', but Vettori's precise demonstration of Cicero's precision was irresistible.

65

CALVINISM

Jean Calvin (1509–64). Christianae Religionis Institutio. Basle: [Thomas Platterus & Balthasar Lasius], 1536

Calvin's 'Institution of the Christian Religion' was the first systematic statement of a Reformed Church. It is the most important doctrinal work of the Reformation as a whole and provided a comprehensive theological system rivalling those of the Middle Ages, particularly Thomas Aquinas's (30). It discusses ancient and medieval philosophy, the Church Fathers, the contemporary Roman Church and the Reformers. Calvin is much indebted to St Augustine (3)—four thousand quotations from him have been counted in Calvin's works—Luther (49), Zwingli (56) and Martin Bucer, but he was greatly influenced also by his classical training, quoting Plato (27), Seneca and other ancient writers.

Calvin, a Swiss, though born in France, published the Institutio at the age of twenty-six. The dedication to Francis I of France contains a passionate appeal for freedom and justice for the Protestants in France whom Calvin characteristically defends from the accusation that they are rebels against state domination. The other parts of the book deal with the duties and conduct laid down in the ten commandments, faith, prayer, sacraments as given in the scriptures and as enforced by Roman Catholic tradition, Christian liberty and the relations between ecclesiastical and civil authorities.

Calvinism is the 'Reformed' as distinct from the 'Lutheran' Church. Though chiefly allied in ecclesiastical policy to Presbyterianism, it has in fact been associated with many other forms of church government. Its cardinal point was the absolute rule of God in the natural and spiritual world, and complete dependence on Him, by whose grace only is man relieved of the consequence of sin. Calvin fully accepted the doctrine of predestination, though its importance was later to be somewhat exaggerated.

Of particular historical importance was Calvin's attitude to the civil power. His ideal was Augustinian—to build God's empire on earth. Therefore secular government was the proper sphere for the Christian. Rulers should be obeyed as Ministers of God, but if they failed to carry out God's will, resistance was permissible. Calvin preferred representative government with an aristocratic flavour, but the emphasis on duty, independence, responsibility and the highest ethical standards in the individual Christian citizen encouraged a taste for liberty and free institutions, an orderly system of Christian government. Martin Bucer had preached the 'Gospel of hard work' and Calvin, too, insisted on thrift and diligence. It has been disproved, however, that he gave his special blessing to business enterprise and accumulation of capital or regarded business success as evidence of God's favour. Calvinism's most important role, despite Calvin's authoritarian influence, was to support the movement for liberty and independence in many parts of the world. Outside Switzerland its most potent influence was exercised in Holland and Britain. Puritanism and the ruling theology of the late sixteenth and early seventeenth century in England was Calvinistic; the Scottish reformation was Calvinistic throughout. Through these countries Calvinism exerted considerable influence on the recognition of the liberal democratic rights of the individual as eventually expressed in the Constitution of the United States of America. There was a revival of Calvinism in the nineteenth century, particularly in Holland, and one of its most eminent representatives today is Karl Barth.

The Institutio was much revised, taking its final form in 1559; Calvin himself translated it into French in 1545, and thereby created one of the finest early prose writings in the language. It has been printed in innumerable editions and translations including Hungarian, Greek and Arabic.

Calvin was a voluminous writer and Biblical commentator and his works fill fifty-nine volumes in the collected edition.

BIBLIOGRAPHY: In Johannes Calvin, Opera (Brunswick & Berlin, 1863–1900), vol. 59.

66

BALLISTICS

Niccolo Tartaglia (1500–77). Nova Scientia. Venice: Stephano da Sabio, 1537

Tartaglia's 'The New Science' stands at the threshold of a new age in the history of mechanics. Niccolo Fontana—known as Tartaglia (the stammerer), a defect he owed to a mutilation he suffered at the hands of French soldiers at the sack of Brescia in 1512—taught mathematics at Brescia, Verona and Venice. He was a self-taught engineer, surveyor, book-keeper and mathematician.

Medieval thinkers such as Albert of Saxony, Jean Buridan and others had begun to modify the Aristotelian theory of movement according to which a body was kept in motion only so long as a mover was actually in contact with it. They had replaced it by the theory of 'impetus', a quality inside the body itself which it acquired from the fact of being set in motion. Tartaglia's work carried this theory a step further.

In the *Nova Scientia* he deals with ballistics, surveying, engineering and fortification. He sought—but did not find—a mathematical theory defining the flight of projectiles. In some respects his views were anti-Aristotelian, e.g. he thought that the path of a projectile is at all points curved towards the ground, owing to its weight. He learned from gunners that the longest range was obtained at 45° elevation. The elucidation of true mechanical principles, however, and the deduction of mathematical ballistics from them, were first perfected by Galileo (130). A copy of Tartaglia's book with notes by Galileo is (still, one hopes) preserved in Florence.

Tartaglia made one of the most important mathematical discoveries of his time by developing a comprehensive system for solving cubic equations. He first kept this secret, but was induced to communicate it to Cardanus, who published it in his *Artis Magnae sive de Regulis Algebraicis Liber Unus* (1545). A famous quarrel ensued.

Tartaglia also published works on arithmetic, commercial arithmetic and mathematical puzzles. In 1543 he issued the first Italian translation of Euclid and the earliest version of any of the works of Archimedes, including his *De Insidentibus Aquae*. An English edition of the *Nova Scientia* was published in 1588.

67

ENGLISH GRAMMAR

WILLIAM LILY (*c.* 1468–1522). Institutio Compendiaria Totius Grammaticae. *London: Thomas Berthelet, 1540*

William Lily was the godson of Grocyn and he followed Colet to Magdalen in 1486. Like them he studied Latin and Greek in Italy (on his return from a pilgrimage to Jerusalem), and shared with them the introduction of Greek to England. For some years he taught in London, and was a friend of Sir Thomas More (47), with whom he published translations from the Greek Anthology. When Colet was founding his new school in St Paul's Churchyard, he chose Lily as its first High Master; he was formally appointed in 1512 and there remained until his death.

The origins of his famous grammar are confused. He contributed a short Latin syntax, with the rules in English, called *Grammatices Rudimenta* to one of Colet's works; his *Absolutissimus de Octo Orationis Partium Constructione Libellus*, a syntax with the rules in Latin, was published

in 1513. Colet sent a draft of the combined work to Erasmus who made substantial revisions; so substantial, in fact, that from 1517 the Basle editions carried his name only on the title-page. These two works were revised and combined in 1540 into the 'Compendium of All Grammar' (here cited), which was designated by royal command as the national Latin grammar. This edition is thought to have been produced for the young Prince Edward, and from this and a proclamation of 1548 enjoining its use the compendium is often called 'King Edward's Grammar'. In 1542 the book was translated into English as *An Introduction of the Eyght Partes of Speche compiled and sette forthe by the Commandement of Henry VIII*. In 1571 a canon was drawn up by the upper house of Convocation with the intention of making its use compulsory and a similar measure was brought before the House of Lords in 1575.

In 1549 it had been again revised, from Erasmus's text, under a new title, *A Short Introduction of Grammar generally to be used*. In this form it was used by Shakespeare (122) who quotes familiar sentences from it in *Love's Labours Lost* and *Twelfth Night*. It was further revised in 1732 and in this form was used by St Paul's, Eton (for which yet another recension was made in 1758) and other schools well into the nineteenth century. Considering its slight beginning, Lily's work achieved a remarkable fame and durability.

68

PHYSIOLOGY AND PATHOLOGY

JEAN FERNEL (1485–1558). De Naturali Parte Medicinae. Paris: [Adam Saulnier for] Simon de Colines, 1542

With his insistence on personal observation and experiment, Fernel was one of the most influential representatives of a new school of medicine. A very successful physician in Paris, he cured the sterility of Catherine de Medici and the ill-health of Diane de Poitiers, and later became physician to Henry II.

'On the Natural Part of Medicine' was later revised and published as the first part of his great general book, the *Medicina*, Paris, 1554. In that edition it was first called 'Physiologia', thus giving the subject the name by which it has been known ever since. The orthodox theories of the four humours (blood, phlegm, yellow and black bile), the four qualities (hot, cold, wet, dry), and the four elements (earth, air, fire and water), on whose proper interrelations the functions of a healthy body were believed to depend, still prevailed in Fernel. But he entirely rejected all magic and superstition as irrelevant to the study of bodily functions, and clearly stated that anatomy shows only the location and not the nature of these processes. Fernel included in 'physiology' the study of the mind and brain.

Equally important was the second part of the 1554 *Medicina*, the *Pathologia*. The first book on pathology was *De Abditis Causis Morborum*, Florence, 1507, by the Italian physician Benivieni (*c.* 1440–1502); it was a pioneer work in which for the first time post-mortem studies were used for finding internal causes of diseases. But Benivieni was a Galenist and did not develop a new system. It was Fernel who first used the term 'pathology' and his was the first systematic essay on the morbid phenomena of the human body, examined methodically organ by organ. Hitherto pathological study had been confined to collections of case-histories without any attempt at a logical or methodical system. Fernel's work included a number of notable observations—in the 1567 edition there is a case-history which has been claimed as the first description of appendicitis. Everything that was a cause of an ailment was part of his conception of pathology; later the term was identified more closely with morbid anatomy alone, until at the end of the nineteenth century Cohnheim initiated a return to Fernel's wider concept.

Both physiology and pathology had, of course, existed in rudimentary form before Fernel; but he was the pioneer who gave these subjects their names and established them as separate systems. His books were very widely studied; the *Physiologia* went through thirty-four editions in the next hundred years and was translated into French and English.

BIBLIOGRAPHY: Sir Charles Sherrington, *The Endeavour of Jean Fernel, with a list of the Editions of his Writings* (Cambridge, 1946).

69

A CLASSIC HERBAL

LEONHARD FUCHS (1501–66). De Historia Stirpium Commentarii. *Basle: Officina Isingriniana, 1542*

From classical times to the early sixteenth century not much progress had been made in medical botany. It all stemmed from Dioscorides (20). Text and illustrations of botanical works—both manuscript and printed—were derived from classical sources and had on the whole altered only for the worse, through continued copying from generation to generation. Consequently the numerous printed herbals of the fifteenth century, books such as the *Hortus Sanitatis*, were crude in text and woodcuts. But a change took place early in the sixteenth century. It is first manifested in the work of Brunfels, who engaged the artist Hans Weiditz to illustrate his *Herbarum Vivae Icones*, Strasbourg, 1530–6. This in turn inspired Leonhard Fuchs to publish his 'Commentaries on the History of Plants', perhaps the most celebrated and most beautiful herbal ever published.

Fuchs was professor of medicine at Tübingen; and as such his primary objectives were to improve the knowledge of *materia medica* and to show the largest possible number of plants useful as drugs and herbs. He described four hundred German and one hundred foreign plants and illustrated them in five hundred and twelve superb woodcuts. These were designed by Heinrich Füllmauer and Albert Meyer, and executed by Veit Rudolph Speckle, whose portraits appear in the book—one of the earliest examples of such a tribute paid to artists in a printed book. Yet Fuchs's interest in plants was not wholly

pharmacological; he dilates upon the beauties of nature, and he is enough of a true botanist to describe the characteristics of plants, their habits, habitats, and forms.

In the text the plants are arranged in alphabetical order: there is no classification, no plant geography, nothing about their relations with other living things. Fuchs's text still draws heavily on classical learning—he was a Renaissance man—but he was acquainted with northwestern European species and even American plants like

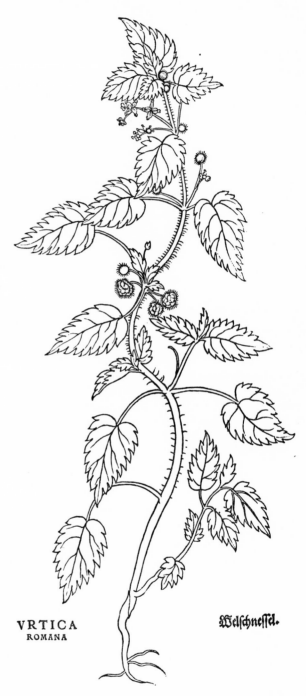

VRTICA
ROMANA

Welſchneſſel.

maize. The fuchsia, when it was brought from America, was named after him. However, the air of modernity is clearest in the woodcuts, based on first-hand observation of the living plant and establishing a standard of plant illustration which has been followed until our own day.

Fuchs's Herbal, as it is generally known, was an immediate success; it was frequently reprinted and freely translated, at first in folio, but later in pocket editions.

70

THE HELIOCENTRIC UNIVERSE

NICOLAUS COPERNICUS (1473–1543). *De Revolutionibus Orbium Coelestium. Nuremberg: Johannes Petreius, 1543*

The publication of 'On the Revolutions of the Celestial Spheres' in 1543 was a landmark in human thought. It challenged the authority of antiquity and set the course for the modern world by its effective destruction of the anthropocentric view of the universe. We owe this book, which was more or less completed as early as 1530, to Georg Joachim Rheticus of Wittenberg, who persuaded Copernicus to allow him to publish it; for until 1540 the author himself had permitted only preliminary statements to circulate in manuscript. He died on the eve of its publication.

Nicolaus Copernicus studied at Cracow, Bologna and Padua. Returning to his native Poland he eventually became Canon of the cathedral at Frauenberg, where he lived quietly until his death. He was a physician—having studied medicine at Padua—diplomat, economist, Doctor of Canon Law, and artist—a self-portrait survives.

Renaissance mathematicians, following Ptolemy (18★), believed that the moon, sun and five planets were carried by complex systems of epicycles and deferents about the central earth, the fixed pivot of the whole system. In Copernicus's day it was well known that conventional astronomy did not work accurately, nor did further study of Ptolemy seem to put the matter right. Copernicus, stimulated by the free entertainment of various new ideas among the ancients, determined to abandon the fixity of the earth, and all the complexities in the treatment of the motions of the celestial bodies that follow from such a conception. With the sun placed at the centre, and the earth daily spinning on its axis and circling the sun in common with other planets, the whole system of the heavens became clear, simple, and harmonious. The revolutionary nature of his theory is evident in his famous diagram illustrating the concentric orbits of the planets.

Moreover, the new system worked mathematically as well as the Ptolemaic though not, indeed, much better. Like Ptolemy, Copernicus believed that the heavenly motions must be perfect, uniform and circular; he still employed epicycles. It was Tycho Brahe who finally destroyed the heavenly spheres, and Kepler (112) who destroyed the myth of the circle.

In the first book of the *De Revolutionibus* Copernicus explains how the daily rising and setting of the heavenly bodies is a consequence of the daily diurnal rotation of the earth on its polar axis. The course taken by the sun through the zodiacal constellations and the phenomena of the seasons are shown to be due to the annual revolution of the earth about the sun. Book 2 contains the mathematics of astronomy and a star catalogue based on Ptolemy; Books 3–6 treat of the particular motions of the earth, moon and planets. The relative distances between the earth and the planets are now determined.

Copernicus (who dedicated his book to Pope Paul III) expected to be ridiculed by the unthinking for supposing that the earth moved; but he did not anticipate that it would attract religious prejudice. The early neglect of *De Revolutionibus* was due to its difficulty and strangeness; later the fundamentalist issue became critical and it was condemned by the Church in 1616. The Church had no objection to the Copernican system as a mere calculating device, in the manner disarmingly proposed in the anonymous preface inserted in the first edition, without Copernicus's knowledge, by the Lutheran minister Andreas Osiander; it was the reality of the earth's motion that was at stake.

Within a century the Copernican view was generally accepted by the leaders of science; Galileo (128) and Gilbert (107) were strong supporters as well as Mästlin

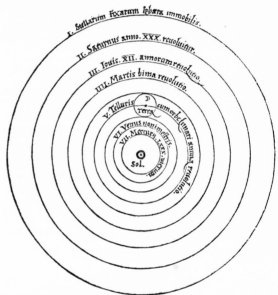

and Kepler. Newton (161) finally established its truth and his views were further developed by the eighteenth-century mathematicians to find their final summing up in the *Traité de Mécanique Céleste* of Laplace (252). When it was stated in modern times that the planets were originally ejected from the sun by centrifugal forces a new significance was given to the heliocentric theory, but it must be said that with the arrival of Einstein's theory of relativity (408) any statement about the absolute motion or rest of bodies has become somewhat irrelevant. But beyond these influences on astronomical science, it is obvious that the publication of this book at that particular moment in history powerfully helped to re-direct the whole outlook and thinking of mankind.

BIBLIOGRAPHY: Henryk Baranowski, *Bibliografia Kopernikowska, 1509–1955* (Warsaw, 1958)

71

THE BIRTH OF MODERN ANATOMY

ANDREAS VESALIUS (1514–64). De Humani Corporis Fabrica. *Basle: Johannes Oporinus, 1543*

Vesalius, born in Flanders but of German extraction, was (in Garrison's words) the most commanding figure in European medicine after Galen (33) and before Harvey (127). He began the study of medicine when Galen's anatomical work was just becoming known, with revolutionary effect on both the method and spirit of anatomical research. Galen, as he himself complained, had been forced to rely upon the dissection of animals; the more fortunate physicians and surgeons of the sixteenth century were able to make use of both animal and human subjects. The young Vesalius, with an iconoclastic zeal characteristic of the sixteenth century, and a forcible style all his own, endeavoured to do all that Galen had done and to do it better.

The result was 'The Structure of the Human Body', published when he was twenty-nine; a complete anatomical and physiological study of every part of the human body, based on first-hand examination and his five years' experience as public prosector in the medical school at Padua. The five books deal with the bones and muscles, blood vessels, nerves, abdominal viscera, thoracic organs and the brain. Galen was not merely improved upon: he was superseded; and the history of anatomy is divided into two periods, pre-Vesalian and post-Vesalian.

The *Fabrica*, a handsomely printed folio, is remarkable for its series of magnificent plates, which set new technical standards of anatomical illustration, and indeed of book illustration in general. They have generally been ascribed to an artist of Titian's school, long (but no longer) thought to be Jan Stephen van Calcar (1499–c. 1550). Vesalius's was the most splendid and the most comprehensive of a large number of anatomical treatises of the sixteenth century. The second edition (1555) used the same plates (the woodblocks indeed survived in Germany until the Second World War) but contains minor variations in the text. No other work of the sixteenth century equals it, though many share its spirit of anatomical enquiry. It was translated, reissued, copied and plagiarized over and over again and its illustrations were used or copied in other medical works until the end of the eighteenth century.

BIBLIOGRAPHY: Harvey Cushing, *The Bio-Bibliography of Vesalius* (New York, 1943); C. D. O'Malley, *Andreas Vesalius of Brussels, 1514–1564* (Berkeley and Los Angeles, 1964).

72

'GIVE ME A PLACE TO STAND, AND I WILL MOVE THE EARTH'

ARCHIMEDES (287–212 B.C.). Opera Omnia. *Basle: Johannes Hervagius, 1544*

Archimedes, the greatest mathematician and engineer of antiquity, studied at Alexandria and lived most of his life at Syracuse. He was killed at the capture of Syracuse by the Romans under Marcellus in 212 by a Roman soldier whom he rebuked for trampling on a diagram he had drawn in the sand.

Many stories circulate about Archimedes, some of which are certainly apocryphal; but their persistence testifies to his continuing repute. To prove to King Hiero that a small force could move a great weight, he is said to have moved a large ship on the shore easily by an arrangement of pulleys. According to Pappus of Alexandria the discovery of this phenomenon caused Archimedes to exclaim: 'Give me a place to stand, and I will move the earth'. Vitruvius tells the story that, while sitting in a bath, Archimedes discovered that the amount of water that overflowed was equal to the amount by which his body was immersed, which suggested to him one of the fundamental laws of hydrostatics. He leapt out of the bath and, running naked to his home, cried out in his joy: 'Eureka, Eureka' ('I have found it').

Archimedes was above all a great mathematician, developing further many ideas of Eudoxus and Euclid (25). In plane geometry he wrote on circle measurement, the quadrature of the parabola and spirals. In his 'The Method', discovered in 1906 by the Danish scholar J. L. Heiberg, he explains how he obtained the solution of certain mathematical problems by comparing (with the aid of his study of centres of gravity) elements of an unknown figure with those of a known figure, thus using his knowledge of mechanics to advance his knowledge of mathematics. It also enables Archimedes's other method of analysis by 'exhaustion' to be reconstructed. In working out these problems, Archimedes used techniques which permit him to be regarded as an important forerunner of the mathematicians who developed the infinitesimal calculus. One of Archimedes's greatest achievements was his calculation that the area of the surface of a sphere is four times that of the great circle of the sphere and that the volume of the sphere is two thirds the volume of its circumscribed cylinder.

In the *Arenarius*, or 'Sand-reckoner', he invented a system of numeration by which he could express any number however large, e.g. the number of grains of sand which could be contained in a sphere the size of the universe. His works on theoretical mechanics and hydrostatics are classics of their kind. He is said to have invented the water screw, but it is probable that this had already been used in Egypt earlier for the purposes of irrigation. Through his researches on statics he discovered the fundamental principles relating to the lever and the centres of gravity of triangles, parallelograms and parallel trapezia. In hydrostatics he described the equilibrium of floating bodies and stated the famous proposition—known by his name—that, if a solid floats in a fluid, the weight of the solid is equal to that of the fluid displaced and, if a solid heavier than a fluid is weighed in it, it will be lighter than its true weight by the weight of the fluid displaced. We owe to Archimedes the full exposition of the doctrine of levers and pulleys. He constructed many machines, a planetarium, burning mirrors, a ship-launching mechanism, etc. In the *Arenarius* he quotes a passage from Aristarchus which is the earliest evidence we now have that the latter had conceived the heliocentric system long before Copernicus (70).

Archimedes—together with Newton (161) and Gauss (257)—is generally regarded as one of the greatest mathematicians the world has ever known, and if his influence had not been overshadowed at first by Aristotle, Euclid and Plato, the progress to modern mathematics might have been much faster. As it was, his influence began to take full effect only after the publication of this first printed edition which enabled Descartes (129), Galileo (113, 128, 130) and Newton in particular to build on what he had begun.

Apart from one small tract published in 1503 and an imperfect edition by Tartaglia (66) in 1543, the edition cited above is the first complete edition of Archimedes's works. The text is in Greek and Latin, edited by Theodore Gechauff, with commentary by Eutocius Ascolonites.

It is significant that major editions of Archimedes's works have been published in modern times: in Greek, by J. L. Heiberg, 1910–15, in English by Sir T. L. Heath, 1897, in French by Paul van Eecke in 1921 and in German in various works by Czwalina-Allenstein in 1922–5.

73
BOOK ABOUT BOOKS

CONRAD GESNER (1516–65). Bibliotheca Universalis. *Zurich: Christopher Froschauer, 1545*

The compilation of bibliographical catalogues of books was attempted by St Jerome who made lists of Christian writers and their works which were continued by Gennadius. Some progress was made in the Middle Ages and in the late fifteenth century, notably by Johannes Trithemius, Abbot of Spanheim, in his *De Scriptoribus Ecclesiasticis*, Basle, 1494. These writers, however, confined themselves to Christian literature. Gesner, the German–Swiss naturalist and polymath, attempted to describe all the existing books in Latin, Greek and Hebrew (though not those in the vernacular) in a majestic series of volumes. These are the earliest systematic 'books about books' to be published and they mark the beginning of modern critical bibliography. For Gesner was no mere enumerator of titles; he gave also his considered estimate of their comparative worth.

The present ample folio, the first of the series, is the author-bibliography, in which the writers are arranged under their names. Their books are listed with particulars of the various printed editions, as well as critical notes; even manuscripts and projected and unfinished works are mentioned. In 1548 followed the second part, the

Pandectarum... libri XXI (actually nineteen), in 1549 the *Partitiones Theologicae*, and in 1555 an Appendix. These three volumes contain the subject index, each book of which is dedicated to a famous contemporary printer, a list of whose productions is added. Of the projected twenty-one books only twenty were actually produced; the volume which was to deal with medicine and natural science was never completed.

Gesner's other achievements are surveyed under No. 77; but if he was best known to his contemporaries as a botanist, 'The Universal Library' and its sequels qualify him also for the title of protobibliographer of the printed book.

74
THE SOCIETY OF JESUS

IGNATIUS OF LOYOLA (1491–1556). Exercitia Spiritualia. (Translated from the Spanish by A. Frusius.) *Rome: Antonio Blado, 1548*

The 'Spiritual Exercises' form the most famous modern textbook on ascetic discipline, the nature of sin and Christian perfection by grace.

St Ignatius of Loyola was born Inigo Lopez de Recalde, a member of a noble Basque family in the province of Guipuzcoa in Spain. In his youth he led the normal life of his class, but during his convalescence after having been wounded fighting the French at Pamplona in 1521, he decided to do penance for his sins. In 1522 he went first to Montserrat and then to the neighbouring Manresa where during a retreat lasting from March 1522 to February 1523 he first sketched out his 'Exercises'. After a pilgrimage to Jerusalem, he returned in 1524 to study for the priesthood, mainly in Paris and Rome, but also visiting England in 1530. His ideas were disapproved by the several religious orders with whom he studied, but eventually he was ordained in 1537. During this period disciples had gathered round him, and were formed by Ignatius into an informal association which he called the 'Company of Jesus'. They moved to Rome, and after some difficulties Pope Paul III in 1540 approved this new community. The Society of Jesus was formally established with Ignatius as its first General. He was beatified by Paul V in 1609, canonized by Gregory XV in 1622 and declared Patron of all Spiritual Retreats by Pius XI in 1922.

The 'Exercises', though undoubtedly influenced by the ascetic teachings of Garcia de Cisneros of Montserrat and the Brothers of the Common Life, form a unique book, inspired by a remarkable fixity of purpose and designed for a clearly defined and practical end: the moulding of character by the precepts of the Gospel. Its asceticism is not one of resignation and withdrawal, but full of a positive recognition of active life. It is this characteristic in particular which made the book such a powerful influence when it became (with the *Constitutiones*, on which Ignatius was still at work when he died) the handbook of the Society of Jesus, which is devoted to educational, missionary and other active works.

St Ignatius introduced many innovations when founding the Jesuit Order; the abandonment of such traditional forms of worship as chanting the divine office, a monarchical rather than collegiate constitution, and much simpler vows. These elements, together with the spiritual

EXERCITIA
SPIRITVALIA.

M.D.XLVIII.

power of the 'Exercises', gave the Order its militant character and enabled it to exercise its great influence on the world. As a work of religious inspiration the impact of the 'Exercises' has been almost as great outside the Society of Jesus as within.

75
THE ENGLISH LITURGY

THE BOOKE OF COMMON PRAYER. *London: Edward Whitchurch, 1549*

The English *Book of Common Prayer* was the first single manual of worship in a vernacular language directed to be used universally by, and common to, both priest and people.

Its original simplicity, which has not been lost in the many subsequent revisions, has ensured its permanence; and deservedly so, because it is one of the greatest of all liturgical rationalizations, combining as it did the four main service books of pre-Reformation days, the Missal, Breviary, Manual and Pontifical, and abolishing all the different regional variations contained in the diocesan uses. From these four service books came the main structure of the Prayer Book, and with translations from other liturgical sources, they formed the contents. To these were added the Collects, which were Archbishop

Cranmer's own contribution, along with the translation into English whose simplicity and vigour are still apparent.

The Litany was compiled and published in 1544, the English version of the Epistles and Gospels followed in 1548 and the first complete Book of Common Prayer was issued and enjoined by the Act of Uniformity of 1549. A considerably altered text was introduced in 1552 to satisfy a more extreme Protestant point of view, and minor alterations of a catholicizing tendency were made in 1561 and again in 1604. The last major alteration took place after the Restoration in 1662, when several hundred alterations were made, ranging from a single word to the substitution of the Authorized Version of 1611 for the Great Bible of 1540 for all passages of scripture except the Psalms; but from then on the liturgy has remained substantially unaltered.

It is not least among the achievements of the original compilers that most of what they wrote should still be in use four hundred years later. The language of the Prayer Book is now part of the whole language, often quoted and used even when the original itself is unknown. And, as a source of spiritual inspiration, it is for most Englishmen second only to the Bible.

BIBLIOGRAPHY: Edward C. Ratcliff, *The Book of Common Prayer: its Makings and Revisions, 1549–1661* (London, 1949).

76
THE SCIENCE OF NAVIGATION

MARTIN CORTES (1532–1589). Breve Compendio de la Sphera y de la Arte de Navegar. *Seville: Anton Alvarez, 1551*

The 'Brief Treatise on the Sphere and on the Art of Navigation' contains the most complete statement of navigational science to date. The author was a Spanish cosmographer of whose life little is known. His book is divided into three parts: (1) on the cosmos, the size of the earth, geographical climates; (2) the courses of the sun and moon, the seasons, tides and weather; (3) a practical manual of navigation, how to draw a sea-card, how to plot or 'prick' a position upon the chart, with a section on the compass and other instruments. The descriptions for making navigational instruments are particularly good, especially those of the cross-staff and astrolabe. William Bourne, who was inspired by Cortes to write his *Regiment of the Sea* [1574], the first printed original treatise on navigation by an Englishman, added instructions for their use.

Cortes supplies a table of the sun's declination for four years and another of the distance between meridians at every degree of latitude, but he has been wrongly credited with first thinking of the enlargement of the degrees of latitude towards the pole, which was the work of Mercator (100) and Wright (106). His instructions for making charts and for plotting courses of ships on them were widely followed. Most important of all, he first understood and described the magnetic variation of the compass, suggesting that the magnetic pole and the true pole of the earth were not the same.

Medina's similar but less accurate manual, the *Arte de Navegar* of 1545, was widely used in France and Italy; but Stephen Borough, one of the men behind Queen Elizabeth's measures to advance Britain's maritime

power, brought Cortes's book back from Seville and persuaded the Muscovy Company to have it translated into English. This translation was published in 1561 and reached its eighth edition in 1615. It was one of the most decisive books printed in the English language, as it supplied to the Elizabethan navigators their first key to the mastery of the sea, which remained in English hands for centuries. It was eventually superseded by the even more advanced works of Mercator and Wright, but it is significant that one whole chapter in the latter's famous *Errors in Navigation* is a translation from Cortes.

77
RENAISSANCE ZOOLOGY

CONRAD GESNER (1516–65). Historia Animalium. 5 vols. *Zurich: Christopher Froschauer, 1551–87*

Conrad Gesner was one of the great polymaths of the Renaissance. He was a German–Swiss who studied at Basle, Paris and Montpellier, became professor of Greek at Lausanne and finally professor of medicine at Zürich where he died of the plague.

His 'History of Animals' is an encyclopaedia of contemporary knowledge, intended to replace not only

medieval compilations but even Aristotle's work of the same title. Like any modern encyclopaedist Gesner drew upon the best sources of information available to him, and although borrowing a great deal from his predecessors (including Aristotle), also commissioned many articles from contemporary experts. He had himself a competent knowledge of natural history, a great love of nature, and a healthy scepticism towards most of the old myths and legends.

The work consists of five large volumes containing some three thousand five hundred pages and one thousand woodcuts. The first four volumes—published 1551–8—deal with quadrupeds, birds and fishes; the posthumous fifth volume with snakes and, in an appendix, scorpions. The animals are arranged alphabetically, each being discussed under eight sections: (1) name in different languages; (2) habitat, origin, description of internal and external parts; (3) environment, movement, diseases, intellectual faculties; (4) mental life, habits, instinct; (5) animal's use to man; (6) animals as food; (7) animals for medical purposes; (8) literary history, fables and anecdotes, sacred and emblematical animals, etc.

Like contemporary herbals, and some earlier works on zoology, Gesner's encyclopaedia was enriched by crude but often lively woodcuts. Most were prepared specially for this work; others—like the rhinoceros after Dürer—were borrowed. They are realistic enough to act as a valuable supplement to the text.

Although the *Historia Animalium* does not yet show any recognition of a connexion between different forms of living nature and fails to conform to our modern ideas of biological research, it was a great step forward and remained the most authoritative zoological book between Aristotle and the publication of Ray's classification of fauna in 1693.

It was many times reprinted and although it often suffered at the hands of editors, it remained the standard reference book even as late as Linné (192) and beyond, because neither Linné nor Ray included illustrations. Editions were published in German in 1557–1613, an English abridgement by Topsell in 1607; and Gesner's unpublished notes on insects formed the basis of Moffet's *Insectormu sive Minimorum Animalium Theatrum*, 1634. Cuvier (276) was one of his greatest admirers and named him the 'German Pliny'.

Gesner was distinguished in many other fields (see 73): he wrote some important botanical works though most of them were not published until C. C. Schmiedel's edition of 1753–9. In his *Mithridates* he studied the comparative philology of one hundred and twenty languages, with twenty-two versions of the Lord's Prayer. He also published a study of fossils: and he was one of the very first men who climbed mountains not only for the sake of collecting botanical specimens, but for pure enjoyment and exercise, an attitude most unusual for his time; his *Descriptio Montis Fracti sive Montis Pilati*, 1555, describes his ascent of the Gnepfstein (6,299 feet).

78

PRELUDE TO HARVEY

MICHAEL SERVETUS (1511–53). Christianismi Restitutio. [*Vienne: Balthasar Arnollet*], *1553*

Michael Servetus, a native of Tudela in Navarre, was primarily a theologian and a religious reformer, and the statement of his anti-Trinitarian doctrine—chiefly in 'The Restoration of Christianity'—aroused the opposition of both Roman Catholics and Protestants. Following Cellarius, *De Operibus Dei*, 1527, he rejected the orthodox and generally accepted theory of the Trinity; he believed in the essentially intellectual recognition of sin and disapproved of infant baptism. He was a forerunner of modern biblical criticism.

As a theologian, Servetus's direct influence was not considerable; the most prominent of his followers was Bernardino Occhino, and eventually his sect was merged with that of the Socinians in Poland. But even if he had no direct followers, his teachings have influenced Unitarians ever since.

While in Paris Servetus had studied anatomy under Günther of Andernach at the same time as Vesalius (71), and it is from a small section of about half-a-dozen pages on physiology that this book derives its medico-historical importance. Here he clearly describes the pulmonary or lesser circulation of the blood, the passage of the blood from the right side of the heart through the lungs to the left side after having been mixed with air, and he rejects the supposed passage of some blood through the septum. The disclosure in recent times that the first description of the pulmonary circulation was given by Ibn al-Nafis, a thirteenth-century Egyptian physician, and the fact that it was also taught by Realdo Colombo and Valverde, two of Servetus's contemporaries, has given rise to controversy over priority in the actual discovery; but Servetus was the first to print it.

Following his rejection of the Trinity, Servetus also denied the traditional physiological theory of the three concepts of natural, vital and animal spirits and once this view, that there were three different physiological fluids in the body, had been demolished, the way to the circulation theory became very much clearer. He challenged the opinon that there were two kinds of blood divided by natural and vital spirits and taught that there was only one kind of blood and that 'the soul itself is the blood'.

Both his religious and physiological views were held to be heretical and he had to flee from the Inquisition in France, where he had been practising medicine at Vienne. He passed through Geneva where he was detained by the Calvinists and died a martyr's death in 1553. Calvin (65) wanted him beheaded, but he was burnt. One of the arguments advanced against him was his unorthodox view of physiology which implied that the soul (being in the blood) perished with the body.

Servetus's books were burned with him and are therefore among the rarest in the world; only three copies of the *Christianismi Restitutio* are known to survive: in Vienna, Paris (once in Dr Richard Mead's collection in London) and Edinburgh (incomplete). There is good reason for believing that the Edinburgh copy belonged to Calvin. The book was reprinted from the Vienna copy in 1790 by Rau of Nuremberg.

BIBLIOGRAPHY: John F. Fulton, *Michael Servetus, Humanist and Martyr* (New York, 1953)

79

TECHNOLOGY AND MODERN GEOLOGY

GEORGIUS AGRICOLA (1494–1555). De Re Metallica. *Basle: J. Froben & N. Episcopius, 1556*

Agricola's best-known work, 'On Metals', is the first systematic treatise on mining and metallurgy and one of the first technological books of modern times.

Agricola—he latinized his name from Georg Bauer—studied at Leipzig, Bologna and Padua, became town physician of the mining centre of Joachimsthal in Bohemia and physician at Chemnitz in Saxony from 1534 until his death. Living in mining regions all his life made it possible for him to study mining practices at first hand and these direct observations made his books particularly valuable and effective.

Mining has been practised from primitive times; gold and silver, copper and lead have been used for thousands of years, and even iron, a late-comer, is prehistoric. Though the actual consumption of metals was slight in the Middle Ages as in preceding epochs, craftsmen then wrote the first coherent treatises on the treatment and fabrication of metals (e.g. the *Schedula Diversarum Artium* of Theophilus Presbyter). In the late Middle Ages there were very important advances in mining and metallurgy, reflected first in the *Probierbüchlein* of c. 1510 (the first printed book on the subject), then in Biringuccio's fine *Pirotechnia* (1540) and finally in this great work of Agricola's, by far the most authoritative account of south German technology.

The *De Re Metallica* embraces everything connected with the mining industry and metallurgical processes, including administration, prospecting, the duties of officials and companies and the manufacture of glass, sulphur and alum. The magnificent series of two hundred and seventy-three large woodcut illustrations by Hans Rudolf Manuel Deutsch add to its value. Some of the most important sections are those on mechanical engineering and the use of water-power, hauling, pumps, ventilation, blowing of furnaces, transport of ores, etc., showing a very elaborate technique.

In Book V, and also in the *De Ortu et Causis Subterraneorum*, Basle, 1546, Agricola made an important contribution to physical geology. He recognized the influence of water and wind on the shaping of the landscape and gave a clear account of the order of the strata he saw in the mines. Writing on the origin of mountains, he describes the eroding action of water as their cause with a perspicacity much in advance of his time.

The most important of Agricola's many other treatises was the *De Natura Fossilium* (also Basle, 1546), which has earned him the title of 'Father of Mineralogy'. After the

NO. 79, AGRICOLA

classical writings of Pliny (5) and Theophrastus on the subject, mineralogy during the Middle Ages was chiefly concerned with the medicinal and magical properties of stones. Agricola supplied a new scientific classification of minerals based on their physical properties. He described eighty different minerals and metallic ores (including twenty new ones), their mode of occurrence and mutual relation.

The *De Re Metallica* was frequently reprinted and is said to have reached China in the seventeenth century. Interest in it was revived in the eighteenth century by Abraham Gottlieb Werner; and in 1912 it was translated into English by Herbert Hoover, afterwards President of the United States.

BIBLIOGRAPHY: E. Darmstaedter, *Georg Agricola* (Munich, 1926).

80

AGAINST FEMALE MONARCHY

JOHN KNOX (1505–71). The First Blast of the Trumpet against the Monstrous Regiment of Women. [*Geneva: Jean Crespin*], *1558*

John Knox was the first among writers of English to use the printing press as a means to overthrow the Scottish episcopal organization and replace it by a presbyterian system conforming to the practical politics of the day.

In exile since 1551, Knox worked in Frankfurt-am-Main and later in Geneva as chaplain to the English refugees from the Marian persecution. Here at last he had access to the printing press for his *Admonition* addressed to the 'Professors of God's Truth in England'. In 1554 he began his pamphleteering, which was to consist of some ten polemical tracts, all couched in a style of violent invective extreme even in an age which delighted in the exchange of theological billingsgate.

While Knox's theological doctrine was that of Calvin (65), his political agitation was personal, and his most famous pamphlet embarrassed Calvin. *The First Blast* was printed without place, or name of author or printer, and was not entered in the Register of Permits kept by the Syndics of Geneva, where it was evidently foreseen that publication might have political consequences. The authorship was soon known, as Knox no doubt anticipated. The objects of his onslaught were Mary I, Queen of England, and Marie of Lorraine, Regent of Scotland, and indirectly the latter's daughter, Mary Queen of Scots. It required courage from Knox to issue his *Blast*, for the consequences might be serious. It could not then be expected that Mary I's life would so soon end or that her sister Elizabeth would, on her succession, overlook the force of the general argument of the *Blast* that a woman monarch was contrary to Scripture.

Queen Mary died on 17 November 1558 and Calvin soon found it desirable to inform Cecil that he knew nothing of Knox's *Blast* until after it was printed. In the circumstances Calvin was highly embarrassed in England, and Knox endangered there. His use of the press prepared

the way for his ascendancy among the Protestants of Scotland. He led a campaign of political and religious agitation for which Mary Queen of Scots and her party were no match.

81

THE THEORY OF MODERN MUSIC

GIOSEFFO ZARLINO (1517–90). Le Istitutioni Harmoniche. *Venice: printer unidentified, 1558*

Zarlino enjoyed a long and successful career as a composer, becoming in 1565 choirmaster of St Mark's at Venice, where he spent all his life. Most of his major musical compositions have disappeared, but his fame rests on his theoretical works, which remain, and of these 'The Rules of Harmony' is the chief.

The first book, which deals mainly with the arithmetical foundations of musical science, differs little from the traditional view, but in the second Zarlino attacks the false system of tonality to which the exact mathematical proportions of the Pythagorean tetrachord must, if strictly observed, inevitably lead. Ancient and medieval theory had always maintained the validity of the mathematical proportion, and despite the fact that practice, at least after the invention of counterpoint, did not strictly follow it, for the simple reason that the ear automatically rebels against the mathematical analogy, it required Zarlino's pioneering work and some consequent controversy to establish it.

His contention that the diatonic scale was the only form of progression which could reasonably be sung is now universally accepted, and is termed 'just intonation'. Keyed and fretted instruments, which are mechanically tuned, cannot follow the free intonation of the voice, but for them Zarlino proposed a compromise by which the octave is divided into twelve equal semitones, and this has been finally adopted for them also. Altogether, Zarlino's treatise had the most far-reaching effects in musical theory, in the practice of composition, and in the construction of musical instruments. 'The Rules of Harmony' opened the way for the new tonality which has governed music from the seventeenth century to the present day.

82

CENSORSHIP

INDEX LIBRORUM PROHIBITORUM. *Rome: Antonio Blado, 1559*

The 'Index of Prohibited Books' is the classic example of censorship. It is a catalogue published by papal authority of books considered to be dangerous to religion and morals which Roman Catholics should not read without dispensation.

Prohibition of books is suggested in Acts xix, 19, where St Paul approves the burning of 'bad' books by recently converted Christians. In the year 325 the Council of Nicea

INDEX AVCTORVM,

ET LIBRORVM, QVI

*tanquam hæretici, aut suspecti, aut pernicio-
si, ab officio. S. Ro. Inquisitionis re-
probantur, et in vniuersa Chri-
stiana republica inter-
dicuntur.*

ROMAE apud Antonium Bladum
Impressorem Cameralem.
M . D . LVII.

editions of Holy Scripture by non-Catholics; any book on liturgy and dogma not approved by the Holy See; immoral and obscene books. In 1949 all books defending Communism were placed on the *Index*.

At first the penalties for infringement of the *Index* were very severe, but over the centuries they became more lenient. Of late a much more liberal attitude has prevailed and dispensations have been freely granted to readers by the authority of the Holy See or the bishops.

The first Roman *Index*, of which the title-page is here reproduced, was printed by the Inquisition in 1557 but it was not published, probably because the Pope objected to some of its features. The first published edition is a quarto volume of thirty-four leaves issued by Pope Paul IV in January 1559, followed immediately by a 12mo edition and three others in the same year. It consists of an alphabetical list of authors, starting with those whose complete works are forbidden, followed by a list of single works and finally by anonymous books. In 1571 Pope Pius V established the Congregation of the Index which operated until 1917, when the Holy Office reassumed its duties. The discipline was at that time based on the papal constitution *Officiorum ac Munerum* of 25 January 1897, but was more recently revised by the *Sollicita ac provida* of Pope Benedict XIV. In December 1965, with a change in the name and procedure of the Holy Office, the Pope entrusted the conduct of these matters to the newly named Congregation for the Doctrine of the Faith; *reprobare* replaces *prohibere* for its condemnation of reading matter, and the defence is given wider scope.

Over forty *Indexes* have been published since the Renaissance. The latest was issued in 1948, with Supplements down to 1961; it runs to five hundred and ten pages and contains over six thousand titles. The Vatican announced in 1966 that there would be no further issues.

BIBLIOGRAPHY: Dr H. Reusch, *Der Index der verbotenen Bücher*, 2 vols. (Bonn, 1883–5); Joseph Hilgers, S.J., *Der Index der verbotenen Bücher* (Freiburg, 1904).

forbade the *Thalia* by the heretic Arius and its destruction was ordered by the Emperor Constantine. The first formal catalogue of prohibited books is the *Decretum Gelasianum* issued in Rome in the year 496. During the Middle Ages and the early Renaissance censorship was exercised chiefly locally by universities (notably Paris and Cologne) and by individual bishops, a few of whom issued their own lists of forbidden books.

With the invention of printing and the resulting enormously wider circulation of books a more systematic control seemed to the authorities to be necessary. The earliest printed lists were published in the Netherlands between 1524 and 1540; in Paris 1544–56; and in Louvain from 1546 to 1558 (this last was also published in Valencia in 1551). In England decrees with lists of forbidden books were issued by Henry VIII and Queen Mary between 1526 and 1555; however, it was in 1543, under Pope Paul III, that the Holy Office issued for the first time a list of forbidden books—the first catalogue with the title *Index* and the first Roman list intended for the whole world. The ten rules, *De Libris Prohibitis*, a product of the Council of Trent (118), were promulgated in 1564. Until the end of the sixteenth century the *Index* was used mainly to help in the Vatican's fight against the Reformation; later it was also used against movements inside the Roman Church. The forbidden books are chiefly: all heretical and superstitious writings;

83

THE GENEVA BIBLE

THE BIBLE AND HOLY SCRIPTURES. *Geneva: Rouland Hall, 1560*

This version of the English Bible was made by English Protestants who, in Mary's reign, had taken refuge in Geneva where they found they could draw on 'the store of heavenly learning and judgement, which so abounds in this city'. More scholarly than any previous translation, it was largely the work of William Whittingham (1524?–79) afterwards Dean of Durham, Thomas Sampson (1517?–89) and Anthony Gilby (d. 1585).

They may have had some help from other English exiles, including Miles Coverdale, who was certainly in Geneva during part of the time the translators were at work. While Tyndale's (58) and Coverdale's earlier versions and notes were in the Lutheran tradition, the arguments and explanatory notes of the Geneva Bible were Calvinist in tone; Whittingham, who had previously translated the New Testament and published it in Geneva in 1557, was related by marriage to Calvin (65). The Geneva Bible was never officially approved in England, where in 1568 the ecclesiastical authorities produced as a rival to it the so-called Bishops' Bible. But from 1575 onwards it was openly printed in London and from then until the publication of the Authorized Version in 1611 (114) the clergy made use of the one or the other according to their Puritan or Episcopal leanings. With the laity, however, the Geneva Bible achieved immediate popularity and exerted an extremely powerful influence. At least one hundred and forty editions were printed between 1560 and 1644 when, thirty-three years after the publication of the Authorized Version, the last Geneva Bible appeared. It was also adopted in 1579 by the Scots Kirk as its official version.

A new feature was the use of roman rather than black letter type; the Geneva Version included prefaces, maps and tables; and for the first time in an English Bible the verses were divided and numbered—invaluable for reference, but with disastrous effects on the flow of the narrative. The translation introduced many famous phrases which retained their place in the Authorized Version, such as 'smite them hip and thigh', and 'vanity of vanities'; and it was heavily relied on by the 'companies' of revisers working on that version.

The name 'Breeches Bible', often applied to this version, derives from the rendering of Genesis iii, 7 as 'and they sewed fig leaves together, and made themselves breeches' instead of the aprons of other versions. It has been more properly called the Elizabethan family Bible, since it was this version which was the first to enter the English home, where it soon became 'the chief book of scientific lore, the source of all religious truth, the matter of devotional meditation, the light of the conscience and the basis of moral principle; and possibly the only book in the house'.

BIBLIOGRAPHY: Darlow & Moule, no. 77.

84

GRESHAM'S LAW

Proclamation for the Valuation of certain Base Monies, called Testoons. *London: Rychard Jugge and John Cawood*, [27 September 1560]

Were Sir Thomas Gresham (1519–79), royal agent in the Netherlands, the first builder of the Royal Exchange and the founder of Gresham College, to revisit this earth, he might be surprised to learn that he was supposed to have discovered a fundamental economic law—that 'bad currency drives out good'. This was not christened 'Gresham's Law' until 1858 when H. D. MacLeod, in his *Elements of Political Economy*, mentioned (p. 475) 'the illustrious Gresham who has the great merit of being, as far as we can discover, the first who discovered the great fundamental law of the currency, that good and bad money cannot circulate together'. The fact had been repeatedly observed before (MacLeod cites a relevant quotation from *The Frogs* of Aristophanes), but no one, that we are aware, had discovered the necessary relation between the facts before Sir Thomas Gresham. MacLeod pointed out that in 1558, soon after Queen Elizabeth's accession, Gresham wrote her 'a letter of advice...explaining how, among other things, all the fine money had disappeared from circulation. The cause of this he attributed to the debasing of the coinage by Henry VIII. Now, as he was the first to perceive that a bad and debased currency is the cause of the disappearance of the good money, we are only doing what is just, in calling this great fundamental law of the currency by his name'.

It is interesting, after this, to note what Gresham actually said. His 'letter of advice' is not upon the currency, but is headed 'Information of Sir Thomas Gresham, Mercer, touching the fall of the exchange, MDLVIII'. The actual passage on which MacLeod relied, but which he never quoted in full, reads: 'Ytt may pleasse your majesty to understande, thatt the firste occasion off the fall of the exchainge did growe by the Kinges majesty, your late Father, in abasinge his quoyne ffrom vi ounces fine too iii ounces fine. Whereuppon the exchainge fell ffrome xxvis. viiid. to xiiis. ivd. which was the occasion thatt all your ffine goold was convayed ought [i.e. out] of this your realme.' As Professor de Roover has pointed out, all that Gresham said was that a fall in the exchange made the exportation of fine coins profitable, and that their place in circulation was then taken by over-valued base monies. The real basis of 'Gresham's Law', as cited by MacLeod, is that the excessive issue of base moneys drove good coins out of circulation, because the latter were either hoarded, carried abroad or sent to the melting pot. This appears to have been appreciated in Gresham's time and earlier, e.g. by Copernicus (70); but nobody formulated a 'law' on the subject and in the sixteenth century the idea (though found in various manuscript sources) does not seem to have achieved the dignity of print. It was, however, the basis of the Elizabethan reform of the coinage in 1560—in which Gresham's memorandum had no doubt been an influence—and is therefore a landmark in British economic practice.

Here is a relevant quotation from the Proclamation: 'The Quenes most excelent Maiestie...hath founde by consente of all sortes of wyse men, that nothyng is so grevous...as the suffraunce of the base monies, being of dyvers standards and mixtures, to be so aboundantly currant within this Realme, which haved been coyned in the same, before her Maiesties raigne...: Nor contrarywyse anye one thyng so profitable...for al maner of people, as to have in place of the same base and copper monies, fine and good sterlying monyes of sylver and gold.'

85

THE FIRST HISTORY OF EUROPE

FRANCESCO GUICCIARDINI (1483–1540). L'Historia d'Italia. (Edited by A. Guicciardini.) *Florence: Lorenzo Torrentino, 1561*

'The basis of all later works on the beginnings of modern history' Ranke called 'The History of Italy' when his *Kritik* (286) destroyed the reputation as an original source which it had enjoyed for three hundred years. At the

same time Ranke sagaciously expounded the reasons for the book's immediate and tremendous influence upon the statesmen no less than the historians of the sixteenth to eighteenth centuries.

For Guicciardini wrote the first history of all Italy within the larger context of the European system of states and thus demonstrated the synchronistic interdependence of political events all over the continent. He was less interested in the facts themselves (which he often derived from quite unreliable sources) than in their causes and effects; these he discussed with the perspicacity of a Renaissance politician and diplomatist, dissecting the intentions and actions of the chief players on the European stage and proving—to his own satisfaction and that of his readers—that worldly passion, ambition and self-interest are the mainspring of human activity.

Guicciardini was the scion of a noble Florentine family and gained his first experience of world affairs as ambassador to Ferdinand of Aragon, where England, France, the

Indies and America impinged upon his horizon; served the Medici popes Leo X and Clement VII as governor in various parts of the papal states; became generalissimo of the anti-imperial league of Cognac and as such was held responsible for the sack of Rome by the Spaniards and Germans in 1527 and dismissed. The ingenious and ostensibly ingenuous defence of his own political and military activities is on a par with that of retired politicians and generals of every age. Returning to Florence, where Machiavelli (63) was his neighbour and friend, Guicciardini supported the rule of the Medici despite his oligarchic inclinations, and became the chief adviser of the first duke, Cosimo. Although a prolific writer of diaries, memoranda, memoirs, political and historical tracts, Guicciardini published nothing himself. *L'Historia d'Italia* was edited by his nephew Agnolo twenty-one years after his death; the first complete edition came out in 1567 in Venice, where an abridgement had already appeared in 1544. Within the sixteenth century at least ten editions were issued in Italian, three each in Latin, French and Spanish, and one in English, German and Dutch respectively; Bodin (94) and Montaigne (95) were early among Guicciardini's fervent admirers.

86

PROTESTANT MARTYRS

JOHN FOXE (1516–87). Actes and Monuments of these Latter and Perillous Dayes, touching Matters of the Church. *London: John Day, 1563*

'Foxe's Book of Martyrs', as it has been called ever since its first English publication, was for more than two centuries one of the most widely read books in England. Appearing when the memory of the treatment of the Protestants in Mary Tudor's reign was fresh in the minds of its readers, it built up an image of the persecuting papist which not only resulted in the fierce hatred of the Inquisition, and hence Spain, in Elizabethan times, but has strongly coloured English thinking on Roman Catholicism to this day.

The book had a long history before reaching its definitive form in the second English edition of 1570. John Foxe was a fellow of Magdalen College, Oxford, but resigned his fellowship in 1545 on religious grounds. He spent the next four years tutoring the children of Henry Howard, Earl of Surrey, and in 1552 began to compile information on the lives and deaths of the early reformers. When in 1554 he had to leave England and reached Strasbourg, he had with him an early draft, in Latin, which was hurriedly printed by Wendelin Richel, with the title *Commentarii rerum in Ecclesia gestarum, maximarumque, per totam Europam, Persecutionum*—'Commentaries on the Activities of the Church and the very great Persecutions throughout Europe'. This octavo of 212 leaves included a few foreign martyrs—Huss, Jerome of Prague and Savonarola—but it was mainly concerned with the Lollards and with Wycliffe. It made some impact on foreign scholars, but was not a commercial success, for its unsold sheets were reissued in 1564 by Josias Richel with a new title, *Chronicon Ecclesiae*.

Moving on to Basle, where he earned his living as corrector of the press for the printer Oporinus, Foxe began to amass material for an enlarged Latin edition which would include the victims of the Marian persecution. Edmund Grindal, the future Archbishop of Canterbury, then in Strasbourg, was intending to produce a similar work in English and passed on the material he received to Foxe. When Mary died in 1558 Grindal returned to England and abandoned his project, but Foxe remained in Basle to complete the first part of his new work, which was published there by Nicolaus Brylinger and Oporinus in August 1559 with the title *Rerum in Ecclesia gestarum...Commentarii*. This was a folio of 750 pages in six books, of which the first was a revised version of the Strasbourg volume; the second and third books dealt with the reigns of Henry VIII and Edward VI; and the last three were intended to cover the martyrdoms of Mary's reign. They reached the death of Cranmer in 1556, but this is succeeded only by a list of the later martyrs. The second part, planned to cover victims of religious persecution on the continent, was eventually written by his Basle friend Heinrich Pantaleon and published in 1563.

As soon as this Latin edition was published, Foxe returned to England and for the next ten years appears to have lived in the house of his former pupil, now Duke of Norfolk, while working on the English edition of *The Book of Martyrs* in the house of the printer John Day. He found a mass of new material available in England and he concentrated on editing this, while friends translated the Latin edition—not always accurately. The first English edition appeared in March 1563 and became an immediate best-seller despite its bulk—it was a folio of 1741 pages—and its consequent high cost, which distressed the thrifty soul of John Knox. It was inevitably the target of furious attacks from the Catholics and for the second edition of 1570, in two large folio volumes, Foxe corrected many errors of fact, as well as carrying the story right back to Apostolic times and including the stories of many European martyrs. The two later editions in the author's lifetime (1576 and 1583) contained only a few additions.

In 1571 a decree of Convocation ordained that copies were to be placed in all cathedral churches and that the houses of archbishops, bishops, archdeacons and resident canons should all have copies for the use of servants and visitors. There was no instruction that it should also be provided in parish churches, but it very often was, and chained examples (often seventeenth-century editions) survive not infrequently. The lively style of the book, not to mention the gruesome illustrations, which first appeared in the English edition of 1563, was thus given an opportunity to influence—and prejudice—the minds of people in all classes of society, including those who could not otherwise have afforded it.

87

THE NATURE OF THINGS

TITUS LUCRETIUS CARUS (*c.* 98–55 B.C.). De Rerum Natura, libri sex, a Dionysio Lambino commentariis illustrati. *Paris: Rouille, 1563*

Of very few languages can it be said that the first surviving major poem in it is an exposition of a philosophical system of considerable subtlety, but, first or last, Lucretius's 'On the Nature of Things' would have been an unique contribution to any literature. In it the atomic theory, the most vivid and tender depictions of nature, and a sense of the beauty and rhythm of words which triumphs over the early unsophisticated form of the Latin hexameter, all these combine in the most astonishing way to produce one of the grandest and most moving poems in the Latin language.

Little is known of the life of Lucretius; and he died leaving his poem in the unrevised form in which it has come down to us. According to an ancient legend, it was finally corrected by Cicero (64). This does not seem very likely; Cicero, as a Stoic, was opposed to Epicureanism, as his own philosophical writings show. Nothing else about Lucretius, beyond the scope of his reading, can be gleaned. Foremost among his masters was Epicurus, whose writings provide the theme of the poem. That Lucretius chose verse as his vehicle is due to western Greek philosophers, who preferred it to prose; the influence of Empedocles, in particular, is strong. Among other writers, Thucydides (102), Hippocrates (55) and Homer (31), for whom he expresses the highest admiration, are quoted and imitated. In his own language, Lucretius is most dependent on Ennius, whose rough but splendid epics had been written a century earlier: indeed, the style of Lucretius, an imitation of this early model, is often deliberately archaic, and he stands apart from the development of the metre which was to achieve its perfection in the works of Virgil (6).

Lucretius's subject is complex. Briefly, his passionate desire to free the mind from the bonds of superstition is expressed in an exposition of the laws of nature, which are shown to depend on the natural movements of the atoms of which all matter is constructed. These movements are in no way controlled by any supernatural beings, such as were traditionally supposed to have created and to influence the universe. The understanding of nature will serve to free men from the fear of such influence, and above all from the fear of death which lies at the source of all human misfortune and misdoing: *tantum religio potuit suadere malorum*. Thus the first two books are devoted to an explanation of the construction and working of the universe; how all matter and movement are built up from the motion of the atoms, which, with space itself, are the only imperishable substances. In the third book Lucretius applies these principles to the mind and body of an individual man, to show that the soul perishes with the body—an essential Epicurean doctrine. The fourth deals with another Epicurean tenet: the theory of images cast by substances which do not perish with the dissolution of the atoms of which the substances are made up. The fifth deals with the origin of the world, of life, and with the progress of mankind; and the last shows how natural are those phenomena—thunderstorms and earthquakes—which are commonly thought to be evidence of supernatural powers.

Although his muse sometimes staggers under the weight of the matter, Lucretius, by the intensity of his vision, power of reason, and variety of invention, carries his theme along: never more successfully than in his paeans on the all-pervading subtlety of nature and its endless powers of creation, which he personifies (in apparent self-contradiction) under the name of Venus, *Alma Venus*, whom he invokes in the magnificent opening lines of the poem.

The first printed edition of Lucretius was published in Brescia about 1473; the second in Verona in 1486 (he was not a popular author with the early printers). The edition here cited was the *chef d'œuvre* of Denys Lambin, the great French classical scholar. Scholarly yet passionate, his editorial work expresses a deep sympathy for his subject and the prefaces and notes are a monument of erudition and fine vigorous Latinity.

BIBLIOGRAPHY: C. A. Gordon, *A Bibliography of Lucretius* (London, 1962).

88

ART HISTORY

GIORGIO VASARI (1511–74). Le Vite de'piu Eccellenti Pittori, Scultori e Architettori. 3 vols. *Florence: Giunta, 1568*

'The Lives of the Most Excellent Painters, Sculptors and Architects' is the first modern history of art. It has made Vasari's name immortal, though in his own day he was considered first and foremost a painter and architect (he worked mainly in Rome and Florence where he was a protégé of the Medici).

His book contains the biographies of Italian painters, etc., from the thirteenth to the sixteenth century. They are based on earlier written and printed sources, on oral accounts, on his knowledge of works of art and his own large collection of drawings. Vasari travelled extensively to collect personal information, meeting most of the artists of his time. Though he took the conventional view of his day that the Middle Ages was a barren period between antiquity and the Renaissance, he was in advance of his time in his admiration for Cimabue and Giotto. It was the Florentine school, however, which he considered pre-eminent, and Michelangelo was his great hero.

'The Lives' are freely laced with stories and anecdotes, some of which are certainly apocryphal; so that modern research, with its more exacting standards, has revealed inaccuracies and critical short comings in the book. Vasari's excellent sense of narrative, however, and lively style combined with his wide personal acquaintance makes his 'Lives' a vital contribution to our understanding of the character and psychology of the great artists of the Renaissance, a term (*rinascita*) which he was the first writer to use.

The book first appeared in Florence in 1550 in two volumes with one hundred and thirty-three lives; but the 1568 edition in three volumes, bringing the biographies up to 1567, is the first complete one, with one hundred and sixty-one lives, and the first to be illustrated

PAVLO VCCELLO PITTOR FIORENT.

with woodcut portraits. It also contains an autobiography and a valuable treatise on the technical methods employed in the arts. It became a model for subsequent writings on the history of art and was the forerunner to the remarkable series of studies on the various Italian schools of painting produced in Italy during the seventeenth and eighteenth centuries. For its period it has remained the chief authority and new editions both learned and popular are published regularly.

BIBLIOGRAPHY: Sidney J. A. Churchill. *Bibliografia Vasariana* (Florence, 1912)

89

PRECEDENT AND COMMON LAW

HENRY DE BRACTON (d. 1268). De Legibus et Consuetudinibus Angliae. *London: Richard Tottel, 1569*

This treatise, 'On the Laws and Customs of England', written in the middle of the thirteenth century, is the 'classical exposition of the common law' (D. M. Stenton), was cited in the courts down to the eighteenth century, and has remained 'a model for legal literature until the present day' (P. M. Barnes).

Henry of Bracton (or Bratton) based his book on the cases decided by the great judges of the first half of the century—such as Martin of Pattishall and William of Raleigh whose clerk he had been—as well as on his own twenty-year experience as 'justice itinerant' in the northern, midland and western counties. He combined a systematic inquiry into the legal maxims of general validity with their practical application in the common-law courts. Thus he arrived at a formulation of principles which have determined the whole development of English law, of which the use of precedents is perhaps the most characteristic. His method was adopted and carried on by Littleton (23) and Coke (126).

Bracton composed the *De Legibus* between 1250 and 1256. Richard Tottel (died 1594), who printed the first complete edition in 1569, was the leading English publisher of law books in the second half of the sixteenth century. Edward VI granted him in 1553 a privilege for 'all and all manner books of our temporal laws' and he was one of the original members of the Stationers' Company when it received its charter in 1557.

90
HUMANE EDUCATION

ROGER ASCHAM (c. 1515–68). The Scholemaster. *London: John Daye, 1570*

Roger Ascham was born in Yorkshire and went to St John's College, Cambridge, of which he became a fellow. Under the influence of Sir John Cheke, he learned Greek and the beautiful 'chancery' italic handwriting for which both became famous. Ascham taught Greek and mathematics, and on Cheke's retirement in 1546 became Public Orator to the University. Shortly afterwards he was appointed tutor to the Princess Elizabeth, to which circumstance he owed his preferment after her accession.

In 1553 he began the work which has made him famous, *The Scholemaster*. The book was occasioned by a debate at dinner with Sir William Cecil and others on the pros and cons of flogging in schools, with Ascham the protagonist of the anti-floggers. Afterwards Sir Richard Sackville begged him to write a treatise 'on the right order of teaching', and the result was *The Scholemaster*.

It is not a general treatise on educational method, nor was it intended for use in schools, but 'a plaine and perfite way of teachyng children to understand, write and speake in Latin tong...for the brynging up of youth in gentlemen and noblemens houses'. Nor was it really an original or revolutionary work, for the famous plea for gentle persuasion, as opposed to flogging, had been anticipated at Winchester and had already found support in England. The expression of this humane spirit, however, and the lively defence of the vernacular in *The Scholemaster*—and perhaps also the touching description of Lady Jane Grey reading the *Phaedo* while everyone else was out hunting—have made it famous.

91
POPULAR CARTOGRAPHY

ABRAHAM ORTELIUS (1527–98). Theatrum Orbis Terrarum. *Antwerp: Ægidius Coppenius Diesth, 1570*

'The Picture of the World' is a landmark in cartographic publication, for it is the first large modern atlas (a name in fact first used fifteen years later by Ortelius's friend Mercator (100)).

The rediscovery of Ptolemy's 'Geography' in 1410 (18*), combined with the great geographical discoveries of the fifteenth and sixteenth centuries, stimulated the drawing of maps and charts of the old and new worlds. While cartographers like Mercator were interested in new techniques of map-making, men like Ortelius, scholar though he was, were primarily publishers, appealing to the ever-increasing public demand for descriptions and maps of known and unknown lands. He developed a wide circle of acquaintances among European cartographers, whose maps he began publishing some years before he collected them into the *Theatrum*.

This was an immediate success, since it gathered together (engraved by F. Hogenberg) the best available maps, and thus presented as complete a picture as was then possible of the whole world, with scholarly citations of authorities and descriptions of the topography and antiquities. So popular was the *Theatrum* that the letterpress was translated into many vernaculars and there were in all forty-one editions between 1570 and 1612. This original edition contained fifty-three maps; by 1595 the corpus had been increased to one hundred and fifteen.

Ortelius published a number of other scholarly works: the *Nomenclator Ptolemaicus*, an edition of Caesar, a book on his own fine collection of medals and sculpture, and *De Recta Pronuntiatione Linguae Latinae*, which contains a vivid account of his first visit to Italy. In 1575 he was appointed geographer to King Philip II of Spain. Before he died he received a presentation from the city of Antwerp, such as was later to be bestowed on Rubens.

The true measure of Ortelius's achievement, however, was the practical success of his atlas. It convincingly demonstrated his belief that no literate person should be without a knowledge of geography, and the letterpress which accompanied the maps was designed to appeal not merely to those interested in pure geography. If every home now owns an atlas of some sort, it is due ultimately to the conviction and example of Ortelius.

92
THE PALLADIAN STYLE

ANDREA PALLADIO (1508–80). I Quattro Libri dell'Architettura. *Venice: Domenico de Franceschi, 1570*

'The Four Books of Architecture' contain the principles of the architectural style which later became known as 'Palladianism'.

Andrea Palladio was born at Padua as Andrea di Pietro. It was his patron Giangiorgio Trissino, the Italian humanist, who gave him the name 'Palladio' after the angel in Trissino's epic poem *L'Italia Liberata da' Goti*, Rome, 1547–8, who signifies the beauty of classical architecture.

Palladio's lasting influence on architectural style in many parts of the world was exercised less through his actual buildings than through his textbook. This is divided into four sections: orders and elementary problems,

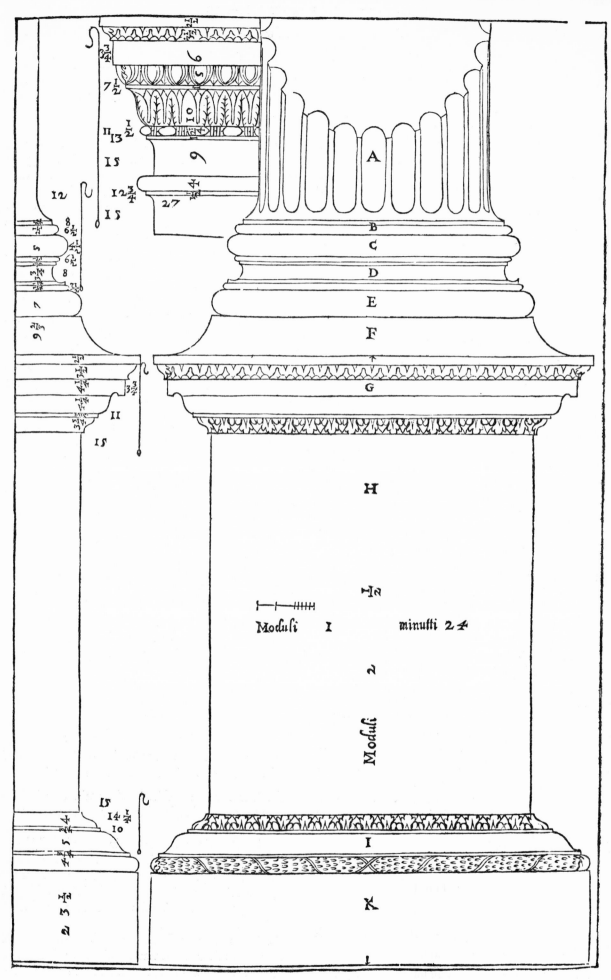

Moduli I   minutti 24

Moduli 2

NO. 92, PALLADIO

56

domestic building, public building and town planning and temples. Palladio's style was directly inspired by Roman classical models through the writings of Vitruvius (26) and Alberti (28). Its characteristics are those of classicism: symmetry, order, fixed mathematical relations of the parts to each other and to the whole, logic and monumentality. Though it is true that Palladio in his later period adopted some of the mannerist vernacular, his buildings remained essentially classical, in contrast to the baroque style of the period in Rome and Piedmont.

Palladio followed the rules of classical Roman architecture more closely than any other architect, even sometimes at the cost of practicability and domestic comfort. In spite of the vogue for the baroque and the fact that Palladio left no immediate successors, his book exerted a powerful influence on contemporary architecture and classical ideals until the end of the eighteenth century. In England this was due in the first place to his enthusiastic follower Inigo Jones (1573-1632) who designed the Queen's House at Greenwich in the new severe, simple, classical style. He copiously annotated his copy of the *Architettura* and these notes were incorporated into the first English translation made by Giacomo Leoni and published in 1715-16. Lord Burlington, Kent, Campbell, Chambers, Adam and others followed. 'Palladianism' became a party label in the world of connoisseurship and England blossomed with buildings 'in the Palladian style'—two centuries after Palladio had created it. From England the style made its way into Scotland, Ireland and America.

Palladio's influence began to wane only with the break-up of the structure of classical aesthetics under the impetus of the new sciences and of such writers as Burke (239) and Hume (194) in the eighteenth and Ruskin (315) in the nineteenth century. The Palladian ideal could not be reconciled with romanticism and its revivals.

As a practising architect Palladio worked mainly in Vicenza, Venice and the Venetian countryside, especially along the Brenta River. His Villa Capra (known as La Rotonda) near Vicenza became virtually a prototype of the Palladian style, and it was widely and faithfully copied. At the end of his life he left plans for that *tour de force* of *trompe l'œil*, the Teatro Olimpico in Vicenza, which was finished by his pupil Vincenzo Scamozzi.

Palladio also provided illustrations for D. Barbaro's edition of Vitruvius (Venice, 1556), and he published a guide-book to the antiquities of Rome, *L'Antichita di Roma*, 1554, often reprinted, which was related to the earlier *Mirabilia Romae* (12) which it extended and helped to replace.

93
HISTORIAN AND SCHOLAR

PUBLIUS CORNELIUS TACITUS (*c.* A.D. 55–*c.* 120). Historiarum et Annalium libri qui exstant, Justi Lipsii studio emendati & illustrati. *Antwerp: Christopher Plantin, 1574*

Tacitus is the outstanding historian and the principal prose writer of the Silver Age of Latin letters. He was the son-in-law of the great Roman general Agricola, under whom the Roman conquest of Britain was completed, and whose biography Tacitus wrote.

His chief works were the 'Annals' and the 'Histories', which covered the period from the accession of Tiberius in A.D. 14 to the death of Domitian in 97. He is by far the most reliable authority for the history of the period. His own high position—he eventually rose to become Senator and Consul—gave him access to all the information which was not locked up in the imperial chancery. A natural pessimism had been confirmed by the reign of terror in the last years of Domitian's reign, but looking back on the history of the century there was little to combat his theory that it was a period of gradual degeneracy to which the reign of Trajan had put a welcome period. Tacitus's standpoint is fundamentally ethical—he sees the woes which he describes as a warning to future generations, yet his sentimental longing for the heroic age of liberty under the republic is tempered by the realization that the strong central Imperial government is—or could be—a beneficial necessity. His much admired style, antithetical, terse and rhetorical, drives home his meaning with unrivalled force.

Relatively unknown during the Middle Ages, Tacitus, whose works were first printed in Venice about 1473 and several times reprinted before the end of the century, exercised great influence on Renaissance historians. Justus Lipsius (1547-1606), the Netherlands scholar, knew the whole of Tacitus by heart, and his great edition (here cited), nineteen times reprinted, is one of the monuments of sixteenth-century scholarship. In a life much vexed by the violence of governments, he found much, as his notes declare, in common with Tacitus's ironic and cynical records of first-century Rome.

94
CONSTITUTIONAL GOVERNMENT

(*a*) JEAN BODIN (1530-96). Les Six Livres de la Republique. *Paris: Jacques du Puys, 1576*

(*b*) HUBERT LANGUET (1518-81). Vindiciae contra Tyrannos. '*Edinburgi*' [*Basle*]: *printer unidentified, 1579*

Jean Bodin was trained to the law and quickly established a successful practice. An early work on the economic predicament of France (a clear-sighted appreciation of the financial revolution of the sixteenth century) brought him to public notice and gained him the favour of Henri III who made him his attorney at Laon in 1576. This was Bodin's *annus mirabilis*, for in the same year he married, published his 'Six Books of the Republic', and rendered his most lasting service to the state. Elected to the States-General of Blois, he almost single-handed fought off the extreme demands of the League, and at the same time moderated the financial demands of the King. There can be no doubt that this achievement postponed and to some extent diminished the force of the outbreak of civil war. At the same time it cost him the favour of the King, and though all his later efforts were devoted to a policy of moderation, he was unable to repeat his success.

Bodin came to England with the Duc d'Alençon in 1581, and finding that the 'Republic' was widely read, although in a bad Latin translation, he determined to produce a better translation himself. In doing so he altered his text considerably and this version, published in Paris in 1586, became the standard one.

The 'Six Books of the Republic' went through many editions in the author's lifetime and after, and had an immense influence all over Europe. It is, in effect, the first modern attempt to create a complete system of political science. Its basis was the *Politics* of Aristotle (38), and it was through Bodin that Aristotle's work came to exercise the influence on modern political thinking which has made him the father of modern democracy. Bodin was not content merely to reproduce his master, however; he added considerably from his own experience. Although like most sixteenth-century writers he approved of absolute government, he demanded its control by constitutional laws, in which respect he foreshadowed the development during the seventeenth century of the idea of the 'social contract' (see 207). Thus Bodin was the first to set out clearly the argument round which most political discussion centred in the seventeenth and eighteenth centuries, that law is merely an expression of the sovereign will, but that where this reposes in an absolute monarch, it must be mitigated by a customary or natural law. When the lawgiver's law becomes unjust, it ceases to be valid and must be resisted.

Hubert Languet, French by birth but a true European, was, like Bodin, a diplomatist. He achieved a considerable reputation as a scholar, and while at the University of Bologna read a book of Philip Melanchthon's which so impressed him that he went to see the author, and shortly afterwards became a Protestant. From then on he was an exile, although he represented Augustus I of Saxony at the court of France from 1561 to 1572. As the official apologist of a Protestant court he narrowly escaped death on St Bartholomew's Eve, and thereafter became ambassador at the imperial court. In 1577 he retired, and it was then that the work for which he is famous was written. (If, that is, he wrote it, for there is still some doubt about the authorship—it was published under the pseudonym 'Stephanus Junius Brutus, Celta' —and it has sometimes been attributed to Du Plessis Mornay, named by Barbier as its publisher.)

'A Counterblast against Tyrants' was probably printed at Basle, outside the jurisdiction of popes, emperors and kings, but it was prudently given a bogus imprint. It is an eloquent vindication of the people's right to resist tyranny, while affirming that resistance must be based on properly constituted authority. It is in fact the practical demonstration of Bodin's theory, and some measure of its impact and continuing relevance may be estimated from a study of the places and dates at which it has been translated or reprinted—London, 1648, London, 1689, Paris, 1789, Berlin, 1848. Like *Rights of Man* (241), it is one of the perennial documents of anti-tyranny.

95
ENLIGHTENED SCEPTIC

MICHEL DE MONTAIGNE (1533–92). Essais. 2 vols. *Bordeaux: S. Millanges, 1580*

Montaigne devised the essay form in which to express his personal convictions and private meditations, a form in which he can hardly be said to have been anticipated. The most elaborate essay, the *Apologie de Raimond Sebonde*, is second to no other modern writing in attacking fanaticism and pleading for tolerance.

He finds a place in the present canon, however, chiefly for his consummate representation of the enlightened

scepticism of the sixteenth century, to which Bacon (119), Descartes (129), and Newton (161) were to provide the answers in the next.

The dominance of Aristotelian science (38) had been weakened by the rediscovery of other ancient philosophers and this fostered a sceptical outlook towards the possibility of acquiring any knowledge of the fundamental nature of reality. Montaigne was the leading exponent of this school of thought and it is interesting to recall that his favourite expression in voicing his doubts, 'Que sais-je?', is now the title of the French series of paperbacks corresponding to the English 'Pelicans'.

The early seventeenth-century philosophers and scientists were primarily and expressly concerned with combating this point of view and it is possible to regard the *Discours* of Descartes as a counterblast to Montaigne.

In 1588 a new edition of the *Essais*, the last published in the author's lifetime, included a third volume, and this became the definitive text on which all later editions are based.

96

THE BEGINNINGS OF RATIONALISM

FRANCISCO SANCHEZ (?1552–1632). Quod Nihil Scitur. *Lyons: Antonius Gryphius, 1581*

Sanchez, of Portuguese and possibly Jewish origin, became professor of medicine at Montpellier and Toulouse. He was one of the first to develop a full system criticizing the scholastic philosophy, whose textbooks he was obliged to use in his teaching. Together with his contemporaries Montaigne (95), to whom he is said to have been distantly related, Bruno, Telesius and others, he represented the new school of philosophic scepticism, particularly in regard to the natural sciences.

Though recognizing the importance of Aristotle (38) as a natural scientist, Sanchez opposed uncritical acceptance of his views and the prevalent unquestioning belief in his authority in philosophical and scientific thought. He taught that knowledge cannot be reached through the syllogistic method of reasoning employed by the scholastic philosophers; based as it was on certain arbitrary definitions, the validity of which Sanchez considered to be doubtful. True scientific knowledge—'scientia est rei perfecta cognitio' (science is the perfect knowledge of things)—cannot be reached by this method. Perfect knowledge is impossible to men—hence the slightly Delphic title of his book, which might be translated 'Why nothing can be known', or 'Nothing is certain'—but through the recognition of his limitations man can yet find a limited knowledge by experiment, empiricism and rational judgement (cf. Nicolaus Cusanus, his fifteenth-century predecessor, no 45). Sanchez strongly attacked the superstitions of his age such as astrology and prophecies.

Even though his influence was perhaps more negative through criticism than positive through creating a new system, his work together with that of some of his contemporaries paved the way for the system created by Descartes (129). His views were also taken up by Bacon (119) and later by the rationalist philosophers and scientists of the seventeenth and eighteenth centuries.

97

PLANT CLASSIFICATION

ANDREAS CAESALPINUS (1519–1603). De Plantis. *Florence: Giorgio Marescotti, 1583*

During the Middle Ages and the early Renaissance botanical literature was largely confined to herbals closely related to pharmacology and books restricted to the botanical knowledge of the ancients. With the knowledge of new fauna and flora coming into Europe from the New World and the East, and the creation of many new botanical gardens, the need was felt for a more scientific classification of plants. Illustrations and descriptions of plants followed at first a 'natural' pattern, based on their form and structure, naming as many characteristics as possible and classifying them accordingly.

With Andreas Caesalpinus a new era begins. He was professor of materia medica and director of the botanical garden at Pisa and later professor in Rome and physician to Pope Clement VIII. His book 'On Plants' was the first attempt to classify plants in a systematic manner based on a comparative study of forms; a similar study had been made by Gesner (77) but was not published until the eighteenth century. The traditional division into trees, shrubs, half-shrubs and herbs is retained, but they are now subdivided into different categories according to their seed, fruit and flower.

The first section contains the general system, while the other fifteen sections describe 1,520 plants in fifteen classes. Caesalpinus's philosophy is Aristotelian: plants have a vegetable soul which is responsible for nutrition and for the reproduction of organisms. Nutrition was believed to come from the roots in the soil and to be carried up the stems to produce the fruit. Hence, the roots, stems and fruit are the main characteristics selected by Caesalpinus as the basis for his classification. His descriptive terminology was finally based on the fruits of plants. Lower plants such as lichens and mushrooms, having no reproductive organs, were believed to arise by spontaneous generation from decaying matter. They were placed at the lower end of the hierarchy of plants, providing the link between plants and inorganic nature. Sex in plants had not yet been discovered; and leaves were considered simply as a protection for the seed.

Imperfect as it was, Caesalpinus's was the first rational system of plant classification by which their ever-growing number (six thousand were known in 1600, but nearly twenty thousand by the beginning of the eighteenth century) could be described. The discovery of sex in plants by Camerarius (165) further supported Caesalpinus's method, as reproductive organs could now be used as classifying elements in greater detail. His influence on his contemporaries was not at first very great; they continued to use empirical descriptions. His chief follower was J. Jung (1587–1657). Within one hundred years, however, the need for a system based on comparative morphology was clearly recognized, culminating in the work of Linné (192) who was greatly indebted to this book as well as to Bauhinus (121). A modern basis for classification of plants was eventually provided by the theory of organic evolution.

98

THE CHRONOLOGY OF HISTORY

JOSEPH JUSTUS SCALIGER (1540–1609). De Emendatione Temporum. *Paris: Mamert Patisson, 1583*

Scaliger was the greatest scholar of his age, and has been described as 'the father of modern criticism'. His penetrating scholarship and powerful gift of analysis were magisterially demonstrated in his edition (1579) of one of the most difficult of Latin texts, the *Astronomica* of Manilius, and this was a forerunner to his greatest work.

The *De Emendatione Temporum* revolutionized ancient chronology; it showed that ancient history was not restricted to that of the Greeks and Romans, but also involved that of the Persians, Babylonians and Egyptians, and that of the Jews, hitherto treated as 'sacred history', a subject apart. With incredible diligence Scaliger compared critically the surviving histories and chronicles of each civilization and evolved out of their several chronologies a continuous narrative in the light of the new understanding of the calendar achieved by the Copernican system. When one considers the disorder, the isolated bits and pieces, which comprised ancient history at this date, Scaliger's achievement in 'A Correct System of Chronology' towers above that of his contemporaries: it is difficult now to imagine how history could be written without an adequate and continuous chronology, based on Scaliger's synchronistic principles.

Scaliger ended his days at Leiden, king of the world of letters. Scholars from all over the world came to visit him, and a word from him could make or mar a scholarly reputation. Among his pupils were Grotius (125) and the Latinist Heinsius. On his death he left a reputation to which no successor has attained.

99

THE DECIMAL SYSTEM

SIMON STEVIN (1548–1620). De Thiende. *Leiden: Christopher Plantin, 1585*

Though he made many important contributions to statics, hydrostatics, mechanics and engineering, Stevin is best remembered for this book, called 'The Tenth', a thin pamphlet of thirty-six pages only, in which he propounded the first systematic treatment of decimal fractions.

Simon Stevin, Flemish mathematician, military engineer and Quarter-Master General of Holland, invented a defence system for Holland consisting of dykes and sluices, constructed windmills and made a famous land yacht which could carry twenty-eight passengers. It was destroyed on Napoleon's order in 1803.

Decimal fractions had been suggested much earlier for the extraction of square roots, but Stevin advocated their daily use and held that common fractions are quite superfluous, because every computation could be carried out with whole numbers. This discovery was probably the most important development in arithmetic since the introduction of Hindu–Arabic numerals.

Stevin's system was intended to replace the sexagesimal fractions used in astronomy as well as common fractions, and he urged its general introduction for decimal coinage, weights and measures. It was eventually used in coinage and after the French Revolution was adapted for weights and measures as 'the metric system' (see 260*).

In the science of mechanics and hydrostatics his work

DE
THIENDE

Leerende door onghehoorde lichticheyt allen rekeningen onder den Menschen noodich vallende, afveerdighen door heele ghetalen sonder ghebrokenen.

Beschreven door SIMON STEVIN *van Brugghe.*

TOT LEYDEN,
By Christoffel Plantijn.
M. D. LXXXV.

followed on that of Tartaglia (66) and preceded Galileo's (113, 128, 130), but their investigations were carried on quite independently. His book, *De Beghinselen der Weeghconst*, 1586, is based on the contention that perpetual motion is impossible. He used this hypothesis to give a remarkable proof of the law of the parallelogram of forces. In hydrostatics he examined the conditions for the equilibrium of floating bodies and discovered the principle that the pressure at any point in a liquid is the same in all directions—later confirmed by Pascal. He also established the so-called 'hydrostatic paradox', i.e. that the downward pressure of a liquid on the base of its containing vessel is independent of the vessel's shape and size and depends only on the depth of the liquid and the area of the base.

De Thiende was translated into French in 1585 and into English in 1608.

100

MERCATOR'S PROJECTION

GERARDUS MERCATOR (1512–94). Atlas sive Cosmographicae Meditationes de Fabrica Mundi, 3 vols. *Duisburg & Düsseldorf: Albertus Busius, [1585]–1595*

It is due chiefly to Mercator and to Ortelius (91) that geography was first freed from the Ptolemaic cosmogony whose authority had lasted over a thousand years (18*). Ortelius published in 1570 the first modern atlas in which uniform principles were brought to bear on the construction and appearance of maps: but the name 'Atlas' was for the first time applied to Mercator's collection, with the sub-title 'Cosmographical Meditations on the Structure of the World'.

Gerardus Mercator, of Flemish origin—his name was latinized from Gerhard Kremer—became a pupil of the cosmographer Gemma Frisius and established himself as an instrument maker and surveyor at Louvain where he issued his first maps. In 1541 and 1551 he constructed his famous pair of globes which were presented to Charles V in 1552. He became a teacher at Duisburg where his best-known maps appeared.

Down to Mercator's time map-making and geographical knowledge were dominated by Ptolemy who devised his navigational courses largely from travellers' tales; his cartographical data were quite unscientific and his maps full of errors. In 1569 Mercator first exemplified his new method of projection in a world map; in this the meridians remain parallel and a great circle on the globe is a straight line. Hence, using Mercator's projection, the mariner could draw his course with a ruler. Mercator did not disclose the projection upon which his maps were based, which was first described by Edward Wright (106); it has been used for practically all nautical charts ever since. From a purely geographical point of view, however, a map of the world constructed on his principles still shows considerable errors, chiefly because the northern latitudes are out of proportion and too far north.

Mercator's maps for France, the Netherlands and Germany were issued in 1585, in 1589 those for Italy and south-eastern Europe, in 1595 those for northern Europe and the Arctic. This last part was published posthumously by Mercator's son Rumbold and was dedicated to Queen Elizabeth I. In the same year the whole collection was re-issued with a total of 107 maps under the above title. Thirty-one editions in folio were published in fairly quick succession (sixteen Latin, eight French, three German, two Dutch and two English), and there were at least twenty-seven editions of the *Atlas Minor*, in a smaller format, including one in Turkish. Owing, perhaps, to the innate conservatism of seamen, Mercator's principles were not immediately accepted, but by the end of the seventeenth century they were in universal use. It is only in very recent times, chiefly owing to the requirements of the aeroplane, that they have been partially abandoned.

Mercator believed in a navigable North-West Passage and a great southern continent; he also confirmed that the magnetic pole was not the same as the pole of the earth. He went further by stating that it was on the earth and not, as was generally believed, in the heavens and he tried to calculate its position.

BIBLIOGRAPHY: F. von Ortroy, 'Bibliographie sommaire de l'Œuvre de Mercator'. In: *Revue des Bibliothèques*, vols. 24 and 26 (Paris, 1914–16); J. Keuning, 'The History of an Atlas; Mercator–Hondius'. In: *Imago Mundi*, vol. 4 (Stockholm, 1947).

101

ANTIQUARIAN STUDIES

WILLIAM CAMDEN (1551–1623). Britannia. *London: Radulph Newbery, 1586*

William Camden has some claim to be considered as the founder, not merely of antiquarian studies, but also of the study of modern history. His name was distinguished in his lifetime, and his works enjoyed a long popularity after his death. It is, however, as the founder of the chair of history at Oxford, still known as the Camden professorship, and the first at any university in the country, that his name is preserved today. It is also commemorated in the Camden Society, founded in 1838 to print unpublished historical documents. He was born in London, the son of a member of the Painter-Stainers' Company, and was educated at Christ's Hospital and St Paul's School, and thence in 1566 went to up Magdalen College, Oxford. His career at the university did not achieve the success his merits deserved: he failed, largely through sectarian prejudice, to obtain a fellowship, and in 1571 he returned to London.

Camden spent a good deal of time, to begin with, in travelling round England, collecting material for his great work. Through his Oxford friendship with the Dean of Westminster, Gabriel Goodman, he was made second master of Westminster School, of which in 1593 he became headmaster. In 1597 he became Clarenceux King of Arms, a position which no doubt left him better opportunities for scholarship. From then on until his death he pursued his antiquarian and historical studies. His industry was colossal—he refused a knighthood for fear it should involve time-consuming duties. Among his friends were Archbishop Ussher, Sir Robert Cotton and John Selden; his fame spread abroad and he was on intimate terms with the French jurist Brisson, and Isaac Casaubon.

The first edition of Camden's *Britannia* came out in 1586. Its full title is *Britannia, sive florentissimorum regnorum, Angliae, Scotiae, Hiberniae et insularum adjacentium ex intima antiquitate Chorographica Descriptio.* By 1623 it had been reprinted half-a-dozen times and was already twice its original size. It was reprinted for the last time to date, expanded into four enormous folio volumes, as late as 1806–42. If Camden was not the first English historian (in the modern sense of the word), topographer and antiquarian, he was certainly the first to relate the three studies, and his *Britannia*, primarily topographical, is the first book which shows, even in a rudimentary form, the need to evaluate sources. It was the revolutionary subject matter, and its even more revolutionary treatment of the subject, which made it at once the vehicle and the model for research in all three subjects for the next two hundred and fifty years. Camden was fully conscious of the importance of his work; and his other books—the *Annales* of the reign of Queen Elizabeth I, the editions of the early chroniclers, the collection of epitaphs, and above all his *Remaines concerning Brittaine*, derived from his *Britannia*, and one of the most popular English works of the seventeenth century—served to confirm it. He himself took the most important step towards putting it on a permanent footing by providing the endowment from lands at Bexley of his Oxford professorship, and by appointing to it his friend, the learned Degory Wheare.

The long tradition of accurate and co-ordinated antiquarian study in Great Britain is almost entirely due to Camden. Other countries developed their own traditions of antiquarian writing on similar lines; though Flavio Biondo and his followers followed a different path in Italy. The *Recherches de la France* of Etienne Pasquier (1529–1615) has many points of resemblance to Camden, whose work typifies the new antiquarian taste.

effect of this can be seen in the speeches of opposing generals before a battle, where one will quite clearly answer the other as if they were debating the issues at stake. Thucydides has been valued as he hoped: statesmen as well as historians, men of affairs as well as scholars, have read and profited by him.

The text was first printed by Aldus in 1502. The edition of Henri Estienne, a member of the famous French family of printers, who corresponded with scholars as an equal, first came out in 1564. The edition cited was improved by the addition of a translation into Latin by Lorenzo Valla and by the notes of another great French scholar, Isaac Casaubon.

102

HISTORIAN OF ATHENS

THUCYDIDES (*c.* 471–*c.* 400 B.C.). De Bello Peloponnesiaco. [*Geneva*]: *Henri Estienne, 1588*

The standards and methods of Thucydides as a contemporary historian have never been bettered. He began work at the very start of the events he records, and the penetration and concentration which he devoted to his account of the 'Peloponnesian War' (the war between Athens and Sparta from 431 to 404 B.C.) were based on the conviction that it would prove the most important event in Greek history.

Thucydides set himself the highest standards of accuracy. 'As to the actions of the war', he says, 'I have not felt free to record them on hearsay evidence from the first informant or on arbitrary conjecture. My account rests either on personal knowledge or on the closest possible scrutiny of every statement made by others. The process of research was laborious, because conflicting accounts were given by those who had witnessed the several events, as partiality swayed or memory served them.' This he did not only from his belief in the importance of the actual events, but in the conviction that the facts would be found of permanent value. He saw his history as a source of profit to 'those who desire an exact knowledge of the past as a key to the future, which in all probability will resemble the past'. It was in this sense, not in any anticipation of his own enduring fame, that he called it, in a memorable phrase, 'a possession for ever'.

This is exactly what it has become. Nothing, not even his own participation in the war or his disgrace in 424, was permitted to divert the historian from the standards he had laid down for himself. It might be supposed that, by introducing the speeches which are among the principal glories of the history, Thucydides was lapsing from this standard. It is obvious that while some, especially the famous 'Funeral Oration' of Pericles, he must have heard, there are others which he could not have heard. It is probably true that Thucydides used this form in obedience to the tradition of first person speech which every Greek history from Homer onwards followed. However, he uses them to make clear, what would have seemed intolerably dry in the abstract, the personal and political motives of the protagonists on either side; the subtle

103

ALGEBRAIC TRIGONOMETRY

FRANCISCUS VIETA (1540–1603). In Artem Analyticam Isagoge. *Tours: Iametius Mettayer, 1591*

The 'Introduction to the Art of Analysis' is the earliest work on symbolic algebra.

Franciscus Vieta (latinized from François Viète), the greatest French mathematician of the sixteenth century, was by profession a lawyer from Brittany who spent his life in the public service, ultimately becoming a member of the King's privy council. He was a wealthy man to whom mathematics was a delightful hobby. While in the service of Henry IV of France he succeeded in putting his mathematical activities to good use by finding the key to a complicated cipher used by the Spaniards.

Vieta's greatest innovation in mathematics was the denoting of general or indefinite quantities by letters of the alphabet instead of abbreviations of words as used hitherto. It is true that arbitrary letters of the alphabet had been used to denote algebraic quantities in the thirteenth century by Jordanus Nemorarius and in the fifteenth and sixteenth centuries by Stifel and Regiomontanus (40) in Germany and by Cardanus in Italy; but Vieta developed the idea systematically and made it an essential part of algebra. Known quantities were represented by consonants, unknown ones by vowels; squares, cubes, etc., were not represented by new letters but by adding the word quadratus, cubus, etc. Vieta also brought the + and − signs into general use, although they are found in some earlier German works and have been traced back to about 1480; the sign of equality = we owe to Robert Recorde (1557). This algebraic symbolism made possible the development of analysis, with its complicated processes, a fundamental element in modern mathematics.

Vieta also wrote *De Numerosa Potestatum ad Exegesin Resolutione*, 1600, in which he demonstrated a method for approximating to the root of an equation, and *De Aequationum Recognitione et Emendatione*, 1615, on the theory of equations, including the solution of the cubic and the quadratic. He constructed trigonometrical tables, derived from those of Rheticus, and described them in his earliest work on mathematics, *Canon Mathematicus seu ad Triangula*, Paris, 1579, which was used by Napier (116). Besides a detailed treatment of the solution of triangles, it contains a celebrated account of the relation between sin $n\theta$ and sin θ. Vieta elaborated the theory of right-angled spherical triangles and obtained the value of π as an infinite product, the first such product to appear in any mathematical work.

By his brilliant researches in mathematics Vieta became a key figure in its development and his influence can be seen on Descartes (129), on Harriot, and even on Newton (161) and Leibniz (160).

All his books were published privately at his own expense for distribution to his friends and are therefore notably rare.

104

CHURCH AND GOVERNMENT

RICHARD HOOKER (1553–1600). Of the Lawes of Ecclesiasticall Politie. *London: John Windet, [1593 or 1594]– 1597*

The monumental work of Richard Hooker was intended as a defence of the Church of England as established in the reign of Elizabeth I, and more particularly as a defence of Episcopacy and the government of the Church against the objections of the Presbyterians. In fact he proceeds to consider the ultimate principles on which all authority rests, which he finds in the concept of law 'whose seat is the bosom of God, whose voice the harmony of the world'. Law, operating in nature, controlling the character and actions of individual men and visible in the formation of societies and governments, is equally to be seen as part of the divine order according to which God himself acts.

'All things therefore do work after a sort according to law: only the works and operations of God have Him both for their worker, and for the law whereby they are wrought. The being of God is a kind of law to His working; for that perfection which God is giveth perfection to what He doeth.' The highest approach which men can make to the law of God is through perfect reason by a deep and absolute regard for facts. 'The general and perpetual voice of men is as the sentence of God himself.' Applying his principles to man in society, he derives the force of government from the general approbation. 'Sith men naturally have no full or perfect power to command whole politic multitudes of men; therefore utterly without our consent we could in such sort be at no man's commandment living. And to be commanded we do consent, when that society whereof we are part hath at any time before consented, without revoking the same after, by the like universal agreement.'

This is the earliest statement of the 'original contract' as the basis of government, which had originated in France and was to become a major issue in the political struggles of the seventeenth century. Hooker's theory formed the basis of Locke's *Treatise of Civil Government* (163) and can thus be considered the first statement of the principles behind the Constitution of England.

Parts 1 and 2, containing Books 1–4 and Book 5 were published as cited above; Books 6 and 8 were published in 1648 and Book 7 in 1661.

105

THE QUEEN'S CAPTAINS

RICHARD HAKLUYT (1552–1616). The Principal Navigations, Voiages, Traffiques and Discoveries of the English Nation. 3 vols. *London: George Bishop, Ralph Newberie and Robert Barker, 1598–1600*

This enormous work—it is said to contain one million seven hundred thousand words—is the most complete collection of voyages and discoveries, by land as well as by sea, and of the nautical achievements of the Elizabethans.

While still at Westminster School, Richard Hakluyt was already inspired with an interest in geography by his cousin, who was adviser to the Muscovy Company. After studying at Christ Church, Oxford, where among much else he learned four languages, he became the first lecturer on modern geography. Later he was appointed Chaplain to the Paris Embassy and, after the publication of his book, Chaplain of the Savoy and a Canon of Westminster.

Although Hakluyt himself never travelled farther than France he inspired some of the great overseas explorations of his time and was one of the leading spirits in the Elizabethan maritime expansion. He met many of the great navigators—Drake, Raleigh, Gilbert, Frobisher and others—corresponded with Ortelius (91) and Mercator (100) and collected all the material on voyages he could find. At first he mainly instigated the translation of such accounts into English, but by 1589 he had collected enough material himself to publish the first edition of his famous book, which ran to 825 pages. He continued to assemble material, so that by 1600 he was able to fill the three folio volumes of the definitive edition of the *Principal Navigations*: called by Froude 'the prose epic of the modern English nation'.

The arrangement is both chronological and regional, with personal reports by explorers and navigators, merchants and diplomats, the reproduction of documents, sailing directions, etc. Book I covers the voyages to North and North-east, Book II South and South-east, and Book III America.

Hakluyt was a vigorous propagandist and empire-builder; his purpose was to further British maritime enterprise and to intensify British expansion overseas. He saw Britain's greatest opportunity in the colonization of America and his first literary production had been the editing of a translation of Cartier's voyage to Canada by Florio. In 1579 he recommended the capture of the Magellan Strait from Spain. He advocated the colonization of America chiefly for economic reasons, but also to spread the gospel and to oust Spain. He pleaded for a voyage to find the North-West Passage, in the existence of which he believed, and for the expansion of English interests in India. In 1599 he became a consultant to the East India Company, whose income is said to have been increased by £20,000 from information given in Hakluyt's book, and in 1606 he became a patentee of the Virginia Company.

Hakluyt instigated numerous publications in the geographical literature of his time, usually contributing prefaces. He suggested De Bry's publication of John White's drawings of America and Hariot's *True Report*, which became part 1 of De Bry's great collection of voyages. His own manuscripts were made accessible to Samuel Purchas, who used them for his *Hakluytus Posthumus or Purchas his Pilgrimes*, a collection of voyages published in five volumes in 1625.

Later in the century and during the eighteenth century the interest in Hakluyt declined somewhat, but in the nineteenth century it revived and the Hakluyt Society was founded in his honour in 1846.

106

MERCATOR FOR THE NAVIGATORS

EDWARD WRIGHT (1558–1615). *Certain Errors in Navigation... Corrected. London: Valentine Sims, 1599*

John Dee, William Bourne and Edward Wright encompass the highest achievement of English navigational science in Tudor times. They solved practical problems relating to the compass, latitude and geography.

An Instrument for the ready finding out of the magneticall azimuth of the Sunne by the ordinary Compasse.

Edward Wright, Fellow of Caius College, Cambridge, apparently had very little practical experience of seamanship; his only journey overseas was to the Azores with the Earl of Cumberland in 1589. He nevertheless brought about a revolution in navigational science, which for the first time he based firmly on mathematical principles. His book includes translations from Roderico Zamorano, Nuñez and Cortes (76), yet his own contribution was of the greatest value. His fame chiefly rests on his tables for the construction of maps using 'Mercator's projection'. On the old charts the degrees of latitude and longitude were shown as of equal length, a distortion which made the plotting of a course at sea extremely difficult. Mercator (100) had first published a chart on which a straight course plotted on a globe could be drawn as a straight line on the map or chart by lengthening the degrees of latitude in greater proportion than the degrees

of longitude; but he had not made it practically applicable. Wright devised and published a set of tables by which Mercator's projection could be put to navigational use; the method still used today.

Wright also formulated instructions for the use of the compass and the cross-staff, made improvements in navigational instruments and gave tables of magnetic declinations. He had communicated his ideas to Hondius, the Dutch map-maker, who immediately produced a chart on his principles, even before Wright himself had published his own book which included a chart of the Azores based on Mercator's projection. In 1600 a world map was engraved in England on Wright's system and published in Hakluyt's *Principal Navigations* (105).

Wright was much concerned with the training of seamen in England. He suggested the appointment of a grand pilot to examine navigators, a reform which was not introduced in England until the mid-nineteenth century. Wright also translated Napier (116) into English having at once realized the great importance of the invention of logarithms for the application of mathematical science. His interest in the problems of latitude found expression in his translation of Stevin's *The Haven-finding Art*, 1599.

107

THE EARTH A MAGNET

WILLIAM GILBERT (1544–1603). *De Magnete. London: Peter Short, 1600*

The magnetic properties of the lodestone were known in ancient Greece, but it was only in the later Middle Ages that knowledge of the magnetic compass spread to Europe from China, where also the mysteries of magnetism had long been studied. But it is with Gilbert, who was physician to Queen Elizabeth I, that the modern development of electricity and magnetism really starts.

His book 'On the Magnet' was the first major English scientific treatise based on experimental methods of research. Gilbert was chiefly concerned with magnetism; but as a digression he discusses in his second book the attractive effect of amber (electrum), and thus may be regarded as the founder of electrical science. He coined the terms 'electricity', 'electric force' and 'electric attraction'. His 'versorium', a short needle balanced on a sharp point to enable it to move freely, is the first instrument designed for the study of electrical phenomena, serving both as an electroscope and electrometer. He contended that the earth was one great magnet; he distinguished magnetic mass from weight; and he worked on the application of terrestrial magnetism to navigation.

Gilbert's book influenced Kepler (112), Bacon (119), Boyle (141), Newton (161) and, in particular, Galileo (128), who used his theories to support his own proof of the correctness of the findings of Copernicus in cosmology. It was printed eleven times, four in Latin, six in English and once in Russian.

BIBLIOGRAPHY: S. P. Thompson, *Notes on the De Magnete of Dr. Gilbert* (London, 1901); Duane H. D. Roller, *The De Magnete of William Gilbert* (Amsterdam, 1959).

108

IL BEL CANTO

GIULIO CACCINI (*c.* 1545–1618). Le Nuove Musiche. *Florence: Marescotti, 1601* [*1602*]

In order to put Caccini's 'The New Music' in its right perspective, it should be considered in relation to his life as a whole and his other work as a composer. Born in Rome in about 1545, he entered the musical service of the Medici at Florence in 1564, mainly as a singer, but also as a player and musical director. Apart from visits to Rome in 1592 and to Paris in 1604–5, his whole life was spent at the Florentine court. He died there in 1618. His life was thus contemporaneous with the rise of Italian opera, to the theory and practice of which he made an important contribution.

By about 1590 Caccini had become a prominent member of the circle of poets and musicians who were centred on the palace of Giovanni de' Bardi, Count of Vernio. Their aim was to discuss the lost music of Greek drama. It has sometimes been claimed that Caccini invented monody: this is incorrect, but it can certainly be allowed that he made a great contribution to the composition of music for a single voice. After small-scale experiments, Caccini completed his setting of Peri's *Euridice* late in 1601, which was the first opera ever printed.

Le Nuove Musiche contains three airs and two choruses from another stage work, *Il Rapimento di Cefalo*, and a number of other separate airs and madrigals. The latter especially are used to express Caccini's innovation of giving musical point to the texts by emphasizing their emotional qualities. He does this chiefly by the use of elaborate, florid ornaments, known as 'gorge'. The preface to the book is extremely important, because it discusses this new technique in detail, and it remains a landmark in the history both of music and of singing. It may, indeed, be regarded as the foundation of the Italian method of voice-training, *bel canto*, universally adopted until the introduction of the declamatory style by Wagner (333) and still characteristic of Italian opera. An English translation of the preface was included in Oliver Strunk's *Source Readings in Music History* (1952).

109

POLITICS: THE LAW AND THE PEOPLE

JOHANNES ALTHUSIUS (JOHANN ALTHAUS) (*c.* 1557–1638). Politica, Methodice Digesta. *Herborn: Christopher Corvinus, 1603*

'The Science of Politics, systematically set out', is now recognized as one of the most important documents in the history of political science: indeed, it is arguable that the modern meaning of the word politics is due to Althusius. It is the codification and final expression of a significant trend of political thought which developed in the sixteenth century out of biblical, classical and medieval sources, and through the ferment of the con-temporary scene. It is also a work of prophetic insight: it could appeal across the centuries to Otto Gierke (360★), whose own writings have done much to establish the form of political science as we know it. The *Politica* was a famous and popular work in its own time: at least six, perhaps eight editions were published, the last in 1654. Then for over two hundred years it was entirely forgotten; no political writer, with the single and notable exception of Spinoza (153), appears to have read it, until it was rediscovered by Gierke, who in 1880 made it the basis of his revolutionary monograph on the growth of the theory of natural right.

Althusius was born, not before 1557, at Diedenshausen in Westphalia and in 1586 took his doctorate in civil and ecclesiastical law at Basle. Immediately thereafter he moved to the University of Herborn, where he became a professor a year or two later. There he remained, taking a prominent part in the affairs of the university and the political affairs of the country, and increasing his reputation as an academic and practical lawyer, until 1604. Then he accepted the offer of the city of Emden to become its Syndic, or legal adviser. As the leading permanent official, the Syndic had considerable influence in its internal affairs; moreover, in foreign affairs, he was the chief diplomatic representative of one of the great mercantile centres and one of the most influential strongholds of Calvinism in northern Europe. Here Althusius remained for the rest of his life; despite his legal practice and municipal business, he contrived to produce more theoretical works—an enlarged and revised edition of the *Politica* among them; his reputation also led him to be called on as legal adviser to other political bodies.

What struck his contemporaries, as it strikes us now, is the skill and ingenuity with which Althusius, from sources widely disparate in matter and intention, built up in the *Politica* a system not only coherent but highly individual. From philosophical works like Aristotle's 'Politics' (38), to which Althusius owes much, not least in his arrangement, and from propaganda works like the *Vindiciae Contra Tyrannos* (94b), Althusius borrowed and improved. To him the essence of 'politics' was what he called a *consociatio symbiotica*, a natural co-operative group. 'Politics', he says, 'is the science of linking human beings together for a social life.' Where Machiavelli (63) saw it as the authority of the prince over people and Bodin (94a) as the authority of the people over their prince, Althusius saw it in the fact of the existence of social groups. This system derived clearly, from his Calvinistic point of view, from God, a God deterministically remote, of whom Althusius could write, in one of his most famous dicta: 'Quod Deus est in universo, lex est in societate'.

This is the beginning of the modern development of the theory of natural right: the point from which the political speculation of Locke and Spinoza started; and in Althusius's corollary of the natural 'sympathy' upon which co-operative living depends we have the essence of Rousseau's theory of the natural state. Such a degree of abstraction was something new at the beginning of the sixteenth century: it has since become the subject-matter of political science.

110

THE END OF THE
'PHILOSOPHER'S STONE'

THEOPHRASTUS BOMBAST VON HOHENHEIM, known as PARACELSUS (1493 or 1494–1541). Opera Medico-chemico-chirurgica. 11 vols. *Frankfurt: A Collegio Musarum Palthenianarum, 1603–5*

Paracelsus (the name was invented by his admiring friends—it is not known that he ever used it himself; it probably signifies 'surpassing Celsus', the author of a famous medical textbook of the first century) was a Swiss physician and one of the most colourful characters of the Renaissance north of the Alps. He made the startling assertion that 'The true use of chemistry is not to make gold but to prepare medicines'. A restless and aggressive man, an extraordinary mixture of the mystic and the patient observer of nature, who combined in his system magical and scientific elements, Paracelsus was soon at loggerheads with the orthodox medical establishment of his time. He spent a large part of his life as an itinerant doctor and chemist, theologian and lay-preacher.

His central idea was that man is a microcosm; that each component of the body and each function has its parallel in the greater world, particularly in the stars with the regularity and interdependence of their movements. He believed the human body to be controlled by an occult vital force, the Archeus, situated in the stomach, whose function it was to separate the healthy from the poisonous elements. A healthy body needs an equilibrium of the mystic elements of salt, sulphur and mercury, and disease was caused by their disturbance. Disease was also seen, not simply as a disturbance of normal functions, but as a parasite; it was, therefore, an extraneous influence— quite a modern idea, though of course Paracelsus had no inkling of the modern theory of infection. Hence, the physician must be familiar with alchemy and the physical sciences; especially with astrology, since the stars influence diseases and astral bodies penetrate the human body, and with theology, since man has a soul in addition to his body and mind.

Paracelsus's significance in the history of medicine lay therefore not so much in his discovery of specific cures as in his general approach and his ideas on methods. The most important of these are two. First, he applied chemical techniques to pharmacy and therapeutics, and he had some inkling of the fact that bodily functions are of a chemical character, so that their disorders can be cured by chemical counter-measures. This is not to maintain that Paracelsus was a chemist in our sense—too much of his thought was bound up with alchemy, mystical cosmology and philosophy for that—but in an empirical way he succeeded in finding some effective drugs. Secondly, in his medical teaching he abandoned the ruling system of 'humours'; and the beginnings of modern pathology can be discerned in his work, even if one cannot claim for him a modern outlook on anatomy and physiology. He left some notable descriptions of diseases: among them 'miner's lung'—the beginning of occupational disease (see Ramazzini, 170)—and goitre with or without feeble-mindedness. He used mercury as a diuretic and demonstrated albumen in the urine; he prescribed opium and ether-like substances as sedatives; he made poisons such as arsenic available for medicinal purposes by special methods of detoxication; he rejected at least some of the crude demonological ideas of his time when considering mental disease.

His influence on the later sixteenth and seventeenth centuries was profound. What is known as 'iatrochemistry' (medical chemistry) which added greatly to our knowledge of compounds, sprang from his inspiration, and the work of Helmont (135), a scientific investigator in the modern sense, is unthinkable without him.

Paracelsus's theological works, now being published from the manuscripts, are planned in fourteen volumes.

BIBLIOGRAPHY: Karl Sudhoff, *Versuch einer Kritik der Echtheit der Paracelsischen Schriften*, 2 vols. (Berlin, 1894–9).

111

DON QUIXOTE

MIGUEL DE CERVANTES SAAVEDRA (1547–1616). El Ingenioso Hidalgo Don Quixote de la Mancha. *Madrid: Juan de la Cuesta, 1605 (Second part 1615)*

Cervantes was born at Alcalá de Henares and died after a long and adventurous life at Madrid. His first verses, on the death of Philip II's third wife, appeared in 1569, but from then on he served as a soldier, fighting with great bravery at Lepanto, and in several actions thereafter. In 1575 he was given leave to return to Spain, but en route his ship was captured by Barbary corsairs and he was taken prisoner to Algiers. After several attempts to escape, which seem to have won him the respect of his captors, he was ransomed and returned to Spain at the end of 1580. For the next ten years he tried without much success to make a living as an author, and his increasing responsibilities (he had married in 1584) forced him to enter government service: with even less success, for between 1597 and 1602 he was more than once imprisoned; and it was in prison, it seems, that his masterpiece was begun.

The first part of *Don Quixote* came out in 1605. What had begun as a simple satire on the tedious chivalric romances of the time broadened into a sweeping panorama of Spanish society; and it was this, the variety, the liveliness, and the gibes at the famous, which won it instant fame. Its larger claims, the subdued pathos, its universal humanity, were slower to be appreciated. But within months Don Quixote and Sancho Panza had become legendary; the book was pirated by three separate publishers and two more authorized editions appeared, all in 1605. Before the publication of the second volume the first had been printed in England, France and Italy, and Cervantes was known throughout Europe. The writing of the second part was stimulated by the publication of a spurious 'second part' in 1614; and it was an even greater success. There is less knockabout, and Cervantes had come to love and understand the two heroes, whom he had at first introduced to ridicule. He died on 23 April 1616, on the same day as Shakespeare.

Don Quixote is one of those universal works which are read by all ages at all times, and there are very few who have not at one time or another felt themselves to be Don Quixote confronting the windmills or Sancho Panza at the inn.

BIBLIOGRAPHY: Leopold Rius, *Bibliografia Critica de los Obras de Miguel de Cervantes Saavedra* (Madrid, 1895–1905).

112

THE LAWS OF PLANETARY MOTION

JOHANNES KEPLER (1571–1630). Astronomia Nova. [*Heidelberg: E. Vögelin*], *1609*

Johannes Kepler stands, with Galileo (113), between Copernicus (70) and Newton (161) among the founders of modern astronomy and of a new conception of the universe. 'The New Astronomy' is perhaps his most important book.

Kepler studied mathematics, astronomy and theology at Tübingen. Compelled as a Protestant to give up his post as a teacher of mathematics at Graz, he joined Tycho Brahe, the famous Danish astronomer, at Prague and on his death became mathematician to the Emperor Rudolf II, a great patron of science.

It was fortunate that Kepler was able to use the mass of material collected by Tycho Brahe. Brahe had greatly improved the construction of astronomical instruments and with these had made systematic and accurate observations over many years. Although he departed from the traditional picture of the universe on some critical issues, he regarded the idea of the motion of the earth as absurd: but he had lacked time to construct his own system of the universe from observation. This task he left to Kepler.

Copernicus had shown the sun to be the centre of the universe round which the earth and planets revolve, but his description of their movements was still strongly

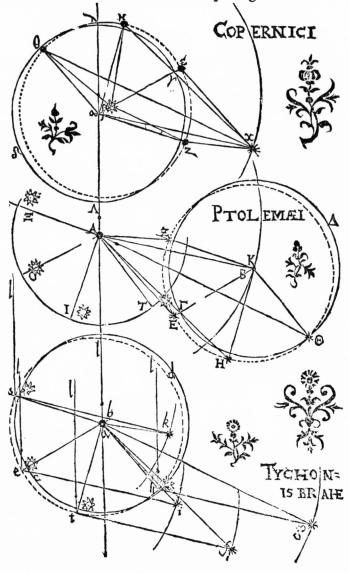

influenced by ancient conceptions of order and harmony. It was Kepler's aim to determine the true movements of the planets and the mathematical and physical laws controlling them. In this task he succeeded brilliantly.

In the *Astronomia Nova* and in his *Harmonices Mundi*, published in 1619, Kepler explained his revolutionary discoveries, the three laws of planetary motion: (1) the planets move around the sun not in circles, but in ellipses, the sun being in one focus; (2) a planet moves not uniformly, but in such a way that a line drawn from it at any point in its orbit to the sun sweeps out equal areas of the ellipse in equal times; (3) the squares of the periods of the planets round the sun are proportional to the cubes of the distances. Kepler attempted to construct a new physical cosmology into which his laws would fit, but he had no conception of the inertia of matter and still believed, like Aristotle, that movement was due to 'animal force or some equivalent'. He had an inkling of a universal force analogous to that of gravity but he identified it with magnetism. Thus, though Kepler sought for a physical system in the universe, he could not deduce the laws of planetary motion from the universal laws of motion. Of these Galileo was laying the foundations in Kepler's time, and Newton was to bring the whole into one great synthesis with the aid of the concept of universal gravitation.

Kepler was a voluminous writer, and his other contributions to science are also of importance. His 'Rudolphine Tables', 1627, inherited from Brahe, remained the standard astronomical tables for one hundred years. His *Epitome Astronomiae Copernicanae*, 1618–21, an account of the Copernican system, was put on the *Index* (82). He welcomed the invention of logarithms by Napier (116) and his *Chilias Logarithmorum*, 1624, made them popular in Germany. He prepared the way for the discovery of the infinitesimal calculus (160). In optics he gave a correct theory of vision, found that the velocity of light is infinite, came very near the correct law of refraction, and described various forms of the newly invented telescope.

BIBLIOGRAPHY: Max Caspar, *Bibliographia Kepleriana* (Munich, 1936).

113

THE TELESCOPE DISCOVERS NEW WORLDS

GALILEO GALILEI (1564–1642). Sidereus Nuncius. *Venice: Thomas Baglionus, 1610*

'The Starry Messenger', a thin pamphlet of twenty-four pages only, contains some of the most important discoveries in scientific literature.

Learning in the summer of 1609 that a device for making distant objects seem close and magnified had been brought to Venice from Holland, Galileo soon constructed a spy-glass of his own which he demonstrated to the notables of the Venetian Republic, thus earning a large increase in his salary as professor of mathematics

at Padua. Within a few months he had a good telescope, magnifying 30 diameters, and was in full flood of astronomical observation.

Through his telescope Galileo saw the moon as a spherical, solid, mountainous body very like the earth—quite different from the crystalline sphere of conventional philosophy. He saw numberless stars hidden from the naked eye in the constellations and the Milky Way; there were far more bodies in the universe than had ever been imagined. Above all, he discovered four new 'planets', the satellites of Jupiter that he called (in honour of his patrons at Florence) the Medicean stars.

Thus Galileo initiated modern observational astronomy, which studies the universe as a physical structure; and he announced himself as a Copernican. By so doing and by asserting, with the evidence of his instrument, that the universe was very unlike what Aristotle and the ancients had described, Galileo revived the smouldering Copernican dispute. His discoveries in the *Sidereus Nuncius* did not prove that Copernicus (70) was correct. Not even his later discoveries (of sunspots and the phases of Venus) did this; nor did any of Galileo's later polemical writings. But Galileo did prove that the Aristotelian–Ptolemaic world-view *must* be wrong. Even his clerical opponents (like the Jesuit astronomers Clavius and Scheiner) were soon compelled to admit it.

With the publication of the *Sidereus Nuncius* Galileo was drawn into a long defence of the telescope, of his discoveries, and of Copernicus, in which he developed formidable powers of persuasion and invective. This period of his life was to end, in 1633, with the Pyrrhic victory of his opponents at his trial in Rome (see 128).

BIBLIOGRAPHY: Dino Cinti, *Biblioteca Galileana* (Florence, 1957).

114

THE AUTHORIZED VERSION

THE HOLY BIBLE...Newly Translated out of the Originall Tongues. *London: Robert Barker, 1611*

The King James Bible, or the Authorized Version, as it is now commonly (but not strictly accurately) known, was the outcome of the conference summoned at Hampton Court by the King in January 1604, in an attempt to settle the quarrels in the Church of England, arising from the Puritan zeal of some of its members. It was the leader of the Puritan party, John Reynolds, the President of Corpus Christi College, Oxford, who first suggested the idea of a new translation. The King took up the idea enthusiastically and gave it his full support.

It has been described as 'the only literary masterpiece ever to have been produced by a committee' and was the work of nearly fifty translators, organized in six groups. Two of these met at Westminster under the Dean, Lancelot Andrewes (1555–1626), and were allotted the Old Testament from Genesis to Kings, and the Epistles. At Cambridge two companies, at first under Edward

Lively (1545?-1605), the Regius Professor of Hebrew, translated the Old Testament from Chronicles to the Songs of Songs and the Apocrypha. The director of the translators at Oxford was also the Regius Professor of Hebrew, John Harding (d. 1610), and among the translators in his two teams, working on the Old Testament from Isaiah to Malachi, and the Gospels, Acts of the Apostles and Revelation, were Sir Henry Savile, Provost of Eton, and George Abbot, the future Archbishop of Canterbury.

After they had completed their allotted tasks, the six companies of translators studied and criticized the work of the other groups, and then a representative committee of six, sitting daily in London at Stationers' Hall for nine months, undertook the final revision. Miles Smith (d. 1624), who was to become Bishop of Gloucester, and Thomas Bilson (1547-1616), Bishop of Worcester, saw the book through the press and are believed to have composed the dedication, preface, and chapter headings.

Being based on a wider range of classical and oriental scholarship than its predecessors, the Authorized Version was a more learned text. Fortunately, however, no attempt was made to produce a completely new translation. While consulting the original Hebrew and the 'received' Greek text as printed by Robert Estienne in 1550, the translators took as the basic English text that of the Bishops' Bible, as revised in 1572. They were instructed that it was to be 'as little altered as the text of the original will permit', but they were enjoined to consult the Tyndale (58) and Coverdale versions and the Geneva Bible (83). It is also clear that they borrowed quite freely from the Catholic translation of the New Testament issued at Rheims in 1582.

Above all the translators lived at a period when the genius of the language was in full flower. Though few of them were possessed individually of literary genius, 'they had, so to speak, a collective ear and taste, and above all, they had intense and reverent zeal' (D. Bush). They succeeded superbly in their aim, not to create a new translation 'but to make a good one better', so that the noble prose of Tyndale and Coverdale remained the backbone of what Macaulay described as 'a book, which if everything else in our language should perish, would alone suffice to show the whole extent of its beauty and power'.

No new English translation was produced until the Revised Version of 1881, and the influence of the Authorized Version may best be described in the words of G. M. Trevelyan. 'For every Englishman who had read Sidney or Spenser, or had seen Shakespeare acted at the Globe, there were hundreds who had read or heard the Bible with close attention as the words of God. The effect of the continual domestic study of the book upon the national character, imagination and intelligence for nearly three centuries to come, was greater than that of any literary movement in our annals, or any religious movement since the coming of St Augustine.'

BIBLIOGRAPHY: Darlow & Moule, no. 240.

THE FIRST STANDARD DICTIONARY

VOCABOLARIO DEGLI ACCADEMICI DELLA CRUSCA. *Venice: Giovanni Alberti, 1612*

The Accademia della Crusca (the 'Bran Academy') was founded in 1582 with the express purpose of 'separating the grain from the husk', that is to say, of purifying and cultivating the Italian language. Under the inspired leadership of Leonardo Salviati (1540-89) the academicians fulfilled their task with an undreamt-of success. Their 'Dictionary', begun in 1591, propagated the Tuscan dialect as the norm of literate Italian, based on the usage of the great Florentine writers from the fourteenth century onward, with Dante (8), Petrarch and Boccaccio as the lodestars. No Italian author or printer of any significance has since written or printed anything except pure Tuscan. Alessandro Manzoni's *I Promessi Sposi* ('The Betrothed'), perhaps the most famous Italian work of fiction, was originally written in the dialect of his native Milan; but after its initial success in 1827 he rewrote it, for the 1840 edition, to conform with the standard established by the Academy two centuries earlier and sedulously maintained ever since.

Beyond the frontiers of Italy, the principles incorporated in the *Vocabolario* served as the model for all subsequent dictionaries. Those of the French (1694) and Spanish (1726-39) academies and Samuel Johnson's *Dictionary* (201) expressly or implicitly acknowledged their debt to this Italian work which, in a long series of editions, has maintained its unchallenged position as one of the most authoritative productions of its kind.

LOGARITHMS

JOHN NAPIER (1550-1617). Mirifici Logarithmorum Canonis Descriptio. *Edinburgh: Andrew Hart, 1614*

John Napier of Merchiston lived most of his life on his family estate; but apart from his scientific studies he was active in the political and religious controversies of his time.

His 'Description of the Wonderful Table of Logarithms' is unique in the history of science in that a great discovery was the result of the unaided original speculation of one individual without precursors and almost without contemporaries in his field. Napier began work on his tables in 1594, but it was twenty years before he was ready to publish them, in this thin quarto volume of ninety pages.

Napier must have recognized the need to simplify the immensely complicated methods employed by contemporary mathematicians for their astronomical calculations. Rheticus, the friend of Copernicus (70), and Vieta (103) in particular had attempted to construct tables for this purpose. In his book Napier explains the nature of logarithms and gives a logarithmic table of the natural sines of a quadrant from minute to minute. His logarithms reduced multiplication and division to a process of addition and subtraction and extraction of roots to division.

The essence of Napier's method is his ingenious use of a relation between an arithmetical and a geometrical progression. Unlike modern logarithms, however, Napier's decrease as the numbers increase. Also his logarithms had no explicit 'base'.

The new technique was immediately adopted. Henry Briggs (1556–1631), Gresham professor of geometry (and afterwards Savilian professor at Oxford), published in 1624 the first table of logarithmic sines to the base 10 of our scale of numeration and the logarithms of numbers from 1–20000 and 90000–100000. These were afterwards supplemented by the table of those between 20000 and 90000 compiled by the Dutch mathematician Adrian Vlacq (1600–67) and published in 1633. Edmund Gunter (1581–1626) constructed rulers with a logarithmic scale for ease of calculation, and he and William Oughtred (1574–1660) eventually discovered by these means the principle of the modern slide rule. Kepler (112) popularized them in Germany and dedicated one of his books to Napier in gratitude for his use of them.

In 1619 Napier's *Mirifici Logarithmorum Canonis Constructio* appeared posthumously, although it was written before the *Descriptio*. In it he explained how he had calculated his table. The modifications which he worked out with Briggs form the basis of our modern system of decimal logarithms. The *Descriptio* was translated into English by Edward Wright (106), who recognized its importance for navigation, and was published after his death by his son Samuel in 1616.

Napier also did work in spherical trigonometry and in his *Rabdologiae seu Numerationis per Virgulas libri II*, Edinburgh, 1617, announced another important invention, 'Napier's Bones'. These were rods which could be used to find the product of two numbers in a mechanical way, the quotient of one number divided by another, and square and cube roots. They were the precursors of seventeenth-century and modern calculating machines and computers.

BIBLIOGRAPHY: W. R. Macdonald, *The Construction of the Wonderful Canon of Logarithms* (Edinburgh, 1889).

117
HISTORY THE TUTOR OF POLITICS

SIR WALTER RALEIGH (*c.* 1552–1618). The History of the World. *London:* [*W. Stansby for*] *Walter Burre, 1614*

The success of Raleigh's *History*, which, apart from numerous abridgements, ran through ten editions between 1614 and 1687, can perhaps be explained by the very fact that it is not a work of history in the academic sense but a political tract of immediate applicability. Its author was listened to, not so much because he was a scholar (which he certainly was by contemporary standards of scholarship), as because he embodied all the glories of the reign of Elizabeth I, which at the time of publication had already begun to be transfigured into a golden age.

Raleigh's death a few years later made him the hero of anti-Stewart and Puritan sentiment, and the *History* proved an arsenal of political ammunition to the Englishmen who overthrew the absolutism of the Stewarts at home and laid the foundations of New England beyond the seas. Raleigh's concern was less with the history of the ancient world than with the fight against the divine-right pretentions of James Stewart, who considered the author 'too saucy in censuring princes'. James was the actual butt of the severe strictures Raleigh passed upon ancient rulers who set themselves above the law; and Raleigh was thinking of England when he assessed the value or worthlessness of ancient institutions according to the eternal standards of right and justice as understood by him—and soon afterwards by all opponents of royal absolutism.

Sir Walter Raleigh or Ralegh can be taken as the epitome of the Elizabethan idea of a courtier and politician, sailor and explorer, writer and poet, full of avid interest in philosophy and the sciences, who, with his sword and his pen, made his mark at court and in parliament, on the high seas and in economic enterprises at home and abroad. He was among the first Englishmen to envisage clearly that the Americas should be the principal goal of English overseas expansion, the ultimate aim of which was to be the supersession of the Spanish by an English empire. The reversal of Elizabeth's policy by James I encompassed Raleigh's ruin: imprisoned in the Tower of London from 1603 to 1616 on a trumped-up charge, he finally fell a victim to James's pro-Spanish inclinations, and the last Elizabethan died by the executioner's axe.

During his confinement in the Tower, which was alleviated by the company of his wife and the visits of his friends, Raleigh conducted scientific experiments (which earned him the suspicion of witchcraft and atheism), wrote essays and verse, and brought out the *History*, which was originally to be dedicated to his friend Henry, Prince of Wales. Though intended to cover all history, it reached only down to 130 B.C. A commonplace book (Phillipps 6339, now in the British Museum), only recently identified as Raleigh's, reveals another aspect of the *History*, which to the present generation is perhaps of greater interest than those political implications on which the seventeenth century fastened: viz. Raleigh's perception that geography, 'the knowledge of the places wherein it [i.e. history] is performed' is fundamental to the right understanding of historical events.

118
THE COUNCIL OF TRENT

PAOLO SARPI (PIETRO SOAVE, pseudonym) (1552–1623). Historia del Concilio Tridentino. *London: John Bill, 1619*

The Council of Trent, the turning-point in the Counter-Reformation, created the modern Roman Catholic Church. It represents not merely one of the decisive moments of the sixteenth century, but a moment whose influence is still felt all over Europe.

HISTORIA
DEL
CONCILIO
TRIDENTINO.

NELLA QVALE SI SCOPRONO
tutti gl' artificii della Corte di Roma, per impedire
che né la veritá di dogmi si palesasse, né la
riforma del Papato, & della Chiesa
si trattasse.

DI
PIETRO SOAVE
POLANO.

DIEV ET MON DROIT.

IN LONDRA,
Appresso *GIOVAN. BILLIO.*
Regio Stampatore.
M.DC XIX.

Forced upon an unwilling papacy by the Emperor Charles V, who was anxious to put an end to the dissensions caused by religious strife, the Council first met in 1545. From the beginning, however, its proceedings were under papal domination, and, so far from effecting a reconciliation with Protestantism, its pronouncements on undecided points of dogma and the bold front it thus put forward gave its members the new confidence they needed to resist the Evangelical threat. No compromise was offered, and when, after numerous delays and evasions designed to frustrate the intentions and representations of the non-Italian members, the Council closed at the end of 1563, an instrument had been placed in the hands of the papacy which determined the evolution of the Roman Church for the next three centuries, culminating in the pronouncement of the dogma of papal infallibility in 1877. Only now is some relaxation beginning to take place.

The full force of the acts of the Council was not lost either on those who desired a reconciliation between the Church and the new schismatics or on those who distrusted the centralization of power in Rome. It was both these motives which prompted the Venetian patriot, scientist, scholar and reformer, Paolo Sarpi, to compile his memorable 'History of the Council of Trent', which was published pseudonymously in London. A member of the Servite Order, hated yet never excommunicated by the Papal See, Sarpi was the devoted and honoured servant of the Venetian Republic. Like the author in his lifetime, so in later years his book formed a nucleus of opposition to the papacy of Pius IV. Translated and reprinted over and over again, the masterpiece of 'Father Paul of Venice', as he was known to generations, is still read. Ranke (286) made a minute study of it and of the papal counterblast by Cardinal Pallavicini and found not much difference between the two in point of impartiality, though he preferred Sarpi in point of style. Only now are the issues debated between the two beginning to recede from the forefront of theological controversy.

119

THE ADVANCEMENT OF LEARNING

FRANCIS BACON (1561–1626). Instauratio Magna. *London: John Bill, 1620*

Sir Francis Bacon, Baron Verulam, Viscount St Albans, statesman, essayist and philosopher, studied law and rose to high office as Lord Chancellor under James I in 1618. Accused of accepting bribes from litigants, he was deprived of his offices and spent the last years of his life in retirement.

Bacon conceived a massive plan for the reorganization of scientific method and gave purposeful thought to the relation of science to public and social life. His pronouncement 'I have taken all knowledge to be my province' is the motto of his work.

The frontispiece to his *magnum opus* shows a ship in full sail passing through the Pillars of Hercules from the old to the new world. It symbolizes the vision of its author whose ambitious proposal was: 'a total reconstruction of sciences, arts and all human knowledge...to extend the power and dominion of the human race...over the universe'. The plan for this was to be set out in six parts: (1) a complete survey of human knowledge and learning; this was expounded in the *De Augmentis Scientiarum*, 1623 (a greatly extended version of *The Advancement of Learning*, 1605); (2) a new method for acquiring true knowledge, contained in the *Novum Organum* ('The New Instrument') forming the largest part of the present work; (3) a collection of empirical data, a whole natural history of facts, to which only the introduction, under the title *Parasceve ad Historiam Naturalem et Experimentalem*, is here printed; (4) examples for further investigation by the new method; (5) some provisional speculations and solutions in anticipation of the new philosophy itself; (6) the new philosophy. Of parts (3) to (5) only fragments were ever published; part (6) remained unwritten.

Bacon made no contributions to science itself, but his insistence on making science experimental and factual, rather than speculative and philosophical, had powerful consequences. He saw clearly the limitations of Aristotelian and scholastic methods and the growing breach between the thinking of his time and that of the Middle Ages is more precisely formulated in his work than in that of, say, Tommaso Campanella or Giordano Bruno. As a philosopher Bacon's influence on Locke (163, 164) and through him on subsequent English schools of psychology and ethics was profound. Leibniz (177), Huygens (154) and particularly Robert Boyle (141, 143) were deeply indebted to him, as were the *Encyclopédistes* (see 200), and Voltaire (202), who called him 'le père de la philosophie experimentale'.

Bacon believed passionately in education, and he held the view that the educated should be socially superior to the ignorant—a progressive notion at present unpopular in his own country. He held that the executive rather than the legislature should administer the state, as the latter could be just as tyrannical as the former; and (although—or perhaps because—he had been Lord Chancellor) that the judiciary should not direct policy, but only administer the law made by the other two powers of the state. He examined the whole problem of the relations between scientists and statesmen, science and government, science and social order; and his notions for a planned development of science and social organization based on scientifically ascertained facts are still relevant to what has become one of the crucial problems of the twentieth century.

To the general reader Bacon is better known by his *Essays*, first published in 1597. There is also a school of believers in his authorship of the works of Shakespeare, dating from Herbert Lawrence, *The Life and Adventures of Common Sense*, 1769.

BIBLIOGRAPHY: R. Gibson, *A Bibliography of the works of Francis Bacon and of Baconiana to the year 1750* (Oxford, 1950; supplement, 1959).

120

THE ANATOMY OF MELANCHOLY

ROBERT BURTON (1577–1640). The Anatomy of Melancholy. *Oxford: John Lichfield and James Short for Henry Cripps, 1621*

Robert Burton went up to Oxford in 1593 and in 1599 was elected to a studentship at Christ Church where he lived for the rest of his life. He wrote a lively Latin comedy rather in the manner of Ben Jonson, and some other minor pieces, but his masterpiece was *The Anatomy of Melancholy*, first published in quarto in 1621 and reprinted in folio in 1624, 1628, 1632, 1651, 1652, 1660 and 1676. In the third edition he promised that he would make no alterations, but the fourth was revised, the fifth edition differed from the fourth, and the sixth was printed posthumously from a copy containing his last corrections: if ever a single book deserved to be called the work of a lifetime, it is this.

THE
ANATOMY OF
MELANCHOLY,
VVHAT IT IS.
VVITH ALL THE KINDES,
CAVSES, SYMPTOMES, PROG-
ꓠOSTICKES, ᴀND SEVE-
RALL CVRES OF IT.

IN THREE MAINE PARTITIONS
with their feuerall SECTIONS, MEM-
BERS, and SVBSEC-
TIONS.

ꓑHILOSOPHICALLY, MEDICI-
ꓠALLY, HISTORICALLY, OPE-
NED ᴀND CVT VP.

BY
DEMOCRITVS *Iunior.*

With a Satyricall PREFACE, conducing to
the following Difcourfe.

MACROB.
Omne meum, Nihil meum.

ᴀT OXFORD,
Printed by IOHN LICHFIELD and IAMES
SHORT, for HENRY CRIPPS.
Anno Dom. 1621.

Burton had read much, and all that he had read, or nearly all, was refined and incorporated in the *Anatomy*. If it were objected that some of the matter was irrelevant, the reply would be that the anatomy of melancholy, like the study of jurisprudence, demands a knowledge of all things, human and divine. The whole book is elaborately divided and subdivided into partitions, divisions, sections, members and sub-sections. The first partition is devoted to the definition of his subject and its species and kinds, the causes of it and—at length—the symptoms: 'for the Tower of Babel never yielded such confusion of Tongues as the Chaos of Melancholy doth of Symptoms'. The second deals with the cure, and Burton's demonstration that it is necessary to live in the right part of the world to avoid melancholy occasions a long digression: a delightful account of foreign lands based—for Burton never travelled—on a wide reading of the cosmographers, and a powerful advocacy of the delights of country life. The third part deals with the more frivolous kinds of melancholy and the fourth with the serious, Religious Melancholy, with some moving reflections on the 'Cure of Despair'.

The *Anatomy*, as its publishing history shows, was one of the most popular books of the seventeenth century. All the learning of the age as well as its humour—and its pedantry—are there. It has something in common with Brant's 'Ship of Fools' (37), Erasmus's 'Praise of Folly' (43), and More's *Utopia* (47), with Rabelais and Montaigne (95) and like all these it exercised a considerable influence on the thought of the time. Dr Johnson deeply admired it, and Charles Lamb's often and strongly expressed devotion served to rescue the *Anatomy* from a brief period of oblivion; its admirers will continue to read and re-read it.

121

THE NOMENCLATURE OF PLANTS

CASPAR BAUHINUS (1560–1624). Pinax Theatri Botanici. *Basle: Ludovicus Rex, 1623*

'The World of Botany Illustrated' marks a most important scientific advance in botany. Great confusion still reigned in botanical nomenclature, since different names had been given to the same species by different writers, each constructing his own system.

Caspar Bauhinus, born at Basle and later professor of anatomy and botany there, a brother of Johannes Bauhinus, another notable naturalist, first established a scientific system of nomenclature. His *Pinax* describes six thousand species: it is the beginning of a modern 'natural' classification based on general morphology. Bauhinus realized the convenience of the binominal nomenclature which later became a central feature of Linné's system (192). He decisively differentiated genera and species, giving names to genera, but without descriptions, while distinguishing species by diagnostic phrases.

Bauhinus's book is still our most important source for the investigation of the botanical literature preceding him, and from it the way leads through Ray to Linné.

122

'ALL THE WORLD'S A STAGE'

WILLIAM SHAKESPEARE (1564–1616). Comedies, Histories, and Tragedies. *London: Isaac Jaggard and Ed. Blount, 1623*

The magic of Shakespeare's poetry is potent only in his own tongue; but the great theatrical scenes, the great dramatic figures are universal. Hamlet's doubts, the doomed love of Romeo and Juliet, Brutus's dilemma, the

73

Falstaffian image, the characters of Iago, Petruchio, and Lady Macbeth, are part of the fabric of western (and not only of western) civilization. Henry V's summons to Agincourt, Othello's stand before the Signoria, Mark Antony's funeral oration for Caesar, Portia at Shylock's trial: these are more real to us than the history books.

This first collected edition of Shakespeare's plays, commonly known as 'The First Folio', was published seven years after his death.

BIBLIOGRAPHY: Charlton Hinman, *The Printing and Proof-Reading of the First Folio of Shakespeare* (Oxford, 1963).

123

DEISM

EDWARD HERBERT, LORD HERBERT OF CHERBURY (1583–1648). De Veritate. [Paris] : *printer unidentified, 1624*

Lord Herbert of Cherbury seemed to have been born for success; he was carefully educated, and when he came to Court in 1605 he already looked to be on the threshold of greatness. A successful military career as a volunteer in the Low Countries, which won him the friendship of the Prince of Orange, confirmed his stature, and in 1619 he became Ambassador at Paris. He was very popular, and his success in achieving the marriage of Charles I and Henrietta Maria made him more so.

His failure, however, in his second object of inducing Louis XIII to assist the Elector Palatine, husband of James I's daughter Elizabeth, 'The Winter Queen', led to his recall in 1624. From then on his career suffered a decline. On the outbreak of the Civil War he refused to take any part in the struggle, but came to terms with Parliament in 1644 and died in London. His character is curiously elusive and it seems typical that his autobiography (published by Horace Walpole in 1764) deals only with his social successes and omits mention of his achievements in diplomacy, his friendships with Donne, Jonson, Selden, Casaubon, Gassendi and Grotius, or even his writings, which constitute a wholly original contribution to English thought.

Of these, the *De Veritate* ('On Truth'), is the most important. At first sight its prolix style and rambling method, the vanity of Herbert's claim to reject all previous theories, seem to confirm the frivolous character revealed by the autobiography. But in fact he justifies his claims. The book contains an elaborate theory of knowledge linked with some penetrating psychology, to which is added a scheme of natural religion: it is in many ways an English precursor of the natural theology and rationalist philosophy expressed by Descartes (129).

Herbert defines truth as the correct equation of the human faculties of apprehension with one another and with their objects. The faculties of the mind are four: natural instinct, which is given by God, and is indisputable; internal perception, under which he deals with love, hate, conscience and free will; external perception, by the senses; and reason, the least certain means, only employed as a supplement to the other means when they fail of themselves. The objects are similarly divided into those which are true in themselves, those which are true in appearance, those which are apprehended to be true, and those whose truth is determinable only by reason. The most striking thing about the *De Veritate* is not its theory of knowledge, but its metaphysical sophistication, especially in the theory of *notitiae communes*, the absolute truths. 'So far are these elements or sacred principles from being derived from experience or observation that without some of them we can neither experience nor even observe.' Kant might well have said that.

In fact, despite Herbert's avowed preoccupation with the intellect, not faith, it is the basic notions of religion which really form his subject matter. His statement of these—that there is one supreme God, that He is to be worshipped, that worship consists of virtue and piety, that we must repent of our sins and cease from them, and that there are rewards and punishments here and hereafter—came to form the 'Five Articles' of Deism, the great theological controversy of the eighteenth century. But it is clear that Herbert's purpose was to do for natural religion what his friend Grotius (125) had done for natural law, and in doing so he produced the first modern work of metaphysics by an English writer.

The London edition of 1645 includes the treatise *De Causis Errorum*.

124

'AMERICA, MY NEW-FOUND LAND'

JOHN SMITH (1580–1631). A Generall Historie of Virginia, New England and the Summer Isles. *London: Michael Sparkes, 1624*

By the beginning of the seventeenth century the piratical adventuring of Elizabethan captains up and down the Spanish Main had begun to be transmuted into merchant adventuring farther north on the American coastline. To the motives of maritime power and trade in the direction of overseas colonization was now added the strong desire of many Puritans among King James's subjects to seek freedom of conscience beyond his immediate reach. Accordingly, there was formed in 1606 the London Company—a joint-stock affair for the establishment of a plantation in the territory which Drake had already christened Virginia.

Captain John Smith, an enthusiastic supporter of Britain's expansionist policies, was among the Company's founders and accompanied the colonists on their voyage in 1607. He was the leading spirit in the colony during the very difficult period of its establishment, and finally became its President. The first settlement at Jamestown in Virginia became the first permanent English colony in America. This marked the beginning of a new age for the American continent, rivalling in world importance the voyage of Columbus itself (35).

Whether or not he had been rescued by the Princess Pocahontas from her father's braves, John Smith certainly surveyed Chesapeake Bay, went up the Potomac river as far as the site of the present-day Washington and up the Rappahannock as far as the present site of Fredericksburg. He returned to England in 1609; but he sailed again in 1614 and surveyed the New England coast from the Penobscot to Cape Cod. He named the region 'New England' and the mainland opposite Cape Cod 'Plymouth'. In 1616 he published *A Description of New England*, with an excellent map, pleading for further colonization. One consequence was the *Mayflower* landing of the Pilgrim Fathers on Plymouth Rock in December 1620, the accepted birth-date of modern America.

Smith published numerous books and pamphlets, all designed to encourage trade and colonization overseas. His masterpiece is the *Generall Historie*, which was the first sizeable work written in English about the new-found continent. Though not wholly reliable in every respect, it remained a standard work, the foundation of England's knowledge of America during the early period of colonization.

BIBLIOGRAPHY: Wilberforce Eames, *A Bibliography of Captain John Smith* (New York, 1927: incorporated in Sabin's *Dictionary of Books relating to America*, nos. 82812–82865).

125

INTERNATIONAL LAW

HUGO GROTIUS (1583–1645). De Jure Belli ac Pacis. *Paris: Nicolas Buon, 1625*

In a lifetime spent seeking to promote peace in an age of controversy and war, Hugo de Groot, always known as Grotius, could not claim any signal success. An infant prodigy, he entered the University of Leiden at the age of twelve, and early attracted the attention of the great J. J. Scaliger (98). He took the degree of Doctor of Law, and decided to practise as an advocate. He was successful in his profession, but he was as much interested in its theory as in its practice.

In 1604, at the age of twenty-one, he composed the treatise *De Jure Praedae*, as a result of a case concerning the ownership of a Portuguese galleon captured in the Straits of Malacca; and this was to become the basis of his most famous work. A diplomatic visit to England followed, but on his return he found the religious and political difference between the Calvinist anti-Spanish party, under Prince Maurice, and the more moderate Remonstrants, who inclined to peace with Spain and were supported by the government of the States, raised to such a pitch that strife was inevitable. Despite the efforts of Grotius to find a formula of compromise, the Calvinists were victorious. Prince Maurice, as Stadtholder, saw to it that his opponents were penalized and Grotius was condemned in 1618 to life imprisonment, from which he escaped to Paris in 1621.

In France he returned to his early work, and in a single year completed his masterpiece, 'On the Law of War and Peace', which made him famous thoughout Europe. Naturally enough, his preoccupation was with the latter

HVGONIS GROTII

DE IVRE BELLI AC PACIS

LIBRI TRES.

In quibus ius naturæ & Gentium : item iuris publici præcipua explicantur.

PARISIIS,

Apud NICOLAVM BVON, in via Iacobæa, fub fignis S. Claudij, & Hominis Siluestris.

M. DC. XXV.

CVM PRIVILEGIO REGIS.

part of his subject, and the questions which he put forward have come to be the basis of the ultimate view of law and society. This was the first attempt to lay down a principle of right, and a basis for society and government, outside Church or Scripture. The distinction between religion and law or morality is not clearly made, but Grotius's principle of an immutable law, which God can no more alter than a mathematical axiom, was the first expression of the 'droit naturel', the natural law which exercised the great political theorists of the eighteenth century, and is the foundation of modern international law.

126

LAW AND DEMOCRACY

EDWARD COKE (1552–1634). The First Part the Institutes of the Lawes of England; or, a Commentarie upon Littleton. *London: The Society of Stationers, 1628*

The first half of the career of Sir Edward Coke might be that of any successful lawyer of his time. Called to the Bar in 1578, his wide and exact knowledge of the law soon brought him a vast practice. By 1594 he had been successively Recorder of Norwich and of London, Solicitor-General, Speaker of the House of Commons, and Attorney-General. In all this, and most notably in his brutal prosecution of Raleigh (117), he differed only from the lawyers of his time in his greater industry and energy. Yet as a judge, despite a harshness and an abuse of authority which again might have been expected, he showed an independence (based on a determination to defend the common law he knew so well against all encroachment) very different from his more time-serving contemporaries. In three famous cases he thwarted the wishes of the King, to demonstrate in each that the royal prerogative could not over-ride the Law; and after a fourth, which resulted in a direct confrontation with James I, he was dismissed from all his offices.

Coke then began a new career as a leader of the constitutional party and himself led the Commons to enter in the journal of the House the famous petition of 18 December 1621 insisting on the freedom of parliamentary discussion. After supporting the popular cause in the first three parliaments of Charles I, in the last of which he was largely instrumental in drawing up the great Petition of Right, he retired in 1628 and spent his last years in compiling the works which have secured his immortality.

If Bracton (89) first began the codification of the Common Law, it was Coke who completed it. Ranging over the whole field of law, in comment, report, argument, and decision, the *Institutes* is a disorderly, pedantic, masterful work in which the common thread is a national dogmatism, tenacious of its continuous self-perpetuating life. With it the lawyers fought the battle of the constitution against the Stewarts; historical research was their defence for national liberties. In the *Institutes*, of which a revised and corrected edition was published in 1629, the tradition of the common law from Bracton and Littleton (23), whose name Coke's commentary—the first part of the *Institutes*—made famous, firmly established itself as the basis of the constitution of the realm.

127

MODERN PHYSIOLOGY

WILLIAM HARVEY (1578–1657). Exercitatio Anatomica de Motu Cordis et Sanguinis in Animalibus. *Frankfurt: William Fitzer, 1628*

The physiology of the blood vessels had been much studied but little understood until the time of Harvey. In this 'Anatomical Treatise on the Movement of the Heart and Blood in Animals', a tract of only seventy-two pages, he solved the problem by demonstrating the circulation of the blood.

William Harvey, educated at Cambridge and Padua, became a successful physician in London. He was appointed physician to St Bartholomew's Hospital and to both James I and Charles I and he accompanied the latter at the battle of Edgehill.

Galen (33) had regarded the veins as serving to convey to all parts of the body the nourishing blood elaborated in the liver. He recognized that both veins and arteries contained blood, and assumed that the arterial blood—clearly differentiable from the venous blood by its colour—was replenished where necessary from the venous supply through the septum of the heart. Sixteenth-century anatomists like Vesalius (71) recognized that the

septum was solid. The earliest published reference to the pulmonary or lesser circulation—passage of the blood from the right to the left side of the heart through the lungs—is in Servetus's theological treatise of 1553 (78); but as this was virtually unknown to medical men, the first real public enunciation must be regarded as the clear statement by Realdus Columbus in *De Re Anatomica* (1559). In 1603 Harvey's teacher, Fabricius of Aquapendente, published a monograph on the valves in the veins—previously noted by others—the purpose of which he only partially understood.

It was left for Harvey to combine these discoveries, to conceive the idea of a circulation of the entire blood system, and demonstrate it conclusively by an exhaustive series of dissections and physiological experiments. For twenty years Harvey pursued his objective in both human and comparative anatomy. He proved experimentally that the blood's motion is continuous and always in one direction, and that its actual amount and velocity makes it a physical impossibility for it to do otherwise than return to the heart by the venous route, the heart being itself a muscle and acting as a pump. He showed how the whole of the blood passes through the lungs, is returned to the left side of the heart, then passes through the general circulation and returns to the right side; he even suspected the existence of the capillaries connecting the smallest arteries with the smallest veins, but without the microscope he could not see them. They were discovered in 1661 by Malpighi.

The arguments and demonstrations marshalled by Harvey were too cogent to admit of long resistance, and his work was accepted by medical men in his lifetime. Descartes (129) used the discovery as a basis for his mechanistic physiology; English experimental scientists regarded the discovery as of equal importance with Copernican astronomy or Galilean physics; Lower (149) supplemented Harvey's work by discovering the role of the lungs in supplying the arterial blood with air. With all this, Harvey's work did not effect any change in medical practice nor fundamentally alter contemporary views on physiology.

Harvey's other book 'On Generation' was less successful, though equally firmly based upon experiment. It is notable for the insistence that all living matter is generated out of eggs, so that spontaneous generation is impossible.

William Fitzer, the Frankfurt publisher of Harvey's *De Motu Cordis*, was an Englishman. It was Harvey's friend Robert Fludd, the Rosicrucian, some of whose books Fitzer had printed, who recommended him to Harvey. Fludd had found that by publishing in Frankfurt he not only did not have to pay for publication, but actually received some free copies and even a fee. Thus it came about that one of England's greatest books was published abroad.

BIBLIOGRAPHY: Sir Geoffrey Keynes, *A Bibliography of the Writings of Dr William Harvey* (Cambridge, 1953).

128

'EPPUR SI MUOVE'

GALILEO GALILEI (1564–1642). Dialogo sopra i Due Massimi Sistemi del Mondo, Tolemaico e Copernicano. *Florence: Giovanni Batista Landini, 1632*

Although Galileo's 'Dialogue on the Two Chief Systems of the World' is neither a very rare nor a very costly book, few others can rival its dramatic history. If it was not exactly written in defiance of the Inquisition, it was composed with the deliberate intention of bamboozling the censors and of outwitting Galileo's clerical enemies. The censors were the more easy to deceive; after the book was published Galileo's enemies dragged him to Rome in 1633, set him before the Inquisition, and forced him to abjure all that the *Dialogo* professed. (The tradition that after recanting he muttered *eppur si muove*—'all the same it does move'—is now considered apocryphal.) The book itself remained on the *Index Librorum Prohibitorum* (82) until 1823. It is an eternal reminder of human endeavour and human fallibility.

As everyone knows, it was a historical accident, the invention of the telescope, that converted an obscure, fifty-year-old professor at Padua into Galileo, the celebrated international crusader for the Copernican hypothesis. During an earlier decade Galileo had remained a silent revolutionary, fearing to court ridicule if he advocated heliocentric astronomy; for even sixty years after Copernicus's death men were largely indifferent to a seemingly implausible hypothesis. Copernicus (70) was a mathematician; it was Galileo, a physicist and philosopher, who showed that his work had to do with the reality of things. Perhaps the greatest discovery Galileo made with his telescope (113) was that the earth-centred philosophy of Aristotle (38), like the earth-centred epicycles of Ptolemy (18*), was utterly false.

Galileo's first publications had little circulation. Then in 1615 he was officially silenced as regards the truth of astronomy. The *Dialogo* was designed both as an appeal to the great public and as an escape from silence. In the form of an open discussion between three friends—intellectually speaking, a radical, a conservative, and an agnostic—it is a masterly polemic for the new science. It displays all the great discoveries in the heavens which the ancients had ignored; it inveighs against the sterility, wilfulness, and ignorance of those who defend their systems; it revels in the simplicity of Copernican thought and, above all, it teaches that the movement of the earth makes sense in philosophy, that is, in physics. Astronomy and the science of motion, rightly understood, says Galileo, are hand in glove. There is no need to fear that the earth's rotation will cause it to fly to pieces.

So Galileo picked up one thread that led straight to Newton (161). The *Dialogo*, far more than any other work, made the heliocentric system a commonplace. Every fear of Galileo's enemies was justified; only their attempts to stifle thought were vain.

BIBLIOGRAPHY: See 113.

129

'COGITO, ERGO SUM'

RENÉ DESCARTES (1596–1650). Discours de la Méthode pour bien conduire sa Raison & chercher la Verité dans les Sciences. *Leiden: Jan Maire, 1637*

The life of Descartes was entirely devoted to the progress of philosophy and science. Refusing to allow any involvement with current affairs to obstruct his thoughts he left France and in 1629 settled in Holland, where there was greater tranquillity and intellectual freedom. He remained there for twenty years, leaving only to go to the Court of Queen Christina of Sweden where he died a year later.

It is no exaggeration to say that Descartes was the first of modern philosophers and one of the first of modern scientists; in both branches of learning his influence has been vast. Although his scope was less comprehensive than Bacon's (119), his great predecessor seems nearer to medieval than modern learning by comparison. The revolution he caused can be most easily found in his reassertion of the principle (lost in the Middle Ages) that knowledge, if it is to have any value, must be intelligence and not erudition. His application of modern algebraic arithmetic to ancient geometry created the analytical geometry which is the basis of the post-Euclidean development of that science. His statement of the elementary laws of matter and movement in the physical universe, the theory of vortices, and many other speculations threw light on every branch of science from optics to biology. Not least may be remarked his discussion of Harvey's discovery of the circulation of blood (127), the first mention of it by a prominent foreign scholar.

All this found its starting-point in the 'Discourse on the Method for Proper Reasoning and Investigating Truth in the Sciences'. Descartes's purpose is to find the simple indestructible proposition which gives to the universe and thought their order and system. Three points are made: the truth of thought, when thought is true to itself (thus *cogito, ergo sum*), the inevitable elevation of its partial state in our finite consciousness to its full state in the infinite existence of God, and the ultimate reduction of the material universe to extension and local movement. From these central propositions in logic, metaphysics and physics came the subsequent inquiries of Locke (164), Leibniz (177) and Newton (161); from them stem all modern scientific and philosophic thought.

130

MECHANICS AND MOTION

GALILEO GALILEI (1564–1642). Discorsi e Dimostrazioni Matematiche. *Leiden: Elzevir, 1638*

The 'Mathematical Discourses and Demonstrations' is now considered by most scientists as Galileo's greatest work.

It falls into three sections. The principal theme of the first two days of the discourses between Salviati, Sagredo and Simplicio, the interlocutors of the earlier *Dialogo*

(128), is a theoretical investigation of the strength of materials, a subject which Galileo considered quite novel, and which he was able to put on an almost correct mathematical basis. In the same two days a number of other questions in physics are discussed, such as motion, infinity, the existence of a vacuum and the weight of air, the cohesion of bodies, etc. The two later days of discussion are devoted to the science of motion. In the *Dialogo* Galileo

DEL GALILEO. 229

drante fuerit minor. nam perpendicularis D B circulum fecabit C I B : quare D I quoque, cum ipfi D B fit æqualis. & angulus D I A erit obtufus,& ideo A I N circulum quoque B I N fecabit : cumque angulus A B C minor fit angulo A I C, qui æquatur ipfi S I N; ifte autem eft adhuc minor eo , qui ad contactum in I fieret per lineam S I ; ergo portio S E I eft longè major portione B O. unde & quod erat demonftrandum.

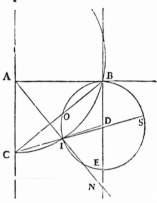

THEOR. XXII. PROPOS. XXXVI.

Si in circulo ad horizontem erecto ab imo puncto elevetur planum non majorem fubtendens circumferentiam quadrante, à terminis cujus duo alia plana ad quodlibet circumferentiæ punctum inflectantur ; defcenfus in planis ambobus inflexis breviori tempore abfolvetur , quam in folo priori plano elevato , vel quam in altero tantum ex illis duobus , nempe in inferiori.

Sit circuli ad horizontem erecti ab imo puncto C circunferentia C B D, non major quadrante,in qua fit planum elevatum C D, & duo plana à terminis D, C, inflexa ad quodlibet punctum B in circunferentia fumptum : Dico, tempus defcenfus per ambo plana D B C brevius effe tempore defcenfus per folum D C,vel per unicum B C ex quiete in B.Ducta fit per D horizontalis M D A;cui C B extenfa occurrat in A : fintque D N , M C ; & B N ad B D perpendiculares : &

Ff 3 circa

had treated motion philosophically ; here, continuing the medieval mathematical tradition, he proceeded to define uniform and accelerated motion correctly, and then to develop kinematics in a series of geometrical theorems, of which the most important is the result already announced in the *Dialogo*, that a uniformly accelerated body (such as a falling weight may be considered to be) travels over distances proportional to the square of the time taken in the descent. Here also is found Galileo's *reductio ad absurdum* proof that acceleration is proportional to time.

Galileo's later theorems in the *Discorsi* treat of motion on inclined planes, from which he is able to consider (though inadequately) the movement of pendulums, and the trajectories of projectiles *in vacuo*, which he proved to be parabolical. In considering Galileo's mechanics this book and the *Dialogo* must always be considered together, the philosophical discussion of the one complementing the mathematical analysis of the other. Mathematicians and physicists of the later seventeenth century, Isaac Newton among them, rightly supposed that Galileo

had begun a new era in the science of mechanics. It was upon his foundations that Huygens (154), Newton (161) and others were able to erect the frame of the science of dynamics, and to extend its range (with the concept of universal gravitation) to the heavenly bodies.

The *Discorsi* was printed at Leiden because Galileo was unable to obtain an ecclesiastical licence to have it printed in Venice, as he had intended. It was his last work, and he spent the few remaining years of his life improving and enlarging it.

BIBLIOGRAPHY: See 113.

131

RELIGIO MEDICI

THOMAS BROWNE (1605–82). Religio Medici. *London: Andrew Crooke, 1642*

'To pursue my reason to an *O Altitudo* !' is perhaps the underlying theme of *Religio Medici*. It was its author's first book and not designed by him for publication (the first two editions were unauthorized).

By turns credulous and sceptical, Sir Thomas Browne is one of the most unusual of the great writers of the seventeenth century. He spent his working life as a doctor practising at Norwich, and not least remarkable is his aloofness from all the political disturbances through which he lived. A Platonist by temperament, the world to him was only an image, a shadow of the real, and all existence is merely the substance of reflexions. Nothing is too minute to be considered: the smallest trifle may provide the key to the problems of existence and what lies beyond death. Browne's inimitable style mirrors the peculiarity of his thought: in an age given to erudition, metaphor and elaborate diction, his writing has an individual excess of all three of which the reader never tires.

The *Religio* is not, as its many imitators were to be, a defence of its author's calling, nor is it the expression of heterodox opinion: Browne's opinions were free from heresy, and his book's title would be better translated as 'philosophy' or 'faith' than as 'religion'. What he demands is the liberty to be guided by his own reason in cases where no exact guidance is laid down by Scripture or the teaching of the Church. The book was a puzzle to his contemporaries; it was published in Paris as the work of a Roman Catholic; in Rome it was placed on the *Index Expurgatorius* (82). So, in a way, it has remained ever since. But it is not the matter only which makes the *Religio Medici* still so universally read. The combination of detachment from the world with fascination with its smallest physical objects, the style, and the mind which both style and contents reveal, has absorbed the interest of readers of all kinds ever since its first appearance.

BIBLIOGRAPHY: Geoffrey Keynes, *A Bibliography of Sir Thomas Browne* (Cambridge, 1924); Elizabeth Cook, in *Harvard Library Bulletin* (Cambridge, Mass., 1948), vol. II, no. I.

132

TRUTH DEFIES TRADITION

Acta Sanctorum, vol. 1, *Antwerp, 1643*; later vols. *Tongerloo, Brussels, Paris (still in progress)*

'The Acts of the Saints' is a critical publication of the lives of the Christian Saints—perhaps the most remarkable collective scholarly undertaking of all ages. Never in the field of scholarship was so much owed by so many to so few: this can truly be said of the small band of Belgian Jesuits who for over two hundred and fifty years have been editing the series. The editorial staff at no time exceeded six and for the greater part consisted only of three or four men, all drawn from the Flemish and Walloon regions of Belgium.

The begetter of the enterprise was Heribert Rosweyde of Utrecht (1569–1629) who in 1607 drafted the first prospectus for a collection of saints' lives arranged according to the calendar. It was to be based on authentic documents which were to be critically examined with the same scrupulous and impartial scholarship which the great French and Dutch philologists—Budé (60), Estienne (62), Lipsius (93), Scaliger (98) and others—had applied to secular texts. Rosweyde's aim was to penetrate the fog of unsubstantiated legends, edifying fairy tales and pious fraud, and to raise hagiography to the rank of an historical science.

Rosweyde's project was realized by Jan Bolland (1596–1665) and his pupils, among whom Godfried Henskens (1601–81) and Daniel Papebroech (1628–1714) were the first and perhaps greatest 'Bollandists'. They added the Greek to the Latin saints and thereby stressed the truly catholic character of the enterprise. Henskens achieved a record, not likely ever to be broken, in working on twenty-four volumes—Papebroech reaching 'only' eighteen. Papebroech's ruthless destruction of every doubtful tradition and his disdain of every kind of superstition brought him perilously near to the attention of the Inquisition, and his hypercritical attitude towards quite genuine documents provoked Mabillon (158) to a rejoinder of which Papebroech was the first to acknowledge the convincing power.

The invasion of Belgium by the French revolutionary armies in 1794 interrupted the work of the Bollandists. It was resumed only in 1837, by which time their methods and technique had been superseded by those employed in the *Monumenta Germaniae* (287). Completely reorganized and modernized in 1882, the *Acta Sanctorum* reached a new zenith under the guidance of Hippolyte Delehaye (1859–1941) and Paul Peeters (1870–1950).

With nearly seventy huge folio tomes, the work has now proceeded to the beginning of the month of December. When the end of the calendar year has been reached, the whole labour will have to start again with the first of January—with the inclusion of new saints as well as the elimination of others. One sad victim of the Bollandists' search for truth has been, alas, the legend of the patron saint of England, St George.

133

FREEDOM OF THE PRESS

John Milton (1608–74). Areopagitica; a Speech for the Liberty of Unlicenc'd Printing, to the Parliament of England. *London, printer unidentified, 1644*

'Give me liberty to know, to utter, and to argue freely according to conscience, above all liberties.' So Milton concludes his magisterial defence of the freedom of speech, writing and printing against the unwisdom and injustice of the order for licensing books, which in practice constituted a government censorship.

In fact, however, Milton's battle had already been won three years earlier in 1641 when the abolition of the Star Chamber court had taken with it the machinery of censorship. The pamphleteers of the period took full advantage of this, and the government sought vainly to re-establish the licensing laws by the Ordinance of 14 June 1643. It was at this point that Milton, generalizing in his characteristic way on the private experience of his wife's desertion, published his tract *The Doctrine and Discipline of Divorce*. This so shocked clerical opinion that a complaint was laid against him under the new ordinance, to which Milton, again converting his own experience into a public protest, rejoined with *Areopagitica*. But the years of freedom had induced a national political consciousness, and the attempt to revive the censorship came too late. Milton was not prosecuted, and *Areopagitica* in fact fought a battle already won.

Why then is it important now? Partly because the argument for freedom has never, before or since, been so magnificently or forcefully expressed. Yet even Milton's arguments have been falsified in practice. 'Though all the winds of doctrine were let loose to play on earth, so Truth be in the field. We do injuriously by licencing and prohibiting to misdoubt her strength. Let her and Falsehood grapple; whoever knew Truth put to the worse, in a free and open encounter.' This is a splendid piece of idealism but it neglects 'the prejudice, stupidity and gullibility of men'. What we owe to Milton first and foremost is the isolation of the freedom of the press from all the other forms of toleration, especially religious toleration, disputed and advocated at the time; it is this, and the vigour of the matchless prose in which it was advocated, that give Milton's words their life today.

134

ATLAS OF THE SEAS

Sir Robert Dudley (1573–1649). Dell'Arcano del Mare. 3 vols. *Florence: Francesco Onofri, 1646–7*

This magnificent book is the most famous of all early sea atlases. Sir Robert Dudley, natural son of Lord Leicester and self-styled Duke of Northumberland, began as a traveller, going to Trinidad in 1594, taking part in some of Cavendish's voyages and in the expedition of the Earl of Essex to Cadiz. In 1605 he left England and settled in Florence where he was employed by Ferdinand II, Duke of Tuscany, to whom this work is dedicated. He was responsible for draining the marshes between Pisa and the sea and created the great port of Leghorn.

His fame rests on this great sea atlas—'The Mystery of the Sea'—which disseminated the new knowledge of seamanship as developed by Mercator (100), Edward Wright (106) and others. In its six parts it deals with longitude and the means of determining it, naval architecture and warfare, the principles of navigation, and nautical instruments; and it includes charts of ports and harbours, *portolani* and general maps rectified as to longitude and latitude. Its principal importance lies in the fact that all the maps and charts are drawn, for the first time in such a large sea atlas, on Mercator's projection and that it gives the prevailing winds and currents at all important harbours and anchorages and the magnetic declination of a large number of places. In Book v the principle of 'great circle sailing'—sailing along a great circle (all meridians of longitude of the earth are such circles) is the shortest distance between two points—is greatly improved and made practical by developing the earlier ideas of Nuñez and Mercator. It was this principle which enabled modern navigators to find out that the quickest route to fly from Copenhagen to Tokyo is over the North Pole.

135
GAS

JOHANNES BAPTISTA VAN HELMONT (*c.* 1577–1644). Ortus Medicinae. *Amsterdam: Ludovic Elzevir, 1648*

'The Birth of Medicine', edited posthumously by the author's son, is our chief source for the discoveries of Helmont with regard to the chemical nature of living processes. He was a Brabant nobleman and after travelling in France, Switzerland and England settled down on his estate near Brussels and devoted himself for most of his life to chemical studies.

Many of Helmont's general principles were derived from those of his master, Paracelsus (110). Like Paracelsus he did not confine his studies to specific limited fields; his outlook was universal. He sought a cosmological system and a unified view of natural science which would embrace all phenomena. His metaphysics and religion led him to abandon scholastic forms of thinking, and thence, by abjuring theoretical speculation, he was brought to regard experiment and empiricism as the main paths to knowledge. Although he was inclined to mysticism, he nevertheless became a remarkable scientific investigator and made significant contributions to the progress of chemistry and medicine.

In his general view of the bodily functions and of disease Helmont also largely followed Paracelsus. In particular, he believed that the processes in diseased organs are of a chemical nature, due in each case to the action of a specific ferment, and he gave a new impetus to the application of chemical remedies to diseases, especially in asthma, catarrh and the lung diseases.

In medicine, he introduced the examination of the specific gravity of urine for diagnostic purposes. He investigated the fluids in the human body and advanced the study of digestion and other physiological changes by discovering acid digestion in the stomach, coming close to identifying gastric acid with hydrochloric acid some two hundred years before the actual discovery of this fact. He also appreciated the significance of bile in the gut for digestion.

Helmont's significance in the development of chemistry is perhaps even greater; he was the first to use the term 'gas' (derived from the Greek word 'chaos'). He realized that 'gas' was distinct from air and water vapour, and he distinguished the 'gases' derived from various sources, including that which we call carbon dioxide. He used the balance in chemistry, showing in many cases the indestructibility of matter in chemical changes, and he believed that water was the primitive constituent of matter.

Helmont, who was himself an alchemist, marks the transition from alchemy to chemistry in the modern sense, and it is not surprising to find that he was much studied by Robert Boyle (141, 143) who adopted many of his ideas. Helmont therefore stands at the very beginning of the chemical revolution which was completed by Lavoisier (238) in the eighteenth century.

The *Ortus Medicinae* was translated into English by Christopher Packe in 1662.

136
THE PEOPLE'S RIGHTS

JOHN LILBURNE (*c.* 1614–57). An Agreement of the Free People of England. [*London*]: *Gyles Calvert*, [1649]

Out of the endless discussions and controversies about the relative importance of the State and the individual which raged throughout the Civil War were forged those safeguards of the freedom of the people which were finally established in 1688.

These freedoms and the right to demand them were the work of many hands, but none did more than John Lilburne. Where the constitutional controversy of the years before the war had been concerned with the relation and powers of King and Parliament, Lilburne pursued the question to its ultimate conclusion. With Coke's *Institutes* (126) as his bible—as it had been to the proponents of Parliament—he maintained ceaselessly and without regard to the consequences to himself, not the law as expressed by Parliament, but the right of every single freeman to justice and freedom under the law, to which Kings, Parliament and all other forms of authority must be obedient. When the Protector offered him his liberty if he would promise not to act against the government, he answered that 'he would own no way for his liberty but the way of the law'. What he sought for himself, he sought equally for others.

Controversy was in Lilburne's blood; his father was one of the last persons to demand trial by battle in a civil suit. While still an apprentice he was brought before the Court of the Star Chamber for disseminating, among others, the works of Prynne; there he refused to take the oath on the ground that he was not bound to incriminate himself, a typical action which called in question the whole procedure of the court. He was pilloried for his contumacy, and immediately became a popular hero. When war broke out he had a short but brilliant career as a soldier, cut short by his refusal to take the covenant in 1645. Just before this, he published the first of his many

AN
AGREEMENT
OF THE
Free People of England.

Tendered as a *Peace-Offering* to
this diſtreſſed *Nation*.

BY
Lieutenant Colonel *Iohn Lilburne*, Maſter *William Walwyn*, Maſter *Thomas Prince*, and Maſter *Richard Overton*, Priſoners in the Tower of *London*, May the 1. 1649.

Matth. 5. verſe 9. *Bleſſed are the Peace-makers for they ſhall be called the children of God.*

✠✠✦✠✠✠✠✠✠✠✠✠✠✠✠✠✠✠✠✠✠✠✠✠✠✠✠✠✠✠✠✠✠✠✠✠✠✠

A Preparative to all ſorts of people.

IF afflictions make men wiſe, and wiſdom direct to happineſſe, then certainly this Nation is not far from ſuch a degree therof, as may compare if not far exceed, any part of the world: having for ſome yeares by-paſt, drunk deep of the Cup of miſery and ſorrow. We bleſſe God our conſciences are cleer from adding affliction to affliction, having ever laboured, from the beginning, of our publick diſtractions, to compoſe and reconcile them: & ſhould eſteem it the Crown of all our temporal felicity that yet we might be inſtrumentall in procuring the peace and proſperity of this Common-wealth the land of our Nativity.
And therefore according to our promiſe in our late *Manifeſtation* of the 14 of *April* 1649. (being perſwaded of the neceſſitie and juſtneſſe thereof) as a *Peace-Offering* to the Free people of this Nation, we tender this enſuing Agreement, not knowing any more effectuall means to put a finall period to all our feares and troubles.
A

pamphlets, attacking his old associate Prynne and the intolerance of the Presbyterians, and asserting the freedom of conscience and of speech (and 'that the Presse might be as open for us as you'). It was the beginning of the Leveller movement.

Hitherto he had appealed to the Commons as the only judges of a 'free-born Englishman'; but now he had antagonized them, and, from prison (where he still contrived to write and publish pamphlets), he appealed beyond them to the people and in particular to the army (*Jonah's Cry out of the Whales Belly*, 1647). Again disappointed, he published *The Foundations of Freedom*, 1648, seeking to arouse the London mob and the discontented part of the army. He was again imprisoned, and the mutineers rose in May 1649. Lilburne then published the perfected version of his constitutional plan as *An Agreement of the Free People*. But the rising failed and his trial took place in October. He was acquitted and, though later exiled, he contrived to return, was again tried, and again acquitted amid extraordinary scenes of popular enthusiasm. By now his troubles were nearly over; he became a Quaker and was released on a pension of 40s. a week.

Though Lilburne himself achieved no lasting success, his cause endured. Where others had argued the rights of King or Parliament, he always with courage and eloquence spoke for the rights of the people. In 1688, when Halifax (162) took his soundings in the crisis that followed the landing of William of Orange, he followed 'the voice of the people'. It was Lilburne who gave them that voice.

BIBLIOGRAPHY: Edward Peacock, 'A Bibliography of the Writings of John Lilburne'. In: *Notes & Queries* (7th ser.), vols. V and VI (London, 1888), *passim*.

137
HOLY LIVING

JEREMY TAYLOR (1613–67). The Rule and Exercise of Holy Living. *London: R. Norton for Richard Royston, 1650*

Among the many remarkable divines of the seventeenth century, Jeremy Taylor was and remains one of the most famous. Born and educated at Cambridge, he was made a fellow of Caius College in 1633 and soon after became one of Archbishop Laud's protégés. The next ten years of his life are a story of unbroken success. He became a fellow of All Souls, and Chaplain successively to Laud and the King; he was happily married, and Juxon, Bishop of London, gave him the rectory of Uppingham.

But the author of *The Sacred Order and Offices of Episcopacy or Episcopacy Asserted against the Aerians and Acephali New and Old* could not hope to keep his parish after 1644, and for the next fifteen years he was a fugitive, for the most part in Wales. He was three times imprisoned, and, perhaps to avoid further trouble, accepted a lectureship at Lisburn in Ireland. After the Restoration he became Bishop of Down and Connor and Vice-Chancellor of the University of Dublin. Neither post was a sinecure, and the last years of his life were spent in unremitting pastoral labour; his task made harder by the official policy by which the tenets of the Church of England were enforced on the natives. To one who had always preached toleration, the repression of bigoted Presbyterians and ignorant Catholics came equally hard.

In these troubled times his mind must often have returned to the quiet days of exile in the hospitable house of Richard Vaughan, Earl of Carbery, 'Golden Grove' in Carmarthenshire. Here, unoppressed by other cares, most of his best work was written, not least *The Rule and Exercise of Holy Living*. This has proved to be the most famous and popular of all manuals of Christian devotion written in the English language. It offers 'the means and instruments of obtaining every virtue, and the remedies against every vice, and considerations serving to the resisting all temptations, together with prayers containing the whole Duty of a Christian'. It has probably never been out of print from 1650 to the present day, and Taylor's learning, his gift of human understanding, and above all his style, majestic and rhythmical, elevated yet homely, but always clear and lively, typify the tolerant spirit of the Church of England at its best.

BIBLIOGRAPHY: By Robert Gathorne-Hardy in Logan Pearsall Smith's *Golden Grove* (Oxford, 1930).

138
THAT LEVIATHAN

THOMAS HOBBES (1588–1679). Leviathan, or The Matter, Forme, & Power of a Common-Wealth, Ecclesiasticall and Civill. *London: Andrew Crooke, 1651*

Thomas Hobbes of Malmesbury was born in the year of the Armada. His long life spanned one of the most momentous periods of English history, and he was one of its most conspicuous figures, at once celebrated and abhorred. His early education at Malmesbury and at Magdalen Hall, Oxford, served to confirm an original and questioning mind in the habit of not accepting traditional doctrine; but it was not until 1610 when he went on the grand tour as tutor to the son of William Cavendish and discovered the new critical methods of Galileo (113), Kepler (112) and Montaigne (95) that he found his métier. From this period dates his famous translation of Thucydides, which, significantly, he did not publish until 1628, the year of the Petition of Right. Abroad again with the son of his old pupil, he met Galileo and Mersenne, and engaged in correspondence with Descartes. His publications, *Human Nature*, *De Corpore Politico*, and *De Cive*, and other minor papers had made him famous, but it was not until the outbreak of the Civil War, when he fled to Paris and became tutor to the Prince of Wales, that he embarked on his greatest work.

Leviathan is the product of those troubled times. The State, it seemed to Hobbes, might be regarded as a great artificial monster made up of individual men, with an existence which could be traced from its generation through human reason under pressure of human needs to its destruction through civil strife proceeding from human passions. The individual (except to save his own life) should always submit to the State, because any government is better than the anarchy of the natural state. Hobbes was so far from expecting the storm that his work would produce, alike from republicans in England and royalists, that he presented a copy 'engrossed on vellum in a marvellous fair hand' (doubtless the one now in the British Museum, Egerton MS 1910) to his young master, now Charles II. He was soon undeceived. From that day on he found himself in the centre of a controversy which did not end with his death. After the Restoration he was protected by Charles II, who always retained an affection for him. He published more books, principally *Behemoth*, a dialogue on the causes of the Civil War, and an attack on the constitutional theory of government propounded by Edward Coke (126); he also engaged in a violent dispute on the subject of squaring the circle; finally, at the age of eighty-seven, he published a translation of Homer. His last years were spent with his old patrons, the Cavendish family, and he died at Hardwick at the age of ninety-one.

Though Hobbes's ideas have never appealed to proponents of the individual rights of men; or at the other end of the scale to the modern totalitarians with their mystical visions of *Volk*, the fundamental nature of his speculation has stimulated philosophers from Spinoza (153) to the school of Bentham (237), who reinstated him in his position as the most original political philosopher of his time.

BIBLIOGRAPHY: Hugh Macdonald and Mary Hargreaves, *Thomas Hobbes, a Bibliography* (London, 1952).

139
LATIN WITHOUT TEARS

JOHANN AMOS COMENIUS (1592–1670). Orbis Sensualium Pictus. *Nuremberg: Wolfgang Endter, 1654*

'The World around us in Pictures' was the first European schoolbook based on the principle of what is now called visual education. Each page consists of a woodcut of some subject or object and, underneath, a bilingual Latin–German text in two columns, which in simple terms explains the picture, with numerical references to the items shown. The edition cited is the earliest known.

A series of bilingual Latin–French schoolbooks had been edited more than a century earlier by Charles Estienne, brother of Henri II Estienne (62), who printed and published them in 1535–6. But these booklets—on Roman clothes, vessels, plants, etc.—appeared without illustrations, and it is the combination of text and picture which has made *Orbis Pictus* a milestone in the history of education. The term itself has become an accepted cachet for picture-books with or without pedagogical aims.

Ján Amos Komensky, a member of the Czech 'Unitas Fratrum' (Moravian Brethren) whose last bishop he became in 1632, was expelled from Bohemia during the Habsburg counter-reformation in 1620 and spent the rest of his life in travelling all over Protestant Europe and England, finally settling in Amsterdam. His universal importance rests on the pedagogic theories and writings which he eventually expanded into a complete system of education from the ages of four to twenty-four (*Didactica*, written 1632, published 1657). He was interested particularly in pre-school and primary education; his *Informatorium der Mutterschul* (1633) is the first 'Instruction for Nursery-Schools'; his 'Open Door to Languages', *Janua Linguarum Reserata* (written 1628, published 1631), secured the fairly uniform teaching of Latin throughout the continent. In all his writings Comenius appealed to the pupil's intelligence and co-operation rather than to drill, force and punishment. His greatest successors in the field of educational theory and practice were Pestalozzi (258) and Froebel (317).

140
AGAINST CASUISTRY

BLAISE PASCAL (1623–62). Les Provinciales, ou les Lettres Escrites par Louis de Montalte à un Provincial de ses Amis. *'Cologne' [Paris]: Pierre de la Vallée, 1656–7*

The *Lettres Provinciales*, as they are called, are the first example of French prose as we know it today, perfectly finished in form, varied in style, and on a subject of uni-

LETTRE
ESCRITTE A VN PROVINCIAL
PAR VN DE SES AMIS.

SVR LE SVIET DES DISPVTES
preſentes de la Sorbonne.

De Paris ce 23. Ianuier 1656.

MONSIEVR,

Nous eſtions bien abuſez Ie ne ſuis détrompé que d'hier, juſque-là i ay penſé que le ſujet des diſputes de Sorbonne eſtoit bien important, & d'vne extrême conſequence pour la Religiõ. Tant d'aſſemblées d'vne Compagnie auſſi celebre qu'eſt la Faculté de Paris, & où ils'eſt paſſé tant de choſes ſi extraordinaires, & ſi hors d'exemple, en font conceuoir vne ſi haute idée, qu'on ne peut croire qu il n'y en ait vn ſujet bien extraordinaire.

Cependant vous ſerez bien ſurpris quand vous apprendrez par ce recit, à quoy ſe termine vn ſi grand éclat ; & c'eſt ce que ie vous diray en peu de mots aprés m'en eſtre parfaitement inſtruit.

On examine deux Queſtions, l'vne de Fait, l'autre de Droit.

Celle de Fait conſiſte à ſçauoir ſi Mr Arnauld eſt temeraire. pour auoir dit dans ſa ſeconde Lettre ; *Qu'il a leu exactement le Liure de Ianſenius, & qu'il n'y a point trouué les Propoſitions condamnées par le feu Pape ; & neantmoins que comme il condamne ces Propoſitions en quelque lieu qu'elles ſe rencontrent, il les condamne dans Ianſenius, ſi elles y ſont.*

La queſtion eſt de ſçauoir, s'il a pû ſans temerité témoigner par là qu'il doute que ces Propoſitions ſoient de Ianſenius, aprés que Meſſieurs les Eueſques ont declaré qu'elles y ſont.

On propoſe l'affaire en Sorbonne. Soixante & onze Docteurs entreprennent ſa defenſe, & ſouſtiennent qu il n'a pû reſpondre autre choſe à ceux qui par tant d'écrits luy demandoiét s'il tenoit que ces Propoſitions fuſſent dans ce liure, ſinon qu'il ne les y a pas veues, & que neantmoins il les y condamne ſi elles y ſont.

Quelques vns meſme paſſant plus auant, ont declaré que quel-

versal importance. They are second only to the *Pensées* (152), left incomplete and the subject of endless controversy about their text and arrangement, as an expression of one of the finest intelligences of the seventeenth century.

Pascal was born at Clermont-Ferrand, the son of an official in the regional government. He was an infant prodigy, whose work in mathematics and natural science attracted considerable attention before he was sixteen. He completed a treatise on conic sections which was afterwards reported by Leibniz (160), and solved problems in the infinitesimal calculus which had defeated Galileo, Descartes and Fermat. His greatest discovery was in the field of hydrodynamics. He realized that the pressure of the air could be measured, and invented the means for measuring it. His famous experiment, carried out on the Puy-de-Dôme, showed that the column of mercury in a barometer falls as it is carried upwards in the atmosphere (see 145).

But, distinguished though he was as a mathematician and scientist, Pascal will always be chiefly remembered as a moralist, more especially as the great apologist for Jansenism, the seventeenth-century French ascetic movement of reform inside the Roman Catholic Church. Pascal's sister, Jacqueline, became a nun at Port Royal, the monastery famous as the centre of the movement, and after a 'conversion' in the autumn of 1654, Pascal went to live there as a recluse. At the end of 1655, the

movement had been much under attack from the Jesuits, and Pascal was persuaded to write a rejoinder. This he did in a few days. The Jesuits' main ground of attack had been that the tenets of Jansenism came dangerously near to the Calvinist doctrine of predestination. Pascal's counter-attack took the form of a brilliant exposure of the casuistical methods of argument employed by the Jesuits. It was at the same time a magnificent sustained invective, after which the Jesuits never recovered their former position in France (it was largely responsible for the traditional bad name they still, less deservedly, bear), and a noble defence of thought in religious faith.

Pascal's weapon was irony, and the freshness with which the gravity of the subject contrasts with the lightness of the manner is an enduring triumph. The vividness and distinction of his style recalls the prose of Milton at its best.

These letters were originally issued clandestinely in eighteen parts as a series of separate publications by a variety of printers between 23 January 1656 and 15 January 1657. No detailed or authoritative information on these separate issues is available.

141

THE FOUNDATION OF CHEMISTRY

ROBERT BOYLE (1627–91). The Sceptical Chymist. *London: J. Cadwell for J. Crooke, 1661*

Robert Boyle was the best-known English scientist of his day, and the greatest experimental scientist of the mid-seventeenth century. He was a leading proponent of the 'new learning' propagated by the founders of the Royal Society (of which he was one), an eminent natural philosopher, an original chemist and a worthy exponent of the view that the study of nature conduces to belief in divinity.

Robert Boyle thought of himself as primarily a chemist, though much of his best work was in experimental physics. In his time chemical thought was dominated by the view that all chemical changes could and should be explained in terms of 'elements'. These, whether the Aristotelian earth, air, fire and water or the Paracelsian salt, sulphur and mercury, were thought to be the basic ingredients out of which all matter was constructed and into which all matter could be decomposed. This Boyle attacked throughout his life; *The Sceptical Chymist* has achieved great fame as a prime example of this critical point of view, although it is in fact by no means his clearest statement of the position.

Boyle (see also 143) was a firm believer in the particulate nature of matter, and developed his own corpuscular philosophy. Matter to him consisted of particles or atoms of various shapes and sizes arranging themselves into groups which constituted chemical substances; and Boyle found many more of these than the four elements of Aristotle. This view was not reconcilable with a definition of an element as a body that could not be further decomposed nor with the theory that a few elements were

6-2

sufficient to compose all bodies. It is a theory much closer to that of modern physical chemistry with its molecules, atoms and kinetic theories, in which comparatively little attention is paid to the elemental character of the substance concerned. The importance of Boyle's book must be sought in his combination of chemistry with physics. His corpuscular theory, and Newton's modification of it, gradually led chemists towards an atomic view of matter, though this was only finally established by Dalton (261).

Boyle distinguished between mixtures and compounds and tried to understand the latter in terms of the simpler chemical entities from which they could be constructed. His argument was designed to lead chemists away from the pure empiricism of his predecessors and to stress the theoretical, experimental and mechanistic elements of chemical science. *The Sceptical Chymist* is concerned with the relations between chemical substances rather than with transmuting one metal into another or the manufacture of drugs. In this sense the book must be considered as one of the most significant milestones on the way to the chemical revolution of Lavoisier (238) in the late eighteenth century.

BIBLIOGRAPHY: John F. Fulton, *A Bibliography of the Honourable Robert Boyle, F.R.S.* (2nd ed., Oxford, 1961).

142

THE MISSIONARY BIBLE

THE HOLY BIBLE... Translated into the Indian Language. *Cambridge [Mass.]: Samuel Green & Marmaduke Johnson, 1663–1661*

This was not only the first Bible to be printed in the New World, but also the first complete Bible to be printed in a new language as a means of evangelization. As such it may be considered the forerunner of all the missionary translations; the Gospels had been printed in Arabic at Rome as early as 1590, but no complete Arabic Bible appeared until 1671. Some part of the Bible, at least, has now been translated into more than 1,180 languages.

This translation into the Massachusetts dialect of the Algonkin family of languages, which was spoken by a large tribe, now extinct, who lived in Massachusetts in the seventeenth century, was the work of John Eliot (1604–90), the 'Apostle to the Indians'. A graduate of Jesus College, Cambridge, he landed at Boston in 1631 and in the following year was appointed 'teacher' of the church in Roxbury, near Boston, where he remained for the rest of his life. He took some part in the translation from the Hebrew of the first book printed in North America, the *Bay Psalm Book* of 1640. He then began to devote himself to missionary labours among the Massachusetts Indians, had mastered their language sufficiently by 1646 to be able to preach in it, and was instrumental in establishing in England the Corporation for the Promoting and Propagating the Gospel of Jesus Christ in New England. This corporation, generally known as the New England Company, was the first missionary society to

be formed in England. Thanks to the efforts of Robert Boyle (141), who was its Governor, its charter was renewed at the Restoration, and it was responsible for financing all Eliot's missionary publications.

In 1651 he tried his hand at translating some metrical psalms into the Massachusetts language and in 1654 a Catechism appeared. This was followed in the next year by trial issues of Genesis and Matthew. The latter has not survived, but a copy of Genesis was discovered in 1937 in the library of King's College, London. The complete New Testament was published in 1661 in an edition of one thousand five hundred copies of which one thousand were reserved to bind up with the copies of the Old Testament which was ready in 1663.

The book was printed in the printing office established in Cambridge, Massachusetts, by Samuel Green in 1638 where the *Bay Psalm Book* had been printed, and on a new press sent out by the Corporation in London. A new fount of type was also supplied, with one special sort and the additional proportions of the letters k and q required by the language. Finally an experienced young printer, Marmaduke Johnson, was sent from London to assist in the printing, his contract including the clause 'And shall work twelve hours in every day at the least in the same employment (Sabbath days excepted)'.

A second edition was subsequently called for and Eliot was assisted in his revision by John Cotton, minister of Plymouth. Printing of this began in 1680, but the Old Testament was not completed until 1685.

BIBLIOGRAPHY: Darlow & Moule, no. 6737.

143

BOYLE'S LAW

ROBERT BOYLE (1627–91). *New Experiments Physico-Mechanical touching the Air, the Second Edition. Oxford: H. Hall for Thomas Robinson, 1662*

In 1657, hearing of Otto von Guericke's invention of the air pump in Germany, Boyle (see also 141) set his assistants to constructing one for his use. With this, and another constructed by Robert Hooke (147), who was then still learning the art of scientific research, he undertook a complete, well thought out and conclusive series of experiments on the physical nature of air. He was the first to demonstrate experimentally the truth of the belief, held since the time of Aristotle, that sound is conveyed by air and is not transmitted in a vacuum. He proved that it is the weight of the air which supports the column of mercury in a barometer, by performing the Torricellian experiment (145) in the receiver of his air pump and then gradually exhausting the receiver—when the column of mercury gradually fell. He demonstrated the weight of the air, its surprising elasticity, and its necessity for respiration and combustion. At the same time he showed that such properties as light and magnetism were not dependent upon the air for transmission.

All these findings, carefully and simply described, Boyle published in 1660. A second edition of *New Experiments* was soon called for, and to it he added a defence of his views against attacks by Hobbes and others. This second edition (here cited) is particularly important for what Boyle called an 'hypothesis' but what we know as 'Boyle's Law': that the volume of air in a confined space varies inversely as the pressure. He demonstrated this by much experimental detail: with experiments on rarefaction performed by others, including Hooke, and on compression performed by himself.

BIBLIOGRAPHY: See 141.

144

VITAL STATISTICS

JOHN GRAUNT (1620–74). *Natural and Political Observations made upon the Bills of Mortality. London: Thomas Roycroft for John Martin, James Allestry and Thomas Dicas, 1662*

The statistical recording of social and medical phenomena, now an essential feature of modern life and government, was introduced by John Graunt, originally a haberdasher in the city of London, who was elected a Fellow of the Royal Society on the publication of this book.

Lists of births and deaths had been published sporadically in London since the sixteenth century. After the plague in 1603 there were weekly reports of baptisms, burials and deaths from the plague, and after 1629 all causes of deaths were methodically published by the parish clerks in London. From these reports Graunt drew up his statistical tables. He was the first to recognize the importance of vital statistics and the need for reducing them to order, which he found to be possible by mathematical calculation, leading to important conclusions on the social and economic conditions of the people. Graunt constructed the first life tables showing the proportion of persons born alive who live to successive ages and the expectation of life at each age. He collected medical data on a mathematical basis and noted seasonal and annual variations in the death rates, classifying their causes. This became important to future studies of epidemiology by such men as William Farr, John Snow and others in the nineteenth century. The scientific study of the numbers, characteristics and territorial distribution of populations—today called demography—began with Graunt. He formulated some fundamental principles; for example, that certain vital phenomena are regular, that the urban death rate normally exceeds the rural one, that mortality rates are highest in early and late years of life and that male births exceed female.

The application of critical scientific methods to medical and vital statistics, which underlies so much of modern government and economics, can be traced back to John Graunt's remarkable book. His immediate influence was considerable, particularly on Sir William Petty, the author of *Political Arithmetic*. Petty edited the fifth edition of Graunt's book in 1675, which at one time led people to believe erroneously that he, and not Graunt, was the author. Edmund Halley (173) published a paper in the *Philosophical Transactions* (148) in 1693 on the subject of life tables which remained in use until well into the nineteenth century; and his ideas were derived from Graunt. Graunt's own tables were quoted in France until the end of the eighteenth century and his influence was also felt in Holland and in Germany; a German edition of his book was issued in 1702. Graunt advocated a census of populations; but although censuses had been published in Virginia since 1624 and in Canada since 1665, Europe was slow in adopting the idea; the first census in France was taken in 1800, the first in England in 1801. Graunt's importance for the establishment of life insurance offices is obvious.

145

THE BAROMETER

EVANGELISTA TORRICELLI (1608–47). *Experienza dell'Argento Vivo. In: Timauro Antiate (i.e. Carlo Dati), Lettera a Filati. Florence: printer unidentified, 1663*

The 'Experiments on Quicksilver' describe the discovery of the barometer.

Evangelista Torricelli, an Italian physicist and mathematician, was largely inspired in his scientific studies by Galileo (113, 128, 130) whose pupil he became and with whom he lived until his master's death. He became Galileo's successor as grand ducal mathematician and professor of mathematics in the Florentine Academy.

Until the early seventeenth century it had been widely

believed that the phenomena of suction were due to nature's abhorrence of a vacuum—the *horror vacui*, an Aristotelian idea. Galileo knew of the fact, already observed by sixteenth-century mining engineers, that water could not be raised by means of suction pumps to more than about thirty feet. He thought it curious that nature's abhorrence of a vacuum should be limited in this way, but, although he knew that the atmosphere had weight, he did not connect the two phenomena.

About 1630 discussion of the same phenomena led to the making of some experiments at Rome, in which tubes considerably larger than thirty feet were first filled with water, then unstoppered at the base so that the water sank to the level where it was supported by the atmosphere. There was much debate on the vacuity, or otherwise, of the space vacated by the water at the top of the tube. When Torricelli and Viviani, also a pupil of Galileo, took up the same experiments, they realized the convenience of using mercury, for as that metal is fourteen times as dense as water, they expected the column to be only one fourteenth as high. They found that this was so, and assumed the weight of the atmosphere to counterbalance that of the fluid column.

Although Torricelli was prevented by his early death from completing his researches, his name was indissolubly linked with the barometer by Père Marin Mersenne, who learned of them from Peiresc. The news was rapidly spread abroad, even though Torricelli's own narrative remained unpublished until 1663; among the most famous of their continuations was Florin Perier's famous Puy-de-Dôme experiment (1648), suggested by his brother-in-law Blaise Pascal. Périer ascended the mountain with Torricelli's apparatus and found that the height of the mercury column decreased as he went higher, thus proving the connexion between atmospheric pressure and the height of the mercury column.

The term 'barometer', probably coined by Boyle, first appeared in a number of the *Philosophical Transactions* (148). About 1660 Guericke (154) found the correlation between barometric pressure and weather, and from this time onwards the readability of the instrument was improved to the extent that the essential features of the barometer have not changed since the seventeenth century.

Torricelli also did fundamental work in the science of hydrodynamics published in his *De Motu Gravium Naturaliter Descendentium* and *Opera Geometrica*, 1644. These include 'Torricelli's theorem' which deals with the problems of the velocity of outflow of a liquid through a small hole in the walls of a vessel kept filled to a constant level, and describes the parabolic path this outflowing liquid takes. Torricelli also worked on the calculus and the cycloid, and continued and improved Galileo's work on optics.

Torricelli's invention of the barometer was not published in his lifetime, but he had communicated it to M. A. Ricci in two letters of 11 and 28 June 1644.

146
THE BALANCE OF TRADE

THOMAS MUN (1571–1641). England's Treasure by Forraign Trade. *London: Thomas Clark, 1664*

England's Treasure by Forraign Trade was published in the year which saw the eruption of hostilities between the English and the Dutch. These hostilities led to the formal declaration in March 1665 of the second Dutch war, the clearest case in English history of a purely commercial war. Thomas Mun's small book, the bible of later mercantilists, crystallized popular opinion in the months before the English attempted to replace the Dutch at the apex of international commercial and maritime supremacy.

Thomas Mun was a highly successful merchant in Italy (where he tells us he did business with Ferdinando, the first Grand Duke of Tuscany) and the Levant. In 1615 he was appointed a director of the East India Company, and his life and literary productions thereafter became totally involved with the life of the Company. His first book, published in 1621 as *A Discourse of Trade, from England unto the East Indies*, was a defence of the Company's monetary policies which included the exportation of money under certain trade conditions. His ardent role as public guardian of the Company brought him an offer to become its deputy-governor in 1624, but he declined. Yet he continued to work for 'the common good' and the English merchant community by submitting several testimonies to the Standing Committee of Trade which was established in 1622 to inquire into the general depression that had spread over trade and especially the cloth trade. Much of *England's Treasure* was drawn from these submissions.

Mun thought that the best way to increase the wealth of the country was by foreign trade, 'wherein', he said, 'wee must ever observe this rule; to sell more to strangers yearly than wee consume of theirs in value'. In this programme for attaining a favourable balance of trade one prominent plank was the liberation of England from her semi-colonial economic status under the industrious, peace-loving Dutch. The nationalistic tone of this demand anticipated the popular war-cries of the English in the three wars that broke out with the Dutch in 1652, 1665 and 1672. The mercantilist programme in this book clearly symbolized the marriage of economics and national policy in the seventeenth century; a union itself symbolized by the dedication of the book to Thomas Wriothesley, Charles II's Lord High Treasurer, by John Mun, the author's son who brought out *England's Treasure* twenty-three years after Thomas Mun's death.

147
MICROSCOPY

ROBERT HOOKE (1635–1703). Micrographia. *London: John Martyn and James Allestry, Printers to the Royal Society, 1665* (Illustrated opposite).

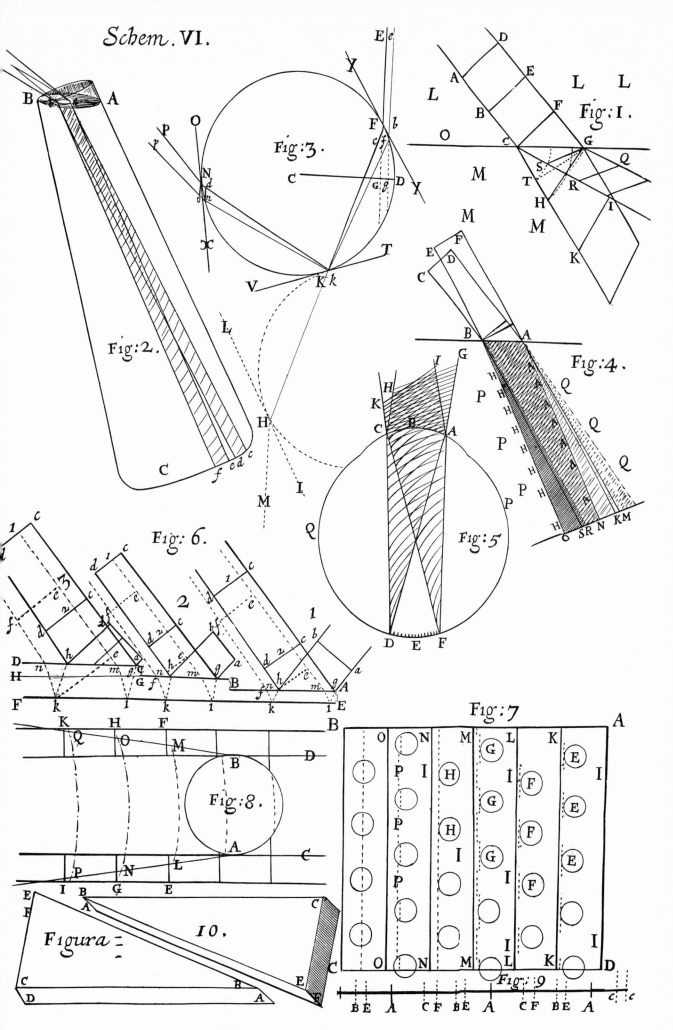

Schem. VI.

Fig: 3.

Fig: 1.

Fig: 2.

Fig: 4.

Fig: 5.

Fig: 6.

Fig: 7.

Fig: 8.

Figura 10.

Fig: 9

Robert Hooke was one of the most versatile and brilliant scientists of all time, and his contributions to astronomy, optics and all branches of physics, mechanics, technology and architecture are innumerable. In 1662 he was appointed curator of experiments to the newly founded Royal Society (see 148) and remained at the centre of the English scientific world until his death. He suggested and inspired scientific work in all fields and carried out an immense number of experiments himself. He left comparatively few printed works, of which the *Micrographia* is the most famous.

It contains fifty-seven microscopic and three telescopic observations, beginning with an examination of inorganic matter and proceeding to the investigation of vegetable and animal bodies. Although ostensibly concerned with microscopy, the book includes scientific observations of high importance in several other fields.

Hooke's main contribution to biology was in microscopy. In Observation No. 18 he describes the structure of cork, comparing it to a honeycomb, being composed of 'cellulae' with walls bounding the 'cells'. A century and a half later the effective study of 'cells'—the word was first used here—led to completely new ideas about the structure of animals and plants. In Observation No. 16 on charcoal Hooke gives his views on combustion: these are very close to those of Boyle (141), with whom he collaborated. Observation No. 58 describes the phenomenon of the diffraction of light, this discovery being independent of Grimaldi's nine years before. In Observation No. 17 Hooke writes of the properties of fossils, which he considers to be shells of certain shell-fish 'which either by some deluge, inundation or earthquake... come to be thrown to that place'. In Observation No. 4 he makes a reference to the possibility of spinning a kind of 'artificial silk' out of some glutinous substance that may be equivalent to natural silk.

In the purely microscopic part of this handsome and copiously illustrated folio, Hooke describes for the first time a polyzoon, the minute markings of fish scales, the structure of the bee's sting, the compound eye of the fly, the gnat and its larvae, the structure of feathers, the flea and the louse. He observed sponges, which he defines as animal structures, not plants, comparing their tissue with horn and hair. He saw the plant-like form of moulds.

Hooke's other experiments, and in particular his work with scientific instruments, are remarkable. He perfected the compound microscope, which he used for his observations; he invented the wheel barometer and other meteorological instruments; and with his new methods of keeping weather records he has been called the founder of modern meteorology. Hooke worked in cartography and geography (assisting Ogilby and Pitt in creating their atlases), improved watches, and made many contributions to optics, physiology, artificial respiration, geology and palaeontology. He invented an apparatus for diving and depth-sounding, and invented or improved a large number of other scientific instruments. He was also active as a surveyor and architect.

The *Micrographia* had an immediate success—many copies have the title-page dated 1666; it was read by Pepys and certainly studied carefully by Newton. The

magnificent plates, mostly from designs by the author himself, but some probably by Sir Christopher Wren, were reprinted in 1745 and some still appear in nineteenth-century books on microscopy. Today it is recognized that Aubrey was right when he said 'He is certainly the greatest mechanick this day in the world', and some think that Hooke was perhaps the greatest mechanical genius science has ever had.

BIBLIOGRAPHY: Sir Geoffrey Keynes, *A Bibliography of Robert Hooke* (Oxford, 1960).

148

A VOICE FOR SCIENCE

PHILOSOPHICAL TRANSACTIONS: giving some Accompt of the Present Undertakings, Studies, and Labours, of the Ingenious in many Considerable Parts of the World, vol. 1. *London: John Martyn and James Allestry, 1665–6*

The *Philosophical Transactions* was the earliest scientific journal. Its first issue was published on 'Munday, March 6. 1664⅘' and it has continued to appear, with brief intermissions, to the present day.

The *Transactions* were dedicated to the Royal Society, which had received its first charter from Charles II nearly three years before. 'In these Rude Collections, which are onely the Gleanings of my private diversions in broken hours', wrote their publisher, Henry Oldenburg, 'it may appear that many Minds and Hands are in many places industriously employed, under your Countenance and by your Example, in the pursuit of those Excellent Ends, which belong to Your Heroical Undertakings.' For the *Transactions* were by no means a record of the activities of the Royal Society and London alone; thanks to Oldenburg's extensive correspondence both at home and abroad, they contained reports and news from all parts of the British Isles and Europe. They formed an international journal, widely circulated on the Continent as they appeared in English, and later translated as a collection into Latin.

The inventor of the journal as a means of communicating new scientific information (which the slightly earlier *Journal des Sçavans* in France had not been) was an industrious German who had come to England in Cromwell's time, and through his connexion with Robert Boyle (141) had entered widely into the scientific life of Europe in the 1650s. He was nominated as one of the Royal Society's two secretaries in its first charter, an office he had for the rest of his life, being virtually responsible for the Society's entire literary business. The *Transactions* were one means by which he tried to compensate for lack of a salary. Begun with the Society's approval, the entire management of the *Transactions* rested with Oldenburg, whose private property they were. They consisted at first of a small monthly pamphlet of about twenty pages, of which some fifteen hundred copies were printed. The contents included extracts or paraphrases from letters written to Oldenburg, or from reports to the Society, and book reviews (usually prepared by the editor). Later, pieces were written specially for publication: 'All for the Glory of God, the Honor and Advantage of these Kingdoms, and the Universal Good of Mankind'.

It was about the middle of the eighteenth century that the responsibility for the *Transactions* was officially assumed by the Royal Society.

149

BLOOD TRANSFUSION

RICHARD LOWER (1631–91). Tractatus de Corde. *London: John Redmayne for James Allestry, 1669*

Richard Lower, trained at Oxford, belongs to that fortunate generation of English scientists who acquired the methods of 'the new learning' from an older generation who practised them: for while Lower was an undergraduate at Oxford, John Wilkins, John Wallis, Thomas Willis and Robert Boyle (141, 143) were all engaged in exploring and promoting experimental science.

Lower's main work was on the anatomy and physiology of the blood system. He gave the most accurate description of the structure of the heart to date, and explored the structure and function of the veins and arteries. He elucidated the mechanism of respiration. It had been known since antiquity that venous and arterial blood differed in colour; Lower showed conclusively that this difference was caused purely by the admixture of air as the blood from the right side of the heart flowed through the lungs. He even showed that venous blood could be made to resemble arterial blood by shaking a sample in air. He concluded that the change in colour was caused by the blood's absorption of air, which explained why air is necessary to life. His experiments were admirably devised and conducted, and *De Corde* ('A Treatise on the Heart') is a worthy successor to Harvey's *De Motu Cordis* (127).

Lower's book also contains an interesting account of the earliest attempts at blood transfusion. Experiments of injections of drugs into the veins of animals were first attempted at Oxford in 1656 by Robert Boyle and Christopher Wren, and later repeated by Lower. As a natural consequence he thought of attempting to pass the blood of one animal into the veins of another, an experiment he successfully performed early in 1666. This was widely discussed by members of the Royal Society, and reported in the *Philosophical Transactions* (148) at the end of the year. The experiment was imitated in France, Italy and Austria; in Paris Jean Denis transfused animal blood into the arm of a man with, at first, apparent success. The Royal Society also appeared to succeed with a poor deranged man named Coga, and in 1668 Denis was emboldened to try repeated experiments upon a madman. However, this last patient soon died (whether or not as a result of the transfusions was never clearly established) and human transfusion was discontinued, though Lower never lost faith in its possible efficacy. Blood transfusion was not attempted again until the early nineteenth century when it was revived for a time in England and Germany. It remained a highly dangerous procedure until Karl Landsteiner in 1900 established the existence of mutually incompatible blood-groups, since when it has become a valuable and universally accepted practice.

BIBLIOGRAPHY: John F. Fulton, *A Bibliography of two Oxford Physiologists, Richard Lower and John Mayow* (Oxford, 1935).

150

QUAKERISM

WILLIAM PENN (1644–1718). No Cross, No Crown. [*London*]: *Printed in the Year 1669*

In 1668 William Penn, later to found the province of Pennsylvania, was imprisoned in the Tower of London for publishing his unorthodox view of the Trinity in a once notorious but now forgotten tract, *The Sandy Foundations Shaken*. It was certainly a tactical error to place so much leisure time at the young religionist's disposal, for in his view to have sat idle in the Tower would have been to neglect his duty. Penn used his time in writing and as a result there was published in the year of his release (1669) his most ambitious and most learned work, *No Cross, No Crown*.

This was not a theological treatise in the ordinary sense but rather what might be called a guide to practical Christianity and a commentary on daily Christian living. Its novelty, and the source of its influence on the development of Protestant ethics, lies in its insistence upon self sacrifice and good works as opposed to blind faith, and on inner spiritual feeling instead of form and dogma. 'Christ's cross is Christ's way to Christ's crown', Penn wrote in the preface to the second edition in 1682 'with great enlargement of matter and testimony', and it is in this later form as revised by a more mature Penn that it has been transmitted to subsequent generations. Like most of Penn's works, *No Cross, No Crown* was printed at the author's expense and distributed free to all interested persons.

The original version of 1669 has never been reprinted. Many of the erudite references which still cause commentators to remark on the astonishing maturity of Penn in his twenties were in fact added to the second edition.

A translation was made into Dutch in 1687, French in 1746, and German in 1825. For two centuries it remained the basic guide for Quaker living, going through no less than twenty-four London editions by 1857 as well as other editions published in Dublin, Boston, New York, and Philadelphia. Since that time it has been only rarely reprinted and yet it remains generally accepted as the clearest exposition of the beliefs of members of the Society of Friends, which has always been strongly represented in the State which bears his name.

BIBLIOGRAPHY: M. K. Spence, *William Penn, a bibliography* (Philadelphia, 1932).

151

FOSSILS

NICOLAUS STENO (1638–86). De Solido. *Florence: sub signo Stellae, 1669*

Nicolaus Steno (Niels Stensen), the Danish geologist and anatomist, travelled extensively in Europe before settling in Florence as physician to the Grand Duke Ferdinand II. While there, he became converted to catholicism in 1667, largely under the influence of Bossuet (157). He was appointed Vicar Apostolic for the 'Northern Missions' and died at Schwerin in 1686.

The ancient belief that fossils are merely imitative forms of natural organisms produced by a 'plastic force' in the earth had first been challenged by Leonardo da Vinci, who declared that fossil shells are in fact remains of organisms that once lived. Fracastoro had similar ideas and Agricola (79) did work on the same lines. But the greatest advance in this field is due to Steno.

In 'A Dissertation concerning a Solid Body' he described the composition of the earth's crust in Tuscany and a famous diagram in his book shows six successive types of stratification: the first attempt ever made to represent geological sections. This was a sequence which he believed would be found all over the world. He explained the true origin of fossils found in the earth as being remains of once living things and he discriminated between the volcanic, chemical and mechanical modes of the origin of the rocks. He was the first clearly to recognize that the strata of the earth's crust contain the records of a chronological sequence of events from which the history of the earth can be reconstructed. He attempted to find the principles of stratigraphy. Seeing that most strata had not remained in their horizontal position, he attributed their disturbance and tilting to the collapse of cavernous spaces below them and to volcanic action. He deduced that these changes in the original position of the strata are the real causes of the unevenness of the earth's surface. This was in direct contradiction to the accepted belief that mountains had existed ever since the beginning of things or had simply grown. He also recognized that some mountains had been shaped by denudation and explained how one of the effects of the dislocation of the strata was the opening of fissures through which water could escape, the origin of springs.

Like those of other investigators before him, Steno's conclusions were sometimes stultified by the theological conviction that the earth could not be more than six thousand years old and that the fossils had been chiefly deposited during or since the deluge. As Steno turned towards religion, such theological concepts prevented him from further developing his theory, which might have led to charges of heresy, and he virtually abandoned scientific studies in later life. In spite of such limitations his book marks a great advance in geology and it cleared the path for the modern sciences of palaeontology and geology as they were gradually established by Leibniz (160), Lamarck (262) and particularly by James Hutton (247).

Steno also made important and original observations on the forms and manner of formation of crystals; he discovered for instance that, although quartz crystals may differ in appearance from one another, the angles between corresponding faces are always the same.

In physiology his researches into the anatomy of the glands led to his discovery of the parotid and lachrymal ducts: the excretory duct which leads from the parotid gland, one of the three salivary glands near the ear, into

NICOLAI STENONIS
DE SOLIDO
INTRA SOLIDVM NATVRALITER CONTENTO
DISSERTATIONIS PRODROMVS.
A D
SERENISSIMVM
FERDINANDVM II.
MAGNVM ETRVRIÆ DVCEM.

FLORENTIÆ
Ex Typographia fub figno STELLÆ MDCLXIX.

the mouth, is still named 'Steno's duct'. He also did important work on the anatomy of the muscles, in particular the muscular nature of the heart, and on the anatomy of the brain.

The *De Solido* was intended only as an introduction to a larger work; but this was never written.

152

REVELATION v. RATIONALISM

BLAISE PASCAL (1623–62). Les Pensées. *Paris: Guillaume Desprez, 1670*

When Pascal (see also 140) died, he left a considerable amount of unpublished material, some of which has only recently been printed. It was however only eight years after his death that there appeared the first edition of his *Pensées*, with an introduction by his nephew Périer, from which it appeared that these 'Meditations' were fragments of a vast apology for Christianity, which Pascal had planned long since. These fragments were in themselves confused, and it is difficult to believe that they formed part of any such grand design. In fact, they were a selection made under the authority of a group of distinguished Jansenists, and the book carried the imprimatur of a number of others, all testifying to its orthodoxy. It is patently clear from these circumstances, and indeed from the still extant manuscript, that the text was considerably modified (a fact which would have caused little surprise or horror at the time) to avoid provoking any further outburst against the Jansenists—in 1670 Port Royal was enjoying an unaccustomed lull in its troubles. From then on, the text of the *Pensées* has been the subject of endless controversy, as has Pascal's purpose and standpoint in writing them. In 1776 Condorcet (246) even published a revised selection in the interests of unorthodoxy, and it was not until 1844 that Faugère produced the first text with any pretensions to accuracy. Modern scholarship is still wrestling with the problem.

What then are the *Pensées*? They are certainly not a mere defence of orthodoxy, nor an appeal to faith from one whose scientific attainments had brought with them a fear of scepticism; even less are they concealed freethinking. But if they attack rationalism as seen in the works of Descartes (129) or scepticism as typified by Montaigne (95), it is with the methods of reasoning developed by Descartes and in a style which acknowledges its debt to Montaigne. To the rational sceptic, Pascal proposes a deeper scepticism, which he called Pyrrhonism. If the sceptic denies everything that cannot be demonstrated by reason, Pascal denies the power of reason also, whose capacity to reach conclusions exists only in the power of God; 'Cogito, ergo sum' is only true if there is a Being which can give the existence and grant it the power of thought. Thus he goes beyond the scope of 'natural theology' to explain all the contradictions and vicissitudes of human experience entirely in terms of faith and revelation, the one justifying the other.

It is impossible to elevate the disconnected reflexions of the *Pensées* into a system, or a complete answer to other systems. The reader will find questions asked and unanswered which take him far beyond the age-old controversy between faith and reason, and an equally penetrating light cast on some relatively minor problem. Pascal's work has, in fact, the marks of genius, exploring and stating all that can be said on both sides of the question it investigates. Since these are notes, and unfinished, conclusions are not always reached. This is not a book which one can measure as a totality in terms of orthodoxy or the reverse. It is, however, a book for which the enquiring mind has had solid reason to be grateful from its first imperfect publication to the present day.

153

THE ETHICS OF POLITICS

BENEDICT DE SPINOZA (1632–77). Tractatus Theologico-Politicus. '*Hamburg: Heinrich Künraht*' [*Amsterdam*], *1670*

Born in Amsterdam to a distinguished family of Sephardic exiles from Spain, Spinoza early absorbed all the theological and philosophical knowledge that the rabbis of his community were able to impart. Latin he learnt from an eccentric physician of materialistic tendencies, which brought him in contact with Giordano Bruno and Descartes (129). From this followed his break with Jewish orthodoxy, and the excommunication imposed upon him on 27 July 1656. From then on Spinoza, adopting the Latin form Benedict of his birth name Baruch, led a wandering life. Like all his Jewish contemporaries, he had learnt a handicraft: the grinding of lenses. In this, as in the theory of optics, he showed great ability. His lenses were in considerable demand, and his skill brought him in contact with Huygens (154) and Leibniz (160): a tract on the rainbow, long thought to be lost, was published as recently as 1862. Thus Spinoza was able to support himself as the guest of a friend, a member of the Collegiants, an Arminian religious community, in the country outside Amsterdam out of reach of his late co-religionists, and to devote himself to concentrated thought and study. There he found himself the centre of a small philosophical club, which, originally meeting to study Cartesian philosophy, eventually parted company with Descartes; it was for them, in all probability, that Spinoza wrote his 'Ethics'.

Early in 1661, Spinoza's host, and Spinoza with him, moved to Leiden. There he met Henry Oldenburg, first secretary of the Royal Society (see 148). His fame spread and when he left Leiden for the Hague in 1663 he was already finding it difficult to prevent the surreptitious printing of his first great work, the *Tractatus Theologico-Politicus* ('A Treatise on Political Theology'). It constituted an extension to political thought of his ethical views. Man is moved to the knowledge and love of God; the love of God involves the love of our fellow men. Man, in order to obtain security, surrenders part of his right of independent action to the State. But the State exists to give liberty, not to enslave; justice, wisdom and toleration are essential to the sovereign power.

Spinoza's thought, a fusion of Cartesian rationalism and the Hebraic tradition in which he grew up, is a solitary but crystal-clear exposition of the theory of natural right. He defends with eloquence the liberty of thought and speech in speculative matters, and the *Tractatus* contains the first clear statement of the independence of each other of philosophy and religion, in that speculation and precepts of conduct cannot collide. Spinoza, to whom any controversy was abhorrent, did not publish the *Tractatus* until 1670, and then anonymously with a bogus imprint. In 1675 he contemplated publishing his 'Ethics', but baseless rumours, later idly repeated by Hume (194), of his atheism, decided him against it. On 20 February 1677 he died of consumption and his funeral was attended by a devoted and distinguished gathering. The lenses found in his cabinet fetched a high price: the *Opera Posthuma*, published in the same year, have served, then and since, with the *Tractatus Theologico-Politicus*, to immortalize his name.

BIBLIOGRAPHY: Fritz Bamber, 'Early Editions of Spinoza'. In: *Studies in Bibliography and Booklore*, vol. V (Cincinnati, Ohio, 1961).

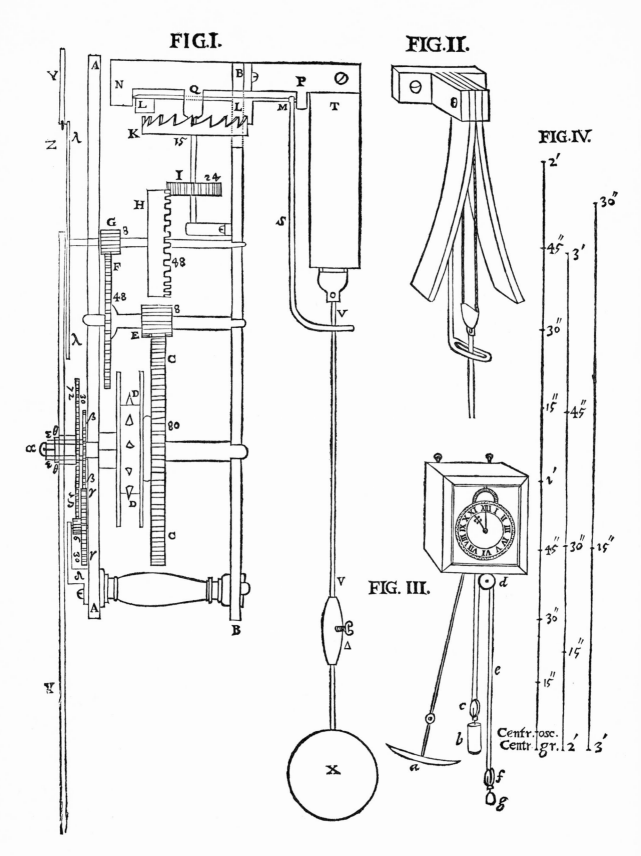

NO. 154, HUYGENS

THE PENDULUM CLOCK

CHRISTIAN HUYGENS (1629–95). *Horologium Oscillatorium. Paris: F. Muguet, 1673*

Christian Huygens, mathematician, physicist and astronomer, came of a rich and noble family; his father was the most cultivated Dutchman of his age. He soon became an international figure in science, spending the years from 1666 to 1681 in Paris where he was the leading light of the Académie Royale des Sciences. He was also, from 1663, a Fellow of the Royal Society; he met Newton twice during his third visit to England (1689), and exchanged some important letters with him. In the history of mathematical science Huygens stands next to Newton, drawing (as he did too) upon Galileo (130) and Descartes (129).

After displaying himself as an infant prodigy in both pure and applied mathematics, Huygens first won public fame by his improvement of the telescope and his discovery that the changes in the appearance of the planet Saturn (first noted by Galileo) are due to a ring surrounding the planet, whose inclination to the line of sight varies; he also discovered the first satellite of Saturn (*Systema Saturnium*, 1659). Huygens's equal interest in the theory of optics and light found expression only much later in his *Traité de la Lumière* (1690). From Galileo he learned of the isochronism of the pendulum: that is, its property of swinging in a constant time, irrespective of the width of the swing. In 1657 Huygens adapted the pendulum to a clock escapement, unaware that this idea too had been anticipated, though not realized, by Galileo. This invention set Huygens off on the pursuit, over many years, of a marine chronometer for determining longitude, a device of inestimable value to mariners.

Important as Huygens's clock was from both a practical and a scientific point of view (it could be used by astronomers), the *Horologium* ('The Oscillating Clock') is a general work on dynamics and especially a mathematical analysis of pendulum motion. It was the most original work of this kind since Galileo's *Discorsi*, containing the demonstration of the isochronism of the cycloid and other new properties of this curve, of the conical pendulum, and other principles. It ends with thirteen theorems (without proofs) on the dynamics of circular motion. Newton in the *Principia* (161) acknowledged Huygens's priority here, though Huygens's work had little influence on his own.

It is interesting that Huygens presented a copy of *Horologium Oscillatorium* to Newton in 1673 (this copy is now in the collection of Mr Sam Barches of Tucson, Arizona) for which Newton repaid him with a copy of the *Principia* in 1687. Huygens's countrymen, unlike Newton's, have honoured his memory with a magnificent edition of his letters, writings, and notebooks in twenty-two volumes (1888–1950).

THE FIRST MODERN ENCYCLOPAEDIAS

(*a*) LOUIS MORÉRI (1643–80). *Le Grand Dictionnaire Historique. Lyons: J. Girin & B. Rivière, 1674*
(*b*) PIERRE BAYLE (1647–1706). *Dictionnaire Historique et Critique. 2 vols. Rotterdam: Reinier Leers, 1695, 1697*

The age of enlightenment produced a spate of encyclopaedias which are either still worth consulting as representing the range of contemporary knowledge and trend of contemporary thought, or deserve our respect as the roots out of which have grown the stately tomes of our present-day store-houses of universal knowledge, the *Encyclopaedia Britannica* (218), Brockhaus (269), Larousse, and the rest.

The first work of this kind to bear the term 'encyclopaedia' on its title-page was Johann Heinrich Alsted's *Encyclopaedia Cursus Philosophici* (Herborn, 1608; later, 1630, expanded to the seven-volume *Encyclopaedia... distincta*). It was one of the last encyclopaedias written in Latin and designed on a systematic plan, as had been the custom from Isidore (9) to Bacon (119). The future belonged to the vernacular and alphabetical type of which Vincenzo Maria Coronelli's *Biblioteca Universale Sacroprofana* is an early specimen; of its intended forty-five volumes only seven were ever published (1701–6).

The first vernacular encyclopaedias to make an impact on the European world of letters were two French works, bringing into focus, as it were, the intellectual preponderance of the age of the Roi Soleil as well as its antithetical aspects of nominal devotion to the Roman Catholic Church and sceptical questioning of the very foundations of revealed religion.

The Abbé Moréri deliberately designed his book as an apologia and defence of his church. It is also noteworthy for its emphasis on historical and biographical entries which for a long time were neglected by other compilers such as Bayle, Harris, and Chambers (171 *b*). Moréri's 'Great Historical Encyclopaedia' had by 1759 gone through twenty editions before it was ousted by the *Encyclopédie* (200): a useful reminder of the strength of the traditional, anti-rationalist forces in the 'age of reason'.

Bayle, a Protestant philosopher, wrote his 'Historical and Critical Encyclopaedia' in his voluntary exile in Rotterdam as an anti-clerical counterblast to Moréri's work, in order, as he put it, 'to rectify Moréri's mistakes and fill the gaps'. Bayle championed reason against belief, philosophy against religion, tolerance against superstition. In a seemingly detached way he posed arguments and counter-arguments side by side, reserving his most daring insinuations to the *renvois* (references) which supplemented the actual entries. For over half a century, until the publication of the *Encyclopédie*, Bayle's *Dictionnaire* dominated enlightened thinking in every part of Europe.

156
PILGRIM'S PROGRESS

JOHN BUNYAN (1628–88). The Pilgrim's Progress. *London: Nathaniel Ponder, 1678*

Bunyan wrote this book in Bedford Gaol, which may bring hope and consolation to some of the myriads of those imprisoned for conscience' sake since his day.

The popularity of *The Pilgrim's Progress* may be judged from its having been reprinted so early and so often. By the end of the year of publication '10,000 copies had been struck off, 4,000 of them by a pirating rival. When the lawful publisher, Nathaniel Ponder, brought out his fourth edition on 3 February 1680, he knew already of six pirated editions...It has been translated into 147 languages' (Steinberg, *Five Hundred Years of Printing*, 1955, 3rd ed., 1966).

The early demand for the book was not from the learned, but from the pious and the young. It was at first fashionable to sneer at Bunyan as a writer, but the approval of such as Swift, Johnson and Walpole marked a change. Now it is universally known and loved, and the parable of salvation is accepted by all denominations. Its language has become common to all and its prose style has profoundly affected later writers.

Another view of its importance is expressed in the following quotation from E. P. Thompson's *The Making of the Working Class*: 'It is above all in Bunyan that we find the slumbering Radicalism which was preserved through the eighteenth century and which breaks out again and again in the nineteenth. *Pilgrim's Progress* is, with *Rights of Man* (241), one of the two foundation texts of the English working-class movement: Bunyan and Paine, with Cobbett (294) and Owen (271), contributed most to the stock of ideas and attitudes which makes up the raw material of the movement from 1790–1850.'

BIBLIOGRAPHY: F. M. Harrison, *A Bibliography of the Works of John Bunyan* (London, 1932). This is a purely functional bibliography and does not note, for example, the considerable additions made in the second and third editions. Thus, in the first edition, Mr Worldly Wiseman, Mr By-ends and his family, and Mrs Diffidence, the wife of Giant Despair, do not appear. Christian's confession to Goodwill, his discourse at the Palace Beautiful and the salute to the pilgrims by the royal trumpeters are among other later additions.

157
ST AUGUSTINE À LA FRANÇAISE

JACQUES-BÉNIGNE BOSSUET (1627–1704). Discours sur l'Histoire Universelle. *Paris: Sebastien Mabre-Cramoisy, 1681*

This 'Treatise on World-History' is the last noteworthy exercise in that type of universal history which, beginning with St Augustine (3), interpreted the course of human history as a continuous manifestation of divine providence leading mankind towards salvation.

Bossuet was the most famous court-preacher of Louis XIV, whose Gallican church-policy he defended against the Roman Curia. His sermons, especially his funeral orations, are impressive showpieces of this genre of baroque literature. He wrote the *Discours* for the instruction of the Dauphin, whose tutor he was from 1670 to 1679; for history, Bossuet declared, is 'the counsellor of princes'. The book extends from the Creation to Charlemagne, thus supplying a direct link between the history of the chosen people and the origins of the French monarchy; the glorification of absolutism—God in heaven, the King on earth—is the *leitmotiv*, and Bossuet was suitably rewarded with a bishopric.

Bossuet's theological and eschatological construction was discredited by Voltaire, whose *Essai sur l'Histoire* (202) was originally designed as a pretended continuation of the *Discours* from Charlemagne to Louis XIII. However, Bossuet's influence is still traceable in popular Roman Catholic history books, and though now valueless as an historical account, his *Discours* can still be enjoyed as a noble specimen of classical French prose.

158
HISTORICAL RESEARCH

DOM JEAN MABILLON (1632–1707). De Re Diplomatica libri Sex. *Paris: Ludovic Billaine, 1681*

The stately folio volume which contains Mabillon's 'Six Books on the Scientific Study of Medieval Charters' created at one stroke the historical disciplines now called by the somewhat misleading term of 'auxiliary sciences', and procured for its author a European reputation which the passage of three centuries has not dimmed.

In 1664 Mabillon joined the Benedictine Congregation of St Maur in St Germain-des-Prés near Paris, which from its foundation in 1618 had been a centre of learning. Mabillon became its most illustrious son. Devotion to the great past of his Order inspired him to produce an edition of the writings of St Bernard of Clairvaux (1667), the *Acta Sanctorum Ordinis S. Benedicti* (9 vols., 1668–1702) and the *Annales Ordinis S. Benedicti* (begun in 1703), all of which are still indispensable to church historians. But Mabillon's chief fame rests on the *De Re Diplomatica*, which came into existence almost as the by-product of a learned dispute and the age-old antagonism of the Benedictine and Jesuit Orders.

Papebroech, the great editor of the *Acta Sanctorum* (132), in 1675 developed a set of rules for the distinction between genuine and spurious documents, and thereby impugned a number of Merovingian charters for the Benedictines as forgeries, mainly because of what seemed to him their incomprehensible and abstruse lettering. Mabillon in his rebuttal of this hypercriticism not only proved the authenticity of the charters but expounded the regular and logical development of the Latin script from the capital letters of imperial Rome down to the handwriting of his time and incidentally taught his readers to decipher the various hands. Mabillon also dealt with other facts determining the outward appearance of medieval documents, and thus put on a secure basis the 'formal' auxiliary sciences of the study of charters (diplomatic), handwriting (palaeography), seals (sphragistics), dates (chronology) and so forth. With the help of these sciences it has been possible to erect a firm scaffold of indisputable principles for historical research.

159

THE ENGLISH HIPPOCRATES

THOMAS SYDENHAM (1624–89). Tractatus de Podagra. *London: Walter Kettilby, 1683*

The greatest advances in medicine in the seventeenth century were made by men whose interest lay mainly in the exact sciences. Pure research and scientific investigation seemed to the anatomist and physiologist of first importance and new theories and doctrines appeared everywhere. This had turned the attention of many leading physicians away from the practical side of medicine and the care of the patient; the laboratory appeared to be more important than the sick-room. It was chiefly due to Thomas Sydenham that this outlook was modified in favour of a return to the Hippocratic ideal.

Sydenham believed that personal observation and the care of the patient were more important than the discovery of new physiological processes or the formulation of yet another general doctrine. The supreme task of the physician was to assist the healing power of nature in the cure of the sick. He must, therefore, most carefully observe each case and its symptoms; he must identify particular diseases by searching for typical pathological processes and by comparing similar individual cases before coming to conclusions. This is essentially the modern view of the task of the practising physician and clinician.

This practical outlook inspired Sydenham's numerous monographs on individual diseases. His epidemiological studies were of great importance. He taught that epidemics are largely dependent upon meteorological conditions (a view derived from Hippocrates (55)): that they can spring from miasmas in the earth, can recur at certain regular intervals, etc. Nevertheless, there are passages foreshadowing the nineteenth-century germ theory of disease.

Among Sydenham's special monographs 'A Treatise on Gout', containing the first distinction between rheumatism and gout, is considered his masterpiece of clinical observation. He was a well qualified observer, since he was himself a sufferer from gout. His other studies include those on 'consumption'—pulmonary tuberculosis—measles and scarlatina (he was the first to distinguish between the two), rheumatic polyarthritis and 'Sydenham's chorea' a mild convulsion of children. In therapeutics he recommended cooling draughts in smallpox, popularized the use of the Peruvian bark, recommended for the first time the use of opium in liquid form ('Sydenham's laudanum') and made many other improvements.

His *Observationes Medicae*, first published in 1676, contained most of his pathological observations and the

TRACTATUS
DE
Podagra
ET
HYDROPE

PER
THO. SYDENHAM, M.D.

Non fingendum, aut excogitandum, fed inveniendum, quid Natura faciat, aut ferat, *Bacon*.

LONDINI,
Typis *R. N.* Impenfis *Gualt. Kettilby* ad Infigne *Capitis Epifcopi* in *Cæmeterio Paulino*. M DC LXXXIII.

Processus Integri (first published in 1693) his therapeutics. Both went into innumerable editions, particularly on the Continent. The great Dutch physician Herman Boerhaave and the medical school in eighteenth-century Vienna were deeply indebted to Sydenham's teachings and transmitted his ideas to their followers.

BIBLIOGRAPHY: Kenneth Dewhurst, *Dr Thomas Sydenham, his Life and Writings* (London & Berkeley, Cal., 1966).

160

THE CALCULUS

GOTTFRIED WILHELM VON LEIBNIZ (1646–1716). Nova Methodus pro Maximis et Minimis. *In:* Acta Eruditorum. *Leipzig: Christopher Günther, 1684*

The German diplomat, historian, theologian, philosopher and mathematician Leibniz (see also 177) was an almost universal genius whose place in the history of mathematics depends on his being an independent inventor of the infinitesimal calculus and on his contributions to combinatorial analysis which foreshadowed the development of modern mathematical logic. Born in Leipzig, he was the son of a professor of moral philosophy.

The *Acta Eruditorum* was established in imitation of the French *Journal des Sçavans* (founded in 1665) in Berlin in

1682 and Leibniz was a frequent contributor. Another German mathematician (E. W. Tschirnhausen) having published in it a paper on quadratures, based on researches that Leibniz had communicated to him, Leibniz at last decided in 1684 to present to the world the more abstruse parts of his own work on the calculus. His epoch-making papers give rules of calculation without proof for rates of variation of functions and for drawing tangents to curves. Two years later he published a paper containing the rudiments of the integral calculus, dealing with quadratures, etc. The first mathematicians to take up the new methods and make effective additional contributions to mathematics with their aid were the Bernoullis (179).

The infinitesimal calculus originated in the seventeenth century with the researches of Kepler (112), Cavalieri, Torricelli (145), Fermat and Barrow, but the two independent inventors of the subject, as we understand it today, were Newton (172) and Leibniz. The subsequent controversy in the early part of the eighteenth century as to the priority of their discoveries—one of the most notorious disputes in the history of science—led to an unfortunate divorce of English from Continental mathematics that lasted until the end of the first quarter of the nineteenth century. Although both Newton and Leibniz developed similar ideas, Leibniz devised a superior symbolism and his notation is now an essential feature in all presentations of the subject.

With the calculus a new era began in mathematics, and the development of mathematical physics since the seventeenth century would not have been possible without the aid of this powerful technique.

BIBLIOGRAPHY: Emile Ravier, *Bibliographie des Œuvres de Leibniz* (Caen, 1937).

161

THE LAW OF GRAVITY

SIR ISAAC NEWTON. Philosophiae Naturalis Principia Mathematica. *London: Joseph Streater, for the Royal Society, 1687*

Following the pioneer researches of Galileo (130) in the study of motion and its mathematical analysis and the important contributions of Descartes (129) and Huygens (154), the scientific revolution of the seventeenth century culminated in the massive achievements of Newton in dynamics and gravitational astronomy.

Kepler's laws of planetary motion (112) came to be gradually accepted in the latter half of the century and unsuccessful attempts were made to account for them in terms of a central force emanating from the sun. The dependence of such a force on the inverse square of the distance was suggested by Robert Hooke (147), in particular, but neither he nor his scientific colleagues in London could prove that Kepler's laws follow mathematically from a law of this form. Finally, in August 1684 Edmund Halley (173) went to Cambridge and put the problem to Newton, who immediately replied that

it could be shown that this law would cause a planet to move in an ellipse about the sun as focus. Since he had mislaid his proof of this result, he undertook to send an account of it to Halley. With further prompting from Halley, Newton (see also 172) agreed to lay the details of his mathematical analysis of motion before the Royal Society. Halley assumed full responsibility for seeing the resulting volume through the press and paid for the printing because the Royal Society's own funds were depleted.

'The Mathematical Principles of Natural Philosophy' is divided into three books. Book I contains the basic dynamical theory of the whole work. It begins with the motion of mass-particles under the action of forces, including central forces, and the proof that the orbit is a conic, with the centre of attraction at one focus, if the force varies as the inverse square of the distance. Among other results it is shown that the resultant attractive forces exerted by all the particles of a spherical body act as if the bodies were mass-particles, so that the theory of the gravitational action of the heavenly bodies can be reduced to that of particles. Book II is essentially a treatise on fluid mechanics, including the motion of bodies in a resisting medium. In particular, Newton showed that the Cartesian vortices could not account for the observed planetary motions. Book III is devoted to astronomy and shows how all the known phenomena of the solar system can be predicted on the basis of universal gravitation and the general dynamical theory of Book I. The motions of comets and the gravitational explanation of the tides are among the other important topics treated. Perhaps the most remarkable feature of this book is the *tour de force* by which Newton explained the precession of the equinoxes.

The *Principia* is generally described as the greatest work in the history of science. Copernicus, Galileo and Kepler had certainly shown the way; but where they described the phenomena they observed, Newton explained the underlying universal laws. The *Principia* provided the great synthesis of the cosmos, proving finally its physical unity. Newton showed that the important and dramatic aspects of nature that were subject to the universal law of gravitation could be explained, in mathematical terms, within a single physical theory. With him the separation of natural and supernatural, of sublunar and superlunar worlds disappeared. The same laws of gravitation and motion rule everywhere; for the first time a single mathematical law could explain the motion of objects on earth as well as the phenomena of the heavens. The whole cosmos is composed of inter-connecting parts influencing each other according to these laws. It was this grand conception that produced a general revolution in human thought, equalled perhaps only by that following Darwin's *Origin of Species* (344). It was the final, irrevocable break with a medieval conception based on Greek and Roman cosmology and a scholastic system derived from the medieval interpretation of Aristotle. Although Newton was a profoundly (but not a conventionally) religious man, deeply impressed with the need for a divine power to create and conserve the universe, immutable laws of nature were sufficient sources of scientific explanation; hence Newton's universe, almost independent of the spiritual order, ushered in the age of rationalism, scientific determinism and the acceptance of a mechanistic view of nature.

The *Principia* is a very difficult book, and it is not surprising that only a few of Newton's contemporaries could read it through. It succeeded in time, however, in demolishing Descartes's prevailing theory of the vortices and was gradually accepted. Owing to Descartes's great influence and Newton's dispute with Leibniz (160) the spread of his thought on the Continent took about fifty years. One of his greatest champions in France was Voltaire, whose *Élémens de la Philosophie de Neuton*, 1738, was widely read. The second edition of the *Principia* was not published until 1713 and the first English translation, by Andrew Motte, not until 1729.

Newton's system remained supreme for two centuries. Except in optics, where he espoused a particle theory of light, his scientific views were not seriously challenged until the beginning of this century with the rise of the theory of relativity (see 408) and the quantum theory (see 391). Nevertheless, Newton's principles and methods still remain essential for many scientific problems, in particular those where the velocities concerned are small compared with the speed of light. Apart from his important work in mathematics and in optics (see 172), Newton devoted his energies to alchemy, chemistry, chronology and theology. The co-discoverer with Leibniz of the differential calculus, he is generally regarded as one of the greatest mathematicians of all time and the founder of mathematical physics.

BIBLIOGRAPHY: G. J. Gray, *Bibliography of the Works of Sir Isaac Newton* (Cambridge, 1907); Henry P. Macomber, *A Descriptive Catalogue of the Grace K. Babson Collection of Sir Isaac Newton and the Material relating to him in the Babson Institute Library*, 2 vols. and supplement (Portland, Me., 1950; reprint, 1955).

162

EXPEDIENCY IN POLITICS

GEORGE SAVILE, MARQUESS OF HALIFAX (1633–95). The Character of a Trimmer. *London: Printed in the Year 1688*

It is not often that a man can be said, either by his actions or his writings, to have changed the course of history, but Halifax did both. He was born to power, of a rich Yorkshire family; he was the great-nephew of Strafford, who watched over his early career, and the nephew not only of Sir William Coventry, who became his political mentor and was the nominal author of *The Character of a Trimmer*, but also of Lord Shaftesbury, who was to become his bitterest opponent. Despite the opposition of Clarendon, he came to power soon after the Restoration, and for thirty years steered a middle course in the violent political scene of the end of the seventeenth century.

At first his energies were devoted to preventing the Exclusion Bill, by which James II would have been cut out of the succession, foreseeing the dangerous precedent it would cause. This earned him the enmity of the Bill's chief promoter, Shaftesbury. Equally, however, he opposed the extremism of James and of Laurence Hyde, Earl of Rochester, and, although he retained his influence while Charles II was still alive, his refusal to support the repeal of the Test and Habeas Corpus Acts was made a pretext for his dismissal in October 1685. In 1687, when James II was courting the Nonconformists (who apparently stood to gain from the repeal of the Test Act as much as the Catholics), he justified his position with the famous *Letter to a Dissenter*, which pointed out the danger of submitting to the royal will in exchange for temporary benefits. It was an immediate success and played a very large part in the frustration of James's policy.

In the following year, a greater crisis called forth an even more remarkable work. The negotiations of James's opponents with William of Orange finally came to a head, and William landed in November 1688. Halifax took a leading part in the negotiations with William, and on James's flight, took charge of the government of the country. In the moderate and comprehensive nature of the terms of the settlement his hand can be seen, and appropriately enough it was he who offered the crown to the joint sovereigns, William and Mary, at the Banqueting House on 13 February 1689. It was a triumph for the policy of trimming, of keeping the boat steady where others desired to weigh it down perilously on one side or the other, which he had set out in brilliant lucid prose a year or two before in *The Character of a Trimmer*, which was first printed and then several times reprinted in the critical months before and during the Glorious Revolution.

Halifax's policy has come to be the essence of constitutional democracy. Though his firm grasp of high moral generalizations is evident, often anticipating the broad concepts of Burke (239), he based himself on the Aristotelian precept that politics is the art of the possible: 'men should live in some competent state of freedom', he wrote. His actions had a lasting effect on the politics of the time, and more lastingly on the government of the country: his writings provide a classic exposition of the empirical character of the British Constitution.

163

THE FOUNDATION OF LIBERALISM

JOHN LOCKE (1632–1704). Two Treatises of Government. *London: Awnsham Churchill, 1690*

John Locke (see also 164) lived his life unvexed by the cares of a profession or public affairs. He was subjected to some persecution, first on account of his connexion with Lord Shaftesbury after the latter's flight in 1682, when Locke was forced to take refuge in Holland. It was there that, at the ripe age of fifty-four, he published his first work, some articles in the miscellany of Le Clerc. In 1689 he was able to return to England, and he spent the last fourteen years of his life in the congenial household of Sir Francis Masham and his wife Damaris, daughter of Ralph Cudworth, one of the Cambridge

Platonists whose views had early engaged Locke's sympathies.

It was during his period of exile that Locke meditated and wrote the *Two Treatises of Government*. Their immediate cause was the *Patriarcha* of Sir Robert Filmer, in which a Hobbesian absolutism was modified to accord with the view of monarchy which Charles II, in emulation of Louis XIV, sought to impose. A confutation of this occupies the first treatise. The second treatise contains

Letters on Tolerance, and they combine with the *Treatises of Government* to provide a classic example of the empirical approach to social and political economy which has remained ever since the basis of the principles of democracy.

BIBLIOGRAPHY: H. O. Christopherson, *A Bibliographical Introduction to the Study of John Locke* (Oslo, 1930).

164

PHILOSOPHY WITHOUT DOGMA

JOHN LOCKE (1632–1704). An Essay concerning Humane Understanding. *London: Elizabeth Holt for Thomas Basset, 1690*

Locke was the first to take up the challenge of Bacon (119) and to attempt to estimate critically the certainty and the adequacy of human knowledge when confronted with God and the universe. In the past, similar enquiries had been vitiated by the human propensity to extend them beyond the range of human understanding, and to invent causes for what it cannot explain. Therefore, Locke's first task was to ascertain 'the original certainty and extent of human knowledge' and, excluding 'the physical consideration of the mind, to show how far it can comprehend the universe'. His conclusion is that though knowledge must necessarily fall short of complete comprehension, it can at least be 'sufficient'; enough to convince us that we are not at the mercy of pure chance, and can to some extent control our own destiny.

The mechanism of comprehension, as Locke saw it, lay in the ability to apprehend ideas. 'Idea' is a typically Lockian concept: 'the term which, I think, stands best for whatsoever is the object of the understanding when a man thinks'. Ideas are 'neither true nor false, being nothing but bare appearances'. Ideas are derived from experience, and experience comes from the perceptions of our senses or from reflective consciousness—a kind of internal sense perception. There are no 'innate' ideas: even the most complex ideas are built up from simple ideas stemming from one or other of these two sources. The ideas derived from the perception of our senses are produced in us by material bodies: the 'qualities' of material bodies produce simple ideas in us. Locke divided these qualities into 'primary'—e.g. solidity and extension—and 'secondary'—e.g. colours and tastes. Secondary qualities are merely the powers in the objects to produce sensations in us by the primary qualities of their insensible parts. Thus the ideas we have of secondary qualities in no way *resemble* those qualities. But, Locke claimed, primary qualities produce simple ideas in us that are actual resemblances of those qualities. Elsewhere in the *Essay*, however, he stressed the point that only the ideas representing or signifying material things, not the things themselves, are present to the mind, and according to this view—the theory of Representative Perception—we can never know whether our ideas resemble the real qualities of material bodies or not.

TWO
TREATISES
OF
𝕲𝖔𝖛𝖊𝖗𝖓𝖒𝖊𝖓𝖙:
In the former,
The *falſe Principles*, and *Foundation*
OF
Sir *ROBERT FILMER*,
And his FOLLOWERS,
ARE
𝕯𝖊𝖙𝖊𝖈𝖙𝖊𝖉 and 𝕺𝖛𝖊𝖗𝖙𝖍𝖗𝖔𝖜𝖓.
The latter is an
ESSAY
CONCERNING THE
True Original, Extent, and End
OF
Civil Government.

LONDON,
Printed for *Awnſham Churchill*, at the *Black Swan* in *Ave-Mary-Lane*, by *Amen-Corner*, 1690.

---

a plain statement of the principles of democracy. In an age and country in which the practice of democracy had just been triumphantly vindicated, Locke's theories, although anticipated to some degree by the 'Whig' tradition of political thought—Aristotle, Aquinas, Hooker, Grotius—had all the freshness of novelty. Like Hooker (104), Locke presupposes an original and necessary law of reason, and bases the constitution of society on it, rather than on the *de facto* existence of a government based on the actual submission of the governed to the rulers. This consent is thus a prior condition of the 'social contract', not a result of it, so that civil rulers hold their power not absolutely but conditionally; government being essentially a moral trust, which lapses if the trustees fail to maintain their side of the contract.

Locke was to reinforce these liberal opinions by his

When Locke came eventually to consider the question of real existence and the reality of human knowledge he accepted the implications of Representative Perception and admitted that a man cannot penetrate beyond his own ideas to the real world, which is never itself present to the mind. He was driven to the conclusion that our *certain* knowledge is limited to an 'intuitive' knowledge of our own existence—by an 'internal infallible perception that we are'—from which the existence of God can be proved by 'demonstration'. That knowledge which we have of other human spirits, and of the material world—he calls it 'sensitive knowledge'—has only a certainty 'as great as our condition needs'.

Locke's investigation was continued by Hume (194) and Kant (226); Hume enquired critically into 'the nature of that evidence which assures us of any real existence...beyond the testimony of our senses'; Kant tried to explain the rational constitution of experience. Locke's design was less penetrating and subtle but it covers a remarkably wide field of investigation into human knowledge: it is the first modern attempt to analyse it.

BIBLIOGRAPHY: See 163.

ACADEMIÆ CÆSAREO LEOPOLD. N.C. HECTORIS II.

Rudolphi Jacobi Camerarii, Professoris Tubingensis,

AD

THESSALUM,

D. Mich. Bernardum Valentini, Professorem Gießensem Excellentißimum,

DE

SEXU PLANTARUM

Epistola.

————————

TVBINGÆ,
Typis Viduæ Rommeii,
A. M DC XCIV.

165

SEED POLLINATION

RUDOLPH JACOB CAMERARIUS (1665–1721). De Sexu Plantarum Epistola. *Tübingen: Vidua Rommeii, 1694*

Before the publication of this treatise man's knowledge of the problem of the sex of plants was almost non-existent. The opinion of Aristotle (38) and Theophrastus that the sexes were separated in animals but united in plants was still prevalent. There was no proper conception of sexual origins, and spontaneous generation was accepted as a fact. The English botanist Nehemiah Grew (1641–1712) first discovered that there are two sexes in plants, but it was Camerarius who demonstrated it experimentally.

Camerarius, professor of medicine at Tübingen, addressed this 'Letter on the Sex of Plants' to M. B. Valentini, a professor at Giessen, in 1694. It contains the first experimental proof that in flowering plants the anthers are male organs, the ovaries and styles female, and that viable seeds cannot be formed without the addition of pollen. No reproduction is therefore possible without the co-operation of the two sexes: a discovery which established the relationship between the vital processes of plant and animal life. Camerarius also recognized the importance of the flower in the proper classification of plants.

This slim pamphlet marks, therefore, the beginning of our scientific and experimental knowledge of fertilization and hybridization in plants, though it attracted little notice until it was rediscovered by the botanist J. G. Koelreuter (1733–1806). Camerarius's discoveries were then entirely adopted by Linné (192) and led to great advances in the study of fertilization by C. K. Sprengel, Charles Darwin (344), G. B. Amici and many more recent workers.

166

MICROBES

ANTON VAN LEEUWENHOEK (1632–1723). Arcana Naturae Detecta. *Delft: Krooneveld, 1696*

Leeuwenhoek was a brilliant example of the amateur scientist. Originally a draper by profession, he became one of the most remarkable microscopists of all time. During his long life he used two hundred and forty-seven microscopes with four hundred and nineteen lenses, varying in their construction according to the kind of material to be observed. All his microscopes were of the simple type, rather than the compound ones then generally used, particularly by his predecessor in the field, Robert Hooke (147), and he used lenses of very short focal length.

Leeuwenhoek made remarkable discoveries in the anatomy of man and the higher and lower forms of animal and plant life—he investigated two hundred and fourteen animal types. He gave the first reasonably accurate account of the red blood corpuscles in both vertebrates and invertebrates by studying the walls of the vessels that controlled the movement of the blood in the capillaries (first seen by Malpighi) and tried to measure the blood velocity. Together with the work of Malpighi these studies completed Harvey's discoveries (127). Leeuwenhoek examined the fibres of the muscles and their increased size in contraction, the structure of the lens of the eye, of the skin and the teeth. On the teeth he found certain micro-organisms and he gave the first illustrations of various kinds of bacteria (on 17 September 1683), without realizing the special nature of this discovery and without connecting it with morbid infections; for this the world had to wait another one hundred and fifty years, in particular for the work of Pasteur (336).

Leeuwenhoek first fully described spermatozoa (though he had been partially anticipated by Stephen Hamm, who had observed similar forms a few months earlier) and protozoa. He discovered infusoria and rotifera, the insect nature of cochineal, viviparous reproduction in aphids and the harmful effect of these insects on plants. He studied the development of mussels and eels and the spinning and poisonous apparatus of spiders. He described the life-history of the ant and proved that what had been believed to be ant eggs were really their pupae and that their real eggs were much smaller. He noticed starch granules in the tissues of plants and the minute globular particles of which yeast consists.

These researches provided evidence against the theory of spontaneous generation, the belief that animal forms 'breed from corruption', which was then generally held. Leeuwenhoek proved that living organisms are always the product of pre-existing parents of their own species.

Nevertheless it must be admitted that, brilliant as was the work of both Leeuwenhoek and Hooke, they inspired no school. Their work raised problems on the concepts of creation, sexual generation, genetics, the structure of plants and animals and their relations, which they themselves could not solve. Though one can say with truth that (in spite of some earlier speculations, particularly by Fracastoro) protozoology, bacteriology and microbiology begin with Leeuwenhoek, his work remained a collection of valuable observations; no general system or theory was developed from it. There were no successors until the nineteenth century when Ehrenberg, Pasteur and others refounded these sciences.

Leeuwenhoek's work was published mainly in a series of three hundred and seventy-five letters sent to the Royal Society in London, and subsequently in various collections in Dutch and Latin of these and other papers, of which the 'Secrets of Nature Discovered' has been selected as a representative example. How widely known his work was in his own time is illustrated by a story that an old lady living in Djakarta in the Dutch East Indies, having read one of his papers, sent him the trunk of a coconut palm for investigation.

BIBLIOGRAPHY: Clifford Dobell, *Anthony van Leeuwenhoek and his 'Little Animals'* (London, 1922).

167
S.P.C.K. AND S.P.G.

THOMAS BRAY (1656–1730). An Essay towards promoting all Necessary and Useful Knowledge, both Divine and Human, in all the parts of His Majesty's Dominions. *London: E. Holt for Robert Clavel, 1697*

In 1695 the Governor and Assembly of Maryland wrote to the Bishop of London asking for his aid in ordering their church affairs. Bishop Compton offered the task to Thomas Bray, an eminent Oxford divine; but his departure was delayed by legal difficulties. Meanwhile he busied himself with recruiting volunteers to serve in foreign missions. Finding that most of them were too poor to buy books, Bray persuaded a group of prelates to institute a fund for the establishment of parochial libraries at home and abroad.

His pamphlet resulted in the enlargement of the scheme and the foundation of the Society for the Promotion of Christian Knowledge (1698–9).

In December 1699 Bray himself went out to Maryland. After a comparatively brief stay he returned home in order to straighten out legal and other complications relating to the colonial churches.

Impoverished by his journeys, he was reimbursed by generous patrons. Characteristically he devoted these gifts to the furtherance of what had become his life's work—missions to the heathen.

The S.P.C.K. had been founded to provide missionaries and other clergy with the literature required for their personal use. Bray now saw that much more was needed to spread a knowledge of the Gospel among, for example, the Indians of North America. On 16 June 1701 he received from William III a patent for the foundation of a Society for the Propagation of the Gospel in Foreign Parts and thus became the founder of England's two oldest church societies.

168
THE LEGENDS OF THE NORSEMEN

SNORRI STURLASON (1179–1241). Heims Kringla eller Snorre Sturlusons Nordlänska Konunga Sagor. Sive Historiae Regum Septentrionalium...illustravit Johann Peringskiöld. *Stockholm: Literis Wankiwianis, 1697 (vol. 1; vol. 2, n.p., n.d.)*

Iceland is the main source of all Norse literature and history, and if one name must be chosen to stand for the whole body of literature which has come down, partly as writing proper and partly as written record of an earlier oral transmission, sometimes anonymous and sometimes with an author's name, the justest choice may well be that of Snorri (or Snorro, or Snorre) Sturlason (or Sturluson, or Sturleson). He was in many ways a rather unsympathetic character, even in the violent times in which he lived. Achieving some prominence in his native land, he used his power to his own advantage in a series of equivocal negotiations between his own country and Norway. Finally, he fell out with the King of Norway and was assassinated by his orders.

Snorri's contribution to the literature of Iceland is of inestimable importance. It was he who collected and preserved the great prose *Edda* (first published in 1665), which contains, with some tracts on composition and metre of considerable importance, the *Gylfaginning*. Part mythology and part history, it is this which gives us the earliest version of the story of the Aesir and their leader Odin, whose invasion of the North became the religion of Scandinavia. From this were spun the *Nibelungenlied* and *Beowulf*; it left its mark on the Arthurian legend (29) and found new life in Wagner (333).

Even more important than this is Snorri's own contribution, the great collections of the Sagas of the Norse Kings called the *Heims Kringla*, first published in full in 1697 in the original Icelandic, with translations into Latin and Swedish, edited by Johann Peringskiöld. This opens with the Ynglinga saga, an account of the coming of the Aesir seen as history, which compared with the *Gylfaginning* shows Snorri's critical powers and confirms his stature as a historian. The series of connected biographies continues down to Sverri, King of Norway in 1177. The fullest and most detailed lives are those of the missionary Kings Olav Tryggvason and St Olav. The account of the defeat and death of the former at the hands of the Danes shows Snorri's magnificent terse prose at its best; it is one of the greatest of historical epics. The life of St Olav contains the famous account of the sacking of Southwark in 993 (or 991). In addition to this, there are early accounts of the western voyages of Erik the Red and Leif the Lucky and the early settlements in 'Vinland', as the Norsemen called the north-eastern coast of the American continent; and the equally daring eastern voyage of Sigurd the Crusader.

Snorri's work is the stem and source of the legend of the Norsemen: a legend which is still potent today.

BIBLIOGRAPHY: C. G. Warmholtz, *Bibliotheca Sueo-Gothica* (Stockholm and Uppsala, 1782–1817); T. Mobius, *Catalogus Librorum Islandicorum Aetatis Mediae* (Leipzig, 1856); Halldór Hermannsson, *Bibliography of the Sagas of the Kings of Norway*. Islandica, vol. 3 (Ithaca, N.Y., 1910).

169
THE MISSING LINK

EDWARD TYSON (1650–1708). Orang-Outang; or the Anatomy of a Pygmie compared with that of a Monkey, an Ape, and a Man. *London: Thomas Bennet and Daniel Brown, 1699*

Comparative zoology was largely forgotten between the publication of the writings of Aristotle (38) and the revival of the study of comparative anatomy at the end of the sixteenth and during the seventeenth century by such writers as Fabricius, Ruini, Perrault, Grew and Blasius. Edward Tyson, physician at Bridewell and Bethlehem Hospitals, was the first to publish monographs on the subject, the chief of which is this book on the orang-outang, with illustrations and a chapter on muscles supplied by the physician William Cowper. It is the earliest important study in comparative morphology.

Up to this time little was known of the higher anthropoid apes and their anatomy. Tyson compared the anatomy of men and monkeys, and he placed between them what he thought was a typical pygmy—it was, in fact, an African chimpanzee, the skeleton of which sur-

Orang-Outang, sive Homo Sylvestris:
OR, THE
ANATOMY
OF A
PYGMIE
Compared with that of a
Monkey, an *Ape,* and a *Man.*

To which is added, A
PHILOLOGICAL ESSAY
Concerning the
Pygmies, the *Cynocephali,* the *Satyrs,* and *Sphinges* of the ANCIENTS.

Wherein it will appear that they are all either *APES* or *MONKEYS,* and not *MEN,* as formerly pretended.

By *EDWARD TYSON* M. D.
Fellow of the Colledge of Physicians, and the Royal Society: Physician to the Hospital of *Bethlem*, and Reader of Anatomy at *Chirurgeons-Hall.*

LONDON:
Printed for *Thomas Bennet* at the *Half-Moon* in St. *Paul's* Church-yard; and *Daniel Brown* at the *Black Swan* and *Bible* without *Temple-Bar* and are to be had of Mr. *Hunt* at the Repository in *Gresham-Colledge.* M DC XCIX.

vives to this day in the Natural History Museum in London. The chimpanzee first appeared in zoological literature in 1625 and was described by Dr Tulp (of Rembrandt's *Anatomy Lesson*) while the orang-outang, mentioned in 1658, was first scientifically described by Camper in 1778 and 1782.

Tyson's work is less important for its anatomical descriptions than for the fact that he established a new family of anthropoid apes standing between monkey and man, and recognized that man was probably a close relative of certain lower animals. Popularized as the 'missing link', the theory that man shares some remote common ancestry with the apes was not clearly expounded until the publication of Huxley's *Man's Place in Nature* in 1863 and Darwin's *Descent of Man* in 1871. Tyson did not foresee the theory of evolution; but his work contributed substantially to its formulation and in that sense he was a forerunner of Blumenbach, Buffon (198), Huxley and Darwin (344). In literature Sir Oran Haut-Ton in Peacock's novel *Melincourt*, 1817, and the orang-outang in Shelley's *Queen Mab*, derive from Tyson—even if at second hand.

In the last part of his book Tyson writes about satyrs and certain other ancient mythical creatures which he believed to have been monkeys and not men. Though accepted by Buffon, the existence of prehistoric ape-like races of men was not finally established until the time of the anthropologists Quatrefages, in 1887, and Kollman, in 1894.

170

OCCUPATIONAL DISEASES

BERNARDINO RAMAZZINI (1633–1714). De Morbis Artificium Diatriba. *Modena: Antonio Capponi, 1700*

Bernardino Ramazzini was professor of medicine at Padua and Modena. He had a great reputation as a general clinician and published a number of books on medical and therapeutic subjects. But it was his 'Essay on the Diseases of Artisans' which earned him the title of 'the father of industrial hygiene'.

Occasional references had been made to occupational diseases in general medical works since the time of Hippocrates (55) and Galen (33): and both Helmont (135) and Paracelsus (110) wrote specifically about the diseases of miners. Ramazzini methodically collected all this material and added the results of his own investigations into the diseases of manual workers and the relation between their occupations and diseases, besides drawing on the observations of others who had direct experience of such cases. He described miner's phthisis, lead-poisoning of potters, eye-trouble of gilders, printers and other artisans, and included diseases peculiar to doctors.

Ramazzini was the first to recognize the social significance of occupational diseases and his book appeared at a most opportune time, since, with the beginning of industrial development in the eighteenth century, prevention of accidents from machinery and the general health of workers became increasingly important. He influenced Charles Turner Thackrah, who in 1831 published the first original English contribution to the subject, Ludwig Hirt in Germany, Sir Thomas Oliver and others in our own time. The leading Italian journal on social hygiene, published since 1907, is entitled *Il Ramazzini*.

The revised edition of 1713 was the definitive one, containing many corrections to the first and a supplement of twelve new chapters. Apart from reprints in Ramazzini's collected works there were twenty-five editions and translations published before the middle of the nineteenth century; the latest edition in English by Wilmer Cave Wright was published in New York in 1940.

171

THE FIRST ENGLISH ENCYCLOPAEDIAS

(a) JOHN HARRIS (1667?–1719). Lexicon Technicum, or an Universal English Dictionary of Arts and Sciences. *London: Daniel Brown (and others), 1704*
(b) EPHRAIM CHAMBERS (1680?–1740). Cyclopedia, or an Universal Dictionary of Arts and Sciences, 2 vols. *London: James and John Knapton, 1728*

John Harris, clergyman, mathematician, and (from 1709) secretary of the Royal Society, produced the first English encyclopaedia arranged in alphabetical order. He was the earliest lexicographer to distinguish between a word-book (dictionary, in modern parlance) and a subject-book (encyclopaedia proper), thereby overcoming the confusion which Isidore (9) had introduced a thousand

years earlier. His *Lexicon Technicum* appears to be the first technical dictionary in any language. The most famous of his contributors was Isaac Newton (161, 172).

Ephraim Chambers was a native of Cumberland and no connexion of the Scottish publishers William and Robert Chambers who in 1859 brought out *Chambers's Encyclopaedia* of still enduring fame. Apprenticed to a London cartographer, he was seized by the idea that Harris's *Lexicon* needed bringing up to date and that he was the man to do this 'work so seemingly disproportionate to any single person's experience'. A good French scholar, he adapted Moréri and Bayle (155) to the common-sense climate of the English Enlightenment. Moreover, he introduced a novel device that has proved indispensable to every subsequent lexicographer and encyclopaedist, namely, cross-references; so that 'a chain may be carried on from one end of an art to the other'. Thanks to his editorial accomplishments the *Cyclopedia* was revised, translated, and imitated throughout the eighteenth century. The *Encyclopédie* (200) was originally planned as a translation of it and Dr Johnson told Boswell that he formed the style of his *Dictionary* (201) partly on Chambers's book.

The titles and subtitles of these two books reflect the fluctuating conception, not yet completely resolved, of the purpose of this kind of reference-book. For a long time, France and Spain used the term 'dictionary', Germany and Scandinavia 'lexicon', the United States 'cyclopedia', whereas Britain, the Netherlands, Italy and Russia seem always to have preferred 'encyclopaedia'— which has steadily been gaining ground and may now be considered the internationally accepted term.

172

THE COLOURS OF LIGHT

SIR ISAAC NEWTON (1642–1727). Opticks. *London: Samuel Smith and Benjamin Walford, 1704*

Isaac Newton began his study of light and optics while an undergraduate at Cambridge, and continued it at his Lincolnshire home during the plague years 1665–6 when (he recalled) 'I was in the prime of my age for invention'. Then, as today, the behaviour of light was investigated experimentally and mathematically; Newton adopted both means, but the core of his work was the observation that the spectrum of colours (formed when a ray of light shines through a glass prism) is stretched along its axis, together with his experimental proof that rays of different colours are refracted to different extents. This causes the stretching, or dispersion, of the spectrum.

All previous philosophers and mathematicians had been sure that white light is pure and simple, regarding colours as modifications or qualifications of the white. Newton showed experimentally that the opposite is true: there are pure coloured rays which cannot be analysed by refraction, such as the green of the spectrum; just as there are coloured rays which can be analysed, such as the green formed by mixing blue and yellow light. Natural white light, far from being simple, is a compound of many pure elementary colours which can be separated and recompounded at will.

Since the lenses of optical instruments analyse light into colours of different dispersions, Newton believed (wrongly) that the coloration of their images was beyond remedy; hence he proposed, and made in 1668, a form of telescope magnifying by reflexion. (All the largest telescopes of today are reflectors.) This he presented to the Royal Society in 1671, shortly afterwards communicating a famous letter (published in the *Philosophical Transactions* for March 1671/2) in which he set out his new view of light and the experiments justifying it.

ADVERTISEMENT.

P*Art of the enſuing Diſcourſe about Light was written at the deſire of ſome Gentlemen of the* Royal Society, *in the Year 1675. and then ſent to their Secretary, and read at their Meetings, and the reſt was added about Twelve Years after to complete the Theory; except the Third Book, and the laſt Propoſition of the Second, which were ſince put together out of ſcattered Papers. To avoid being engaged in Diſputes about theſe Matters, I have hitherto delayed the Printing, and ſhould ſtill have delayed it, had not the importunity of Friends prevailed upon me. If any other Papers writ on this Subject are got out of my Hands they are imperfect, and were perhaps written before I had tried all the Experiments here ſet down, and fully ſatisfied my ſelf about the Laws of Refractions and Compoſition of Colours. I have here Publiſhed what I think proper to come abroad, wiſhing that it may not be Tranſlated into another Language without my Conſent.*

The Crowns of Colours, which ſometimes appear about the Sun and Moon, I have endeavoured to give an Account of; but for want of ſufficient Obſervations leave that Matter to be further examined. The Subject of the Third Book I have alſo left imperfect, not having tried all the Expe-

Newton's innovations were hotly criticized, not least by Robert Hooke, exponent of a different hypothesis of colour in *Micrographia* (147). Nevertheless, in 1675 Newton submitted further long papers, in which he discussed particularly the coloration seen in thin plates and films, and in the following years wrote most of the text of *Opticks*. However, Newton's unhappy earlier experience of controversy (see his *Advertisement,* here reproduced) induced him to refrain from printing *Opticks* until after Hooke's death in 1703. Thenceforward, for over a century, it remained a work of great authority; 'supreme' in Andrade's words 'as a record of experiment and scientific deduction from experiment'.

Opticks is also distinguished in two other ways: the first edition contained Newton's first mathematical papers in print (the dispute with Leibniz (160) had already begun), and in the later editions it was embellished with a set of *Queries* long supposed to represent Newton's opinions on the chief mysteries of Nature.

BIBLIOGRAPHY: See 161.

173
HALLEY AND HIS COMET

EDMUND HALLEY (1656–1742). A Synopsis of the Astronomy of Comets. Translated from the Original, printed at Oxford. *London: John Senex, 1705*

Edmund (or Edmond) Halley was long considered the most important English natural philosopher after Newton. We owe to him the publication of the *Principia* (161). His own scientific work was chiefly in astronomy, the present book containing his classic study of comets.

In ancient and also in medieval times comets were considered to be exhalations from the earth or were looked upon with suspicion and fear as divine portents supposed to be omens of events calamitous for mankind. Tycho Brahe was the first astronomer to conclude that comets are true astronomical objects: in 1577 he observed a brilliant comet necessarily much farther away than the moon, in a region where according to Aristotelian ideas no changes could occur at all. Kepler (112), Hevelius and Cassini attempted to describe the orbits of comets, but with little success; it seemed impossible to reduce their motions to any laws. Newton, by the application of his theory of gravitation, first observed that the orbit of a comet should be an ellipse or parabola according to whether it returned or was seen only once.

Halley collected all the observations of comets he could find. He worked out the orbits of twenty-four comets seen between the years 1337 and 1698. He found the orbits of three of these (of 1531, 1607 and 1683) to have been closely similar; and from this he deduced that they were one and the same, and that their orbit was not a parabola, but a very elongated ellipse traversed in about seventy-five years. He correctly explained that the small difference of about fifteen months between these returns was due to the effect of perturbations caused by the gravitational pull of Jupiter and Saturn. He predicted the return of his comet about the end of 1758 and it duly appeared on Christmas Day. It reappeared in 1835 and and 1910, and previous returns back to 240 B.C. have now been calculated. This was a striking verification of Newton's theory of gravitation: Halley had proved that comets belong to the solar system and move in eccentric orbits round the sun.

In 1679 Halley had published the first catalogue of the southern stars. In 1698–1700, while in command of the *Paramour* cruising in South American waters and on the West African coast, he went on the first sea voyage ever undertaken for purely scientific purposes. He discovered the importance of the transits of Venus and Mercury for determining the solar parallax, the changes in the apparent relative positions of some fixed stars, the acceleration of the moon's mean motion, etc. He studied the magnetic declination and in 1702 prepared a chart of the Atlantic Ocean showing lines of equal declination. This was the first map of its kind and remained in force for about one hundred years, the lines being known as 'Hallean Lines'. He made contributions to gunnery and ballistics, improved the diving bell and used the barometer to measure heights. In 1693 he published mortality tables of the city of Breslau, one of the first attempts to found tables of annuities on a basis of fact (see Graunt 144). Halley was the first to suggest the use of graphical methods to represent the geographical distribution of the physical features of the earth on maps and the first meteorological chart prepared by him appeared in 1688.

BIBLIOGRAPHY: Eugene F. McPike, *Dr Edmund Halley, a Bibliographical Guide to His Life and Work* (London, 1939).

174

THE ENGLISH HYMN

ISAAC WATTS (1674–1748). Hymns and Spiritual Songs. *London: J. Humfreys for John Lawrence, 1707*

Watts is generally regarded as the single-handed founder of English hymnody. This is hardly an exaggeration and the full transcription of the title-page given here shows exactly what he accomplished. (In Three Books. I. Collected from the Scriptures. II. Composed on Divine Subjects. III. Prepared for the Lord's Supper. With an Essay towards the Improvement of Christian Psalmody, by the use of Evangelical Hymns in Worship, as well as the Psalms of David.)

Singing in churches was born of the Reformation. Luther (49) was a music-lover and hymn-singing became popular through the Protestant Church in Germany. Calvin (65) on the other hand favoured the chanting of psalms. Hence the frequent occurrence in or with English Bibles from the mid-sixteenth century onwards of a supplement consisting of Sternhold and Hopkins's metrical version of the Psalms. The versification is dreary in the extreme and much of the music is singularly uninspired. Hence also contemptuous references to the Puritans as 'psalm-smiters'.

Poets like Donne, Gascoigne, Quarles and Herbert wrote much devotional verse, but this was seldom sung, although Thomas Campion's *Two Bookes of Ayres, c.* 1612, include many devotional songs. George Wither was granted a royal patent which required the inclusion of his *Hymns and Songs of the Church*, 1623, to accompany every copy of the Psalter; but this practice expired for lack of interest.

Watts set himself the mission of revolutionizing this situation and a comparison of the post-Watts with the ante-Watts period in the contents of *Hymns Ancient and Modern* clearly shows not only how well he succeeded but how little he was anticipated by other British writers. He was a prolific hymn-writer, with about six thousand five hundred hymns—many of them translations from the German—to his credit, and a master of the art. His best-known hymns include 'When I survey the wondrous cross', 'Our God, our help in ages past' and 'Jesus shall reign'. As a writer of children's verse he was also a pioneer. His *Divine Songs for the use of Children*, 1715, struck a new note and some of them are still familiar.

BIBLIOGRAPHY: A. P. Davis, *Isaac Watts* (London, 1948) contains a check-list of his works.

175

SCIENTIFIC GREEK

BERNARD DE MONTFAUCON (1655–1741). Palaeographia Graeca. *Paris: Ludovic Guerin, the widow of Jean Boudot & Charles Robustel, 1708*

What Mabillon (158) did for the study of medieval Latin documents, Montfaucon, after Mabillon's death the leading member of the congregation of St Maur, achieved in the field of Greek studies. His monumental work, published a year after Mabillon's death, also created a new discipline, that of Byzantine palaeography. Like Mabillon's work, his results have had to be modified only in details, chiefly due to the application of technical inventions such as photography and, in Montfaucon's case, to the discovery of Greek papyri which has immensely widened the scope of modern research.

Montfaucon applied his vast knowledge of Greek manuscripts to exemplary editions of the writings of Anastasius, Origen, and John Chrysostom which provided reliable texts, not yet entirely superseded, of these Fathers of the Church and stimulated patristic studies. Moreover, he eventually branched out into a new field of learning. His *Antiquité expliquée et représentée en Figures* surveyed in fifteen volumes the social and artistic aspects of the ancient civilizations; and the unfinished *Monuments de la Monarchie Française* tried to do the same for early French history. These works can well be called foundation stones of scientific archaeology. Montfaucon's last completed work, *Bibliotheca Bibliothecarum Manuscriptorum nova* (2 vols., 1739), is a comprehensive catalogue of the manuscript collections of Europe, a bibliographical masterpiece and the fruit of one man's lifework.

176

DOES THE EXTERNAL WORLD EXIST?

GEORGE BERKELEY (1685–1753). A Treatise concerning the Principles of Human Knowlege. *Dublin: Aaron Rhames for Jeremy Pepyat, 1710*

Berkeley was born in Ireland, and there the major part of his life was spent. He went to Trinity College, Dublin, in 1700, at a time when traditional scholasticism was being rapidly supplanted by the work of Descartes and Newton, and Locke's *Essay* (164) and the new theory of knowledge it put forward were gaining currency.

Here Berkeley, with his determination to accept nothing on the evidence of authority and his innate subtlety and originality of mind, had little use for the curriculum, but his ability was recognized and he became a fellow in 1707. The speculations which were later to lead to the first application of his theory in the *New Theory of Vision*, 1709, and then in the *Principles* are recorded in his *Common Place Book*. (This remarkable autobiographical document provides a detailed record of the progress of his mind towards his conclusions.) In 1711 he followed this with the *Discourse on Passive Obedience*, in which he

A

TREATISE

Concerning the

PRINCIPLES

OF

Human Knowlege.

PART I.

Wherein the chief Caufes of Error and Difficulty in the *Sciences*, with the Grounds of *Scepticifm, Atheifm*, and *Irreligion*, are inquir'd into.

By *George Berkeley*, M. A. Fellow of *Trinity-College, Dublin.*

DUBLIN:

Printed by A ARON RHAMES, for JEREMY PEPYAT, Bookfeller in *Skinner-Row*,1710.

ceivable or possible which is not conscious spirit or the ideas of which such a spirit is conscious. This presupposes complete equation of subject and object: no object can exist without a Mind to conceive it. Without the pre-existence of the Mind, matter and substance, cause and effect, can have no meaning. In the *Principles*, externality absolutely independent of all mind is shown to be an unreal, impossible conception: true substance is the conscious spirit and true causality the free action of such a spirit. Physical substance and causes are relations among phenomena, arbitrary though (by the action of the Mind) constant. Connexions between them are viewed subjectively as the suggestion or associations of the human mind, and objectively as the operation of the Universal Mind. Thus the universe is the sum of human experience, and forms a symbol of the divine universal intelligence: *esse est percipi.*

In this empirical attitude to the perceptions of the human mind, Berkeley is on common ground with Locke; it is in the theory of causality, with its distinction between the perceptions of sense and imagination that the essential difference lies. To Berkeley the ideas of sense are not due to our own activity; they must therefore be produced by an external, that is divine, will. But he does not predicate a simple division into human ideas, and sensible things which exist only in the Mind of God. A perception is not a mere thing, but an association of sensations which is somehow assured to us. As such, they do not define the permanent existence of real objects, which are known only to God. The difficulty here involved in estimating the degree of reference Berkeley is content to leave as a question. It is a question which Locke evaded, and which Hume (194), following Berkeley, was to develop to its final form. Nevertheless it raises metaphysical speculation to a higher level than before; it is a measure of Berkeley's greatness that the difficulties in his theory have been the subject matter of later philosophical thinking.

BIBLIOGRAPHY: T. E. Jessop, *A Bibliography of George Berkeley, with an Inventory of his Manuscript Remains* by A. A. Luce (Oxford, 1934).

deduces the moral rules which derive from God's intentions for human happiness, which foreshadows the utilitarianism of J. S. Mill (345). In 1712 he went to London, where the *Dialogues*, 1713, popularized his views. From then until 1721, when he returned to Ireland, he travelled on the Continent. In 1722 he became Dean of Dromore, and in 1724 Dean of Derry. The next eight years were occupied with his scheme for founding a college in the Bermudas, during which he spent three years in Rhode Island; but, owing to the failure of the government to support it, his great plan came to nothing, and he was compelled to abandon it and return to Ireland. In 1733, he published *Alciphron*, a series of dialogues in which he applied his principles to refute the current forms of free-thinking, and in the following year he became Bishop of Cloyne. Here he occupied himself with pastoral work and continued his controversial writing. He died at Oxford while on a visit to England.

The principle which underlay all Berkeley's philosophical writing was based on a rejection of all speculation, such as Locke's, about the meaning and necessity of matter as a primal necessity to any theory of human understanding. Briefly, Berkeley maintained that no existence is con-

177

A NEW PHILOSOPHY

GOTTFRIED WILHELM VON LEIBNIZ (1646–1716). (*a*) Essai de Théodicée. *Amsterdam: Isaac Troyel 1710*; (*b*) Lehrsätze über die Monadologie. *Jena: Mayer, 1720*

Leibniz was one of the last 'universal men' of the type which the Italian Renaissance had ideally postulated: philosopher, historian, mathematician, scientist, lawyer, librarian, and diplomat. In all these fields either his actual achievements or his seminal suggestions have become part and parcel of European thought.

Although trained for the law, mathematics was his favourite subject. Independently of Newton (172) he worked out the infinitesimal calculus (see 160), introduced a number of mathematical symbols now in general use, and constructed an early calculating machine, the ancestor of our computers.

Mathematical conceptions also determine his philosophy. In it, Leibniz tried to combine physics and metaphysics and to reconcile philosophy and theology. The 'Essay on a Theodicy' is the only larger philosophical work published by himself; but his fame as a philosopher rests on his 'Theory of Monads'. The original French text of this was published for the first time in 1840; but it had circulated in manuscript in its initial form of a letter addressed to Prince Eugene of Savoy (1714) and it was printed in German (as above) and Latin (1721) translations. Leibniz proclaimed a 'pre-established harmony' of the universe which he explained as composed of hierarchically ordered 'monads', i.e. the ultimate substances of mind as well as matter. This concept clearly reflects the ideal of the properly organized absolutist state of the baroque period and derives partly from the 'idées simples' of Descartes (129) whom Leibniz greatly admired. A generation later, Voltaire ridiculed the 'pre-established harmony' in Candide (204); but modern nuclear science has vindicated Leibniz's basic ideas, albeit from different presuppositions.

From 1676 Leibniz lived in Hanover in the service of the Guelph dynasty. He was instrumental in raising the duke to the electoral dignity and in assisting the succession of George I to the British throne. He wrote a voluminous history of the house of Guelph, which embodies much source material since lost or destroyed. He reorganized the magnificent library at Wolfenbüttel, to which Lessing, later librarian, gave a new fame; and with the encouragement of the Guelph queen of Prussia he founded in 1700 the Berlin 'Society of Sciences', the nucleus of the Academy. Although Leibniz wrote almost exclusively in Latin and French, he championed the use of the German language in learned publications and urged the study of German philology—an early precursor of the Grimm brothers (281).

Leibniz's political ideas were considered chimerical at the time: they have become commonplace in our own days. Thus he suggested plans for a reunion of the Christian churches, which is now actively pursued by the World Council of Churches and favoured by the Vatican Council. He advised the western powers to admit Russia to the peace congress of Utrecht (1713) and thereby to include this then 'underdeveloped country' in the comity of nations. He put it to Louis XIV that France's future was not to be secured by perpetuating her enmity with Germany but that she should look across the seas: he pointed to Egypt and the Near East as goals for French expansion and the building of the Suez Canal (see 339) as a desirable task for European co-operation.

BIBLIOGRAPHY: see 160.

178

THE GOLDEN MEAN

QUINTUS HORATIUS FLACCUS (65–8 B.C.). Opera, ed. Richard Bentley. Cambridge: [University Press], 1711

Horace's life spanned the decline and downfall of the Roman republic, and the secure establishment of the Empire under Augustus. He was young when the civil war broke out, and just finishing his studies at Athens. With other students he joined Brutus, and on the collapse of the republican cause found himself stranded penniless in Rome. Then he was introduced to Maecenas, the great literary patron, by Virgil. Maecenas encouraged him, helped him to publish his first book of Satires, and gave him a farm, which provided the independence he so much valued. He soon became a great favourite of Augustus, to and for whom some of his most famous work was written. When he died, famous and acknowledged since the death of Virgil as the greatest Roman poet, Augustus was his executor.

Despite his familiarity with all the great men of his time, there was nothing servile in Horace's life or writings. His early experience, when the whole social structure seemed to have been torn up by the roots, had left him determined to be independent of all pressures; neither rich nor poor, neither too involved nor too set apart from life and affairs. It is this calm independence, the moderate Epicureanism which he professed, that has ensured Horace his immortality. To it is added a deep feeling for natural beauty and the contentment it bestows, and a perfect control of and feeling for language and metre: all this expressed with a magical certainty and harmony. To accept what fortune sends and not to grieve when, as it must, it departs—this is Horace's creed:

immortalia ne speres, monet annus et almum
quae rapit hora diem.

Probably no other poet's works have been so often copied or printed, and hundreds of versions in every modern language have been made of the least translatable of poets. Certainly Horace far outstrips all competitors when it comes to pocket editions: all over the world, where the libraries or even the smaller collections of personalia of the great have been preserved, a well-worn pocket Horace is very frequently among them. The directors of a small company in the last century used to open and close all board meetings by reading one of the Odes together. But one of the most remarkable uses to which Horace has been put is shown in the present edition. In 1711 Bentley was fighting against the angry fellows of Trinity College, Cambridge, who were petitioning the College Visitor, the Bishop of Ely, to remove him from the Mastership. Bentley wished to enlist the support of the Crown (which appoints the Master), and he did it —by dedicating his edition of Horace to Harley, then Prime Minister.

Bentley (1662–1742) was and remains the greatest of English classical scholars. His reputation was made by his Dissertation on Phalaris, the final crushing blow in the 'Battle of the Books' (see Swift, 185*). His immense learning was combined with an equal control in its deployment. Although he here restricted himself entirely to criticism of the text, and refrained from comment or explanation, in fact his feeling for Horace is revealed in the seven or eight hundred emendations, many of which have found permanent acceptance. Bold yet sensitive, deeply learned and at the same time understanding, his edition is a compound, as Bentley was himself, of temerity, authority and subtlety.

BIBLIOGRAPHY: A. T. Bartholomew, *Richard Bentley, a Bibliography of his Works*, etc. (London, 1908).

179
FAMILY OF MATHEMATICIANS

JACOB BERNOULLI (1654–1705). Ars Conjectandi. *Basle: Impensis Thurnisiorum fratrum, 1713*

This entry covers an erudite family of refugees from Spanish persecution in Antwerp, who settled in Basle in 1622, and in three generations produced eight mathematicians.

JACOBI BERNOULLI,
Profeff. Bafil. & utriufque Societ. Reg. Scientiar. Gall. & Pruff. Sodal.
MATHEMATICI CELEBERRIMI,

ARS CONJECTANDI,

OPUS POSTHUMUM.

Accedit

TRACTATUS

DE SERIEBUS INFINITIS,

Et EPISTOLA Gallicè fcripta

DE LUDO PILÆ
RETICULARIS.

BASILEÆ,
Impenfis THURNISIORUM, Fratrum.

cIɔ Iɔcc XIII.

Like their father, Nicolaus senior (1623–1708), his three sons Jacob I, Nicolaus II (1662–1716) and Johann I (1667–1748) all married the daughters of merchants with large fortunes and all distinguished themselves brilliantly in various scientific fields. All three were primarily mathematicians.

Jacob was among the first to develop the calculus beyond the point at which it was left by Newton (172) and Leibniz (160). His brother Johann and Euler (196) between them perfected the calculus to a point which made it of almost everyday use in Europe, while its development was virtually neglected in England.

Jacob was both a Cartesian and a Newtonian and did much to further the spread of Newton's ideas in Europe. Johann, however, felt his discipleship of Leibniz to be inconsistent with approval of Newton. He was a man of strong, if not always creditable character. He more than once laid claim to achievements of his brother Jacob and he turned his son Daniel (1700–1782) out of the house for winning the prize in a competition in which his father had unsuccessfully competed.

Jacob's great treatise (*conjectandi* means literally 'casting', *sc.* dice) was published posthumously. It was the first systematic attempt to place the theory of probability on a firm basis and is still the foundation of much modern practice in all fields where probability is concerned—insurance, statistics and mathematical heredity tables. Other researches by Jacob, once regarded as curiosities, are now found to have practical application to the construction of suspension bridges and in the transmission of high voltages.

The second brother, Nicolaus, emigrated to Russia and was given a state funeral by Catherine the Great. Johann's sons, Nicolaus III (1687–1759) and Daniel (1700–82), were both appointed to the staff of the Academy of St Petersburg. Daniel is also famous in mathematical physics for his proposed dynamic model of a gas (*Hydrodynamica*, 1738).

180
DESERT ISLANDS

DANIEL DEFOE (1660?–1731). The Life and Strange Surprizing Adventures of Robinson Crusoe, of York, Mariner. *London: W. Taylor, 1719*

After twenty years of enormously prolific pamphleteering, political and sectarian, sometimes in verse, Defoe suddenly disclosed a genius for devising a tale of adventure. The special form of adventure that he chose, and even the name of his hero, have been adopted by countless imitators—Campe's 'Robinson Junior' and Wyss's 'Swiss Family Robinson' being among those not altogether unworthy of mention alongside Defoe himself. This influence is not yet dissipated, for much of science fiction is basically Crusoe's island changed to a planet.

At least equally relevant to the present purpose is the figure of the lonely human being subduing the pitiless forces of nature; going back to nature, indeed, and portraying the 'noble savage' in a way that made the book required reading for Rousseau's Emile.

Robinson Crusoe has long since been more widely read in the abridged versions for young people, in which his breast-beating and philosophizing are less prominent than the footprint in the sand, Man Friday, the threatening savages, and the endless ingenuity and contrivance that make the hero's island life tolerable. But the pious sections of the book are also relevant in the religious inferences drawn by Crusoe from his communings with nature.

Two further volumes, one of *Further Adventures* and one of *Serious Reflections* were published in 1719 and 1720 respectively.

BIBLIOGRAPHY: H. C. Hutchins, *Robinson Crusoe and its Printing, 1719–1731* (New York, 1925).

181
ITALIAN SCHOLARSHIP

LODOVICO ANTONIO MURATORI (1672–1750). Rerum Italicarum Scriptores. 28 vols. *Milan: Societas Palatina, 1723–38, 1751*

The collection of 'Writers on Italian Affairs' from 500 to 1500 is the first of its kind to comprise the entire corpus of medieval sources relating to a whole country, including annals and chronicles, laws and ordinances, letters, poems and inscriptions: an achievement which put Italy a century ahead of similar undertakings such as the *Monumenta Germaniae Historica* (287) or the Rolls series.

The man who achieved this amazing performance, Muratori, was successively librarian of the Biblioteca Ambrosiana in Milan (1695) and to the Este Duke of Modena (1700). Italian patriots and scholars formed the Palatine Society to carry out his project; the Emperor Charles VI accepted the dedication of the first folio volume. Muratori followed up the *Scriptores* series by two works of hardly less significance, the *Antiquitates Italicae Medii Aevi* (6 vols., Milan, 1738–43), which amounted to a documentary history of Italian civilization in the Middle Ages, and his own chronological summary of all his material, the *Annali d'Italia* (12 vols., Milan, 1744–9). By applying the critical methods of Mabillon (158) to the sources of Italian history, Muratori became the founder of modern Italian historiography. Gibbon (222) acknowledged him as his 'guide and master'.

A large number of Muratori's texts are still available only in his original edition; and it is a deserved tribute to his genius that the new edition of the *Scriptores*, edited from 1900 by a host of Italian medievalists, bears his name on the title-page.

BIBLIOGRAPHY: T. Sorbelli, *Bibliografia Muratoriana*, 2 vols. (Modena, 1943–4).

182
MEASURING TEMPERATURE

GABRIEL DANIEL FAHRENHEIT (1690–1740). Experimenta circa Gradum Caloris. *In:* Philosophical Transactions of the Royal Society. *London, 1724*

Galileo (113, etc.) is said to have been the first to devise an instrument for measuring temperature. He is credited by Viviani, his biographer, with the use of this 'thermoscope' as early as 1592, and Castelli wrote to Cesarini in 1638 giving a detailed description of Galileo's demonstration of it in 1603.

A form of clinical thermometer was devised and used by Sanctorius early in the seventeenth century. The authorities are at variance on the book in which it was first described and on the date of publication—all the way from Wolf (1612) by way of Foster (1614) to Garrison (1625) and to Garrison-Morton (1626)—the last two references are to the same book, Sanctorius's 'Commentary on the first book of Avicenna', in which the instrument is actually illustrated.

Bacon, Boyle, Guericke, Jean Rey (first liquid thermometer), the Grand Duke Ferdinand II of Tuscany (first use of coloured alcohol—c. 1641–54), Hooke, Huygens and many others had attacked the problem with minimal success.

(2)

Præparato ejufmodi thermometro (licet in multis adhuc imperfecto) voto tamen meo eventus refpondebat; magnâ enim animi voluptate rei veritatem contemplabar.

Tres jam erant anni elapfi, in quibus opticis aliifque incubuiffem laboribus, cum cupidus fierem experimentis explorare, an etiam alii liquores fixo ebullituri effent gradu caloris. Exitus experimentorum fequenti continetur tabula, cujus prima columna exhibet liquores adhibitos; fecunda illorum gravitatem fpecificam; tertia graduin caloris, ad quem unufquifque liquor ebulliendo pertigit.

Liquores.	Gravitas fpecifica Liquorum ad 48 Gr. calidorum.	Gradus ebullitione acquifiti.
Spiritus vel Alcohol vini.	8260	176
Aqua Pluvia.	10000	212
Spiritus Nitri.	12935	242
Lixivium cineris clavellati	15634	240
Ol. Vitrioli	18775	546

Gravitatem fpecificam cujufcunque liquoris addendam necefe judicavi, ut fi aliorum experimenta jam inftituta, vel adhuc inftituenda, a memoratis differrent, colligi poffit, an e variatione gravitatis fpecificæ, vel ex aliis differentia petenda fit caufis. Experimenta præterea non eodem tempore funt facta, & inde etiam liquores vario temperamenti vel caloris gradu erant affecti, fed quoniam illorum gravitas diverfimode & inæqualiter turbatur, calculo illorum gravitatem ad 48 gradum (qui in thermometris meis medium tenet locum inter terminum intenfiffimi frigoris arte commixtione aquæ, glaciei, falifque Armoniaci, vel etiam maritimi, confecti, & inter

With his 'Experiments concerning the Degrees of Heat' Fahrenheit perfected the modern instrument, his principal innovation being a 'fixed point' of departure, namely the temperature to which water can be cooled when mixed with ice and salt. This he called zero. At the ends of his scale were normal human blood-heat—which he took as 96°—and the normal freezing point of water, 32°. When this scale was later extended upwards, the boiling point of water fell at 212°. He may have been the first to use mercury as a thermometric fluid.

Réaumur (c. 1730–1) and the Swedish astronomer Anders Celsius (1742) introduced other methods of scaling. The centigrade system, now on the point of virtually universal adoption, seems to have been introduced by one Christin of Lyons as early as 1743, but a *locus classicus* for this appears not to be known. Celsius himself called the boiling point 100° and the freezing point 0°.

183

A NEW COUNTERPOINT

Johann Joseph Fux (1660–1741). Gradus ad Parnassum, sive Manuductio ad Compositionem Musicae Regularem. *Vienna: J. P. van Ghelen, 1725*

The author of this guide to contrapuntal music, 'Steps to Parnassus', sprang from Austrian peasant stock and matriculated in 1680 at the Jesuit University of Graz, to study for the priesthood. But he soon fled to Vienna, where in 1696 he became organist in the Schottenkirche. Two years later, Fux was appointed a court composer, and by 1712 first Kapellmeister at St Stephen's Cathedral. Ultimately he became chief Court Composer and was highly esteemed in royal circles, where he received many tokens of favour.

Fux was a prolific composer, though not exceptionally so by the standards of his age. He left over four hundred compositions, of which nearly three hundred consisted of church music. But though he has been described as the Austrian Palestrina, practically all of these are forgotten today. Some of his instrumental and dramatic music has, however, proved more enduring. In his lifetime it was as a master of the practice and theory of music that he was chiefly appreciated, and it would therefore probably have been gratifying to him that his posthumous fame has been largely based on his *Gradus ad Parnassum*.

This is one of the most influential and long-lived of all works of musical theory. It was originally written in Latin, and cast, like not a few others of its kind from the time of Thomas Morley onwards, in the form of a dialogue between master and pupil. By the 1770s it had been translated into German, French, Italian and English. Many great teachers of musical theory, such as Vogler and Martini, based their work on it. Mozart and Haydn used it in their pedagogic work. An abridged English edition appeared in New York in 1943, well over two hundred years after the appearance of the original. Perhaps the nicest tribute to Fux was paid by Debussy when in 1906 he entitled the first of his pieces in *Children's Corner* 'Doctor Gradus ad Parnassum'.

184

THE HISTORY OF CIVILIZATION

Giovanni Battista Vico (1668–1744). Principi di una Scienza Nuova intorno alla Natura delle Nazioni. *Naples: Felice Mosca, 1725*

The 'Principles of a New Science regarding the Character of Nations' has been justly called 'the vehicle by which the concept of historical development at last entered the thought of western Europe'.

Vico was of very humble parentage. He became a professor of rhetoric at Naples and Historiographer-Royal in 1735. Working in virtual isolation he laid the foundations of our modern conception of sociology. He boldly attacked the widely accepted theories of Descartes (129) that mathematical proof was the one criterion of truth in every sphere of thought. Natural phenomena, he maintained, are the works of God; mathematics is an arbitrary human invention and there is no reason to suppose that God observes its principles.

Vico believed that a genuine if limited knowledge of the external world was possible to man and he did not despise the use of mathematical method; but the Cartesian idea that full and perfect knowledge of the universe awaited only the perfection of geometrical knowledge was quite unacceptable to him. Human knowledge of the universe could never be perfect, owing to the imperfection of our nature and our limited powers of observation. Only to God was perfect knowledge possible.

Again in direct contrast to Descartes, Vico taught that our knowledge of history could approach much nearer to perfection than our knowledge of the phenomena treated by the natural philosophers. The past history of the human race, unlike the history of the physical universe, is due to the actions of creatures like ourselves. We can project our minds into theirs, and by patient record and interpretation we can reconstruct the series of cause and effect by which modern societies developed. Historical study of what man has done is as much entitled to the status of a science as is natural science.

Vico inherited the conception of a cyclical pattern in history, an idea revived in our own day by Spengler (410) and Toynbee (421). This old principle he put to strikingly original use. Just as the individual man passes through successive stages of feeling, imagination and finally of thinking, so does the history of civilizations pass through the age of gods, heroes and men. At the beginning a barbarian stage develops out of a purely animal or bestial one; there follows a transitional period of intellectual and spiritual refinement, leading to the era of humanity. The energies of civilizations then become gradually enfeebled; they relapse into barbarism and the whole cycle begins again.

Vico was the first to recognize the importance of language, myth and tradition as a source for understanding the primitive stages of man's history, before intellectual and historical consciousness developed. Poetry, for example, enshrines much early history, and historical facts can be deduced from philology. The concept of a history of human ideas, the principles of a universal history and its philosophical criticism, a recognition of the importance of social classes, all begin with Vico. Many twentieth-century notions of anthropology, comparative law, literature, religion and linguistic philosophy can be found in the pages of this book.

Vico's idea of an historical cycle ending in decline was essentially pessimistic and entirely out of sympathy with the concept of human progress and enlightenment prevailing in his time, as was his recognition of barbaric elements in ancient Greece. It is not, therefore, surprising that Vico remained unrecognized by his contemporaries (although his book was in fact printed three times in his lifetime). He became known through Conti to Montesquieu (197), but it was only in the nineteenth century that he was rediscovered and his influence has greatly increased ever since. In Germany Herder (216) and Goethe (298) took up his fundamental contributions to historical philosophy and method (W. E. Weber published a German translation in 1822) and in France Michelet (324) was his protagonist. In our day Benedetto Croce has done much to spread the knowledge of Vico's contribution to historical scholarship.

BIBLIOGRAPHY: Benedetto Croce, *Bibliografia Vichiana*, edited by Fausto Nicolini (Naples, 1947–50), 2 vols. (and supplement).

185*

GULLIVER'S TRAVELS

JONATHAN SWIFT (1667–1745). Travels into Several Remote Nations of the World. By Lemuel Gulliver, First a Surgeon, and then a Captain of several Ships. 2 vols. *London: Benjamin Motte, 1726*

Dean of St Patrick's, the prince of pamphleteers and satirists, Jonathan Swift, was born in Dublin and educated at Trinity College. In 1689 he became secretary to Sir William Temple, in whose service in England he remained until his patron's death in 1699. While thus employed, he became involved in the controversy about the merits of ancient and modern literature to which the most famous contributor was Richard Bentley (178). Swift's share was *The Battle of the Books*, from which sprang the even more remarkable *Tale of a Tub*, 1704, which established his reputation as the most original of contemporary writers.

He became the friend of Pope, Addison, and Steele; by 1708, he was being courted by both political parties, and his High Church sympathies detached him from his early Whig alignment towards the Tories. He had arrived at the right time, when the nation was tiring of the long domination of the Whigs, and *The Conduct of the Allies*, 1711, had a notable part in their downfall. Swift was now at the height of his power; but its roots were shallow. Indecision about the succession and the fatal quarrel between Harley and Bolingbroke brought an end to the short Tory government, and Swift, now Dean of St Patrick's, retreated into exile in Ireland.

For some years he remained quiet. The injustices inflicted by the English on the Irish aroused him, however,

and he achieved a new popularity with the *Drapier's Letters*, 1724. These, purporting to be written by an Irish draper, were in fact a brilliant and incisive onslaught on the government's decision to debase the Irish coinage through the introduction of 'Wood's halfpence'. In 1726 came *Gulliver's Travels*, which achieved immediate success, and then some lighter works, *Directions to Servants* and *Polite Conversation* among them. By now Swift's powers were failing. Although he continued to rule his cathedral as punctually as ever, he had begun to suffer from fits of giddiness, and the last three years of his life were passed in a semi-coma.

Gulliver's Travels has given Swift an immortality beyond temporary fame. Before leaving London, he had joined Pope and Arbuthnot in founding the Scriblerus Club, with the object of satirizing current follies. It was then perhaps that *Gulliver's Travels* was conceived. Certainly the bitterness of the satire on the court and the parties suggests that recent wounds were still rankling. However, two greater gifts, a sustained logic in invention and a facility for absorbing the reader till fiction becomes reality, brought Swift a different and far wider readership than he had envisaged. All those who had been fascinated by the realism and vivid detail of Defoe's *Robinson Crusoe* (180) were captivated again, even though they knew that Gulliver must be fiction. The brilliance and thoroughness with which his logic and invention work out the piquancies of scale involved by the giant human among the Lilliputians, and then by a minikin Gulliver among the Brobdingnagians, ran away with the author's original intention.

Gulliver's Travels has achieved the final apotheosis of a satirical fable, but it has also become a tale for children. For every edition designed for the reader with an eye to the historical background, twenty have appeared, abridged or adapted, for readers who care nothing for the satire and enjoy it as a first-class story.

BIBLIOGRAPHY: H. Teerink, *A Bibliography of Jonathan Swift* (The Hague, 1937) (2nd edition, revised and corrected, edited by A. H. Scouter, Philadelphia, 1963); Harold Williams, *The Motte Editions of Gulliver's Travels* (Oxford, 1925).

186

MODERN DENTISTRY

PIERRE FAUCHARD (1678–1761). Le Chirurgien Dentiste. 2 vols. *Paris: Jean Mariette, 1728*

Before Fauchard's time the profession of dentistry was truly a 'mystery', for its practitioners had steadfastly refrained from publishing details of their technique and equipment. Fauchard summarized in his pages with numerous illustrations all that was best in the practice of his day and disclosed what had been hitherto jealously guarded secrets. *Le Chirurgien Dentiste*—'The Surgeon-Dentist, or a Treatise on the Teeth, with instruction on the means of maintaining them Sound and Healthy'—is in fact the first scientific work on its subject, and modern dentistry begins with its publication.

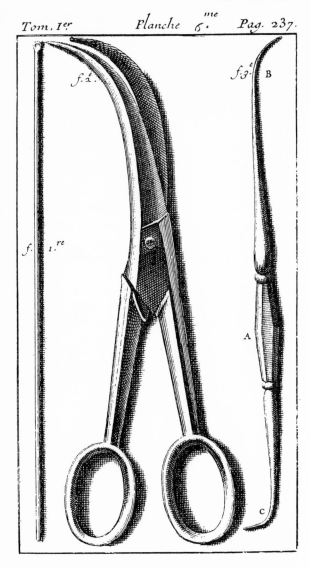

Tom. I.er   Planche 6.me   Pag. 237.

THE SEED OF METHODISM

WILLIAM LAW (1686–1761). *A Serious Call to a Devout and Holy Life. London: William Innys, 1729 [1728]*

William Law was born at King's Cliffe, near Stamford. He was one of eleven children, and was sent in 1705 to Emmanuel College, Cambridge. In 1711 he was elected a fellow and was ordained. He remained at Cambridge, in occasional difficulties due to his High Church and Jacobite opinions. In 1715, when he refused to take the oath of allegiance he was deprived of his fellowship.

By 1727, Law had taken what was to prove a critical step by taking up residence with Edward Gibbon at Putney as tutor to his son Edward, the father of the historian. There he remained for over ten years, acting as a spiritual adviser not only to the whole family, but to a number of the serious-minded who came to consult him. Among these were George Cheyne the physician, Archibald Hutcheson, M.P. for Hastings, John Byrom, poet, hymnographer and pioneer of shorthand, and, most notably, John and Charles Wesley. It is difficult to over-estimate the influence which Law had on the brothers at this critical stage in their career. They themselves spoke of him in the highest terms and their praise is not likely to be an over-estimate, for by 1736 they had drifted away from him, their practical minds out of sympathy with his new-found enthusiasm for mysticism in general and the works of Boehme in particular.

Law's writings fall roughly into three groups. He was best known in his earlier career as a controversialist. His first work was the *Three Letters to the Bishop of Bangor*, 1717, which made it clear that only Bentley (178) was his equal in controversy. The *Remarks on Mandeville's Fable of the Bees*, 1723, is a devastating defence of religion and morality; it enjoyed a second vogue in the nineteenth century when it was praised by John Sterling and re-published by F. D. Maurice. The *Case of Reason*, 1732, was an equally able onslaught on deism. In the meantime Law had already produced his two best-known works in the second group, practical divinity: *A Treatise of Christian Perfection* came out in 1726, followed by the famous *Serious Call*. After the Gibbon household broke up in 1737 Law, in retirement, devoted himself to the study of mysticism; the works of this period (although not so successful, in that practical age, as the *Serious Call*) are among the most original and fascinating of the century.

It is the *Serious Call*, a plea for a return to the practice of private individual piety, in an unadorned, lucid and deeply moving style, on which his reputation chiefly stands. Its peculiar force is difficult to convey; authorities as different as Gibbon, Lord Lyttelton and George Whitefield spoke enthusiastically of it. Samuel Johnson attributed to it his first earnest attention to religion. But the most significant testimony is that of John Wesley, who reaped where Law had sown. Writing after they had parted company, he said: 'it will hardly be excelled, if it be equalled, in the English language, either for beauty of expression or for justice and depth of thought'.

Fauchard describes in the fullest detail the procedure in operative dentistry, in the filling of teeth and most especially in prosthesis, which is that part of dental surgery concerned with artificial dentures, bridge work and the like. He was especially novel in his methods for correcting irregularities and was the first, for example, to describe the use of metal bands or braces for this purpose. The illustrations he gives of the instruments used in his practice show how advanced his methods were. He used antiseptic methods in filling teeth long before the germ theory of infection.

In the second edition, 1746, he gave the first description of *pyorrhoea alveolaris*, a common affliction of the gums. An English translation of this edition, by Lilian Lindsay, was published in London in 1946.

Fauchard was followed by Philipp Pfaff, whose *Abhandlung von den Zähnen* was published in 1756, and in 1771 by John Hunter's magisterial *Natural History of the Human Teeth*. These three books are categorized by Garrison as 'the most important in the history of dentistry'; and if Hunter was the first to apply medical science to the structure of the teeth (introducing the classes cuspid, bicuspid, molar and incisor), Fauchard was the true pioneer of dental surgery.

188

SCIENTIFIC AGRICULTURE

JETHRO TULL (1674–1741). The New Horse-Houghing Husbandry or an Essay on the Principles of Tillage and Vegetation. *London: Printed for the Author, 1731*

The early advances in eighteenth-century European agriculture were largely based on trial and error; but gradually agricultural phenomena began to be studied scientifically, and Jethro Tull was one of the pioneers in the field. Originally trained for the law, Tull soon became a farmer in Oxfordshire and later in Wiltshire. He toured Europe to study agricultural methods and was much impressed with the results of cultivation in the vineyards of France.

Tull first observed that pulverizing the soil without manuring it allowed improved aeration and freer entrance of water to the roots of plants, thereby increasing their nutriment. His most important invention, however, was the horse-drill, the construction of which was based on the mechanism of the church organ which he had studied as a young man when he was much interested in music. The drill, which he perfected in 1701, enabled him to sow seeds thinly in parallel rows and continuously in each row. Another of his inventions, the horse-hoe, was then used to improve the weeding and aeration of the adjacent soil. He made many other valuable observations on seed and the rate of sowing, and his inventions first made possible the reduction of manual labour on farms, while the use of his drill saved much seed. It was, in fact, the refusal of his labourers to introduce improved methods of sowing which led Tull to the invention of the drill by which he could obtain the desired results with less manual labour.

At first his methods were widely criticized, but gradually they were accepted, and they laid the foundation for mechanizing and rationalizing the growth of crops.

The first edition of this book was comparatively short. In 1733 a much enlarged edition was published, with illustrations. Many other editions followed, and in 1822 it was edited by another reformer, William Cobbett (294). It was translated into French by Duhamel du Monceau and had a considerable influence in France, Voltaire being one of Tull's enthusiastic followers.

189

PLANT NUTRITION

STEPHEN HALES (1677–1761). (*a*) Statical Essays containing Vegetable Staticks: Or an Account of some Statical Experiments on the Sap in Vegetables. (*b*) Haemastaticks or an Account of some Hydraulick and Hydrostatical Experiments made on the Blood and Blood Vessels of Animals. 2 vols. *London: W. Innys & R. Manby, and T. Woodward, 1731–3*

Stephen Hales, a modest country parson at Teddington, had some training not only in biology but also in mathematics and physics. It was this combination which enabled him to make the remarkable scientific investigations which earned him a Fellowship of the Royal Society and its Copley Medal.

He studied the movement of sap in plants and discovered what is now known as root pressure. He measured the amount of water lost by plants through evaporation and related this to the amount of water present in a given area of soil in which the plants were growing. He estimated rain and dewfall in this connexion, measured the rate of growth of shoots and leaves, and investigated the influence of light on plants. He experimented on gases and found that they were obtainable from plants by dry distillation. He was the first to realize that carbon dioxide was supplied to plants by the air and formed a vital part of the plant's food supply. These experiments led the way to those of Ingenhousz and de Saussure, while his ideas on combustion and respiration facilitated the discoveries of Black, Lavoisier (238) and Priestley (217).

The second volume contains the studies on blood pressure which make Hales one of the founders of modern experimental physiology. The application of the principle of the pressure-gauge or manometer enabled him to measure blood pressure during the contraction of the heart. He computed the circulation rate and estimated the velocity of the blood in the veins, arteries and capillary vessels and by showing that the capillary vessels are liable to constriction and dilation he made an important contribution both to the study of physiology and the practice of the physician of today. It became clear that the blood supply is largely determined by the state of contraction of the supply vessels, which are in their turn under nervous control: one of the problems of nervous integration later studied by Sherrington (397). Hales's work marked the greatest advance in the physiology of the circulation between Harvey (127) and the introduction of the mercury manometer and other instruments for the measurement of blood pressure by J. L. M. Poiseuille in 1828.

Hales was also a pioneer of public health. He supported the temperance movement and was responsible for the introduction of the 'gin laws'. He was the inventor of artificial ventilation and in 1757 he constructed a bellows to suck out foul air from houses, hoping thus to prevent the spread of typhus; he developed methods for measuring unfathomable depths, for distilling fresh water from the sea, and for the preservation of meat and water on voyages. He was a trustee of the Colony of Georgia, where the plant *Halesia* was named after him by its Governor, the naturalist John Ellis. Volume I was first published in 1727. The present is the first complete edition.

190

THE LURE OF THE ALPS

ALBRECHT VON HALLER (1708–77). Versuch Schweizerischer Gedichten. *Berne: Niclaus Emanuel Haller, 1732*

This small volume has a twofold importance in the history of European civilization. Although of moderate poetical value, it heralded to its German, French and

English contemporaries 'the beginning of a national German poetry' (as Goethe put it): and it created a new feeling for nature to which the Augustan age had been largely impervious.

The poem *Die Alpen* ('The Alps') is 'the fruit of an extensive journey through the Alps' which Haller had undertaken in 1728. Although didactic and descriptive, and, at least in parts, pedantic, it opened the eyes of the public to the grandeur and beauty of the mountain scenery which had hitherto been regarded with fear and aversion; and, anticipating his compatriot, Rousseau, Haller was the first to extol the simple life of the peasants and shepherds on the Alpine pastures, whom the sophisticated writers had treated as objects of pity or derision. Himself a son of the age of enlightenment, Haller nevertheless prepared the way for the Romantic movement, here represented by Burns (231), Byron (270), Wordsworth and Coleridge (256), and Walter Scott (273).

Haller, a patrician from Berne, is remembered not only for his poetry, although his *Versuch schweizerischer Gedichten* ('Essays in Swiss Poetry'), went through ten editions and takes an honoured place in the history of Swiss literature. He was by profession a naturalist and medical man who had received his training in London and Paris and, from 1736 to 1753, occupied the chair of anatomy, botany and surgery at Göttingen University— where he wished his friend Linné (192) to succeed him when he returned to Berne. His interest in the natural sciences impinged also upon his poetry: 'The Alps' is accompanied by learned footnotes commenting on the botanical, zoological, geological and other features treated in the poem. Moreover, his medical writings make him a precursor of modern experimental physiology and dietetics; he was the first to demonstrate the psychological basis of the physiological phenomena of irritability and sensibility.

191

ZEDLER'S LEXICON

Grosses vollständiges Universal-Lexicon aller Wissenschaften und Künste. 64 vols., and Supplement, 4 vols. *Halle & Leipzig: Johann Heinrich Zedler, 1732–54*

'The Great, Complete, Universal Dictionary of all Sciences and Arts' occupies a significant place in the long history of encyclopaedias. It is always cited as 'Zedler's Lexicon', i.e. by the name of the publisher instead of that of the author or editor, as had been the case from Pliny (5) to Ephraim Chambers (171 b), thus starting the tradition perpetuated by Brockhaus (269), Larousse, and others of giving all the credit to the publishing firm.

It is the first encyclopaedia on which a staff of editors (nine in Zedler's case) was employed, each of whom was responsible for a special subject and its consistent treatment: a sensible innovation which was adopted by the *Encyclopédie* (200) and virtually every subsequent reference book of its kind. The inclusion in the title of 'arts and sciences' shows Zedler's Lexicon in the main stream of eighteenth-century dictionaries, from Harris (171 a) to the *Encyclopaedia Britannica* (218). But it made a momentous new departure by being the first encyclopaedia to include biographies of living persons. Its value is further enhanced not only by the fact that it is one of the largest encyclopaedias ever completed but also by its high degree

of accuracy, achieved in spite of its comparatively rapid production. Zedler is therefore still useful as a storehouse of information on minor eighteenth-century persons and institutions long since excluded from current reference books.

The enterprising Leipzig bookseller and publisher, Johann Heinrich Zedler (1706–70), encountered the hostility of his fellow bookmen who feared or pretended to fear that such an all-embracing compendium might make superfluous all other books and thereby bring about the end of the publishing trade. Zedler therefore transferred his enterprise from Saxon Leipzig to Prussian Halle, where the chancellor of the university, Johann Peter von Ludewig, contributed the preface to the first volume. Zedler was shrewd, or lucky, enough to enlist as his chief editor Johann Christoph Gottsched (1700–66), professor of poetry at Leipzig and a doughty champion of German philosophy, literature and education, whose image has suffered from the ridicule Lessing (213) inflicted upon his narrow and doctrinaire aesthetic theories. As the translator of Bayle's *Dictionnaire* (4 vols., 1741–4; see 155 *b*) Gottsched proved himself an excellent choice as the first editor of Zedler's Lexicon. From the nineteenth volume onward the editorship was entrusted to Carl Günther Ludovici (1707–78), from 1733 professor of philosophy at Leipzig University. Ludovici has left no trace in the annals of science and learning, but the 'Zedler' is an enduring monument to his editorial capability.

192

THE CLASSIFICATION OF NATURE

CARL LINNAEUS, or LINNÉ (1707–78). Systema Naturae. *Leiden: Joannes Wilhelm de Groot for Theodor Haak, 1735*

'The System of Nature' is the starting point of modern systematic botany.

Linnaeus, or Linné, as he called himself from 1762 onwards, went on a journey of exploration to Lapland in 1732, mainly to collect plants. In 1738 he established himself as a physician in Stockholm, became professor of medicine in 1741 at Uppsala, but soon exchanged this for the chair of botany.

He compiled this work, consisting only of seven folio leaves, as a first outline of what in its further development became the foundation of botanical and zoological classification systems. Linné was first and foremost a systematist, subordinating all botanical problems to that of classification. He established the principles of class, order, genus and species for all plants and animals. Attempts at classification had, of course, been made before: Caesalpinus (97), Bauhinus (121) and Tournefort had based their scheme on the qualities of certain single parts—seed and fruit for Caesalpinus, petals of flowers for Tournefort. John Ray had maintained that all characteristics of a plant should be taken into consideration: Linné followed Ray in this and in making the idea of the species his starting point. This is the fundamental difference between what is called an 'artificial' and a 'natural' system of classification.

Linné had read Camerarius (165) and he made his discovery of the sexuality of plants the focal point of his system. He devised a method of twenty-four classes dependent on the number, union and relative length of the stamens: the classes then being subdivided into orders according to the number of the styles. It was the simplest system yet devised and therefore readily accepted. It was, however, not capable of universal application because the development of flowers is less uniform than the Linnaean system assumed. It has, therefore, been superseded by a more natural system. Linné himself stated that eventually a more natural method would have to be evolved, based 'upon the simple symmetry of all the parts'. In his time, however, his classification was the most universal available and was of immense value at a period when there was such a great expansion of botanical knowledge. It was further developed in his *Classes Plantarum*, 1738, and *Philosophia Botanica*, 1751, the latter book being of particularly wide influence.

Linné has been criticized for being a firm believer in the doctrine of the fixity of species and thereby retarding the progress of botany. All his species were sharply separated from the others, and all products of one pair of parents were considered to be produced without change of habit. Actually, there is some evidence in his later writings that he did not regard this invariability of species as unlimited. He experimented with hybrids and saw in these an indication of a new species developing over a period of time; he also admitted that specially favourable conditions of life could lead to the occurrence of new varieties. Linné is, therefore, not so entirely remote from the ideas of Buffon (198) and Darwin (344) as has been supposed.

His second most important contribution to botany was his new nomenclature. Previously this was in a state of great confusion. Naturalists referred to any species (of plants or animals) by the generic name, with only very approximate indications of its specific characters. Linné established the binary system which is still in use today. This designates each species under two words—generally in Latin—first, the genus—including all species sufficiently similar—and, second, the species, detailing its special characteristics, i.e. the lion and tiger belong to the cat genus and are therefore named *Felis leo* and *Felis tigris*. Linné was not the first to invent the system—it had been suggested by Rivinus and Ray before him—but he applied it universally. Some seven thousand three hundred species are described in the *Species Plantarum*, 1753, all arranged according to the sexual system and nearly all examined by Linné himself. The tenth edition of the *Systema Naturae*, 1758, is his final version of the system by which many plants and animals are still named to this day with reference 'Linnaeus', 'Linn.' or 'L.' attached.

He was much honoured in his lifetime, and many societies were founded in his honour, one of the most distinguished being the Linnean Society of London which is the proud possessor of his own library, herbarium and manuscripts, acquired by its founder and first president, Sir James Edward Smith, from Linné's widow in 1783 for £1,000. Today the *Systema* is alone worth several times that sum.

BIBLIOGRAPHY: Basil H. Soulsby, *A Catalogue of the Works of Linnaeus (and publications more immediately relating thereto) preserved in the libraries of the British Museum.* Second edition (London, 1933), with index of Authors, by Charles Davies Sherborn (London, 1936).

193

RELIGIOUS POLEMICS

JOSEPH BUTLER (1692–1752). The Analogy of Religion, Natural and Revealed, to the Constitution and Course of Nature. *London: James, John and Paul Knapton, 1736*

Butler was born at Wantage, the youngest of eight children of a retired, well-to-do linen draper. He was intended for the Presbyterian ministry, but while still at a dissenting academy he joined the Church of England. He was ordained in 1719 and was appointed to the Rolls Chapel, Chancery Lane.

Here he preached a number of learned sermons, a selection of which appeared in 1726 with the title *Fifteen Sermons*. These included his famous discourse on human nature which contained the germ of the *Analogy*. Combating the idea of Hobbes (138) that human nature is naturally inclined to seek enlightened self-interest, Butler contended that man is naturally virtuous. He held that our nature is adapted to virtue as a watch is adapted to the measurement of time. Thus 'as the frame of man reveals a supreme conscience, so that frame of nature shows a moral governor revealed through conscience'.

In 1725 Butler was inducted to the comfortable incumbency of Stanhope in County Durham, where he remained for ten years. Little is known of his life there except that he frequently rode abroad very fast on a black horse and barred his door to beggars and visitors. Answering an enquiry of Queen Anne's about Butler at this time, Archbishop Blackburne remarked that he was 'not dead but buried'. He was neither: he was busy with the preparation of the *Analogy*.

Butler was deeply preoccupied with the prevalence of deism, originating with Herbert of Cherbury (123): and he saw that this was a not unexpected outcome of the overthrow of traditional conceptions of the universe by Copernicus (70) and the Cartesian preparation for the Newtonian concept of the rule of law. Although not explicit, it was to combat this trend that Butler wrote the *Analogy*; and it is sometimes considered that its importance died with the theory of deism itself. The book is grudgingly admitted to be the one lasting memento of the controversy; but that is all. Its inclusion here indicates a contrary view. It is, indeed, one of the bulwarks of Christian apologetics and, although its effect is not always what was intended, its persistent influence is undoubted.

Hume (194), who sent Butler his *Essays* in 1741, ranked him with Locke (164) and Berkeley (176) as one of the originators of the experimental method in moral science. John Stuart Mill (345) considered that the arguments adduced by Butler were the turning point in his father's translation to scepticism. Newman (312) marked a very different era in his religious opinions by his study of this work. Gladstone listed as his 'four doctors' Butler, Aristotle, Dante and St Augustine. Macaulay called him 'a man of real genius'.

Butler's was an empirical approach, similar to Hume's, but he held that philosophic scepticism should not entail religious scepticism. Assuming, as the deists were prepared to, that God is the author of nature, there are no contradictions, obscurities or improbabilities in religious doctrine different in kind from those encountered in science. Thus the religious order and the scientific order are similar in nature, and both show the working of the Supreme Creator.

Butler declined an offer of an archbishopric in 1747 and ended his days as Bishop of Durham, a see to which Horace Walpole wrote that he had been wafted 'in a cloud of metaphysics'.

194

'ESSE EST PERCIPI'

DAVID HUME (1711–76). A Treatise of Human Nature. *London: vols. 1,2, John Noon, 1739; vol. 3, Thomas Longman, 1740*

David Hume early determined to be a writer, and, as a preliminary to achieving that aim, tried the law and business without taking to either. In 1733, his reading of Locke and Berkeley (164, 176)—he had a liking for 'books of reasoning and philosophy'—induced such intellectual activity that he became completely exhausted and went to France to recover. He had found his true métier, and the next three years were spent putting his views into a systematic form for publication.

The *Treatise* appeared in 1739–40, and was—although one must be cautious in accepting Hume's sometimes overmodest view of the reception of his work—a failure. Nevertheless, his circumstances gradually improved. His *Philosophical Essays* (largely a re-statement of parts of the *Treatise*) had greater success, and in 1751 he became librarian of what was in fact the Scottish national library, the Advocates' Library. Then came his *History of England*; and when in 1763 he went as Secretary to the Embassy at Paris his fame was already widespread. His last years were spent at the centre of that group of distinguished men who earned for Edinburgh the title of 'the Athens of the North'.

In the *Treatise* (Hume's philosophical views did not substantially alter), we have the first attempt to apply Locke's empirical psychology to build a theory of knowledge, and from it to provide a critique of metaphysical ideas. His first step was to advance from the positions of Locke and Berkeley. Where the former postulated a material substance existing independently of perception and the latter a spiritual, Hume maintained that the continued existence of objects distinct from perception is illusory. Where hitherto a distinction had been made between reason and the combined product of sensation and experience, he declared that our 'rational' judgements are simply association by custom. All our knowledge is only the sum of our conscious experience. From this Hume proceeds to consider the contents of the mind and the nature of experience, in which he makes a distinction between secondary *ideas*, particular copies of an unknown

A

TREATISE

OF

Human Nature :

BEING

An ATTEMPT to introduce the experimental Method of Reasoning

INTO

MORAL SUBJECTS.

by David Hume Esqr.

Rara temporum felicitas, ubi sentire, quæ velis ; & quæ sentias, dicere licet. TACIT.

VOL. I.

OF THE

UNDERSTANDING.

LONDON:
Printed for JOHN NOON, at the *White-Hart,* near *Mercer's-Chapel,* in *Cheapside.*
MDCCXXXIX.

abstraction, and primary *impressions,* which are themselves original. The distinction between the relation of ideas and matters of fact enables Hume to discuss the formal elements of experience, space and time and the propositions of mathematics, which cannot be matters of opinion. Then he considers the principle of real connexion between experiences, cause and effect, and denies that such a connexion can have a separate existence. Thus a causal chain is merely a series of ideas, which, from the speed with which they follow one another, we assume to be connected. From this it follows that the perceiving self can have no separate identity, a negative conclusion which Hume summed up by asserting 'that all our distinct perceptions are distinct existences, and that the mind never perceives any real connexion among distinct existences'. The extension of this theoretical analysis to ethics involves the rejection of the view that the distinction between right and wrong is one of reason; the subject decides such issues by reference to itself. However, a

moral sense is demanded as the supreme end, by reference to which the happiness of self and others can be related.

Thus Hume decisively sums up a century of speculation on knowledge and of theological discussion. Though universally hailed at the time, the full importance of his conclusions was hardly appreciated until Bentham (237) realized Hume's utilitarianism and Mill (345) his logic.

BIBLIOGRAPHY: T. E. Jessop, *A Bibliography of David Hume and of Scottish Philosophy from Francis Hutcheson to Lord Balfour* (London, 1938).

195

DYNAMICS

JEAN LE ROND D'ALEMBERT (1717–83). Traité de Dynamique. *Paris: David l'aîné, 1743*

Jean d'Alembert, mathematician and philosopher, friend of Voltaire and Madame du Deffand, devoted admirer of Mademoiselle de Lespinasse, was the illegitimate son of General Destouches and Madame de Tençin. Abandoned outside the Church of St Jean le Rond in Paris, he was found and brought up by the wife of a glazier named Rousseau: this explains the name 'Le Rond', to which he later added 'd'Alembert'. After graduating from the Mazarin College, he lived for thirty years with his foster-mother, despite tempting invitations from Catherine of Russia and from Frederick the Great, who repeatedly offered him the presidency of the Berlin Academy.

The 'Treatise on Dynamics' was d'Alembert's first major book and it is a landmark in the history of mechanics. It reduces the laws of the motion of bodies to a law of equilibrium. Its statement that 'the internal forces of inertia must be equal and opposite to the forces that produce the acceleration' is still known as 'd'Alembert's principle'. This principle is applied to many phenomena and, in particular, to the theory of the motion of fluids. It has become useful in the practical solution of many technical and mechanical problems, and is as important for the motion of bodies as is the principle of virtual velocities for their equilibrium—the latter formulated by Johann Bernouilli in 1717 (see 179). It was left to Lagrange to combine both these principles and to construct mechanical equations applicable to the motions of any system of bodies.

Among d'Alembert's earliest works was a paper on the calculus of variations by means of which Lagrange unified mechanics. He cleared up the dispute between Newtonians and Leibnizians on whether 'quantity of motion' (momentum) or 'vis viva' (energy) is conserved in collisions, showing that this dispute was a quibble: either can be consumed, according to the circumstances. He also applied the calculus of differences to the study of vibrations of chords and the oscillations of the air, and published the first monograph on winds. In astronomy he confirmed Newton's theory of the precession of the equinoxes, the nutation of the earth's axis and the perturbations of the planets.

D'Alembert is also remembered for his close association

with Diderot in the founding and editing of the *Encyclopédie* (200). He wrote the *Discours Préliminaire*, a general essay on the origin and relationships of the various sciences, and contributed a number of articles, mainly on mathematics.

BIBLIOGRAPHY: Gustav Eeneström, 'Verzeichnis der Schriften Leonhard Eulers'. In: *Deutsche Mathematiker—Vereinigung Jahresbericht* (Leipzig, 1910-13). Ergänzungsband, IV.

196

ANALYTICAL MATHEMATICS

LEONHARD EULER (1707-83). Introductio in Analysin Infinitorum. 2 vols. *Lausanne: Marc Michel Bousquet, 1748*

Leonhard Euler, the great Swiss mathematician, was born at Basle where he became the pupil of Johann Bernouilli (179), whose sons persuaded Catherine the Great to invite him to St Petersburg. In 1747 he was invited by Frederick the Great to Berlin. In 1766 he became blind, but this did not interfere with his colossal output of work. Altogether he produced thirty-two books in Latin, German and French, and approximately nine hundred memoirs. He covered practically the entire field of pure and applied mathematics, but some of his best and most enduring work was done in analysis, which he established as an independent science.

In his 'Introduction to Mathematical Analysis' Euler did for modern analysis what Euclid (25) had done for ancient geometry. It contains an exposition of algebra, trigonometry and analytical geometry, both plane and solid, a definition of logarithms as exponents, and important contributions to the theory of equations. He evolved the modern exponential treatment of logarithms, including the fact that each number has an infinity of natural logarithms. In the early chapters there appears for the first time the definition of mathematical function, one of the fundamental concepts of modern mathematics. From Euler's time mathematics and physics tended to be treated algebraically, and many of his principles are still used in teaching mathematics. The chief development of his conception of analytic mathematics, however, is due to Lagrange.

Euler published important work in other fields of mathematics and the physical sciences. Many symbols, equations and algebraic expressions are known by his name. He advanced the wave theory of light against the corpuscular theory, thereby weakening the hold of some of Newton's erroneous views (172). He worked out new analytical solutions for the motions of the sun, earth and moon which helped Tobias Meyer in 1755 to construct lunar tables of sufficient accuracy to determine longitude at sea. He investigated the representation of a spherical surface or a plane surface, explaining Mercator's projection (100) and causing great progress to be made in cartography. He wrote on dynamics, chemistry and medicine, and his *Lettres à une Princesse d'Allemagne*, 1768-72 (mainly on cosmology and physics), in which he attacked Leibniz's monadology (177), had an immense success and profoundly influenced contemporary philosophy.

A complete edition of Euler's works was begun in 1911, first published at Leipzig, later at Lausanne. It has reached over fifty volumes and is expected to be completed in about seventy.

197

THE SPIRIT OF LAW

CHARLES DE SECONDAT, BARON DE MONTESQUIEU (1689-1755). De l'Esprit des Loix. 2 vols. *Geneva: Barrillot & fils, [1748]*

In many ways one of the most remarkable works of the eighteenth century, 'The Spirit of Law', owing in the main to the high plane of generalization on which it is written, defies easy classification and for that reason has never enjoyed a great popularity. So, too, its author puzzled his contemporaries, and very diverse opinions were passed on him and his work even by the *philosophes*, whose predecessor Montesquieu was.

Born in the Gironde, he inherited from his uncle the title of Montesquieu and the presidency of the *Parlement* of Bordeaux, an office which he held for ten years. During this period he wrote and published his equally famous *Lettres Persanes*. Conveniently disguised as the correspondence of two Persian noblemen travelling in Europe, Montesquieu satirized, in an unforgivably witty style, the absurdities and abuses of the contemporary social, political, ecclesiastical and literary scene. France was publicly shocked and privately delighted. Four editions appeared in 1721, and then none for nine years; it is not unreasonable to suppose that it was officially suppressed. This success brought Montesquieu into Parisian society, and after publishing some more books of a slighter nature he was, not without some intrigue and counter-intrigue, elected a member of the Academy. He gave up his Bordeaux presidency and embarked on an extensive tour through Austria, Hungary, Italy and Germany, ending in England, where he stayed for eighteen months and developed an admiration for the English constitution and character which never left him. He then returned to his estate in La Brède, and pursued the life of a country gentleman (rather in the English manner) while he worked on his next book.

In 1734 *Considerations sur les Causes de la Grandeur des Romains et de leur Décadence* appeared in Amsterdam. Despite Montesquieu's previous reputation as a wit, this was immediately recognized as a major work, and it has remained the most popular and widely read of his books. Its facts may have been superseded but neither its style, a masterly succinctness, nor its matter—it is the first comprehensive philosophy of society—have lost their value.

Finally in 1743 he began *De l'Esprit des Loix*. It took four years to write, and when it was finished almost all his friends advised him not to publish it. Montesquieu paid no attention and it was printed in Geneva in the autumn of 1748. It consists of six main sections, the first dealing with law in general and different forms of government, and the second with the means of government, military matters, taxation and so on. The third deals with national character and the effect on it of climate; a subject of peculiar originality and the one most discussed at the time. The fourth and fifth deal with economic matters and religion; the last is an appendix on law—Roman, feudal and modern French.

The most distinctive aspect of this immense syllabus is its moderation: a quality not designed to achieve official approval in 1748. It is an always original survey which is neither doctrinaire, visionary, eccentric, nor over-systematic. If it is at fault, it is that in its comparison of the various kinds of constitution it is too prone to reflexion upon the defects of the French monarchy. But the scheme that emerges of a liberal benevolent monarchy limited by safeguards on individual liberty was to prove immensely influential.

In 1750 Montesquieu published a dignified *Défense* of his work, but not long after he died while on a visit to Paris. Curiously enough the *philosophes*, whose views were much in sympathy with his, did not speak much of him. This was partly due to the antagonism of Voltaire, and partly to a feeling that on this subject there was nothing much to be added. Yet his theories underlay the thinking which led up to the American and French revolutions, and the United States Constitution in particular is a lasting tribute to the principles he advocated.

BIBLIOGRAPHY: D. C. Cabeen, *Montesquieu: a Bibliography* (New York, 1947).

198

POPULAR NATURAL HISTORY

GEORGES LOUIS LE CLERC, COMTE DE BUFFON (1707–88). Histoire Naturelle, Générale et Particulière. 44 vols. *Paris: Imprimerie Royale, 1749–1804*

Buffon's 'Natural History, General and Particular' presented for the first time a complete survey of natural history in a popular form.

The Comte de Buffon was the son of a wealthy father. This enabled him to travel widely in Europe and to spend some time in England where he was made a Fellow of the Royal Society. While there in 1733, he translated Hales's *Vegetable Staticks* (189) and Newton's work on fluxions. These were published in France in 1735 and 1740 respectively.

In 1739 he was appointed Director of the Jardin du Roi (now Jardin des Plantes). It would appear that the 'Natural History' germinated in the preparation of a catalogue of the royal collection. Buffon then enlarged its scope to Aristotelian or Plinian proportions and finally transformed it into a conspectus of nature of a breadth and depth previously unknown.

With the help of his assistant, Louis Daubenton, as anatomist, and later of other collaborators (notably the Comte de Lacepède), but always under his supervision and control, this vast enterprise eventually covered not only the entire animal creation, but many other ramifications. Despite its extent and costliness the 'Natural History' was a great popular success, as is proved by the frequency with which it was reprinted and translated.

For us its significance is in point of manner rather than matter. Buffon's early training in England and his later close study of Leibniz (177) imbued him with a strong sense of the universal rule of law in inanimate nature and a compelling conviction that this should be extended to the world of living things. Feeling his way very carefully to this end he opens his great work with an essay

HISTOIRE
NATURELLE,
GÉNÉRALE ET PARTICULIÉRE,
AVEC LA DESCRIPTION
DU CABINET DU ROI.

Tome Premier.

A PARIS,
DE L'IMPRIMERIE ROYALE.
M. DCCXLIX.

called *Théorie de la Terre*, in which for the first time he outlines a satisfactory account of the history of our globe and of its development as a fitting home for living things. In his view the earth had been originally part of the sun which was broken off by the impact of a comet. It gradually condensed from its gaseous state, and the forces shaping its continents and mountains are still active.

This theory was elaborated in a later section of the 'Natural History' called *Des Époques de la Nature*, 1778. Here Buffon distinguished seven geological epochs and extended orthodox chronology, for he found it impossible to encompass the history of creation within six thousand years, which at that time was believed to be the age of the earth calculated from the history of the Bible.

Buffon's ideas led him, like Aristotle, to deny that any clear line of demarcation could be drawn between animal and vegetable life. The powers of reproduction and growth were characteristic of all living things. He seems also in his own mind to have virtually bridged the gap between the organic and inorganic worlds when he stated that life 'is not a metaphysical characteristic of living creatures, but a physical quality of matter'. For Buffon there was nothing in man which gave him any peculiar pre-eminence. He is a part of the animal creation and has to be fitted into a general picture of nature as a whole. This rejection of a rigid system of classification, to which most biologists of his time adhered, and Buffon's belief in the mutability of species, implied clearly some preparation for the thought of Darwin (344).

Buffon lacked the scientific equipment to enable him to set all this out in terms completely acceptable to the modern mind, although his descriptive powers were considerable and his style is admirable. Nevertheless he was the first to present the universe as one complete whole and to find no phenomenon calling for any but a purely scientific explanation.

199*

THE LIGHTNING CONDUCTOR

BENJAMIN FRANKLIN (1706–90). Experiments and Observations on Electricity made at Philadelphia in America. *London: E. Cave, 1751*

Benjamin Franklin, one of the most striking (and endearing) figures in American history, made his mark in many spheres of human endeavour. He was a statesman and diplomat, inventor and scientist, author, printer and publisher, educationalist and public servant. He was the first American scientist to achieve an international reputation, with his work on electricity.

Until the middle of the eighteenth century electricity was known only in its static form, and the most important instrument in use was the Leiden jar for concentrating electricity, discovered accidentally in 1745 by Pieter van Musschenbroek. With this and other instruments Franklin conducted a series of experiments during the years 1746–57. His interest was aroused when he saw some electrical demonstrations performed by an itinerant lecturer.

The most dramatic result of Franklin's researches was the proof that lightning is really an electrical phenomenon. Others had made such a suggestion before him—even Newton himself (161)—but it was he who provided the experimental proof. In 1752 he flew a kite in a thunderstorm and attached a key to its string. From this he collected electric charges in a Leiden jar and showed that atmospheric and frictional or machine-made electricity are the same. He went on to propose the fixing of iron rods at the top of buildings, masts of ships, etc., from which he conducted the electric charges they collected from lightning into the wet subsoil—the invention of the lightning conductor.

Franklin thought that there was a single electric fluid pervading all space and all bodies. If there was an equilibrium of electricity within and outside these bodies, then they were electrically neutral. But if one had more than its normal share, it was positively charged, i.e. 'plus'; if less, it was negatively charged, i.e. 'minus'. These now common terms were invented by Franklin and his 'one fluid' theory was widely accepted until the discoveries of Faraday (309).

His reputation as a scientist was immediately established by the publication of the results of his researches in a series of letters addressed to Peter Collinson, a London merchant and naturalist, in 1751; and the *Experiments and Observations* remains the most important scientific book of eighteenth-century America. By 1769 five editions had appeared (usually with additions by Franklin or others), there were three French editions in 1752, 1756 and 1773, a German one in 1758 and an Italian one in 1774.

200

LES PHILOSOPHES

ENCYCLOPÉDIE ou Dictionnaire Raisonné des Sciences, des Arts et des Métiers, par une Société des Gens de Lettres. Mise en ordre & publié par M. Diderot & quant à la Partie Mathématique par M. D'Alembert, 17 vols. *Paris: Briasson, David l'aîné, Le Breton, Durand, 1751–65*

A monument in the history of European thought; the acme of the age of reason; a prime motive force in undermining the *ancien régime* and in heralding the French Revolution; a permanent source for all aspects of eighteenth-century civilization—and a classic example of how not to arrange a work of reference: thus may be summed up the serried row of twenty-one volumes of text, twelve volumes of plates and two volumes of indexes, which eventually, in 1780, constituted the great French 'Encyclopaedia'.

Its beginning gave no inkling of its future importance. In 1745 the Paris publisher André-François Le Breton was approached by the English agriculturist John Mills and an otherwise unknown German writer, Gottfried Selle, with a proposal for bringing out a French translation of Ephraim Chambers's *Cyclopaedia* (171 b); in fact, the preamble to the first volume of the *Encyclopédie* still refers to the 'dictionnaires anglois de Chambers, d'Harris, de Dyche, etc.' as its main sources. Meanwhile, however, the plan had taken a different, far more ambitious shape. Le Breton went into partnership with the publishers Claude Briasson, Michel-Antoine David and Laurent Durand, each of whom took up a sixth share in the venture, while Le Breton had three-sixths. The royal privilege they obtained was dated 8 February 1746.

Most important, the three partners introduced to Le Breton the man who had just edited for them a *Dictionnaire de Médecine*, Denis Diderot (1713–84). This brilliant young man, unknown to the public and in very straitened circumstances, at once gained for the project the warm support of his already famous friend Jean d'Alembert (195), who not only wrote the *Discours préliminaire*, the general introduction to the *Encyclopédie*, and contributed the articles on mathematics, but used his assured position in society and the world of letters to obtain the moral and financial support of the leading *salons* and the co-operation of the best scholars and *philosophes*.

Each volume as it appeared caused a sensation throughout Europe. The court, the church, the judiciary were outraged; the number of subscribers, originally one thousand, rose to four thousand. In 1759, the seven volumes so far published were banned by the French Attorney-General and condemned by the Pope. Frederic II of

ENCYCLOPÉDIE,

OU

DICTIONNAIRE RAISONNE

DES SCIENCES,

DES ARTS ET DES MÉTIERS,

PAR UNE SOCIETÉ DE GENS DE LETTRES.

Mis en ordre & publié par M. *DIDEROT*, de l'Académie Royale des Sciences & des Belles-Lettres de Prusse ; & quant à la PARTIE MATHÉMATIQUE, par M. *D'ALEMBERT*, de l'Académie Royale des Sciences de Paris, de celle de Prusse, & de la Société Royale de Londres.

Tantùm series juncturaque pollet,
Tantùm de medio sumptis accedit honoris ! HORAT.

TOME PREMIER.

A PARIS,

Chez
{
BRIASSON, *rue Saint Jacques*, à la Science.
DAVID l'aîné, *rue Saint Jacques*, à la Plume d'or.
LE BRETON, Imprimeur ordinaire du Roy, *rue de la Harpe.*
DURAND, *rue Saint Jacques*, à Saint Landry, & au Griffon.
}

M. DCC. LI.

AVEC APPROBATION ET PRIVILEGE DU ROY.

Prussia and Catherine II of Russia offered to have the work published in Berlin and St Petersburg. Le Breton, however, carried on clandestinely and in 1765 completed the tenth volume, the last according to the prospectus. But a rising young publisher, Charles-Joseph Panckoucke (1736–98), continued the work until 1780. By that time, at least seven pirated editions of the *Encyclopédie* had been published in Geneva, Berne, Lausanne, Yverdun, Lucca and Leghorn. Panckoucke's attempt to oust the *Encyclopédie* by his own super-encyclopaedia, the *Encyclopédie Méthodique* in 201 volumes (1782–1832), was a deserved failure. The *Encyclopédie* of Diderot and d'Alembert remained, and remains, unique.

201

STANDARD ENGLISH

Samuel Johnson (1709–84). A Dictionary of the English Language, 2 vols. *London: Printed by W. Strahan, for J. & P. Knapton; T. & T. Longman; C. Hitch and L. Hawes; A. Millar; and R. & J. Dodsley, 1755*

Dr Johnson performed with his *Dictionary* the most amazing, enduring and endearing one-man feat in the field of lexicography. Adam Smith (221) in one of the earliest reviews of the book in the *Edinburgh Review*, 1755, compared it favourably with the best international dictionaries of modern languages then available, those of the French Academy and of the Accademia della Crusca (115), both of which 'were composed by a numerous society of learned men and took up a longer time in the composition than the life of a single person could well have afforded'; whereas the English dictionary was 'the work of a single person and composed in a period of time very inconsiderable when compared with the extent of the work'. In fact, it took Johnson less than ten years from writing his first prospectus in 1746 to publication day, 14 June 1755, when the two folios went on sale at £4. 10s.

The *Dictionary* was originally the project of a group of publishers and booksellers and the great Scottish printer, William Strahan. They recognized that the time was ripe to bring to fruition the idea of a standard English dictionary which the Royal Society had entertained as far back as 1664. In that year it appointed a committee for the improvement of the English language, for which John Evelyn, after a visit to Florence, wrote a report on the activities of the Crusca in 1665.

Johnson's *Dictionary* is divided into four parts: the preface, in which he expounds—largely in the steps of Ephraim Chambers (171 b)—the aims and problems of lexicography; a history and a grammar of the English language, both sections being of interest only in that they show the vast ignorance of eighteenth-century philologists before Sir William Jones (235) and his successors in this field; and finally the dictionary proper. The preface ranks among Johnson's finest writings; the history and the grammar, which did not interest him in the least, are dull rehashes of older compilations. It is the dictionary itself which justifies Noah Webster's statement that 'Johnson's writings had, in philology, the effect which

Newton's discoveries had in mathematics'. Johnson introduced into English lexicography principles which had already been accepted in Europe but were quite novel in mid-eighteenth-century England. He codified the spelling of English words; he gave full and lucid definitions of their meanings (often entertainingly coloured by his High Church and Tory propensities); and he adduced extensive and apt illustrations from a wide range of authoritative writers.

In the field of English lexicography Johnson's greatest followers were the American, Webster (291), and the compilers of the *Oxford English Dictionary* (371); but despite the progress made during the past two centuries in historical and comparative philology, Johnson's book may still be consulted for instruction as well as pleasure.

BIBLIOGRAPHY: W. P. Courtney and D. Nichol Smith, *A Bibliography of Samuel Johnson* (Oxford, 1925); R. W. Chapman and A. T. Hazen, 'Johnsonian Bibliography: a Supplement to Courtney'. In: *Proceedings of the Oxford Bibliographical Society*, vol. v, pt. 3 (Oxford, 1938).

202

PHILOSOPHIC HISTORY

François-Marie Arouet de Voltaire (1694–1778). Essai sur l'Histoire Générale et sur les Mœurs et l'Esprit des Nations. [*Geneva: Cramer*], 1756

The 'Essay on Universal History and the Manners and Mind of Nations' has secured Voltaire the honorary title of the father of the history of civilization (as distinct from political history) and the creator of a '*philosophie d'histoire*' (a term coined by himself) which removed the barriers between the Christian and non-Christian, European and non-European concepts of history.

The slow growth of the book is indicative of the importance Voltaire attached to the theories expounded therein, for as a rule he was a rapid performer and not given to afterthoughts. The first draft, begun about 1740, was entitled *Abrégé de l'Histoire Universelle*; it was mockingly designed as a continuation of, in reality a trenchant attack upon, Bossuet's biblical teleology (157). Some years later this 'summary of world-history' was expanded into the *Essai* as cited above, and this, in turn, received its final form in 1769 when its title was abbreviated to *Essai sur les Mœurs et l'Esprit des Nations*.

Voltaire wanted to explain world-history as a gradual progress of mankind towards the goal of perfection by reason. Each nation and each epoch was represented as an intellectual and cultural organism in its own right. He resolutely abandoned the traditional Europe-centred attitude and included Asia and America in his survey.

Nothing need be said here on Voltaire's eminence in French letters and European thought (see 204). But the fact should be stressed that Voltaire the historian has usually been given less than his due: his *Histoire de Charles XII*, 1731, *Siècle de Louis XIV*, 1751, and the *Essai* mark the watershed in European historiography between Bossuet and Ranke (286).

203

THE BIRTH OF ATOMIC PHYSICS

ROGERIUS JOSEPH BOSCOVICH (1711–87). Theoria Philosophiae Naturalis redacta ad unicam Legem Virium in Natura existentium. *Vienna: in Officina Kaliwodiana, 1758*

The 'Theory of Natural Philosophy' is now recognized as having exerted a fundamental influence on modern mathematical physics. Its author was born at Ragusa (Dubrovnik). He became a Jesuit and spent most of his life in Italy as professor of mathematics at the Collegium Romanum and at Pavia, and as director of the Observatory at Milan, and he also held academic posts in Vienna and Paris.

Boscovich's theories are concerned in the first place with the constitution of matter, the behaviour of physical forces, and the nature of atoms and of light. Lucretius's theory (87) conceived of atoms as hard particles in continual motion in a void, influencing each other by impact. His discussion of their relation to the various substances of nature is of the most general kind. Newton (161) was an atomist with a clear notion of inter-atomic forces. Boscovich's views are different and come nearer certain ideas of modern physics. As the title of his book implies, he considered that a single law was the basis of all natural phenomena and of the properties of matter; that the multiplicity of physical forces was only apparent and due to inadequate mathematical knowledge.

These 'point-atoms' of Boscovish were deemed to have a position—but no extension—in space, and to possess mass. Boscovich believed that each atom is surrounded by a field of force, alternately positive and negative through a number of cycles. The force exists whether there is at any point another atom for it to act upon, or not. Newton (and every other atomist) could not believe in the continuity of matter. Descartes (129) did, for he was not an atomist.

The *Theoria* had an immediate success in scientific circles, even though it was regarded as no more than speculation. Joseph Priestley (217) read it and a century later Faraday (309) was influenced by it. Clerk Maxwell (355) described its contents in his *Encyclopaedia Britannica* article on the atom (1875). Lord Kelvin cited Boscovich frequently, and J. J. Thomson (386) referred to him when describing the electron and his own idea of successive rings or shells of electrons in the atom, only the outer ones of which are chemically operative. This in its turn led to the work of Niels Bohr, who showed that the energy of the electron revolving in its fixed orbit was transformed into light energy of a definite frequency.

Boscovich was a prolific writer and left more than one hundred dissertations and books on most branches of mathematics, geodesy, astronomy, physics, meteorology and other subjects. Together with an English Jesuit, Christopher Maire, he measured in 1750 a meridian between Rimini and Rome on which basis the Papal States were carefully mapped.

An English translation of the *Theoria* was published in Chicago and London in 1922.

BIBLIOGRAPHY: In: A. de Backer and C. Sommervogel, *Bibliothèque de la Compagnie de Jésus*, vol. I (Brussels and Paris, 1890–1911); and in Riccardi, *Biblioteca Mathematica* (Modena, 1893; reprinted Milan, 1952).

204

LE MEILLEUR DES MONDES POSSIBLES

FRANÇOIS MARIE AROUET DE VOLTAIRE (1694–1778). Candide, ou l'Optimisme. [*Geneva? Paris? Amsterdam? London?*]: *1759*

It was Voltaire himself and his long career of disorderly, troubled and occasionally glorious opposition to established authority rather than his books which caught the imagination and occupied the mind of his contemporaries and succeeding generations. Whether writing frivolously to amuse, or seriously to put right injustice, he was never unnoticed: his best-sellers made him a rich man; when he tried to right injustice, as in the case of Lally Tollendal, he was listened to.

Voltaire lived for a very long time and from his youth on was always in some sort of trouble. In 1716 he was exiled for the first time for writing or being thought to have written lampoons against the Regent. In 1718 his first tragedy, *Oedipe*, was produced, and the next year he was exiled again. And so it went on, flattery, scribbling, insult and trouble taking equal shares in his life. In 1726, after some particularly bad trouble, Voltaire went to London. Here he stayed for three years; it was one of the most important visits of his life. The eighteenth-century English were more different from the eighteenth-century French than any two European nations can be imagined to be now, and the piquancy of this difference had the liveliest effect on Voltaire. Moreover, the English, unlike the French, who regarded Voltaire as a writer of elegant trifles, took him seriously, and paid him correspondingly. Voltaire responded by behaving seriously and even gratefully. Much struck by the admirable English phlegm and toleration of free thought and eccentricity, he wrote the *Lettres Philosophiques sur les Anglais*, the most sympathetic of critiques.

Back in France, this only made more trouble, and he took refuge at Cirey in Lorraine with the talented Marquise de Chatelet. In the 1740s he was partially restored to favour and through the influence of Mme de Pompadour he was made historiographer royal on New Year's Day 1745. He was soon back in hiding, and Mme de Chatelet died. So in 1751 Voltaire yielded to the persistent invitations of Frederick of Prussia, and set out for Berlin. There, despite his farcical quarrels with the King, he remained for three years, until the breach became total. Then he fled to Geneva where he found and bought the ideal refuge, Ferney, four miles from the city. Here, just on French soil, he could enjoy the political liberty of Geneva with the social liberty of France. Here *Candide*, the most perfect of the light-weight parables which were his especial and peculiar forte, was written. Typically, it was published anonymously, and many times printed and pirated in its early years. Which of the editions of 1759 is the first is still open to doubt.

But what does it matter? Voltaire would be pleased to know that his attempts to cover his tracks have been successful and even more to contemplate the book's continued popularity. For the optimistic, innocent Candide, and his equally guileless if more worldly-wise mentor, Dr Pangloss, and their delicious adventures, still command our attention. The folly of philosophic and religious optimism is displayed with a vigour and wit that carries the reader away. Irony without exaggeration, a perfect restraint in its admirable humour, a gift for the 'throw-away line' ('pour encourager les autres' is a classic example); all these show Voltaire's style and originality at their incomparable best.

In 1778, possibly piqued by the new success of Beaumarchais (230), he could not resist a visit to Paris. He was fêted to an extraordinary degree and at the performance of his latest tragedy, *Irène*, he was crowned with laurel. It was too much for him and he died on 30 May. His legacy of lively scepticism, perpetuated in the spirit of the *philosophes*, lives on.

BIBLIOGRAPHY: G. Bengesco, *Bibliographie de Voltaire* (Paris, 1882–90); A. Morize, *Candide, édition critique* (Paris, 1913); Ira O. Wade, 'The First Edition of Candide'. In: *Princeton University Library Chronicle*, vol. xx, no. 2 (Princeton, N.J., 1959).

205

THE MEASUREMENT OF LIGHT

JOHANN HEINRICH LAMBERT (1728–77). *Photometria. Augsburg: C. P. Detleffsen for the widow of Eberhard Klett, 1760*

Both Kepler (112) and Huygens (154) had investigated the intensity of light, and the first photometer had been constructed by Pierre Bouguer (1698–1758); but the foundation for the science of photometry—the exact scientific measurement of light—was laid by Lambert's 'Photometry' (Bouguer's treatise, *Traité d'Optique sur la Gradation de la Lumière*, appeared posthumously, also in 1760).

Johann Heinrich Lambert, born in Mülhausen (Mulhouse), Alsace, was the son of a tailor and almost entirely self-educated. He made his own instruments and with them embarked on a series of geometrical and astronomical observations. Lambert on the whole accepted the wave theory of light of Huygens and Euler (196) rather than Newton's corpuscular theory (172). In the *Photometria* he described his photometer and propounded the law of the absorption of light named after him. He investigated the principles and properties of light, of light passing through transparent media, light reflected from opaque surfaces, physiological optics, the scattering of light passing through transparent media, the comparative luminosity of the heavenly bodies and the relative intensities of coloured lights and shadows. His discoveries are of fundamental importance in astronomy, photography and visual research generally. Even in the modern world of wave mechanics (see 417), the *Photometria* remains a significant book. Indeed there is hardly any

I. H. LAMBERT
ACADEMIAE SCIENTIARVM ELECTO-
RALIS BOICAE, ET SOCIETATIS PHYSICO-ME-
DICAE BASILIENSIS MEMBRI, REGIAE SOCIETATI
SCIENTIARUM GOETINGENSI COMMERCIO
LITERARIO ADIVNCTI

PHOTOMETRIA
SIVE
DE
MENSVRA ET GRADIBVS
LVMINIS,
COLORVM ET VMBRAE.

AUGUSTAE VINDELICORUM,
Sumptibus VIDVAE EBERHARDI KLETT
Typis CHRISTOPHORI PETRI DETLEFFSEN.
MDCCLX.

aspect of photometry that was not fully covered by Lambert's investigations.

Lambert also made a notable contribution to the science of cartography. He first suggested the use of perspective as a means of making maps, and proposed several systems of projection in his *Anmerkungen und Zusätze zur Entfernung der Land- und Himmelskarten* (forming part III of *Beiträge zum Gebrauche der Mathematik und deren Anwendung*, Berlin, 1772). Though much of this work has now been superseded, his equal-area conical projection is used to this day. It employs a cone represented as intersecting the sphere at two parallels known as the 'standard parallels' for the area to be mapped. It is a system which compares favourably with gnomonic and Mercator projection (100), because radio and visual bearings can easily be plotted on it and it is widely used in aerial and military maps.

Lambert also wrote on mathematics—his *Theorie der Parallellinien*, 1766 (but not published until 1786), is an early essay in non-Euclidean geometry, although its implications were probably not fully realized by the author himself—on cosmology, and on rationalist philosophy.

BIBLIOGRAPHY: Max Steck, 'Bibliographia Lambertiana'. In: *Johann Heinrich Lambert, Schriften zur Perspektive*, part x (Berlin, 1943).

206

PATHOLOGICAL ANATOMY

GIOVANNI BATTISTA MORGAGNI (1682–1771). De Sedibus et Causis Morborum per Anatomen Indagatis. 2 vols. *Venice: Remondini, 1761*

Morgagni, professor of anatomy at Padua, was an expert clinician and was the first to identify the symptomatic condition associated with many diseases. Theophilus Bonetus, in his *Sepulchretum*, Geneva, 1679, collected three thousand post mortem reports of the sixteenth and seventeenth centuries. Morgagni found their brevity and inaccuracy unsatisfactory and began to compile written records of his own. This book, 'The Origins and Causes of Diseases anatomically investigated', contained reports on an extensive series of post mortems performed by himself, his teacher, Valsalva, and other members of his circle. By comparing the clinical symptoms with the post mortem findings Morgagni laid the foundations of pathological anatomy.

The study of diseased organs finally ousted the old humoral pathology. Morgagni could not have succeeded in 'introducing the anatomical idea into medicine' (Virchow) without the advancement of physiology in the period immediately preceding him. There can be no knowledge of morbid symptoms without the knowledge of normal organ function—physiology. Morgagni's classification was thus one of symptoms rather than of diseases. The book includes a number of brilliant descriptions of new diseases, some of which have remained classics until our own day, particularly those of the heart, blood vessels, lungs and throat. He described syphilitic tumours (gummata) in the brain, recorded a case of heart-block (Stokes Adams disease), identified the clinical features of pneumonia with consolidation of the lungs, described lesions in angina pectoris, acute yellow atrophy of the liver, tuberculosis of the kidney, etc.

Morgagni does not rank with such pioneers as Vesalius (71) and Harvey (127), but he systematized a branch of medicine hitherto studied in isolation and without method. Rudolf Virchow (307c), one of the greatest of modern pathologists, acknowledged his indebtedness to Morgagni.

Besides the *De Sedibus* Morgagni left some valuable studies on normal anatomy and a splendid book on the life and work of his teacher Valsalva. The *De Sedibus* appeared in numerous Latin editions and was translated into English and French.

207

THE SOCIAL CONTRACT

JEAN-JACQUES ROUSSEAU (1712–78). Du Contract Social; ou, Principes du Droit Politique. *Amsterdam: Marc Michel Rey, 1762*

In the course of an incessantly wandering life, for most of the details of which we have only the unreliable authority of his own *Confessions*, Rousseau was perpetually at odds with almost everybody.

After an irregular education and a variety of unimportant employments he came to Paris in the 1740s with only some rather threadbare musical knowledge and some useful introductions as a means of support. He earned his living by music-copying, an occupation which he was always able to fall back on in time of stress, and through his introductions met Diderot (200) and the circle of the *philosophes*. Thus, in circumstances which are still not wholly clear (Rousseau says it was entirely his idea, but it is probable that Diderot had some share in its conception), Rousseau produced his first masterpiece.

In 1749 the Academy of Dijon announced a prize for an essay on the effect of the progress of civilization on morals. Rousseau competed, taking as his thesis the paradox of the superiority of the noble savage, and won the prize. Next year he published it, under the title of *Un Discours sur les Arts et Sciences*, to resounding applause. Madame d'Epinay, the friend of the *philosophes*, lent him a cottage, the famous 'Hermitage' at Montmorency, and for the time being all was well. But in 1758 he contrived to quarrel with all his friends: with Diderot and Madame d'Epinay for some still obscure reason, and with d'Alembert (195) and Voltaire (202, 204) through his *Lettre à d'Alembert contre les Spectacles*, an attack on the performance of plays which, characteristically, damaged himself more than anyone else. Still, he did not lack patrons: in 1760 *La Nouvelle Héloïse* appeared, and in 1762 both the historic *Contrat Social* (to give it its modern spelling) and *Émile, ou de l'Éducation*.

The first and last of these, with their sentimental expression of deism, gave much offence, and Rousseau, like Voltaire, was forced to fly to Prussia. Restless and locally unpopular, he fled again to England, where he had a great welcome. Hume, who had offered him asylum, looked after him patiently, but Rousseau, at once indignant at neglect and too idle to attract attention, grew tired of London and then of England. After several fits of petulance, including wild attacks on the long-suffering Hume, he returned to Paris in 1770. Here he lived for the rest of his life, copying music and completing the *Confessions*, published in 1782–9.

The *Contrat Social* remains Rousseau's greatest work. With no particular learning, no gift for logic, and a total lack of practical experience, he yet contrived to write a work of compelling eloquence. He was, as has been seen, fundamentally at odds with the established beliefs of his time. In the Age of Reason he advocated the greater force of intuition: against artificial refinement, he urged a return to the natural state. So, observing that under the French monarchy the effect of government was the greatest misery of the greatest number, his convinced and sincere republicanism needed to look no further. He had no sense of history, and his theoretical reasoning is faulty: in practice his attempts to balance *volonté des tous* and *volonté générale* could result only in anarchy. Nevertheless, his fundamental thesis that government depends absolutely on the mandate of the people, and his genuine creative insight into a number of political and economic problems, give his work an indisputable cogency. It had the most profound influence on the political thinking of the generation following its publication. It was, after all, the first great *emotional* plea for the equality of all men in the state: others had argued the same cause theoretically but had themselves tolerated a very different government. Rousseau believed passionately in what he wrote, and when in 1789 a similar emotion was released on a national scale, the *Contrat Social* came into its own as the bible of the revolutionaries in building their ideal state. Still in print, translated into every language in cheap editions and paperbacks, it remains a crucial document of egalitarian government.

BIBLIOGRAPHY: J. Dufour, *Recherches Bibliographiques sur les Œuvres Imprimées de J.-J. Rousseau*, 2 vols. (Paris, 1925); J. Senelier, *Bibliographie Générale de J.-J. Rousseau* (Paris, 1950).

208

THE CHRONOMETER

JOHN HARRISON (1693–1776). An Account of the Proceedings in order to the discovery of the Longitude. *London: Printed by T. and J. W. Pasham and sold by the Booksellers, 1763*

Navigation of a sea-going vessel requires determination of its latitude, which is its position north or south of the equator, and of its longitude, which is its position east or west of an accepted meridian, such as that of Greenwich Observatory. Latitude is ascertainable by simple astronomical observation of the sun or the pole-star with a sextant—perfected in 1731 but preceded by the cross-staff, astrolabe, sea-quadrant and backstaff.

One way of measuring longitude is to compare local solar time with the standard time at the prime meridian. Local time is easily ascertained by observing the sun but only a very accurate clock can register a standard time over long periods. The improvements in horology effected by Christian Huygens (154) and others after him about the mid-seventeenth century promised success with this method. But the practical problems associated with temperature-compensation and so forth remained long intractable, although several rewards for an invention were offered. Finally, John Harrison, a clockmaker with several useful inventions to his credit, attracted by a premium of £20,000 offered by the Board of Longitude in 1714 for a solution, perfected a chronometer of the required degree of accuracy, showing a steady rate of gain or loss. He received the maximum award in full only after the direct intervention of George III in 1773.

Harrison's chronometer not only supplied navigators with a perfect instrument for observing the true geographical position at any moment during their voyage, but also laid the foundation for the compilation of exact charts of the deep seas and the coastal waters of the world, now co-ordinated by the International Hydrographic Bureau at Monaco. There has possibly been no advance of comparable importance in aids to navigation until the introduction of radar.

Pierre Leroy, a French horologist, is among other claimants to priority in this connexion. Although his approach was more scientific, whereas Harrison's instruments were the productions of a skilled craftsman, the Englishman's claims appear paramount. In 1735 he had already perfected his first chronometer and although this was a cumbersome instrument it proved equal to correcting an error in dead reckoning of one and a half degrees. His fourth timepiece, a pocket watch about five inches across, was completed in 1759.

The earliest records of any of Leroy's chronometers appear to be his exhibition of an instrument to the Académie des Sciences in 1763, and of another in 1764. It seems advisable to dispose of this point of bitter controversy at the time, echoes of which are still occasionally heard.

209

PENAL REFORM

CESARE BECCARIA (1738–94). Dei Delitti e delle Pene. *[Leghorn: printer unidentified], 1764*

At the beginning of the eighteenth century the methods of criminal justice and punishment were still essentially medieval. The penal system was cruel and arbitrary. Barbarous methods of punishment were used, torture still survived, capital punishment was widely imposed, even for very minor offences, and conditions in prisons were primitive and savage. Court procedure was in most cases secret and inquisitorial and there was little right of defence. Protests against these methods had been made since the sixteenth century, but they remained isolated efforts with no appreciable results.

With the advent of the Age of Enlightenment in the eighteenth century the demands for reform became much stronger. Rousseau, the Encyclopaedists, Frederick II of Prussia and in particular Montesquieu (197), called for a new attitude towards the criminal. In this generally favourable climate of opinion there was published one of the most influential books in the whole history of criminology, 'Crimes and Punishments', issued anonymously in 1764. Its author, only twenty-six years of age at the time, was Cesare Beccaria, Marchese Beccaria-Bonesana, a member of a well-to-do family in Milan, where he became professor of law and economics at the age of thirty. His friend Alessandro Verri was a prison official, and it was through visits he made with him to prisons that Beccaria's interest in the condition of criminal justice was first aroused. Having read Montesquieu's *Lettres Persanes* (in the expanded edition of 1754) and being deeply influenced by the rationalist thinkers of his age, he was appalled at what he saw. His short but pregnant book was the result of these experiences and of his reading.

Beccaria maintained that the gravity of the crime should be measured by its injury to society and that the penalties should be related to this. The prevention of crime he held to be of greater importance than its punishment, and the certainty of punishment of greater effect than its severity. He denounced the use of torture and secret judicial proceedings. He opposed capital punishment, which should be replaced by life imprisonment; crimes against property should be in the first place punished by fines, political crimes by banishment; and the conditions in prisons should be radically improved. Beccaria believed that the publication of criminal proceedings, verdicts and sentences, as well as furthering general education, would help to prevent crime. These ideas have now become so commonplace that it is difficult to appreciate their revolutionary impact at the time.

The success of Beccaria's book was immediate, six editions being published within eighteen months, and it was eventually translated into twenty-two languages. Its principles have been incorporated into the criminal practice of all civilized countries. The Constituent Assembly in Paris inserted in its 'Declaration of the Rights of Man' Beccaria's principle: 'The law must not ordain any penalties that are not evidently and strictly necessary'. Reforms were very soon introduced by the Grand Duke Leopold of Tuscany, Catherine II of Russia, Emperor Joseph II of Austria and the legislators of the French Revolution and of the United States. Voltaire was one of Beccaria's most enthusiastic followers—he published a commentary on the book—as were Blackstone (212), Bentham (237) and John Howard (224). The impact of *Dei Delitti e delle Pene* on the reform of criminal justice can hardly be exaggerated. The next step was the introduction in our own time of psychiatric treatment and analysis.

Beccaria also did some valuable work in economics: his *Elementi de Economia Pubblica* was published in 1804. He was one of the first to apply mathematics to economic analysis and his population studies anticipated those of Malthus (251).

Nachahmung der griechichen Werke in der Malerei und Bildhauerkunst; and in the same year he entered the Catholic Church. He also resigned his employment and travelled to Rome with a pension from Augustus III, Elector of Saxony. In Rome, undoubtedly accompanied by recommendations from the Nuncio, he was befriended by several cardinals, to two of whom he was appointed librarian. He also found employment at the Vatican Library and was appointed a Controller of Antiquities.

Italy became his second home, and when, in 1768, he decided to revisit Germany, after a trying illness in the Tyrol and a successful visit to the Court of Maria Theresa in Vienna, he turned back. On the return journey, while waiting at Trieste for a boat to take him to Ancona, he was murdered at an inn by an Italian who stole some coins presented to Winckelmann by Maria Theresa.

Meanwhile, with the publication of his masterpiece, the 'History of the Art of the Ancients', his fame had become widespread. This was indeed the first work in the German language to achieve universal acclaim. Winckelmann had drawn attention for the first time to the importance of Greek ideals for the modern world, and, with his unique acquaintance with the surviving examples of classical art, amplified by wide and specialized reading, his authority was unquestioned. It is now known that he was sometimes led astray by late Hellenic or Roman copies of Greek works; but this has not weakened the novelty and importance of his thesis.

Lessing was an early and deeply impressed reader of the *Geschichte* and the publication of his *Laokoon* (213) in 1766 was the first example of Winckelmann's influence on the thought of his time.

210

THE NOBILITY OF ANCIENT ART

JOHANN JOACHIM WINCKELMANN (1717–72). Geschichte der Kunst des Alterthums. *Dresden: Walther, 1764*

Winckelmann was born at Stendal in the Altmark of Brandenburg. At school he was befriended by a master who was blind. He there had the run of a fine library and seems to have been especially attracted to Greek antiquity even at this early age. As a poor student at the universities of Halle, Jena and elsewhere he studied theology and medicine. After graduating he spent some years of drudgery first as a private tutor and eventually as an assistant master in a Gymnasium at Seehausen.

The turning point in his life came with his appointment in 1748 as secretary and librarian to Count Bühnau, at Nötheniz near Dresden, for whose history of the Roman Empire he collected material. Opportunities to acquaint himself with the treasures of the Dresden Art Gallery and to meet a number of artists nurtured a natural bent towards the history of art; and an acquaintance with the Papal Nuncio in Dresden eventually inclined him to Catholicism.

In 1754 he published his first book, *Gedanken über die*

211

GOTHICK

HORACE WALPOLE (1717–97). The Castle of Otranto, a Story. Translated by William Marshal, Gent. From the Original Italian of Onuphrio Muralto. *London: Thomas Lownds, 1765*

'*The Castle of Otranto*', wrote Sir Walter Scott, 'is remarkable not only for the wild interest of the story, but as the first modern attempt to found a tale of amusing fiction upon the basis of the ancient romances of chivalry.' The elaborate subterfuge on the title-page created an atmosphere of fabrication which Chatterton thought to justify the Rowley Poems, which affected Ireland, the Shakespeare forger, and others including the whole school of Gothick novelists. Its influence on Poe is manifest, and it has survived in such novels as Bram Stoker's *Dracula* and in modern mystery stories and horror films.

Walpole's letter to William Cole, 9 March 1765, explains that the story was inspired by a dream and that its setting was Strawberry Hill, Walpole's mock-gothick 'castle' at Twickenham.

Walpole was the fourth son of Sir Robert Walpole, afterwards Earl of Orford, the Prime Minister, and later in life (1791) succeeded his father, brother and nephew as the fourth Earl. His private press at Strawberry Hill

Johann Winckelmanns,

Präsidentens der Alterthümer zu Rom, und Scrittore der Vaticanischen Bibliothek, Mitglieds der Königl. Englischen Societät der Alterthümer zu London, der Maleracademie von St. Luca zu Rom, und der Hetrurischen zu Cortona,

Geschichte der Kunst des Alterthums.

Erster Theil.

Mit Königl. Pohlnisch- und Churfürstl. Sächs. allergnädigsten Privilegio.

Dresden, 1764.
In der Waltherischen Hof-Buchhandlung.

was the first of its kind in England. The first book printed there, 1757, was the *Odes* of his friend Thomas Gray.

BIBLIOGRAPHY: A. T. Hazen, *A Bibliography of Horace Walpole* (New Haven, Conn., 1948).

212
THE LAWS OF ENGLAND

SIR WILLIAM BLACKSTONE (1723–70). Commentaries on the Laws of England. 4 vols. *Oxford: Printed at the Clarendon Press, 1765–9*

Blackstone's great work on the laws of England is the extreme example of justification of an existing state of affairs by virtue of its history. The progress of law in England had had but few commentators (see Littleton 23, Bracton 89, Coke 126), all of whom had approached it from an empiric point of view; it lacked the attention of a scientific jurist. Blackstone himself was none such, and not until Bentham (237) and Maine was the English concept of law scientifically examined. But by then it had already undergone a considerable change in the popular mind, and this change was almost entirely due to Blackstone.

Until the *Commentaries*, the ordinary Englishman had viewed the law as a vast, unintelligible and unfriendly machine; nothing but trouble, even danger, was to be expected from contact with it. Blackstone's great achievement was to popularize the law and the traditions which had influenced its formation. He has been accused of playing to the gallery, of flattering the national vice of complacency with existing institutions. The charge is in many respects just; but it is no small achievement to change the whole climate of public opinion. The law might be as much an ass after Blackstone as before, but it was a familiar ass. Public interest in the law can be seen in the change in newspaper reports of cases from a haphazard selection of the spectacular to a detailed presentation of the legal issues. If the English constitution survived the troubles of the next century, it was because the law had gained a new popular respect, and this was due in part to the enormous success of Blackstone's work.

His own career was not markedly brilliant and certainly not unorthodox. Born in 1723 and early orphaned, he was educated at Charterhouse and Pembroke College, Oxford. In 1744 he became a fellow of All Souls and in 1746 he was called to the bar as a member of the Middle Temple. From then on he divided his time between college and university business and practice at the bar. He was notably successful as steward of his college and in the reforms he initiated at the Clarendon Press. His legal practice was less successful, although in 1749 he became recorder of Wallingford, where—in typical eighteenth-century fashion—he succeeded his uncle. In 1752 he retired from the bar to devote himself to academic life; his lectures attracted considerable attention, and in 1758, as Vinerian Professor, he delivered the lecture which was afterwards prefixed to the *Commentaries*. They were an immediate and lasting success. Originally published over

five years in four volumes quarto, they were reprinted in octavo and again a dozen times in almost as many years. They were translated into French, German, Italian and Russian; they remained the textbook for students for many years; they were indispensable to the Justice of the Peace, if not to his clerk. Their success brought Blackstone back to legal practice in London. He became a Member of Parliament, where he was a comparative failure. He declined the place of Solicitor General in 1770, but was soon promoted to the bench, and thence to a seat in the Court of Common Pleas. He died in 1770.

As has been said, Blackstone was not interested in the science of law. All law is the same to him—the law of gravity or the law of the land. The object of the latter is to distinguish between right and wrong. Rights are either the rights of persons or of things; wrongs are either public or private. These theses form the headings of the four books of the *Commentaries*. Blackstone assumes that such distinctions are self-evident, and stem from the law of nature or of God. 'No human laws', he said, 'are of any validity if contrary to this.' This is hardly a lucid basis, and Blackstone's treatment of detail is no clearer. He takes a delight in describing and defending as the essence of the constitution the often anomalous complexities which had grown into the laws of England over the centuries. But he achieves the astonishing feat of communicating this delight, and this is due to a style which is itself always lucid and graceful. This is the secret of Blackstone's enormous influence. He did for the English what the imperial publication of Roman law (see 4 Justinian) did for the people of Rome.

213
DISCIPLINE FOR THE ARTS

GOTTHOLD EPHRAIM LESSING (1729–81). Laokoon, oder über die Grenzen der Mahlerey und Poesie. *Berlin: Christian Friedrich Voss, 1766*

Lessing was born in Saxony, the son of a pastor, and after a brilliant career at school entered the University of Leipzig as a theology student. Here, however, the two interests, literature and the theatre, which were to dominate his life, first discovered themselves, and no amount of persuasion could induce him to abandon them.

He moved in 1748 to Berlin, and there began the outpouring of writing which lasted the rest of his life. Early in 1751 he became literary critic of the famous *Vossische Zeitung*, which gained him a wider reputation as a reviewer of discernment and learning. In 1753–5 his first collected works were published, already in six volumes, including his play *Miss Sara Sampson*, which introduced the drama of real life, first popularized by Richardson, to Germany. After some wanderings, he returned to Berlin, and there, in 1766 and 1767, two of his greatest works appeared, *Laokoon* and the comedy *Minna von Barnhelm*. The foundation of a national theatre at Hamburg drew Lessing there, but it proved a failure, only memorable now through his *Hamburgische Dramaturgie* (1767–8), a commentary on the theatre's productions which is the first modern handbook of the dramatic art. In 1770 he became librarian of the ducal library at Wolfenbüttel, and there he remained for the rest of his life.

He became involved in theological controversy due to his publication of the so-called 'Wolfenbüttel fragments' of the deistic work of H. S. Reimarus. Assailed by every kind of sectarian prejudice, and prevented from answering by the government, Lessing returned to 'my old pulpit, the stage', with *Nathan der Weise* (1779), a noble plea for toleration which put his adversaries to shame. This was backed with *Die Erziehung des Menschengeschlechts* and *Ernst und Falk*, both of which appeared between 1777 and 1780. But by now Lessing was exhausted, and in 1781 he died, worn out with over-work and anxiety. 'We lose much in him', wrote Goethe, 'more than we think.'

Laokoon is perhaps Lessing's best known work outside Germany, and it has had a world-wide influence. It takes its name from the famous statue discovered at Rome in the sixteenth century. It analyses the differences between the sculptor's treatment of Laocoon wrestling with the serpents and Virgil's treatment of the same theme, and from there goes on to discuss the limits and limitations of all the arts. It contains the first clear statement of the truth, which is now considered axiomatic, that every art is subject to limitations, and can achieve greatness only by a clear understanding of and self-restriction to its proper function. The most telling passages, and those which have borne most fruit, are those on poetry. Lessing knew more about this than about painting and sculpture, for which he was entirely dependent on Winckelmann (210). His exposition of the themes of Homer and Sophocles is especially effective, and he opened up a new prospect in the appreciation of Greek literature.

Yet perhaps Lessing is best judged by the sum of his achievement. He was one of the principal figures in the *Aufklärung*, the emancipation of German literature from the narrow classicism of the French school. It was he, more than any other, who laid the foundations of the intellectual primacy of German writers and thinkers in the nineteenth century, a debt which they were not slow to acknowledge. Without attaching himself to any special philosophical school, he consistently opposed error and dogmatism, and in art, in poetry, in drama and in religion he provided new stimulation. In the words of Macaulay, he was 'beyond all dispute the first critic of Europe'.

214
SCIENTIFIC AGRICULTURE

ARTHUR YOUNG (1741-1820). A Six Weeks Tour, through the Southern Counties of England and Wales. *London: W. Nicoll, 1768*

Arthur Young, like Jethro Tull (188), was a great agricultural reformer whose influence reached far beyond his own country. England, however, with its increased acreage of cultivated land resulting from the enclosure system, and the consequent rise of great landowners and farmers in the eighteenth century, especially welcomed innovations in agricultural methods.

Arthur Young applied statistical methods to the study of agriculture, investigating both the statistics of production and the costs of this particular industry. He obtained his information from a series of extensive tours in England, Ireland and France, where he studied the state of agriculture at first hand. These journeys resulted in the publication of about two hundred and fifty books and pamphlets setting out his ideas and theories. The main points in his programme were: the correct rotation of crops, a maximum net production of agricultural produce, the investigation of the chemistry of soils, which he undertook with the help of Joseph Priestley (217), the increase of the fertility of soil by the use of artificial fertilizers, the improvement of stock-breeding, the establishment of larger farm units, security of tenure, and the improvement of the road system. In short, he introduced many new and scientific ideas into agriculture and farm management.

In 1793 Young was appointed the first Secretary of the newly established Board of Agriculture, a private institution, the predecessor of the Royal Agricultural Society. The series of reports issued by the Board on the agriculture of the British counties (Young himself wrote those on Suffolk, Lincolnshire, Hertfordshire, Norfolk, Essex and Oxfordshire) has remained unsurpassed to this day as a model survey of this particular industry. He also issued the *Annals of Agriculture* from 1784 to 1809 in forty-six volumes (with contributions by George III— under the pseudonym of his Windsor gardener Ralph Robinson—Jeremy Bentham, Joseph Priestley and many others) which also did much to raise the standards of British agriculture.

Young accepted pupils from most parts of Europe and America. His books were translated into several languages and were of particular influence in two of the greatest agricultural countries of the period, France and Russia.

215
THE BIBLE OF MATERIALISM

BARON D'HOLBACH (1723-89). Système de la Nature, par M. Mirabaud. *'London' [Amsterdam]: printer unidentified, 1770*

Paul Heinrich Dietrich, Baron d'Holbach, was born at Heidelsheim in Germany and educated in Holland at Leiden University, before settling in Paris and becoming a naturalized Frenchman. He first became known as a scientist and contributed some four hundred articles to the *Encyclopédie* (200) of his lifelong friend and colleague Denis Diderot. Diderot, d'Alembert, Helvetius, Voltaire and others of the *philosophes* met frequently for dinner and philosophical discussion at the Baron's house, which became known as 'the café of Europe' (among foreign visitors to these dinners were Wilkes, Hume and Sterne). Later Holbach turned from science to more dangerous topics: he wrote, and had published abroad, a stream of books attacking religion in all its aspects, which flooded illegally into France. He could not publish safely under his own name, but had had the ingenious idea of using the names of recently dead French authors. Thus, in 1770, his most famous book, 'The System of Nature', appeared under the name of Jean-Baptiste Mirabaud.

SYSTÊME

DE LA

NATURE.

OU

Des Loix du Monde Phyſique & du Monde Moral.

PAR M. MIRABAUD.

Secrétaire Perpétuel, & l'un des Quarante de l'Académie Françoiſe.

Naturæ rerum vis atque Majeſtas in omnibus momentis fide caret, ſi quis modò partes ejus, ac non totam complectatur animo.

PLIN. HIST. NATUR. *Lib.* VII.

PREMIERE PARTIE.

LONDRES,

MDCCLXX.

In the *Système* Holbach rejected the Cartesian mind–body dualism and attempted to explain all phenomena, physical and mental, in terms of matter in motion. He derived the moral and intellectual faculties from man's sensibility to impressions made by the external world, and saw human actions as entirely determined by pleasure and pain. He continued his direct attack on religion by attempting to show that it derived entirely from habit and custom. But the *Système* was not a negative or destructive book: Holbach rejected religion because he saw it as a wholly harmful influence, and he tried to supply a more desirable alternative. In fact he outlined a whole ethical and political philosophy, which he expanded in his later works (especially *La Morale Universelle*, 1776). It was his aim to derive a morality and an ethic from a completely materialistic and atheistic basis. In spite of his hedonistic explanation of human actions he saw man as a social animal; and indeed it is social utility that is the basis of his ethics. The great problem that he faced, and never

really resolved, was to reconcile his complete determinism with a denial of fatalism in the moral sphere: that is, to reconcile the belief that man's every action is determined by his material circumstances with the conviction that man can himself change these circumstances. But, reconciled or not, he retained until his death both his faith in determinism and an even stronger faith in the power of education.

Holbach was not a great original thinker: his important ideas can be found in predecessors such as Hobbes (138), Locke (164) and La Mettrie, all of whom influenced him greatly. But by combining various elements in their thought and pressing to the logical conclusion he reached the most extreme position in eighteenth-century free-thought. He was far too dogmatically atheistic for most of the *philosophes*, who were 'sceptical' and vacillated between atheism and deism. They criticized the established church, whereas Holbach dared to attack the very idea of God. Holbach's influence was perhaps never very great, but the confident dogmatism and the comprehensiveness of the *Système de la Nature*, which even provoked Voltaire to reply in defence of religion, have ensured its survival as the bible of materialism.

216

THE FIRST
MODERN TREATISE ON LANGUAGE

JOHANN GOTTFRIED HERDER (1744–1803). Abhandlung über den Ursprung der Sprache. *Berlin: Christian Friedrich Voss, 1772*

Herder studied under Kant (226) in Königsberg from 1762 to 1764. He met Goethe (298) in 1770 and in 1766 at Goethe's instance was called as court chaplain to Weimar and later became head of the Lutheran state church of the duchy. He lived there until his death.

Against the generally accepted view that language is a direct and specially bestowed divine gift, Herder proved to his own satisfaction that it was not God who invented language for man but man himself who devised it as a natural means of developing his own reason. This, as introduced in the 'Discussion of the Origin of Language', was then a novel and startlingly unorthodox theory. The pioneer nature of this essay of some two hundred pages is not belied by its universal acceptance by philologists today.

Herder went much further than this in his study of languages and although his reasoning is philosophic rather than scientific it is enormously provocative. In 1784, in his preface to Schmidt's translation of Monboddo's *Of the Origin and Progress of Language*, he praised the author's comparisons between various languages and suggested that a true science of philology would emerge only when these comparisons were much more broadly extended, taking in all known languages, past and present. This, at a time when philological studies were confined almost exclusively to Latin and Greek with additions from the Hebraic languages, was farseeing indeed.

Herder suggested further that languages should be related to stages of cultural development—an idea extensively developed by Humboldt (301). There is clear evidence that in his own mind Herder related comparative philology to comparative studies of mythology and religion. Finally he suggested that as speech, the outstanding invention of the human mind, is the true organ of reason, a fundamental contribution to discovering the real nature of reason might result from the comparisons he suggested.

Herder's stimulating influence upon the intellectual life of Germany can hardly be overestimated. His enthusiasm for Shakespeare was decisive in making the English playwright an integral part of German civilization; his collection of folksongs stressed the unity of poetic production in all ages and zones—he called it 'The Voice of the Nations in Poetry', posthumously watered down to 'Voices...'; his numerous theological tracts initiated the growth of liberal protestantism; his philosophical (or, as we should now say, sociological) studies were designed to promote the reconciliation of the ideals of nationalism and cosmopolitanism. Herder's ideas have permeated the whole world-picture of the nineteenth and twentieth centuries, especially in the Slav countries; yet his influence has been almost entirely indirect, as not one of his own writings is read today.

In his *Ideen zur Philosophie der Geschichte der Menschheit* ('Ideas for a Philosophy of the History of Mankind', 4 vols., 1784–91) Herder amalgamated the theories of Vico (184) and Kant—his own master. 'From stones to crystals, from crystals to metals, from these to plants and animals and from animals to man, we see the form of organization ascend; and with it the powers and propensities of the creature become more variant, until finally they all, so far as possible, unite in the form of man.'

217

OXYGEN FORESHADOWED

JOSEPH PRIESTLEY (1733–1804). Observations on Different Kinds of Air. *In*: Philosophical Transactions of the Royal Society. *London, 1772*

By the mid-eighteenth century the study of chemistry seemed to have made less progress than that of physics under the leadership of Galileo (113, etc.) and Newton (161). Boyle (141, 143) besides going far in experimenting, had extended the mechanical philosophy to chemistry under the influence of theories which went back to Lucretius (87). He had attacked the prevailing view, mainly Paracelsian (110), that there were only a few basic elements, which could be found by distillation. In spite of Boyle's theoretical outlook, mid-eighteenth-century chemistry was dominated by the 'phlogiston' school founded on the work of two German chemists, J. J. Becher and G. E. Stahl. They maintained that a body lost phlogiston (a term coined in the 1730s for a hypothetical principle of inflammability) while burning, ashes being lighter than the combustible; and explained many chemical changes as involving the exchange of phlogiston between the reagents. Only late in the day was it discovered that metals, in calcination, both lose phlogiston (in theory) and gain weight (in fact). This discovery was a serious obstacle to the phlogiston theory.

It is ironic that Priestley, in spite of his many chemical discoveries contributing to the 'chemical revolution', stubbornly supported the phlogiston theory to the end of his life, and that this great theoretical revolution was finally carried out not by him, but by Lavoisier (238). For his contributions to the knowledge of gases were crucial. He improved the technique for studying them by collecting them over mercury instead of water, so that many more gases could be observed. He identified nitrous oxide, nitric oxide, carbon monoxide, ammonia, sulphur dioxide, hydrogen chloride, etc.—to use our modern names for them. On 1 August 1774 he carried out his historic experiment of heating calx of mercury (mercuric acid) in a small tube by focusing light from a burning glass on it; and thus discovered oxygen. He found the substance to be five or six times as 'pure' as ordinary air and by suggesting that it would be particularly good for the lungs foreshadowed our use of oxygen tents. This discovery—made a little earlier and quite independently by the Swedish chemist Scheele—brought Priestley fame and led to a meeting in Paris with Lavoisier and other scientists. Lavoisier repeated the experiment and ultimately gave the substance its modern name—oxygen.

The paper here cited, for which the Royal Society awarded Priestley the Copley medal, announced the discovery of hydrochloric acid and nitric oxide and the use of the latter in measuring the purity of air, which led through the work of Cavendish, Fontana and others to exact eudiometry. Priestley also observed that plants consume carbon dioxide and give out oxygen, thereby purifying air which has been vitiated by combustion, respiration or putrefaction, and that this action takes place only under daylight. This proved of the greatest value for the subsequent work on respiration of Ingenhousz and Senebier.

Priestley was a voluminous writer: under the influence of Franklin (199*) he had published the *History and Present State of Electricity*, 1767, and his largest chemical work is *Experiments and Observations on Different Kinds of Air*, 3 vols., 1774–77, with three supplementary volumes 1779–86. He became a Unitarian minister at the age of twenty-two and in 1761 a teacher at the Warrington Academy. His opposition to the established church, his sympathies with the ideas of the French Revolution and his support of the American colonists against the King made him very unpopular in many circles: while minister of the Congregationalists in Birmingham his house and library were pillaged on 14 July 1791. He fled to London and eventually emigrated to America, where he founded one of the earliest Unitarian Churches.

The centenary of the discovery of oxygen was celebrated at Priestley's American home at Northumberland, Pennsylvania, and was followed in 1876 by the foundation of the American Chemical Society.

Encyclopædia Britannica;

OR, A

DICTIONARY

OF

ARTS and SCIENCES,

COMPILED UPON A NEW PLAN.

IN WHICH

The different SCIENCES and ARTS are digested into
distinct Treatises or Systems;

AND

The various TECHNICAL TERMS, &c. are explained as they occur
in the order of the Alphabet.

ILLUSTRATED WITH ONE HUNDRED AND SIXTY COPPERPLATES.

By a SOCIETY of GENTLEMEN in SCOTLAND.

IN THREE VOLUMES.

VOL. I.

EDINBURGH:

Printed for A. BELL and C. MACFARQUHAR;
And sold by COLIN MACFARQUHAR, at his Printing-office, Nicolson-street.
M.DCC.LXXI.

218

THE BRITANNICA

ENCYCLOPAEDIA BRITANNICA, or a Dictionary of Arts and Sciences. 3 vols. *Edinburgh: For A. Bell and C. Macfarquhar, 1771*

The most famous of all encyclopaedias in the English language was sponsored by 'a Society of Gentlemen in Scotland', which may be as mythical as Beaumarchais's one-man *Sociéte Littéraire et Typographique*, the publishers of the Kehl edition of Voltaire. The Edinburgh 'society' could well have consisted only of the editor, the antiquarian William Smellie (1740–95), the engraver, Andrew Bell (1726–1809), and the printer, Colin Macfarquhar (died 1793), the two last-named being the joint proprietors until Bell bought out his partners.

The subtitle implicitly acknowledges the editor's indebtedness to Harris and Chambers (171), though later on (in the third edition of 1801) the dedication to the King sought to create the impression that the *Britannica* had been conceived as a means 'to counteract the tendency [of anarchy and atheism] of that pestiferous work', the French *Encyclopédie* (200). In fact, Smellie defined its purpose far more sensibly and convincingly in the preface of the first edition: 'Utility ought to be the principal intention of every publication'.

The *Encyclopaedia Britannica* appeared first in numbers, each priced 6*d.*, or 8*d.* on better paper, 1768–71. The precedent of Moréri and Bayle (155) was followed when the second edition, 1778–83, included history and biography; Smellie refused to countenance this suggestion of Bell's and resigned the editorship. From the supplement to the fifth edition, 1816–24, onward the *Encyclopaedia Britannica*, following the example of the

Encyclopédie, appended the signatures of the contributors to articles of original value. There appeared the names of Benjamin Robert Haydon (painting), William Hazlitt (arts), Charles Kingsley (Hypatia), Macaulay (Bunyan, Dr Johnson), Malthus (population), Thomas de Quincey (Alexander Pope, Coleridge), Sir Walter Scott (chivalry) James Watt (steam); and leading scholars and men of letters of all nations have continued to lend the lustre of their names to all subsequent editions.

Although most entries in earlier editions have 'dated', some of the individual articles as well as the editions themselves are still of at least historical interest: the former because of their authors (as indicated above), the latter because they exemplify a definite stage in the development of either scholarship in general or lexicography in particular. Thus the ninth edition, 1875–89, will remain memorable as a main contributor to the advancement of biblical criticism in the English world. In fact its editor, William Robertson Smith, lost his professorial chair in Aberdeen and was tried for heresy by the Free Church of Scotland because of his advocacy of liberal Protestantism. Similarly the eleventh edition, 1910–11, is noteworthy for its index which has justly been described as the best index of any work of reference.

While the *Encyclopaedia Britannica* has gone from strength to strength, it has not been without troubles. It was involved in the bankruptcy (1826) of Archibald Constable, who had acquired the copyright in 1812, and has passed through the hands of various publishers (A. & C. Black, The Times Publishing Company and the Cambridge University Press). It was finally bought by an American syndicate and subsequently transferred to the University of Chicago, an editorial office in London being considered to justify the continuous use of the title.

219

THE FOUNDER OF ANTHROPOLOGY

JOHANN FRIEDRICH BLUMENBACH (1752–1840). De Generis Humani Varietate Nativa. *Göttingen: F. A. Rosenbusch, [1775]*

Johann Friedrich Blumenbach was for nearly seventy years professor of medicine at Göttingen. He wrote a number of valuable works on natural history and comparative anatomy, but today he is chiefly remembered for his work 'On the Native Varieties of the Human Race', now considered as the foundation of the science of physical anthropology—the study of the origin and evolution of the races of men.

He was preceded by Tyson (169) and Linné (192) who had prepared the ground for his studies by relating man to the order of the primates. Linné had distinguished four races of man chiefly by the colour of their skin. From these premises Blumenbach was able to develop the thesis that all living races are varieties of a single species, *homo sapiens*, and that their differences were small compared with those between man and the nearest animal; 'innumerable varieties of mankind run into each other by insensible degrees'. It is not surprising therefore that Blumenbach was opposed to the practice of slavery and the then current belief in the inherent savagery of the coloured races.

Blumenbach studied comparative anatomy and craniology; he had a large collection of skulls which formed part of his great anatomical collection, one of the most famous of his time. He measured methodically the shape of skulls and facial configurations, and the results led him to divide mankind into five racial groups: (1) Caucasian or white—a female Georgian skull happened to be the most symmetrical in his collection, which led him to adopt this term for the white races; (2) Mongolian or yellow; (3) Ethiopian or black; (4) Malayan or brown; (5) American or red. This division has survived to our own day, though with some modification. Prichard (303) in particular was greatly indebted to Blumenbach, as were Lambert Quetelet and Paul Broca.

Blumenbach also observed that chimpanzees are essentially quadrupeds in spite of their occasional erect posture, proving this from the structure of their bones and anticipating thereby some twentieth-century analyses of locomotion. He was also an important representative of the eighteenth-century school of vitalism, largely created by Haller. Blumenbach's conception of the *Bildungstrieb* meant that there was an innate tendency in living creatures towards self-development. This impulse was to be added to irritability, sensibility and contractility as an essential feature of vitalism.

Blumenbach had a great influence on the scientific explorers and travellers of the time; among his pupils were Alexander von Humboldt (320*), Georg Heinrich von Langsdorff, John Sibthorp, Prince Maximilian zu Wied and others. His book was originally composed as the thesis for his doctorate, conferred on 16 September 1775.

officials throughout the Colonies and the following day the text of the Declaration made its first newspaper appearance in the *Philadelphia Evening Post*. Its progress up and down the coast can be followed in its subsequent newspaper publication. On 9 July it appeared in Baltimore, on the 11th in Annapolis and finally on the 19th in Williamsburg. Moving north, it was published in New York on 10 July, New London, Connecticut, on the 12th, Providence on the 13th, and on to Portsmouth, New Hampshire, on the 20th. In addition to the twenty-nine known newspaper printings in July nineteen broadside editions have been recorded as published by January 1777. Of the first printing only fifteen copies are at present known to have survived.

The intent of the Declaration of Independence was not to formulate a new political philosophy but to explain in terms of already accepted ideas the justness of the Colonists' action. John Adams said of it that 'there is not an idea in it but was hackneyed in Congress for two years before'. Indeed, the principal concepts it embodies had found their way into print nearly a century before. The philosophy of natural rights to which the Declaration looks for its main support had been used by Locke (163) in his second treatise on government in 1690 to justify another revolution and had been further expanded by later writers in the course of the eighteenth century, most notably by Rousseau in his *Du Contrat Social*, 1762 (207). By 1776 it had gained wide enough acceptance that Jefferson could appeal to it as common sense. 'Neither aiming at originality of principles or sentiments, nor yet copied from any particular and previous writing, it was intended to be an expression of the American mind', he wrote some years later. It remains as a continuing embodiment of both an important historical event and of those truths we hold to be self-evident.

220

THE DECLARATION OF INDEPENDENCE

In Congress, 4 July 1776, A Declaration. *Philadelphia: John Dunlap, 1776*

On 2 July 1776 'the Representatives of the United States of America in General Congress assembled' resolved 'that these United Colonies are, and of right ought to be free and independent states'. Two days later, behind the locked doors of the State House in Philadelphia, the Committee of Five (made up of Thomas Jefferson, John Adams, Benjamin Franklin, Roger Sherman and Robert R. Livingston), presented before Congress the draft of a declaration on which they had been at work since mid-June, intended to justify to the world the action which the Colonies had taken. After some discussion and a number of changes in wording the document was approved. Under the watchful eyes of the Committee of Five it was set in type and sometime on the night of 4 July or the morning of 5 July the historic 'Declaration of Independence' came off the press of the Philadelphia printer John Dunlap.

From Philadelphia the news spread rapidly. Copies of Dunlap's broadside were despatched on 5 July to various

221

THE AGE OF 'LAISSEZ-FAIRE'

Adam Smith (1723–90). An Inquiry into the Nature and Causes of the Wealth of Nations. 2 vols. *London: W. Strahan and T. Cadell, 1776*

Adam Smith was born at Kirkcaldy in Fife, the son of the comptroller of the Customs there. At the age of three he was carried off by tinkers, but was soon recovered. His powers of application and memory developed early, and in 1737 he went to Glasgow University where he studied mathematics and natural philosophy; three years later he went on to Oxford where he remained for seven years, studying moral and political science and ancient and modern languages. In 1748 he gave some lectures in Edinburgh where he became a friend of Hume (194); in 1751 he removed to Glasgow, where for twelve years he was professor of moral philosophy. There he wrote his *Theory of Moral Sentiments*, 1759, which first carried his fame to the outside world; it was, he said later, 'by far the most useful, and therefore by far the happiest period of my life'. Then in 1763 he undertook the charge of the young Duke of Buccleuch on his travels abroad. They spent eighteen months at Toulouse and returned to Paris where they met Quesnay, Turgot, d'Alembert and Helvetius. They returned home in 1766; the Duke kept up his friendship with Smith and obtained for him the appointment of a commissioner of Customs which he held for the rest of his life. The next ten years Smith spent in the writing and perfecting of *The Wealth of Nations*, begun at Toulouse. In 1776 it was published; Smith came to London and remained there for two years, making friends with Gibbon, Burke and Reynolds. Then he returned to Edinburgh, where he died.

The history of economic theory up to the end of the nineteenth century consists of two parts: the mercantilist phase which was based not so much on a doctrine as on a system of practice which grew out of social conditions; and the second phase which saw the development of the theory that the individual had the right to be unimpeded in the exercise of economic activity. While it cannot be said that Smith invented the latter theory—the physiocrats had already suggested it and Turgot in particular had constructed an organized study of social wealth—his work is the first major expression of it. He begins with the thought that labour is the source from which a nation derives what is necessary to it. The improvement of the division of labour is the measure of productivity and in it lies the human propensity to barter and exchange: 'labour is the real measure of the exchangeable value of all commodities...it is their real price; money is their nominal price only'. Labour represents the three essential elements—wages, profit and rent—and these three also constitute income. From the working of the economy, Smith passes to its matter—'stock'—which compasses all that man owns either for his own consumption or for the return which it brings him. *The Wealth of Nations* ends with a history of economic development, a definitive onslaught on the mercantile system, and some prophetic speculations on the limits of economic control.

Where the political aspects of human rights had taken two centuries to explore, Smith's achievement was to bring the study of economic aspects to the same point in a single work. *The Wealth of Nations* is not a system, but as a provisional analysis it is completely convincing. The certainty of its criticism and its grasp of human nature have made it the first and greatest classic of modern economic thought.

such as Voltaire (202), are still quoted with respect, the *Decline and Fall* is the only historical narrative prior to Macaulay which continues to be reprinted and actually read. Gibbon was also fortunate in the choice of his publisher, William Strahan—the friend of Dr Johnson, Benjamin Franklin, David Hume—who, together with Cadell, was also the publisher of Adam Smith and James Macpherson. Strahan was the first to appreciate the importance of Gibbon's work: having read the manuscript of the first volume, he immediately doubled the printing order—and the first edition of one thousand copies was sold within a fortnight.

Gibbon was widely read in the literatures of the Greeks and Romans, French, Italians and English, keenly interested in history and natural science, a student of military and political affairs, a Member of Parliament (1774–83) and of Shelburne's government (1779–82). He was equally at home in France, Switzerland, Italy or England. It was on 15 October 1764 among the ruins of the Capitol, he tells us, that he 'first conceived the idea' of his life-work, which, in twenty years' labour, expanded into a comprehensive picture of the whole Mediterranean world from the death of Marcus Aurelius (A.D. 180) to the fall of Constantinople in 1453.

To this task Gibbon brought a width of vision and a critical mastery of the available sources which have not been equalled to this day; and the result was clothed in an inimitable prose. It was his good fortune, as Lytton Strachey observed, that 'the material with which he had to cope was still just not too voluminous to be digested by a single extremely competent mind. In the following century even a Gibbon would have collapsed under the accumulated mass of knowledge at his disposal.' As it was, he was able to dominate the facts. Gibbon's continuous hold on us is the more remarkable in that his main thesis—that the fall of Rome was chiefly due to the victory of Christianity—has proved untenable. Moreover, his disparagement of genuine Christian piety as well as silly Christian superstitions is often carried to extremes; although he is no less derisive of the shallow rationalism and timid prevarication of Voltaire, with whom he shares the distinction of a permanent place in the *Index Librorum Prohibitorum* (82).

BIBLIOGRAPHY: J. E. Norton, *A Bibliography of the Works of Edward Gibbon* (Oxford, 1940).

222

DECLINE AND FALL

EDWARD GIBBON (1737–94). The History of the Decline and Fall of the Roman Empire. 6 vols. *London: W. Strahan and T. Cadell, 1776–88*

This masterpiece of historical penetration and literary style has remained one of the ageless historical works which, like the writings of Macaulay (328) and Mommsen (337*), maintain their hold upon the layman and continue to stimulate the scholar although they have been superseded in many, if not most, details by subsequent advances of research and changes in the climate of opinion. Whereas other eighteenth-century writers in this field,

---

223

A NEW CONTINENT

JAMES COOK (1728–79). A Voyage towards the South Pole, and round the World. Performed in His Majesty's Ships the Resolution and Adventure, in the Years 1772, 1773, 1774 and 1775. 2 vols. *London: W. Strahan and T. Cadell, 1777*

This is the official account of the second of the three great voyages by Captain James Cook, one of the most illustrious of English navigators. Cook, a native of Yorkshire, was apprenticed to a Whitby shipowner and then joined the Royal Navy as an able seaman, taking part in the Seven Years War and the capture of Quebec by Wolfe. The excellent surveys he made between 1759 and 1767 of the St Lawrence River, Newfoundland and Nova Scotia made him known to the Royal Society and the Admiralty so that in 1768 he was given command of the ship *Endeavour*. Together with a scientific party under Sir Joseph Banks, Cook sailed on to Tahiti to observe the transit of the planet Venus in June 1769, to search for and investigate the supposed southern continent, and to annex any available new territory for Great Britain.

On this first voyage, 25 August 1768 to 12 July 1771, Cook circumnavigated New Zealand and for the first time explored the east coast of Australia (the earlier Dutch navigators, notably Tasman, had explored the northern, western and southern coasts) of which he took possession for Great Britain; he also sailed through the straits separating New Guinea and Australia. On the second, and historically most important, voyage (13 July 1772 to 30 July 1775) he began by cruising as far south as possible round the edge of the antarctic ice. He again visited New Zealand and, cruising through the Pacific, discovered, or explored again, many of the islands, in particular New Caledonia, Palmerston and Norfolk Islands, Easter Island, the Marquesas, New Hebrides, Tonga, the South Sandwich Islands and South Georgia.

The third voyage (11 July 1776 to 4 October 1780) was undertaken in search of the North-West Passage from Europe to the East. After again visiting Tasmania, New Zealand and many Pacific islands, Cook sailed on to North America, discovering on the way the Cook Islands and the Hawaiian group. He charted the North American coast from Oregon as far north as the Bering Strait, where the ice turned him back. On the way back the great explorer was killed in a fight with natives in Hawaii.

Cook earned his place in history by opening up the Pacific to western civilization and by the foundation of British Australia. The world was given for the first time an essentially complete knowledge of the Pacific Ocean and Australia, and Cook proved once and for all that there was no great southern continent, as had always been believed. He also suggested the existence of antarctic land in the southern ice ring, a fact which was not proved until the explorations of the nineteenth century.

Cook was a brilliant navigator and hydrographer, an excellent administrator and planner, and probably the first sea captain to realize the importance of preserving the health and well-being of his crew. He did everything possible to maintain their physical fitness and the cleanliness of both men and ships. He conquered the hitherto prevalent scurvy by cutting down the consumption of salt meat and by always having fresh vegetables and fruit on board; in particular limes (first suggested by James Lind in 1775), whence the terms 'lime-juicer' and 'limey' for a British ship and her sailors. On his second voyage, of 112 men on board the *Resolution*, which he commanded, Cook lost only one by disease—and that not scurvy— a unique achievement in his time.

BIBLIOGRAPHY: Maurice Holmes, *Captain James Cook, R.N., F.R.S., a Bibliographical Excursion* (London, 1952).

224
PRISON REFORM

JOHN HOWARD (1726–90). The State of the Prisons in England and Wales. *Warrington: Printed by William Eyres, and sold by T. Cadell and N. Conant, London, 1777*

From the casual experience of visiting Bedford Gaol—one of the most influential prisons in English history (see 156)—came Howard's determination to improve prison conditions. His single-handed campaign not only caused a revolution in his lifetime, but is the direct progenitor of subsequent work in the most critical branch of penal reform.

Howard, after some early adventures on the continent, might have spent the rest of his life in quiet philanthropy on his paternal estate. However, in 1773 he accepted office as high sheriff of Bedford, and when the assizes were held he insisted on visiting the gaol. The squalor and misery he found made a lasting impression on him; even more did the fact that the gaolers were dependent on the prisoners' fees for their own livelihood and that in consequence many prisoners were wrongly detained because they could not pay the gaol delivery fees. He proposed to the justices that the gaoler should be paid a salary instead, and was told to find a precedent for it. Accordingly he went from county to county, and although he found no precedent he saw enough to determine him to devote himself to prison reform.

The following year Howard gave evidence before a committee of the House of Commons, and received its thanks for 'the humanity and zeal which have led him to visit the several gaols of this Kingdom'. Immediately an Act was passed liberating, free of charges, all prisoners against whom no true bill had been found, and providing a salary for gaolers from the county rate. It was followed by another Act providing for improvements to existing gaols and better care, especially medical care, for prisoners. Howard characteristically had the new regulations printed in large type and sent to every gaoler and warder in the country. Encouraged by this success he then set out on a systematic tour of British and continental prisons. He noticed the comparative absence of crime in the Low Countries and saw the cause in the reformatory treatment there bestowed on criminals. The French authorities tried to prevent his access to their prisons, but he was able to circumvent them and published the results of his inspection. This and the report of his expedition as a whole formed part of *The State of Prisons*, the first major practical work on the subject (Beccaria's book—see 209—was primarily theoretical).

Again the effect was instantaneous, and another bill was passed establishing two 'penitentiaries' on the lines of those Howard had seen in the Low Countries, where, by solitary confinement, adequate religious instruction, and instruction in the habits of industry, prisoners might be better fitted to take a place in society. Further journeys resulted in two large appendixes to his book, separately published in 1780 and 1784. Thereafter Howard's direct involvement with prison reform ceased, and he devoted himself to the study and prevention of gaol fever, a permanent hazard in all prisons. Finally he contracted the disease himself in the Crimea where he died of it in 1790.

Howard's enthusiasm was remarkable not only in its immediate effectiveness, but also in the universal affection which he inspired. His cause found permanent support, and is commemorated in a body of which he would have been proud to acknowledge the foundation, the Howard League for Penal Reform.

225

MESMERISM

FRIEDRICH ANTON MESMER (1733–1815). *Mémoire sur la Découverte du Magnétisme Animal. Geneva; & Paris, P. Fr. Didot le jeune, 1779*

German romanticism and mysticism of the eighteenth century provided a fertile soil for the achievements of Anton Mesmer, an Austrian physician whose name is perpetuated in 'Mesmerism', the manifesto of which is his 'Memoir on the Discovery of Animal Magnetism'.

MÉMOIRE
SUR LA DÉCOUVERTE
DU
MAGNÉTISME
ANIMAL;

Par M. MESMER, Docteur en Médecine de la Faculté de Vienne.

A GENEVE;

Et se trouve

A PARIS,

Chez P. FR. DIDOT le jeune, Libraire-Imprimeur de MONSIEUR, quai des Augustins.

M. DCC. LXXIX.

Since the days of primitive and magic medicines, and later those of the Royal Touch (for the cure of scrofula) curative properties had been attributed to the laying on of hands. Mesmer practised a similar method. He maintained that a magnetic fluid pervades the universe, exists in every living being, and affects the nervous system. Experimenting with the use of this 'magnetism' he

found that there was a healing magnetic power in his own hands and that he could obtain results in treating nervous disorders without a magnet, a faculty he called 'animal magnetism'. Mesmer induced sleep and did, in fact, use hypnotic power (the term 'hypnosis' replaced 'mesmeric sleep' when coined by the Scottish neurologist James Brain in *A Practical Essay on the Curative Agency of Neuro-hypnotism*, 1842). Paracelsus (110) had spoken of the influence of imagination in curing diseases, and Helmont of the occult power of magnetism, but this kind of treatment had never been applied systematically.

Mesmer went to Paris, was patronized by the King and Queen and corresponded with George Washington. Fantastic scenes took place in his magnificent consulting rooms, where patients sat round a special tub, while Mesmer appeared, clad in lilac silk, waving an iron wand: perfume, theatrical costumes and dramatic illumination were all part of the treatment.

Louis XVI set up a committee, with Benjamin Franklin as chairman and Lavoisier, Guillotin and Jean Sylvan Bailly as some of the members, to investigate 'animal magnetism'. Their report condemned 'mesmerism' medically; but the idea had taken hold and spread all over Europe, being exploited by such charlatans as Count Cagliostro, and Elisha Perkins with his metallic tractors in America. There were also many serious disciples such as Puysegur, who developed hypnotism on scientific lines.

Mesmer himself was undoubtedly sincere, despite his theatrics; but he never realized the implications of his discovery and methods. Suggestibility on the part of the patient can, without question, be the key to his recovery; and having found this out Mesmer became, unwittingly, a pioneer of psychotherapy. Since his time the investigation of how to release subconscious states through auto- and hetero-suggestion has continued, and the whole field of extra-sensory perception and spiritualism has affinity with mesmerism. Much more important scientifically were the experiments of Braid in Scotland and Charcot in Paris, and the development of psychoanalysis: Freud's first experiments (389) were on hypnotic patients; and Jung was particularly close to mesmerism in his belief that consciousness could transcend time and space.

226

PURE REASON

IMMANUEL KANT (1724–1804). *Critik der Reinen Vernunft. Riga: Johann Friedrich Hartknoch, 1781*

Kant was born in Königsberg and spent most of his life there. His grandfather had been an immigrant from Scotland, so it is possible to claim him as—however distantly —a fellow-countryman of the only philosopher who had a significant influence on the development of his thought, David Hume (194).

His first published works dealt largely with physical theories. It is enough to notice that Kant's dissatisfaction with the Cartesian (129) and the Leibnizian (177) systems is first made plain in them: they laid the theoretical foundations upon which Laplace (252) built to create the 'Kant–Laplace' theory of the origin of the universe.

Then in 1755 he obtained a post in the university, where his lectures, which had first dealt simply with physical subjects, widened in scope to include almost all branches of philosophy. In 1770 Kant became professor of logic and metaphysics, and at this point there is a sudden falling off in the number of his publications. The cause of

Critik

der

reinen Vernunft

von

Immanuel Kant

Professor in Königsberg.

Riga,
verlegts Johann Friedrich Hartknoch
1 7 8 1.

this became clear eleven years later when 'The Critique of Pure Reason' appeared; and with it Kant became world-famous.

Kant's great achievement was to conclude finally the lines on which philosophical speculation had proceeded in the eighteenth century, and to open up a new and more comprehensive system of dealing with the problems of philosophy. Of the two main systems which preceded his own, Kant had little or no sympathy with the metaphysical categorization of the Cartesians, and inclined more to the empirical methods of Locke (164) and Leibniz. But just as the extension of Locke's thesis by Hume had ended in the apparent negation of real cognition, so, Kant came to realize, there was an equal difficulty in the monads of Leibnizian metaphysics (177),

which produced an equally negative result. Of the two, therefore, Kant leaned towards Hume as presenting the more realistic view, and in doing so discovered that Hume's negative findings could be turned to fruitful use. To Kant the problem was to explain how it is possible for the individual thinking subject to connect together the parts of his experience in the form we call cognition. The essence of cognition is to him a *synthetic* act, an act of combining the detached elements of experience. Synthesis is not explicable as an act of pure thought, which is solely analytic in function, nor simply as the effect of external realities on our faculties. If real experience is a matter of knowledge, it is as the reaction of given material to synthetic combination. Form and matter may be regarded for the purposes of critical analysis as separable, but in experience they are necessarily united.

The influence of Kant is paramount in the critical method of modern philosophy. No other thinker has been able to hold with such firmness the balance between speculative and empirical ideas. His penetrating analysis of the elements involved in synthesis, and the subjective process by which these elements are realized in the individual consciousness, demonstrated the operation of 'pure reason'; and the simplicity and cogency of his arguments achieved immediate fame.

Kant's achievements in other branches of philosophy were equally distinguished and fruitful. The 'categorical imperative'—the foundation of modern ethics—stems from the *Critik der Praktischen Vernunft*, 1788, and the basis of practical pacifism is contained in *Zum Ewigen Frieden*, 1795, which contains an outline of a world league of nations. His methods fascinated Coleridge; they were amplified by Fichte (244); and they dominated western philosophical thought throughout the nineteenth century, as they do today.

227

A NEW PLANET

FREDERICK WILLIAM HERSCHEL (1738–1822). On the Proper Motion of the Sun and Solar System. *In:* Philosophical Transactions of the Royal Society. *London, 1783*

Between 1780 and 1821 Sir William Herschel produced some seventy papers, mostly published in the *Philosophical Transactions of the Royal Society*. These were the results of his astronomical observations which have earned him the title of 'Father of sidereal astronomy'. The present paper is one of the most important in the series.

Herschel (see also 254) was born in Hanover (named Friedrich Wilhelm), the son of a bandsman. He followed his father's profession and became an oboe player in the Guards. In 1757 he left for England where he continued to earn his living as a musician, first as a teacher in Leeds and then as organist in Halifax and Bath. He had already begun to study astronomy in his spare time and in 1772 he brought over his sister Caroline to help him. She proved an invaluable assistant, and became a considerable observer in her own right.

Herschel could not afford to buy expensive telescopes, so he made his own and in 1774 began his observations with a Newtonian reflecting telescope of 6 feet focal length. On 13 March 1781 he made the famous discovery which enabled him to give up his profession and devote the remainder of his life to astronomy. On that day he observed in the constellation Taurus an object which showed as a perceptible disc. He thought at first it was a comet, but on further observation he identified it as a planet moving outside the orbit of Saturn. It was the first planet to be discovered in historic times. Herschel named it Georgium Sidus in honour of George III, but it has since been known as Uranus. Herschel was elected a Fellow of the Royal Society, received the Copley medal and became the King's personal astronomer, with a salary.

Herschel was a very skilful mechanic, constructing many instruments and grinding hundreds of mirrors himself. In 1789 he constructed at Upton, near Slough, the celebrated giant telescope of 40 feet focal length with a 4 foot aperture, which remained a local landmark for many years. With these instruments Herschel carried out his immense survey of the heavens. During the seventeenth century the time-honoured belief that stars are fixed immovably to a crystal sphere had been finally abandoned; Herschel now set himself to finding out how the stars are distributed in space and how they are related to each other. He adopted a method of 'star-gauging', as he called it, by which he counted systematically the stars to be seen in each section of the heavens on which he directed his telescope. He concluded that the entire system of stars is of lens shape, the breadth of the lens being in the plane of the Milky Way and the sun being near the centre of this lens. He discovered hundreds of nebulae and came to the conclusion that these did not all consist of separate stars, but that some at least were 'of a shining fluid'; i.e. that these were the gaseous nebulae from which star clusters or single stars would gradually be condensed. He described the movement through space of the whole stellar system, which he believed to progress gradually towards a point in the constellation Hercules. Perhaps Herschel's most notable discovery was that pairs of stars in close continuity—the binary stars—move around each other according to the laws of gravitation; thus indicating the universality of natural law. Among many other discoveries Herschel identified two satellites of Uranus and two satellites of Saturn.

He had a notable successor in his son, Sir John Herschel (1792–1871), who completed one section of his father's work by his observations carried out at Cape Town for the southern celestial hemisphere.

228

SUNDAY SCHOOLS

ROBERT RAIKES (1735–1811). The Gloucester Journal. *Gloucester: Printed by R. Raikes, 3 November 1783*

Raikes was not a great educationalist like Pestalozzi (258) or Froebel (317). He was, rather, a philanthropist, and his inheritance of a country newspaper, *The Gloucester Journal*, gave him excellent opportunities as a publicist. He did not claim to be the originator of Sunday Schools. On the contrary, it was a Sunday School started a little earlier by Thomas Stock at Ashbury in Berkshire that inspired Raikes in 1780 to set one up at his own parish church, St Mary le Crypt, and he asked Stock to draw up the rules for it.

In 1768 Raikes had appealed in his paper for funds to relieve the wretched lot of prisoners in the local gaol and his efforts are favourably mentioned by Howard (224). On 3 November 1783 he inserted a paragraph on the Sunday School movement in the vicinity of Gloucester without mentioning his own name. Inquiries poured in from all over the kingdom, and one of his correspondents contributed a note on the subject to the *Gentleman's Magazine*.

In 1786 Raikes's friend Samuel Glasse preached an eloquent sermon on behalf of the movement at nearby Painswick, and in the same year published a treatise on *The Piety, Wisdom and Policy of Promoting Sunday Schools*. He stated that two hundred thousand children were then in attendance. In 1789 the movement spread to the United States. The Sunday School Union was founded in 1803; and at the 'jubilee' of Raikes's first school celebrated in 1831—one year late—there were said to be a million and a quarter Sunday scholars. It should be emphasized that for the vast majority of these children, simple and elementary though it might be, this was the only form of education open to them; since, until the middle of the nineteenth century, the education of the poor remained largely in the hands of the Church and other voluntary organizations.

229

THE FIRST AERIAL VOYAGE

BARTHÉLEMI FAUJAS DE SAINT-FOND (1745–1819). Description des Expériences de la Machine Aérostatique de MM. de Montgolfier. 2 vols. *Paris: Cuchet, 1783–4*

There are dual claimants to priority in ballooning, J.A.C. Charles and the Montgolfier brothers. Faujas de Saint-Fond, an eminent French scientist, was at once the sponsor of the Montgolfiers and their chronicler. He set on foot a subscription to repeat an experiment conducted by them in June 1783 when 'a cloud enclosed in a bag', in fact a linen globe of 105 feet circumference in which the air was heated by a straw fire, made a successful ascent at Annonay. The subscribers preferred the hydrogen-filled balloon devised by Charles. This was only 13 feet in diameter and its ascent took place from the Champs de Mars in Paris in August 1783.

This feat, however, was surpassed by the Montgolfiers in September when they successfully launched a balloon carrying a sheep, a cock and a duck, and even more sensationally in November when, after some tethered experiments, Pilâtre de Rozier, accompanied by the Marquis d'Arlandes, made the first aerial voyage in history. They ascended from the Château de la Muette in the Bois de Boulogne, sustained their flight for five-and-a-half miles across Paris and descended after twenty-five minutes on the outskirts of the city.

Faujas de Saint-Fond's 'Description of the Aerial Machine of MM. Montgolfier' was the earliest record of this flight, written and published in the very year of its accomplishment. It is the first serious treatise on aerostation as a practical possibility.

In December 1783 Charles made a much longer ascent in a hydrogen balloon of his own devising. He stayed up for two hours. He is responsible for the main features of modern balloon construction.

(29)

EXPÉRIENCE

FAITE avec un Ballon de 70 pieds de hauteur fur 40 de diamètre, dans le jardin de M. Reveillon, rue de Montreuil, fauxbourg S. Antoine, le 12 Septembre 1783, en préfence de Meffieurs les Commiffaires de l'Académie Royale des Sciences.

LA Machine aéroſtatique que M. de Montgolfier faiſoit exécuter au fauxbourg S. Antoine, étoit en toile de canevas, doublée tant en dedans qu'en dehors d'un fort papier.

Sa coupe géométrique étoit formée ;

1°. Par un priſme de 24 pieds de hauteur :

2°. Par une pyramide de 27 pieds ½ qui devoit couronner le priſme ;

3°. Par un cône tronqué, de 18 pieds ½, deſtiné à former la partie inférieure de la Machine.

Chacune de ces portions étoit compoſée de 24 bandes ou méridiens, réunis & couſus enſemble.

En cet état la Machine développée, pleine de gaz, & tendue dans tous les points, devoit

The balloon was very soon used for scientific research, the ascents of James Glaisher and his meterological observations being perhaps the most important early examples. In 1794 J. M. J. Contelli, a colonel in the French revolutionary army, made the first military reconnaissance by balloon; and the balloon-post during the Siege of Paris in 1870 is familiar. Protracted efforts towards dirigibility culminated in the success of Graf Zeppelin early in the present century; the Germans used airships extensively in the First World War and the U.S. Navy in the Second. But some spectacular disasters put an end, seemingly for good, to the development of dirigibles for civilian transport.

230

FIGARO

PIERRE AUGUSTIN CARON DE BEAUMARCHAIS (1732–99). La Folle Journée, ou le Mariage de Figaro. [*Paris*]: *Ruault, 1785*

Beaumarchais was a watchmaker's son, once a King's favourite, who used to boast that his patent of nobility was among the most genuine extant, for he had bought it, paid cash, and could produce the receipt.

He was undoubtedly a rascal and had built up a great fortune by questionable means, but he had an able pen, and 'The Day of Folly, or the Marriage of Figaro' is acknowledged as his masterpiece.

In 1784, the year of its first performance, it was repeated sixty-six times, and the text was continually reprinted. Cordier's bibliography records fifteen editions in French within twelve months of its first appearance. It was also immediately translated and/or produced in Stockholm, Nuremberg, Lisbon, Madrid, London, Copenhagen, St Petersburg and Buda-Pesth.

Public interest was whetted by its satirical references to the aristocracy, and it was this that first won it fame. Although greeted with enthusiasm by French society, it in fact contributed largely to its destruction. It is, however, the music of Mozart which has immortalized it as the perfect type of comedy. To Beaumarchais, a controversial figure, whose other principal achievement was his edition of the complete works of Voltaire, its transformation would probably be surprising, but no one can doubt its immortality.

BIBLIOGRAPHY: This French edition was preceded by at least one unauthorized edition with an Amsterdam imprint.

231

'THE BOAST OF SCOTLAND'

ROBERT BURNS (1759–96). Poems, chiefly in the Scottish Dialect. *Kilmarnock: Printed by John Wilson, 1786*

There has never been a more truly national poet than Burns. Himself of humble origin, he spoke the language of the people and his songs are part of the air breathed by Scots the world over. It has been said of *Lyrical Ballads* (256) that no clue can be gained from them that 'men eat or drink, marry or are given in marriage'. No one could say that of Burns. He may have gone to the other extreme, but his lyrics are as full of life as he was himself. They are 'the links, the watch-words, the masonic symbols of Scottish life'. The wild enthusiasm of Burns's compatriots, especially the expatriates in England and the U.S.A., and especially on the occasion of 'Burns Nicht', all too easily obscures the fact that Burns is not only the greatest Scots poet but one of the great poets of any age and nation.

BIBLIOGRAPHY: J. W. Egerer. *A Bibliography of Robert Burns* (Edinburgh, 1965).

232

THE ABOLITION OF SLAVERY

(a) THOMAS CLARKSON (1760–1846). An Essay on the Slavery and Commerce of the Human Species, particularly the African. *London: T. Cadell and J. Phillips, 1786*; (b) WILLIAM WILBERFORCE (1759–1833), A Letter on the Abolition of the Slave Trade. *London: T. Cadell and W. Davies, and J. Hatchard, 1807*

A L E T T E R

ON

THE ABOLITION

OF THE

S L A V E   T R A D E ;

ADDRESSED TO THE

FREEHOLDERS AND OTHER INHABITANTS

OF

YORKSHIRE.

By W. WILBERFORCE, Esq.

" There is neither Greek nor Jew, circumcision nor uncircumcision, Barbarian, Scythian, bond nor free: but CHRIST is all, and in all.   Put on therefore bowels of mercies, kindness," &c.—COL. iii. 11. 12.

" GOD hath made of one blood all nations of men, for to dwell on all the face of the earth."—ACTS xvii. 26.

LONDON:
Printed by Luke Hansard & Sons,
FOR T. CADELL AND W. DAVIES, STRAND; And,
J. HATCHARD, PICCADILLY.

1807.

William Wilberforce came of a long established Yorkshire family, and most of his active life was spent representing the county in Parliament. It was in Parliament that the final battle against slavery was fought and won; a battle which Wilberforce undertook in 1787, maintained almost single-handed, and whose successful conclusion followed one month after his death.

Wilberforce was not the first to take up the cause. Granville Sharp had won the Somersett Case in 1772, and when Thomas Clarkson wrote his famous prize essay in 1785, published in 1786 as the first of the works noted above, a group gathered together and determined to take action. But, lacking representation in Parliament, aboli-

tion seemed far off. Then in 1787 two important things happened. First, after some discussion with Pitt, his life-long friend, who told him that he must not 'lose time, or the question would be taken up by another', Wilberforce resolved to espouse the cause in Parliament. The foot of the tree at Holwood Park, Pitt's country house, where the decision was taken, is marked with a stone. Secondly, Clarkson and Sharp formed a permanent committee to lobby for abolition, inaugurated after a dinner at which Wilberforce made his decision public, on 22 May.

The first action of the committee was to produce *A Summary View of the Slave Trade*, compiled by Clarkson from evidence collected in his travels from port to port. This was the prelude to parliamentary action. Wilberforce, who had already spoken for abolition in the House, should have introduced the first measure, but was prevented by ill-health; and it was Pitt who undertook it. He saw the first minor bill, for limiting the number of slaves carried on any ship to a figure in proportion with the tonnage, safely passed in 1788. Then Wilberforce returned to sponsor the main bill. Well aware of the dangers of haste, he was subjected to deferment after deferment forced by those acting in the West Indian planters' interests, and despite the most deliberate and cautious handling of the bill in committee, the motion for abolition was finally defeated in April 1791.

Undeterred by this setback, Wilberforce and the committee set to work once more, and after further delays and setbacks brought the matter up under the new Whig administration in 1806. Several more restrictive measures were passed, and finally on 25 March 1807 the royal assent was given to a bill abolishing the trade in slaves.

This, signalized by Wilberforce's *Letter*, was the first major victory for the movement. There remained some distance yet to go. The 1807 Act was strengthened in 1811 by another making the trade a felony, and in 1823 the Anti-Slavery Society was given permanent form, Clarkson and Wilberforce being Vice-Presidents. In 1825 Wilberforce retired from Parliament, and the struggle was carried on by others. As he lay dying in 1833, news was brought to him of the second reading of the Emancipation Bill, by which all slaves were freed and slavery abolished in all the dominions of the British Crown. Between them, Clarkson and Wilberforce had achieved and seen accomplished the triumphant conclusion of a campaign, carried on by word of mouth and by means of the printing press, for one of the fundamental rights of man.

233

ACOUSTICS

ERNST FLORENS FRIEDRICH CHLADNI (1756–1827). (a) Neue Entdeckungen über die Theorie des Klanges. *Leipzig: Weidmann, 1787*; (b) Die Akustik. *Leipzig: Breitkopf & Härtel, 1802*

The earliest contributions to a scientific study of sound were made almost simultaneously, but independently, in the seventeenth century by Galileo (113, etc.) and Mersenne, both of whom tested and tabulated the sounds produced by strings vibrating at various speeds.

Chladni, professor of physics in Breslau, was the first to reduce the general association between vibration and pitch to a tabular basis and thus to lay the foundation of the modern science of acoustics. His first results were reported in 'New Discoveries in the Theory of Sound', 1787, and were greatly enlarged in 'Acoustics', 1802. He spread sand on plates made of metal and glass, which were fixed in clamps. He then applied a violin bow to the edge of each plate and recorded the patterns produced thereby in the sand. These figures are still known by Chladni's name.

The science of acoustics was further developed by Ohm (289) and by Helmholtz (323) in his *Tonempfindungen*, 1863.

234

THE AMERICAN CONSTITUTION INTERPRETED

ALEXANDER HAMILTON (1757–1804), JAMES MADISON (1751–1836) and JOHN JAY (1745–1829). The Federalist. 2 vols. *New York: J. and A. McLean, 1788*

When Alexander Hamilton invited his fellow New Yorker John Jay and James Madison, a Virginian, to join him in writing the series of essays published as *The Federalist*, it was to meet the immediate need of convincing the reluctant New York State electorate of the necessity of ratifying the newly proposed Constitution of the United States. The eighty-five essays, under the pseudonym 'Publius', were designed as political propaganda, not as a treatise of political philosophy. In spite of this *The Federalist* survives as one of the new nation's most important contributions to the theory of government.

The Federal Convention at Philadelphia (May–September 1787) had drawn up the proposed Constitution which was to be sent to the several States for ratification. Both because of anticipated difficulties in getting it past certain State legislatures, and because it was felt that the Constitution should derive from the people, it was determined that ratification should be by special State Conventions elected for that purpose. Supporters of the Constitution had a twofold battle to wage: first to elect sympathetic delegates to the Conventions, and then to win the debates in the Conventions themselves. It was as a weapon to be used in this battle in New York State that Hamilton conceived *The Federalist*. Yet as a propaganda weapon it failed to achieve its goal: the New York voters elected forty-six members from the party opposed to the Constitution and only nineteen favourable to it. The ultimate thirty to twenty-seven vote for ratification was due less to the arguments contained in *The Federalist* than to the more immediate political consideration that a favourable vote had already been cast in several States, including Virginia, and to the rumoured threat that New York City would secede from the State and apply for admission in its own right.

The first number of *The Federalist* appeared on 27 October 1787 in *The Independent Journal, or The General Advertiser* and newspaper publication continued in this and three other papers, *The New York Packet, The Daily Advertiser*, and *The New York Journal and Daily Patriotic Register*, through number 77, 2 April 1788. The first thirty-six essays were published in book form on 22 March 1788 by J. and A. McLean of New York and a second volume containing essays 37–85 followed on 28 May. Thus numbers 78–85 were published in book form before they appeared in the popular press. Their newspaper publication, 14 June–16 August, was withheld until the New York State Convention met at Albany. In 1799 the two McLean volumes were reissued with cancel title-pages by John Tiebout. The second edition, edited by George F. Hopkins, with revisions which while not by Hamilton apparently had his approval, appeared on 8 December 1802. The last edition with authorial revisions, this time by Madison, came out in August 1818.

All three authors of *The Federalist* represented the anxieties of men of property and show an underlying distrust of popular democracy. Hamilton especially expresses a stronger concern for the rights of property than for the natural rights of 'life, liberty, and the pursuit of happiness' as outlined by Jefferson in the Declaration of Independence (220). These men saw a strong central government as essential to the maintenance of a stable economy. Their conservative views regarding property rights have had a lasting effect on U.S. Constitutional law. As a commentary on the Constitution by men included among its principal architects *The Federalist* has been used from the beginning of the nineteenth century to modern times as an interpreter of the Constitution not only by laymen but by lawyers and Justices of the U.S. Supreme Court.

235

THE INDO-EUROPEAN FAMILY OF LANGUAGES

SIR WILLIAM JONES (1746–94). On the Hindus. *In:* Asiatic Researches or, Transactions of the [Bengal Asiatic] Society. *Calcutta: Printed and sold by Manuel Cantopher, and sold at London by P. Elmsly, 1788*

This slim paper, read to the Bengal Asiatic Society in 1786 and published in its *Transactions*, marks a turning-point in the history of linguistics and signalled the birth of comparative philology.

Jones, a product of Harrow and University College, Oxford (of which he became a fellow in 1766), had established his reputation as an orientalist by his *Grammar of the Persian Language* (1771) and *Poeseos Asiaticae Commentariorum Libri VI* (1774), when in 1774 he became a barrister of the Middle Temple and in his second profession again achieved fame as the author of a standard work on *Bailments* (1781) which for many decades remained a classic on both sides of the Atlantic. In 1783 he was knighted and appointed a judge of the high court in Calcutta, the administrative seat of the East India Company, an office which he held until his death.

Here Jones indulged in his oriental studies, founded the Asiatic Society of Bengal (1784), edited its *Journal of Asiatic Researches*, translated Indian classics into English—such as the *Hitopadesa*, *Sakuntala* and selections from the *Upanishads* and *Vedas*—printed, as the first European, Sanskrit texts in the Devanagari script, and laid down rules for the *Orthography of Asiatick words in Roman Letters*.

In 1786 Jones made his epoch-making discovery of the relationship between the Sanskrit, Gothic, Greek and Latin languages—to which he later, erroneously, thought he could add Egyptian. His clear understanding of the basic principles of scientific linguistics provided the foundation on which Rask (266), Bopp (275) and Grimm (281) built the imposing structure of comparative Indo-European studies.

236

THE CLASSICAL COMPANION

JOHN LEMPRIÈRE (c. 1765–1824). Bibliotheca Classica, or a Classical Dictionary. *Reading: printed for T. Cadell, London, 1788*

'Lemprière's Classical Dictionary' is the first of a new kind of manual: the rendering of a body of knowledge not easily accessible in any other form into a series of alphabetical articles for the use of those who lack the time or the learning to seek out the sources. Dictionaries, literary, geographical and biographical there had been, and encyclopaedias; but Lemprière's is the first specialist work designed as a substitute for, rather than as an aid to, learning. It was in fact an early 'cram-book', 'this book being undertaken more particularly for the use of schools', according to the preface. But what started as a popularizing medium has since become a valued and respected part of the literary scene. The 'Oxford Companion' series is one of its most distinguished descendants.

Of its author's career little is known; as with most popular innovations, it is unlikely that he realized the full novelty of his work. John Lemprière was born in the island of Jersey and was educated at Winchester and Pembroke College, Oxford. While still at the university—not, as is sometimes asserted, when an usher at Reading—he compiled and published the *Bibliotheca Classica*. In 1792 he was appointed headmaster of Abingdon grammar school, and later became vicar of the parish. In 1808 he published a *Universal Biography of Eminent Persons in all Ages and Countries*, a work in the same style as his classical dictionary, but in a long familiar form. In 1809 he moved to Exeter to become headmaster of the free grammar school there, but retired as a result of a disagreement with the trustees and spent the rest of his life as a country clergyman.

Lemprière's dictionary has been frequently re-edited and its accuracy has been greatly improved, although its original style, always lively and unusually readable

for a work of reference, has been largely preserved. Beyond this, finally, it has one quite imperishable claim to fame. Keats owned a copy, and it was the source of much of his knowledge of Latin and Greek mythology; one can sometimes even see the genesis of his lines in Lemprière's humble but lively prose.

237

UTILITARIANISM

JEREMY BENTHAM (1748–1832). An Introduction to the Principles of Morals and Legislation. Printed in the year 1780 and now first published. *London: T. Payne and Son, 1789*

To re-read Bentham now is to realize how much practical good he has done, as well as how much he advanced social and political thinking. Typically, his range is too great to be easily classified (he has left no school or followers) but much of what he taught has become part of the common thought not only of his own but of subsequent time: truths which had not found expression before they were pointed out by Bentham are now so universally accepted as to be thought common-place. Take 'Utilitarianism' for example; although the concept was not wholly original, only Bentham could have summed it up in the succinct aphorism 'the greatest happiness of the greatest number', and only he could have coined the word 'utilitarianism' to label it. (Bentham was a lively neologist: 'utilitarian', 'international', 'codification', all were invented by him; the first he had already used in 1802, long before 1823 when J. S. Mill thought he had coined it.) But his most significant achievement, and the one that would have pleased him most, is his real and practical influence on the machinery of government and upon jurisprudence.

Bentham was born in London, the son and grandson of lawyers. He was an infant prodigy, could read extensively before he was three, and took his B.A. at the age of fifteen. He was called to the Bar, but he had no great enthusiasm for the legal profession, in which his father held such high hopes for him. Instead he occupied himself with speculating on the principles and abuses of the English legal system. He had an almost exclusively logical approach to a subject which is traditionally considered from an historical point of view, and there can be little doubt that no revolution would have taken place if he had mixed the two methods. The *Fragment on Government*, 1776, was the first product of his speculations, an attack on the praise of Blackstone (212), the arch-historian, for his theory of the organic growth of the British constitution. This immediately brought Bentham to notice, and when thirteen years later it was followed by the *Principles* he became known the world over. From then on he worked and wrote almost without stopping until his death in 1832. His inherited wealth enabled him to maintain the necessary secretarial help and to secure the editorial help of such friends as the Mills and the Austens. He negotiated for nearly twenty-five years with the government about the establishment of the 'Panopticon' for the central inspection and housing of convicts, on the lines of Howard (224), but owing to official inertia it was never built. After his death, according to his directions, his body was dissected, and the bones are still preserved at University College London.

All Bentham's reforms or suggestions result from the application of strict common sense to the facts of society. With morals he deals only so far as to show that human impulses must be controlled by law—'ethical utilitarianism' was developed by his pupil Mill. Of all institutions he enquires whether their utility justifies their existence. If not, he suggests a new institution to provide the missing service. Thus he proposes to abolish the discrepancies which have grown up from feudal days onwards, and provides a new code, not mutually conflicting, which forms a consistent whole. Both criminal law and criminal and civil procedure in England have been materially improved by the application of his principles, notably in the legal revolution of 1873 by which law and equity were fused. One day perhaps the expression as well as the content of the law will be changed to accord with his proposals. But even if every one on every subject were adopted, the value of his work would not be exhausted. 'Pillé par tout le monde', said Talleyrand, 'il est toujours riche.'

BIBLIOGRAPHY: *In:* E. Halévy, *The Growth of Philosophic Radicalism* (London, 1934; reprinted with corrections, 1952).

238

A NEW EPOCH IN CHEMISTRY

ANTOINE LAURENT LAVOISIER (1743–94). Traité Élémentaire de Chimie. 2 vols. *Paris: Cuchet, 1789*

This book accomplished a chemical revolution: but Lavoisier's achievement would have been impossible without his knowledge of the works of his predecessors. Priestley (217) had discovered oxygen; Scheele had also found oxygen and proved that air consisted of two different gases, now known as oxygen and nitrogen, and discovered many other substances; Black had proved that there were many kinds of gases differing from air, a fact first recognized by Helmont (135); Cavendish established that water was not an element; and Stephen Hales (189) had even earlier found that gases could be obtained from plants.

Lavoisier made extensive use of the chemical balance when investigating the results of the calcination of metals. He proved that the increase in the weight of the calcined metals was due to something taken from the air, and that this effect was constant in all such processes. He named the substance oxygen. He repeated Cavendish's experiments and concluded that water was a compound of oxygen and hydrogen. Cavendish, still clinging to the 'phlogiston' theory (see 217), had named them phlogiston and dephlogisticated air. Lavoisier perceived that respiration and combustion were similar processes, and, since oxygen was that part of the air that combined with metals in the process of combustion, he named the resulting substances oxides. He finally established the modern conception of elements as substances which cannot be further decomposed. His 'Elementary Treatise on Chemistry' contains a list of twenty-three such elements,

TRAITÉ
ÉLÉMENTAIRE
DE CHIMIE,

PRÉSENTÉ DANS UN ORDRE NOUVEAU

ET D'APRÈS LES DÉCOUVERTES MODERNES;

Avec Figures :

Par M. LAVOISIER, de l'Académie des Sciences, de la Société Royale de Medecine, des Sociétés d'Agriculture de Paris & d'Orléans, de la Société Royale de Londres, de l'institut de Bologne, de la Société Helvétique de Bafle, de celles de Philadelphie, Harlem, Manchester, Padoue, &c.

TOME PREMIER.

A PARIS,

Chez CUCHET, Libraire, rue & hôtel Serpente.

M. DCC. LXXXIX.

Sous le Privilège de l'Académie des Sciences & de la Société Royale de Médecine.

which are still recognized today. Together with Morveau and Berthollet he introduced a completely new system of chemical nomenclature in the *Méthode de Nomenclature Chimique*, Paris, 1787. Thus the great confusion as to the actual number of elements and the very fanciful nomenclature which still included many alchemical terms were finally swept away. Having proved the analogy between combustion and respiration, Lavoisier was able to explain many cyclical processes in animal and vegetable life and to carry out the earliest biochemical experiments.

One of the most important consequences of Lavoisier's work was the establishment of the concept of the conservation of matter. Compound bodies were now found to represent the combined weight of the simple bodies of which they are composed, while, when these simple bodies are withdrawn, they have the same weight as was put into them; i.e. matter remains constant throughout all chemical change. Lavoisier's book put an end to the phlogiston theory and the surviving remnants of alchemy.

Lavoisier was one of the first great scientists to devote

much of his time to public service. He was trained for the law, but in 1768 he became assistant Fermier Général of taxes. In 1775 he was appointed to the Gunpowder Office, and reformed the national supply and the manufacture of gunpowder. He was a great believer in applying scientific principles to agriculture and he conducted extensive experiments on his own estate. Many economic reforms were either carried out or proposed by him; these included a new system of public accounts and improved schemes of taxation; he proposed savings banks, insurance societies and the building of canals to improve economic and social conditions, and he was associated with committees on hygiene, coinage, public education, and the metric system.

Lavoisier recognized the urgent need for social reforms in France, but he refused to support unconstitutional means to bring them about. This attitude and his former connexion with the Ferme Générale made him suspect to the revolutionary régime and on 8 May 1794 he was guillotined. Legend has it that the judge remarked in his summing up: 'The republic has no need of scientists'. Lagrange's comment was: 'It took but a moment to cut off that head which a hundred years would be unable to replace'. Lavoisier himself said, before his execution: 'La revolution en chimie est faite'. He was right.

BIBLIOGRAPHY: Dennis I. Duveen and H. S. Klickstein, *A Bibliography of Antoine Laurent Lavoisier* (London, 1954; Supplement by D. I. Duveen, London, 1965).

239

THE PRICE OF REVOLUTION

EDMUND BURKE (1729–1794). Reflections on the Revolution in France. *London: J. Dodsley, 1790*

It is strange that Burke, who for all his influence enjoyed less experience of the practical business of government than most of his acquaintances, should have written, in defence of an existing régime and against a liberating revolution, one of the most brilliant of all polemics. Yet the paradox may not seem so strange when it is considered that the whole course of Burke's life had been devoted to the practicable in human affairs, and that his great imagination (which transcended his practical ability, and with it gave him the vast influence he enjoyed in or—as more often—out of office) was kindled by the conviction that the existing order in Europe sprang from permanent elements in human nature. It is in Burke's life and the operation of his imagination in it that the real influence of the *Reflections* is to be found.

Burke was born in Dublin, the child of parents not poor—his father was an attorney—but without influence. His education was unremarkable, and in 1750 he crossed to England to keep terms at the Temple. The legal profession was distasteful to him, however, and for the first ten years of his adult life he only just survived in his struggle to establish himself. 1756 brought him some renown; in that year there appeared both *A Vindication of Natural Society*, a satire on the danger of measuring

civil institutions by the test of pure reason in which the principles of the *Reflections* can be seen already formed, and the *Philosophical Inquiry...into the Sublime and Beautiful*, which achieved great popularity and had some influence on Lessing (213). In 1759 he founded *The Annual Register*, a summary of the chief events of the year, of which he was the principal editor for its first eight years.

At last Burke began to make his mark in national affairs. In 1765 he became secretary to Lord Rockingham, and took a distinguished part in the short-lived Whig government which thwarted the absolutist tendencies of George III and attempted to defend the American colonists. Burke was set on the path he was to follow for the next twenty-five years: the transformation of the age of family politics into the age of great principles, and the creation of a new, more soundly based Whig party.

It is not to be wondered at that a man who desired justice for America but rejected Jefferson's doctrines would be deeply stirred by the events of 1789. To Burke an absorption with the end and neglect of the means was the most dreadful of sins. His anger and disgust were exacerbated by the dread that the aims, principles, methods and language which he detested in France might infect the people of England. This it was which provoked the *Reflections*, in which his distrust of the 'Perfectibilitarians' and of mere destructive criticism of institutions was magnificently voiced. To the view that the old régime was so rotten that wholesale revolution was necessary, Burke replied that any revolution that did not bring real liberty, which comes from the administration of justice under a settled constitution without bias from the mob, was no liberty. 'Alas!' he said, 'they little know how many a weary step is to be taken before they can form themselves into a mass which has a true political personality.'

The *Reflections* achieved immediate success all over Europe, even though it cost Burke the allegiance of the Whigs. Lonely now, he finally enjoyed a European authority which he had never attained in his own country or with his own party. The other side found a trenchant spokesman in Paine's *Rights of Man* (241), which took the discussion beyond the limits of the government of France, but as the Terror grew, Burke seemed almost to be a prophet. In the eternal debate between the ideal and the practical, the latter had never had a more powerful or moving advocate, nor one whose own ideals were higher.

BIBLIOGRAPHY: W. B. Todd, *A Bibliography of Burke* (London, 1964).

240

ANIMAL ELECTRICITY

LUIGI GALVANI (1737–98). De Viribus Electricitatis in Motu Musculari. *Bologna: Ex Typographia Instituti Scientiarum, 1791*

By the end of the eighteenth century the connexion between nervous action and electricity had been the subject of investigation for some time. Newton, when discussing the properties of aether, had made suggestions that an electric spirit might convey sensations to the brain along the nerves and produce muscular reactions: see Book III of *Opticks* (172) and the General Scholium concluding the second edition of the *Principia* (161). Haller also made experiments trying to prove a connexion between electrical action and reflexes of the muscles.

It was left to Luigi Galvani, professor of anatomy at Bologna, in 'On the Effects of Electricity on Muscular Motion', to provide, as he thought, dramatic experiments on what was called 'animal electricity' and afterwards 'galvanism'. Galvani observed in his laboratory that when a nerve in a frog's leg was touched with a scalpel, violent contractions of the muscles occurred simultaneously with the sparks discharged from a nearby electrical machine. He further discovered that when one metal was placed in contact with a frog's nerve, another with a muscle, and the metals touched, contraction of the muscle took place, without needing a spark from an electrical machine. As a physiologist, Galvani thought that this action was due to the presence of electricity in the animal itself, as in the 'electric eel', and that the metal wires simply served as conductors. He did not realize that he had not discovered just a new physiological source of electricity, but a new source of continuous electric flow in chemical action. Hitherto electricity had been produced only in high-voltage, intermittent surges from frictional machines. It was Alessandro Volta (255), a physicist, who proved that animals were inessential to 'galvanic' electricity, and who constructed the first battery to cause a current to flow by chemical action. Galvani's paper immediately aroused great interest in the scientific world, and it involved him in controversy with Volta (largely carried on by Galvani's nephew, Giovanni Aldini, on his uncle's behalf).

Galvani's influence on the modern development of energy, electrochemistry and electromagnetism is an indirect one. But there is no doubt that modern electrophysiology, as was emphasized by one of its foremost representatives, Du Bois-Reymond in Germany, derives from those observations of the behaviour of the frog's legs.

BIBLIOGRAPHY: John F. Fulton and Madeline E. Stanton, *A Bibliography of Galvani's Writings on Animal Electricity* (Norwalk, Conn., 1953).

241
THE RIGHTS OF MAN

THOMAS PAINE (1737–1809). Rights of Man. *London: J. Johnson, 1791*

The life of Paine, Quaker and political theorist, defaulting excise-man and revolutionary, is a medley of contradictions. Its apogee came after his return to Europe in 1787 and the publication in 1790 of Burke's *Reflections on the Revolution in France* (239). Burke expressed in a single work all the reactions of horror and dismay with which

the liberal-minded who had hailed its beginning now felt for the French revolutionaries. Paine's 'answer to Mr Burke's attack' took the argument to a higher level. With a force and clarity unequalled even by Burke, Paine laid down those principles of fundamental human rights which must stand, no matter what excesses are committed to obtain them. His own deep and bitter knowledge of revolutionary politics (Benjamin Franklin brought him to America in 1774, so he had experienced the entire course of the War of Independence) enabled him to see where Burke's vision had been clouded both by horror and by his own experience of the stable realities of English politics.

Rights of Man was an immediate success. Although even the radical publisher Johnson took fright, Paine

RIGHTS OF MAN:

BEING AN

ANSWER TO MR. BURKE's ATTACK

ON THE

FRENCH REVOLUTION.

BY

THOMAS PAINE,

SECRETARY FOR FOREIGN AFFAIRS TO CONGRESS IN THE AMERICAN WAR, AND AUTHOR OF THE WORK INTITLED *COMMON SENSE.*

LONDON:
PRINTED FOR J. JOHNSON, ST PAUL's CHURCH-YARD.
MDCCXCI.

found another (Jordan) to take it over. The government tried to suppress it, but it circulated the more briskly. Those who bought it as the work of an inflamed revolutionary were surprised by its dignity and moderation: even Pitt could say that he was quite in the right—'but what am I to do? As things are, if I were to encourage Tom Paine's opinions we should have a bloody revolution'. Considered apart from the turmoil which attended its first publication, however, *Rights of Man* can be seen for what it is: the textbook of radical thought and the clearest of all expositions of the basic principles of democracy.

242

THE RIGHTS OF WOMAN

MARY WOLLSTONECRAFT (1759–97). A Vindication of the Rights of Woman. *London: J. Johnson, 1792*

Mary Wollstonecraft was born at Hoxton, then a suburb of London. Her father had squandered a sizeable patrimony, and after her mother's death in 1780 she and her two sisters had to earn their own livelihood. She went to live with her friend Fanny Blood, whose family was in similar difficulties, and after her sister Eliza's marriage came to an end, the three set up a school, first at Islington then at Stoke Newington. In 1785 Fanny married, and her death in childbed soon after was an indescribable loss to Mary. She closed the school, and briefly became a governess; this too she gave up in 1787 and decided to devote herself entirely to literary work. She became literary adviser to John Johnson, the publisher in St Paul's Churchyard, over whose imprint some of the most distinguished poets and writers of the time, especially those of liberal and advanced opinions, published their books. She herself wrote tales for children, a novel and a number of translations, and in 1792 there appeared the work for which she will always be famous.

A Vindication of the Rights of Woman is dedicated to (of all people) Talleyrand, whom Mary Wollstonecraft still believed to be inspired by the same progressive views as her own. To him she wrote that her main argument was 'built on this simple principle that, if woman be not prepared by education to become the companion of man, she will stop the progress of knowledge, for truth must be common to all'. The main part of her book was written in an equally plain and direct style, and it was this, as well as the idea of writing a book on the subject at all, which caused the outcry which ensued. There was indeed nothing specially shocking in her matter. She did not attack the institution of marriage or the practice of religion. Instead, she argued for equality of education for both sexes, and for state control and co-education. It was a rational plea for a rational basis to the relation between the sexes (here she disagreed with Rousseau (207), with whom in other respects she had so much common ground). Its chief object was to show that women were not the playthings of men but ought to be their equal partners, which they could be only if they were educated in the same way.

After publishing the *Vindication*, Mary Wollstonecraft went to France to observe the Revolution and remained there throughout the Terror. She became involved with an American, Gilbert Imlay, who cruelly deserted her, leaving her with an infant daughter. After a frustrated attempt at suicide, she met and married William Godwin (243) with whom she enjoyed a few months of tranquillity and happiness; but she died a few days after the birth of their daughter Mary, later wife of Shelley. Her memory was lovingly preserved by her husband, who collected her letters and in 1798 published a memoir of her. Her courage and her most famous work were to be remembered years later (see 398) when the struggle which she began was successfully concluded.

243

RATIONAL MAN

WILLIAM GODWIN (1756–1836). An Enquiry concerning Political Justice, and its Influence on General Virtue and Happiness. 2 vols. *London: G. G. J. and J. Robinson, 1793*

William Godwin was born at Wisbech, in Cambridgeshire, the son of a nonconformist minister. He was destined for his father's profession, and educated at the Academy of Hoxton, the birthplace of his future wife (the new development of London north of the City was the home of the prosperous middle class and the centre of the nonconformist sects they supported). He served as a minister in Ware, Stowmarket and Beaconsfield; but in 1782 the teaching of the *philosophes*, to which he had been introduced at Stowmarket, brought him to London, still a minister in name, but by now determined to devote the energy hitherto bestowed on militant Calvinism to pure philosophic radicalism. With the Encyclopaedists he saw no good in human institutions and sought to put an end to all organized politics, religion and society.

For the next ten years Godwin lived by writing books and by journalism, earning barely enough to support life, until the publication of his best-known work brought him fame and a comfortable competence. In 1797 he met and married Mary Wollstonecraft (242), who shared his views, and with whom for a few months he was idyllically happy. Her death left him stunned with grief, but in 1801 he married again. He continued to write voluminously but was more than once in difficulties from which he was rescued by subscriptions from the Whig society to whom he had become, as it were, party theorist. In 1833, when the Whigs had finally achieved power (see 296), Godwin was given a sinecure office with apartments in Palace Yard, where he died. During the latter part of his life, despite his embarrassments, he exercised, through his writings and conversation, an immense influence, especially on the young. Shelley, who married his daughter Mary in 1816, was one of many to whom, with his revolutionary opinions, he seemed almost a prophet.

The *Enquiry* was, and remained, the work by which he was best known. It was one of the earliest, the clearest, and most absolute theoretical expositions of socialist and anarchist doctrine. Godwin believed that the motives of all human action were subject to reason, that reason taught benevolence, and that therefore all rational creatures could live in harmony without laws and institutions. Believing in the perfectibility of man, he thought that 'our virtues and vices may be traced to the incidents which make the history of our lives, and if these incidents could be divested of every improper tendency, vice would be extirpated from the world'. All control of man by man was intolerable and 'government by its very nature counteracts the improvement of original mind'. The time would come, he maintained, when every man, by doing what seemed right in his own eyes, would also be doing what was best for all men, because all, through discussion, would be guided by purely rational principles.

Natural relationship had no meaning—marriage and parental duty were alike irrational, and property the worst form of tyranny.

It is to be doubted if anyone fully accepted this out-and-out radicalism, but Godwin's passionate advocacy of individualism, his trust in the fundamental goodness of man, and his opposition to all restrictions on liberty, have endured. They found a practical exponent in Robert Owen (271), whose philanthropic industrial experiments were deeply influenced by Godwin. They lie at the roots of all communist and anarchist theory.

244

THE FOUNDATIONS OF KNOWLEDGE

Johann Gottlieb Fichte (1762–1814). Ueber den Begriff der Wissenschaftslehre. *Weimar: im Verlage des Industrie-Comptoirs, 1794*

Fichte was born of poor parents at Rammenau, in upper Lusatia. The independence and industry which he early showed attracted the attention of the Freiherr von Miltitz, who provided for his early education. In 1780 he entered the University of Jena as a theology student, and supported himself while there by private teaching. After leaving the university he had various jobs but in 1790, having encountered Kant's works (226), he resolved to undertake the exposition and clarification of his great predecessor's views.

Fichte's first interview with Kant was a disappointment. But later he sent his 'Essay towards a Critique of all Revelation', an extension of Kant's principles to a theological problem, to Kant, who thoroughly approved it and found him a publisher. Fichte's name was omitted from the title-page, and when it was published the book was generally ascribed to Kant. Kant himself having put this right, Fichte's reputation was made; and at the end of 1793 he was offered the chair of philosophy at Jena.

Here his major work was done. The introduction to his philosophy—a term he avoided and replaced by 'Wissenschaftslehre', a neologism coined by himself—was laid down in *Ueber den Begriff*—'On the Idea of a Theory of Science'; followed by 'The Foundation of the Whole Theory of Science', 'The Outline of the Peculiarities of the Theory', and the two 'Introductions', 1797. These covered the theoretical side of his system; the practical was expounded in the 'Foundation of Natural Right', c. 1796, and the 'System of a Theory of Morals', 1798. But in 1799 a misunderstanding of an article he had written led to a charge of atheism, and despite his protests he was forced to resign his chair. He retreated to Berlin, where he remained for the rest of his life, apart from a brief period in 1806–7, when the disastrous course of the war forced him to take refuge first in Königsberg and then in Copenhagen. In 1807–8 he delivered his *Reden an die deutschen Nation*, which did much to cheer and encourage the Prussian people in defeat. In 1810 he was elected rector of the new University of Berlin, which he had done much to plan. In 1813 the campaign for independence began, and Fichte

took an enthusiastic part in it, but in January 1814 he caught a fever and died.

Fichte's last years had been devoted to improving (and considerably changing) the *Wissenschaftslehre*; his last work, the *Tatsachen des Bewusstseins*, appearing posthumously in 1817. Fichte's starting-point was the theory of knowledge as Kant had left it. The defect of Kant's system was that while the method of apprehension had been explored to a degree never before reached, its matter had been largely set aside in such a way as almost to assume that it had a separate existence apart from cognition of it. To complete Kant's work, Fichte set himself to demonstrate that all the necessary conditions of knowledge can be deduced from a single principle, from which a complete system of reason can be constructed. The act of cognition presupposes an existence, an ego, which comes about through what Fichte called *Tathandlung*, a deed-act, a process which happens, although cognition of it is not possible. To this is opposed the non-ego,

Ueber den

Begriff der Wissenschaftslehre

oder

der sogenannten Philosophie,

als

Einladungsschrift zu seinen Vorlesungen über diese Wissenschaft

von

IOHANN GOTTLIEB FICHTE,

designirten ordentlichen Professor der Philosophie auf der Universität zu Jena,

Weimar,
Im Verlage des Industrie-Comptoirs
1794.

which limits the ego to that which it can apprehend. From these oppositions Fichte builds up his system. Later (in the *Tatsachen*) he sought to work back to determine the absolute ego, which becomes conscious of itself in the original *Tathandlung* by defining itself in the multitude of individual egos and constitutes the existence of God.

In this perfected *Wissenschaftslehre* the way is prepared for all the later Hegelian dialectic (see 283). If Kant had opened up the path which German, and indeed all, philosophy was to take in the nineteenth century, the credit for the complete description of its subject-matter belongs to Fichte.

245

PRACTICAL PROOF OF THE EXISTENCE OF GOD

WILLIAM PALEY (1743–1805). (*a*) A View of the Evidences of Christianity. 3 vols. *London: R. Faulder, 1794.* (*b*) Natural Theology or Evidences of the Existence and Attributes of the Deity collected from the Appearances of Nature. *London: R. Faulder, 1802*

The theological controversies of the eighteenth century sometimes seem indescribably remote; even more than that of the Deists, the Latitudinarian controversy seems wholly innocuous two hundred years later. Yet it was his dangerously latitudinarian views that cost Paley a bishopric. But what some eighteenth-century diocese lost (Paley was remarkable in a not always careful age for his painstaking pastoral work) England and the world as a whole have gained.

Paley was educated at his father's school in Giggleswick and at Christ's College, Cambridge, of which he became a tutor in 1768. His lectures on moral philosophy impressed the university, and when Paley married and retreated to a country rectory he set to work to enlarge and publish them. They appeared in 1785 as *Principles of Moral and Political Philosophy*. The book was an instant success, and Paley followed it up with another, *Horae Paulinae*, in 1790. In 1794 one of his two most influential works, the *Evidences of Christianity*, was published, and Paley found himself famous. The rest of his life was spent mainly in his northern rectory.

Until this century 'Paley's Evidences' was the first divinity treatise for all students. It is the epitome of eighteenth-century theological reasoning; rational, empirical, it seeks to demonstrate the truth of the Christian religion by reference to physical phenomena. To a large extent Paley's material, and in some cases his arguments, are derived from earlier writers; but the directness and clarity of his approach make it perhaps the most effective statement of the external evidence for Christianity ever written. He rests his case on 'the necessity, in each particular case, of an intelligent designing mind for the contriving and determining of the forms which organized bodies bear'. This concept of revelation as the purely mechanical relation of God to the world, in which the divine origin of Christianity is isolated from the history of mankind, was superseded in the nineteenth century by the view of revelation as a continuing process. But Paley's view (which controverts the theory of the adaptation of an organism to its circumstances by use) was still a dominant one in the nineteenth century; without an understanding of Paley's position, the opposition to the theory of evolution is meaningless.

It was not for any special subtlety or refinement that his book continued to be valued. It is Paley's strong and continuous reasoning power, his capacity for lucid organization and forceful statement that caused him to be read by generation after generation. He was the first great exponent of the 'common touch'; one of his most effective arguments is brilliantly illustrated by the metaphor of the bridge, the famous New Iron Bridge in his own parish of Wearmouth, so often depicted on contemporary glasses and Sunderland ware. His was the first work (after the *Materia Medica*) to have a whole series of mnemonic rhymes devised for it for the use of examination students. All in all, the *Evidences* is a testimony to a whole climate of thought, which is still alive.

Natural Theology was the last of Paley's major works and it immediately shared the enormous popularity of the others: by 1820 it was in its twentieth edition. The book, as the title indicates, is an exposition of the argument from design—the *a posteriori* proof of the existence of God.

Darwin (344) acknowledged that his study of Paley's works at Cambridge 'was the only part of the academic course which...was of the least use' to him. Given the idea of an evolving world—of which the Natural Theologists had no inkling—he showed that adaptation to circumstances did not imply design and a designer but could be explained as evolving through the action of natural selection. There is much truth in Thiselton Dyer's remark that Darwin 'swept in the whole of Paley's teleology, simply dispensing with its supernatural explanation'.

246

CAN MAN BECOME PERFECT?

MARIE JEAN ANTOINE NICOLAS CARITAT, MARQUIS DE CONDORCET (1743–94). Esquisse d'un Tableau Historique des Progrès de l'Esprit Humain. *Paris: Agasse, 1795*

A belief in the ultimate perfectibility of man lies at the root of all progressive thinking about the human condition. The *philosophes* and Godwin (243) had familiarized the reading public with this notion; it was left to Condorcet to give it its finest and most durable expression. It was the gospel of the nineteenth century that mankind is destined for indefinite future progress. Condorcet, looking back and then forward, saw proof of this in the growing equality between classes and nations, the intellectual, physical and moral improvement of man; and he prophesied that popular education on correct principles would strengthen and assure this progress.

Condorcet was born of an ancient family from the Dauphiné, and distinguished himself at school and college as a mathematician. He became a close and honoured friend of d'Alembert (195), Turgot and Voltaire (202), and was invited to take a part in the preparation of the *Encyclopédie* (200). At the age of twenty-six he was elected to the Academy of Sciences, and became its permanent secretary in 1782. He contributed substantially to its *Mémoires*, and among his articles are many dealing with the most abstruse mathematical problems. But Condorcet's mind was too large and generous for specialization. He was equally attracted by philosophy and literature, and above all by social work.

When the revolution came, Condorcet was indefatigable in promoting its democratic growth. He wrote pamphlets and, when elected to the Legislative Assembly, drafted most of its official documents. Most notable among these was his scheme for comprehensive state education, which, although postponed in his lifetime, became the basis of the modern French system. But the business of preparing the new constitution was interrupted by the fatal trial of the King, and in the dissensions that followed Condorcet's independence and public criticism of the Convention became suspect, despite his unimpeachable republicanism. In the Terror he was outlawed and went into hiding. For a year he remained safe

span the growth of civilizations and knowledge down to Descartes (129), and the ninth describes the revolution of Condorcet's own lifetime, from Newton to Rousseau. The prophetic view of the tenth epoch shows Condorcet at his most original. He forecasts the destruction of inequality between nations and classes, and the improvement, intellectual, moral and physical, of human nature. Unlike Godwin, he does not preach absolute equality, but equality of opportunity. While progress is limited by human nature, as men desire freedom, so they will obtain it and the equality that goes with it. Knowledge of this can come only from proper education, and this explains Condorcet's zeal to improve it. Despite his aversion to religion, his ethical theory stresses human impulses of sympathy and social feelings; it exercised considerable influence on Comte (295). But it is as the most fully developed exposition of the progress of man that Condorcet's work is now remembered, and it is this which has given it its lasting appeal.

E S Q U I S S E

D'UN

TABLEAU HISTORIQUE

DES PROGRÈS DE L'ESPRIT HUMAIN.

Ouvrage posthume de CONDORCET.

———

A PARIS,

Chez AGASSE, rue des Poitevins, N°. 18.

———

L'AN III. DE LA RÉPUBLIQUE, UNE ET INDIVISIBLE.

and wrote the *Esquisse*—'An Historical Outline of the Progress of the Human Mind'—but at length, fearing he had been discovered, he left his refuge and was immediately captured; he died in prison.

In the *Esquisse*, published after his death, Condorcet traces the history of man through epochs, the first three covering his progress from savagery to pastoral community and thence to the agricultural state. The next five

247

THE THEORY OF THE EARTH

JAMES HUTTON (1726–97). Theory of the Earth, with Proofs and Illustrations. 2 vols. *Edinburgh: printed for Cadell and Davies, London, and William Creech, Edinburgh, 1795*. Vol. 3 (edited by Sir Archibald Geikie). *London: Geological Society, 1899*

James Hutton was trained for the medical profession, but never practised it. He lived on his estate in Berwickshire, where he devoted himself to agricultural pursuits and to his scientific researches, culminating in this classic book on geology.

His fundamental conception—now accepted as a matter of course, but then entirely new—was the doctrine of uniformitarianism. The formation of the surface of the earth is one continuous process which can be studied entirely from terrestrial materials without cosmological or supernatural intervention.

According to Hutton the greater part of the world's land mass consists of sediments, due to the denudation of pre-existing continents, which had been deposited in the sea bed. Thus the greater part of the present solid land had once been beneath the ocean. The transformation of some of these sediments into solid rock and the fact that the strata of which the earth is now composed are not now found horizontally, but in every possible position, broken, bent and tilted—this had first been observed by Steno (151)—was attributed by Hutton to the action of subterranean heat. When forced upwards the material is split and cracked, the fissures filling with molten mineral matter. Volcanoes act as safety-valves during this upheaval, providing an exit for the molten rock masses, and thereby preventing the heat expansion from raising the continents too far. This theory became known as 'Vulcanism'.

Another important feature of Hutton's system is his discussion of the erosion of land-surfaces due to atmospheric, chemical and mechanical action of water by which many earlier landscapes and mountains had been destroyed; in the remaining strata we can see 'the ruins of an older world' and we can study in them ancient continents and faunas from which the present ones have developed. Hutton maintained that these natural processes have operated continuously and uniformly through immensely long periods of time and will go on doing so—with 'no vestige of a beginning—no prospect of an end'; a view diametrically opposed to those then generally held by naturalists, according to which every major feature of the earth was formed abruptly by catastrophic forces.

Hutton had no clear idea of the significance of fossils for the theory of gradual evolution and not all his theories are now accepted, but his central ideas of uniformitarianism and of the effect of small changes in nature leading eventually to gigantic transformations have had far-reaching consequences in their influence on Charles Lyell and Darwin (344).

Hutton was nearly sixty years old when he first adumbrated his theories in a paper read to the Royal Society of Edinburgh in 1785 (printed in their *Transactions* in 1788). In 1795 he published a greatly enlarged version in two volumes. A third was added by Sir Archibald Geikie in 1899 from manuscripts Hutton had left. Hutton's style is sometimes obscure and his book is not well organized; so that his views became better known to the scientific world through a work by his pupil John Playfair, *Illustrations of the Huttonian Theory of the Earth*, Edinburgh, 1802. Playfair added another observation which was to have far-reaching consequences, viz. that glaciers can transport large masses of rock (see Agassiz, 309).

248

THE NEW PHILOLOGY

FRIEDRICH AUGUST WOLF (1759–1824). Prolegomena ad Homerum. Vol. 1 [*all published*] *Halle: E Libraria Orphanotrophei, 1795*

Wolf was born at Hagenrode near Nordhausen. He proved a prodigious linguist, absorbing quickly and easily Greek, Latin and modern languages at the local grammar school. When in 1777 he went to the University of Göttingen and was required to choose his faculty, he said 'philology'—a science which was not represented in the syllabus. Perhaps on this account, certainly through a fundamental difference of temper, he did not get on with the university authorities, although he read a great deal. On leaving, he became a successful teacher; but he managed to find time to publish a commentary on Plato's *Symposium*, on the strength of which he was offered, in 1783, a professorship at the Prussian University of Halle. His years at Halle were the happiest and most productive of his life, but in 1807, he, and the university with him, were swept away by the French invasion. The rest of his life was spent, without a proper job and in considerable uncertainty and gloom, at Berlin. Humboldt (301) found him a place in the department of education and he tried to resume teaching, but without his old success.

Finally his health gave way and he went to the south of France, where he died.

When Wolf took up his professorship in 1783, a critical point in the history of education had been reached. New ideas derived from Locke (164) and Rousseau (207) were at work and Wolf longed to enter the fray. He found able and enlightened allies in the ministers of Frederick the Great, and with their help and by his enthusiasm he was able to carry out his long-cherished plan to give a new basis to the science of philology. To Wolf this meant philology in the original sense—love of letters, of learning and of language. He defined it as 'the knowledge of human nature as exhibited in antiquity'; its matter was everything that remained of ancient culture, to which an equal care and scholarship must be devoted. The 'Prolegomena to Homer', the best exposition of Wolf's beliefs, were written in a great hurry to meet the needs of a lecture course, and they have all the merits of good lectures: command of method, the gift of inspiration, penetration and breadth of view. Wolf's thesis is no theory, but a collection of great ideas, which laid the foundations for the dominance of German scholarship in the nineteenth century. They have inspired and given purpose to education ever since.

249

THE BEGINNING OF SOCIOLOGY

SIR FREDERICK MORTON EDEN (1766–1809). The State of the Poor; or an History of the Labouring Classes in England. 3 vols. *London: printed by J. Davis for B. & J. White (and others), 1797*

Sir Frederick Eden was the son of Sir Robert Eden, Governor of Maryland, and Caroline Calvert, sister of the last Lord Baltimore. He entered Christ Church, Oxford, in 1783. The rest of his short life was occupied with business—he was one of the founders of the Globe Insurance Company and afterwards became its chairman—and in the social and political enquiries which were to earn him the admiration of, among others, Karl Marx. His other writings show him to have been a cultivated and public-spirited man. He wrote a poem in Latin hexameters in memory of Nelson, and tracts on Friendly Societies, on improving the Port of London and the establishment of a fire brigade.

The State of the Poor is one of the classical works in the history of economics. Eden was led to embark on the subject by the high prices brought on by the war in 1794 and 1795, and the effect they had on the living conditions of the poorer classes. He established the framework of his investigation by lengthy visits to several parishes; the rest was filled in by his many correspondents up and down the land, and by 'a remarkably faithful and intelligent person, who has spent more than a year in travelling from place to place for the express purpose of obtaining exact information agreeably to a set of queries with which I furnished him'—the first statistical field-worker, in fact. The results were published in three volumes; the first contained a description of the condition of the labouring classes and an analysis of its causes; the other two the supporting facts in the form of parochial reports on the administration of workhouses and houses of industry, friendly societies, and other charitable organizations, with a lengthy series of appendixes, including tables of prices and wages and a list of works on poverty and its alleviation.

Eden's own work, notwithstanding its originality, might now be forgotten if it were not for the invaluable collection of facts attached to it, which can never cease to be of importance. More valuable even than these, however, is the method he adopted of obtaining and systemizing statistically the details of so diffuse a problem; it has proved the basis of sociological investigation ever since. Perhaps the greatest tribute to Eden's achievement is that paid to him by Karl Marx in *Das Kapital* (359). Not forgetting Malthus (251), he described Eden as the only pupil of Adam Smith who achieved anything of any significance in the eighteenth century.

by 1803 the book had been translated into Latin, French, German, Italian, Dutch and Portuguese and had been made known in America by Waterhouse. A Russian translation appeared in 1897. The latest edition was published at Denver, Colorado, in 1949.

Jenner's work is the basis of the modern science of immunology. When Pasteur (336) successfully inoculated sheep against anthrax he called such preventive inoculations 'vaccines' in honour of Jenner, a name which has been kept for the successful Salk and Sabin vaccines against poliomyelitis. Jenner had started one of the greatest practical advances in preventive medicine and today there are inoculations which confer immunity against scarlet fever, typhoid fever, diphtheria, whooping-cough and tetanus, as well as some of the age-old plagues such as bubonic plague, cholera and yellow fever.

BIBLIOGRAPHY: W. R. Le Fanu, *A Bio-bibliography of Edward Jenner* (London, 1951).

250

VACCINATION

EDWARD JENNER (1749–1823). An Inquiry into the Causes and Effects of the Variolae Vaccinae. *London: printed for the Author by Sampson Low, 1798*

Smallpox had for centuries been one of the most devastating diseases. Those fighting it had observed two things: (1) that those who survived an attack of smallpox developed a degree of immunity; (2) that the epidemics varied in severity. In India, China and Turkey the practice had therefore grown up of inoculating patients with small amounts of fluid from human pustules while there was a mild form of the epidemic. This practice was brought to England in 1718 by Lady Mary Wortley Montagu who as wife of the British ambassador in Constantinople had discovered it there. It was generally adopted in England where it was called 'variolation' and soon spread to the Continent. For several reasons variolation was not an ideal preventive method; the disease persisted and many died of it.

Edward Jenner, a pupil of John Hunter and a general practitioner in the small English country town of Berkeley in Gloucestershire, learned of an old west country tradition that milkmaids who had contracted cowpox, a mild infection caught from cattle, did not take smallpox. He decided to make an experiment, and on 14 May 1796 he injected cowpox lymph from an infected milkmaid into a country boy, James Phipps. On 1 July following he inoculated Phipps with the smallpox virus. No infection developed. In due course 'vaccination' replaced 'variolation'—the latter was prohibited in England in 1840—and smallpox has in consequence become a very uncommon disease in the western world.

At first Jenner's book was much criticized; its doctrine was too unfamiliar. Between 1799 and 1806 he issued five supplementary reports, and gradually his system was adopted, not only in England, but all over the world. Parliament voted him £30,000 for his services. The first vaccination in Vienna took place on 30 April 1799 and

251

POPULATION AND SUBSISTENCE

THOMAS ROBERT MALTHUS (1766–1834). An Essay on the Principle of Population. *London: J. Johnson, 1798*

Thomas Robert Malthus, for most of his life professor of modern history and political economy at the East India Company College, Haileybury, was one of the founders of modern economics. His *Essay* was originally the product of a discussion with his father on the perfectibility of society. Malthus senior, who had been a friend of Rousseau, was a supporter of the utopian views of Godwin (243) and others, but he recognized the force of his son's refutation of these views, and urged him to publish. Thus the first edition was essentially a fighting tract, but later editions were considerably altered and grew bulkier as Malthus defended his views against a host of critics.

The central idea of the essay—and the hub of Malthusian theory—was a simple one. The population of a community, Malthus suggested, increases geometrically, while food supplies increase only arithmetically. If the natural increase in population occurs the food supply becomes insufficient and the size of the population is checked by 'misery'—that is the poorest sections of the community suffer disease and famine. Malthus recognized two other possible checks to population expansion: first 'vice'—that is, homosexuality, prostitution and abortion (all totally unacceptable to Malthus); and second 'moral restraint'—the voluntary limitation of the production of children by the postponement of marriage. This was the solution to the population problem that Malthus advocated. The *Essay* was highly influential in the progress of thought in early nineteenth-century Europe. This simple generalization on population increase, and the social policy Malthus advocated were widely discussed. 'Parson' Malthus, as Cobbett dubbed him, was, for many, a monster and his views were often grossly misinterpreted. The socialists universally opposed him—both Marx (359) and Engels later condemned his theories—and the conservatives, while glad of a defence against the spread of revolutionary ideas from the Continent, never fully accepted his ideas. But his influence on social policy, whether for good or evil, was considerable. The Malthusian theory of population came at the right time to harden the existing feeling against the Poor Laws and Malthus was a leading spirit behind the Poor Law Amendment Act of 1834.

The simplicity of the central idea of the *Essay* also caught the imagination of thinkers in other fields. Paley (245) was a convert to the Malthusian view, and both Darwin (344) and Wallace clearly acknowledged Malthus as a source of the idea of 'the struggle for existence'. That Malthus was the only source, as has been traditionally held and as Darwin himself suggested, seems very doubtful, but certainly reading the *Essay* was for both of them an important event in the development of their theory of natural selection, and they were glad to quote such a well-known and weighty source for their ideas.

Since his death Malthusian theory, although always controversial, has, more often than not, been rejected as a part of early Victorian social conservatism and, besides, his central tenet—that food supplies can only increase arithmetically—is now regarded as false. However, Malthus has always had his supporters, often unexpected ones. Keynes (423), while showing that effective demand for many forms of investment is dependent on an expanding population—thus contradicting Malthusian population theory—traced back to Malthus himself the idea that a lack of effective demand can cause economic crises. He also contrasted Malthus's commonsense approach and the rigidly theoretical bent of his contemporary and friend David Ricardo, concluding that 'the almost total obliteration of Malthus's line of approach and the complete domination of Ricardo's for a period of 100 years has been a disaster to the progress of economics'.

252

CELESTIAL MECHANICS

PIERRE SIMON LAPLACE (1749–1827). Traité de Mécanique Céleste. *Paris:* vols. I–III, *Crapelet for J. B. M. Duprat,* [*1799*]–*1802;* vol. IV, *Courcier, 1805;* vol. V, *Huzard-Courcier, 1825*

Laplace has been called the 'Newton of France'. In his monumental 'Treatise on Celestial Mechanics', published over a period of twenty-seven years, he codified and developed the theories and achievements of his predecessors, notably Newton (161), Euler (196), d'Alembert (195) and of his contemporary Lagrange, whose *Méchanique Analitique* had been published in 1788.

Laplace was the son of a small farmer in Normandy. Some rich neighbours recognized his talents and helped with his education. Arriving in Paris at the age of eighteen he met d'Alembert, who secured for him a position as professor of mathematics at the École Militaire, and he soon became a member of the Académie des Sciences. He took a great interest in politics, and managed to re-

main in favour with the governing powers through all the political changes in France. He was honoured by Napoleon, became a Count of the Empire and a Marquis after the restoration of the Bourbons.

Newton had observed in the movements of Saturn and Jupiter anomalies which he could not explain. He, like Euler, was doubtful whether the variable forces acting in the solar system could be permanently maintained in an equilibrium. Newton therefore declared that God must be present in the universe to correct such irregularities. Laplace took a different view. When asked by Napoleon, to whom he presented the first part of the

TRAITÉ

DE

MÉCANIQUE CÉLESTE,

PAR P. S. LAPLACE,

Membre de l'Institut national de France, et du Bureau des Longitudes.

TOME PREMIER.

DE L'IMPRIMERIE DE CRAPELET.

A PARIS,

Chez J. B. M. DUPRAT, Libraire pour les Mathématiques, quai des Augustins.

AN VII.

Mécanique Céleste, why in this survey of creation he had never mentioned its creator, Laplace replied: 'I had no need of such a hypothesis'.

Laplace maintained that while all planets revolve round the sun their eccentricities and the inclinations of their orbits to each other will always remain small. He also showed that all these irregularities in movements and positions in the heavens were self-correcting, so that the whole solar system appeared to be mechanically stable. The universe was really a great self-regulating machine and the whole solar system could continue on its existing plan for an immense period of time. This was a long step forward from the Newtonian uncertainties in this respect, although it left out of account the possibilities of interference by outside forces and assumed that the sun would remain indefinitely in its present physical state.

Laplace also offered a brilliant explanation of the secular inequalities of the mean motion of the moon about the earth—a problem which Euler and Lagrange had failed to solve. He proved that these irregularities are connected with certain solar actions and changes in the orbit of the earth. He also investigated the theory of the tides and calculated from them the mass of the moon.

The *Mécanique Céleste* itself is an extremely difficult and highly mathematical work. Laplace had earlier produced a more popular book, with most of the mathematics left out: the *Exposition du Système du Monde*, 1796. This includes in a footnote his famous 'nebular hypothesis'.

Laplace's other mathematical work included the *Théorie Analytique des Probabilités*, 1812, and a treatise on the attraction of spheroids. 'Laplace's co-efficients' are important in the theory of attraction, hydrodynamics and electrical science. He made discoveries on the velocity of sound in gases, found a formula for measuring heights by the barometer and developed a new theory of capillarity.

The *Mécanique Céleste* was translated into English by the American mathematician Nathaniel Bowditch and published with an ample commentary in Boston, 1829–39, in four volumes; a German edition of the general section was issued by Johann Karl Burkhardt, 1800–2.

253

THE EXPLORATION OF AFRICA

MUNGO PARK (1771–1806). Travels in the Interior Districts of Africa. *London: W. Bulmer and Co., for the Author, and sold by G. and W. Nichol, 1799*

Until the publication of Park's book in 1799 hardly anything was known of the interior of Africa, apart from the north-east region and coastal areas. It is true that in 1768–73 James Bruce had begun to explore Abyssinia and the Nubian desert, but the real opening up of Africa by the white races began with the African Association, founded in 1788 with the express purpose of exploring Africa and of furthering British trade and political influence on the continent. This exercise lasted a century and it was concentrated mainly on exploring the great rivers which would give access to the interior. In the early days it was the Niger and later the Nile, the Zambesi and the Congo, which were the targets (see Baker, 357; Livingstone, 341).

Having sent out four expeditions to the Niger, all of which had failed, the African Association in 1795 charged Mungo Park with the task. Park, a Scot and the seventh of a family of thirteen, had originally studied medicine, but after being employed as assistant surgeon on the *Worcester* for a voyage to Sumatra, his enthusiasm for exploring had been aroused. On 22 May 1795 he set sail to find and explore the Niger. Travelling eastward from the English factory at Pisania (where he had learned the Mandingo language) along the River Gambia, Park reached the Niger at Segou and followed its course for about one hundred miles to Sulla, where difficulties forced him to turn back. He followed its banks as far as Bamako and eventually reached the Kingdom of Mandingo on 14 September 1796. Here he was taken ill, but was brought back to Gambia by a slave trader and finally reached Falmouth on 22 December 1797.

After the publication of his book Park withdrew to a country medical practice at Peebles. He soon got bored with the quiet life; and in 1805 he set out on another voyage to the Niger. This time he actually travelled on the river in a canoe, hoping to follow it to its mouth. But he met great hardships, lost a number of his men, and when he reached the rapids at Boussa, his company consisted only of four other Europeans. Here the canoe foundered, and Park and his companions perished in a fight with the natives. Fortunately, he had earlier sent back his journals to Gambia and they formed the basis of a second account of his voyages issued by the African Association: *The Journal of a Mission to the Interior of Africa in the year 1805... To which is prefixed an Account of the Life of Mr. Park* [by John Wishaw], London, 1815.

Park's *Travels* had an immediate success and was translated into most European languages. It has become a classic of travel literature, and its scientific observations on the botany and meteorology of the region, and on the social and domestic life of the negroes, have remained of lasting value. Park's career was short, but he made the first great practical advance in the opening-up of Central Africa. Park did not solve the problem of the Niger: he believed it to be a tributary of the Nile or to be really identical with the Congo; but he set the further exploration of the region in the right direction. Clapperton, Oudney, Lander, Barth and others followed in Park's footsteps and found the source of the river in Sierra Leone in 1822 and its mouth in the Gulf of Guinea in 1830.

254

INFRA-RED RAYS

FREDERICK WILLIAM HERSCHEL (1738–1822). Three Papers on Radiant Heat, Infra-Red Rays, &c. *In*: Philosophical Transactions of the Royal Society. *London, 1800.* (*a*) Investigation of the Powers of the Prismatic Colours to heat and illuminate Objects; (*b*) Experiments on the Refrangibility of the invisible Rays of the Sun; (*c*) Experiments on the Solar and on the Terrestrial Rays that occasion Heat

Newton (172) had discovered the nature of the prismatic spectrum and in the eighteenth century the Swedish chemist Scheele had found that heat is not only produced as an accompaniment of visible light—e.g. the collection of heat by concave mirrors or lenses from the sun's rays—but that it is also propagated by invisible rays.

Sir William Herschel, the great astronomer (see also 227), further investigated this problem and made a major contribution to physics. He made some delicate experiments at one end of the spectrum with a thermometer and discovered that when sunlight was refracted by a prism, invisible heat-rays fell outside the visible spectrum, being less refracted than red light. He had, in fact, discovered the infra-red rays.

In one of these papers Herschel remarked: 'May not the chemical properties of the prismatic colours be as different as those which relate to light and heat?' Here was a remarkable prophecy; for half a century later the special sensitivity of silver halides to blue, violet and ultra-violet light was discovered, a basic factor of photography (see 318).

255

THE ELECTRIC CURRENT

ALEXANDER VOLTA (1745–1827). On the Electricity excited by the Mere Contact of Conducting Substances of Different Kinds. *In:* Philosophical Transactions of the Royal Society. *London, 1800*

Pursuing the investigations of Galvani (240) Volta took the practical step that produced the first continuous and controllable electric current.

The voltaic pile revolutionized the theory and practice of electricity, so that within one hundred years of Volta's invention more progress was made than in the two thousand four hundred years between the tentative experiences of Thales and the publication of Volta's letter

Philos. Trans. MDCCC. *Plate* XVII. *p.* 430.

addressed to Sir Joseph Banks, President of the Royal Society. The pile consisted of a series of copper and zinc discs separated by pieces of cloth, paper, or paste-board soaked in a saline or acid fluid. Suitable connexion to an electroscope showed that (like a frictional machine) the pile produced an electric charge: but Volta demonstrated also that the action was continuous where an unbroken circuit permitted the flow of what he called, in a gracious gesture, the galvanic fluid.

Within days of the reading of this letter, and certainly before its publication, William Nicholson had built a pile and decomposed water by means of it. Humphry Davy followed this up with electrolytic experiments of his own on which he published his first paper in Nicholson's *Journal* in September 1800. This was the forerunner of a brilliant series of papers to the Royal Institution and the Royal Society culminating in the Bakerian Lectures in 1806 and 1807, in which Davy outlined a theory of mass action, forecast the use of electricity in atomic disintegration and announced the isolation by electrolytic methods of two new elements, sodium and potassium.

The indispensability and ubiquity of electricity, in one form or another, in western civilization today emphasize sharply the fact that before 1800 human environment and existence were closer to life in ancient Egypt than to our own. Volta's invention is one of the earliest and most important causes of the change.

256
MANIFESTO OF THE ROMANTIC MOVEMENT

WILLIAM WORDSWORTH (1770–1850) and SAMUEL TAYLOR COLERIDGE (1772–1834). Lyrical Ballads. 2 vols. *London: T. N. Longman and O. Rees, 1800*

It may have been the bedevilment caused by the clumsy methods of Joseph Cottle, printer and original publisher of the first edition of *Lyrical Ballads*, 1798, that induced Longman, when purchasing the printer's copyrights, to value this one at nothing and to hand it back to Wordsworth. This gift and the eventually unfulfilled promise of *Christabel* by Coleridge encouraged Wordsworth to embark on a second edition, in two volumes. This was fortunate for Wordsworth, who made about £100 out of it, and fortunate for posterity: not only for the fine poems in the second volume, but also for Wordsworth's famous preface defining his theory of poetry which first appeared in this, the second edition. It is not the incidental remarks on diction that are important but Wordsworth's revolt against eighteenth-century artificiality. Its outline of the supreme function of poetry, expressed in such phrases as that poetry 'takes its origin from emotion recollected in tranquillity', set a new tone; and it became in effect the revolutionary manifesto of the romantic poets of the next generation.

257
'THE PRINCE OF MATHEMATICS'

CARL FRIEDRICH GAUSS (1777–1855). Disquisitiones Arithmeticae. *Leipzig: Gerhardt Fleischer, 1801*

Gauss ranks, together with Archimedes (72) and Newton (161), as one of the greatest geniuses in the history of mathematics. Much of his work was not published until long after his death, so that its importance was not fully realized until this century.

He was of humble origin, the son of a bricklayer, but his remarkable gift for calculation soon became apparent and Carl Wilhelm, Duke of Brunswick, looked after his education and sent him to his Collegium Carolinum. He later studied at Göttingen, where in 1807 he became professor of mathematics and director of the observatory. He hardly ever left the town again.

Gauss published his 'Arithmetical Disquisitions' at the age of twenty-four, an astonishing achievement, as it is considered to be a book that begins a new epoch in mathematics, being a fundamental book in the modern theory of numbers. In Part IV it contains a discussion of the theory of quadratic reciprocity, which Gauss had discovered at the early age of eighteen; yet Euler (196) and Legendre before him had failed to prove it. His discovery of a method of inscribing in a circle a regular polygon of seventeen sides is described in Part VII—it was the first new discovery of this kind in Euclidean geometry for over two thousand years. Other sections treat of congruences of the second degree and of quadratic forms. The book is extremely difficult to understand, but due to the comments of Peter Gustav Dirichlet, Gauss's main exponent in the nineteenth century, and others, its ideas have become much more comprehensible to modern mathematicians.

There was hardly a branch of mathematics in which Gauss did not produce important work. He was one of the first to develop a form of non-Euclidean geometry, and it is perhaps worth noting that among his circle of student friends in Göttingen was Wolfgang Bolyai. He developed the method of least squares in the theory of errors and his investigations in geodesy led him to study problems of curved surfaces and thereby introduce the subject of differential geometry which later inspired Riemann (293 *b*) and Einstein (408).

Much of Gauss's time in later life was devoted to astronomy and magnetism. His *Theoria Motus Corporum Coelestium*, 1809, contains an analysis of the problems arising in the determination of the motions of planets and comets from a limited number of observational data. With Wilhelm Weber (1804–91) he worked on magnetism, evolving a theory of terrestrial magnetism and inventing the bifilar magnetometer and in 1833 the electromagnetic telegraph. He also left important studies in geodesy, optics, mechanics and crystallography.

Gauss's works have been published in a monumental edition, the *Gesammelte Werke*, 13 vols., 1863–1933.

258

RADICAL EDUCATOR

JOHANN HEINRICH PESTALOZZI (1746–1827). Wie Gertrud ihre Kinder lehrt. *Berne & Zürich: Heinrich Gessner, 1801*

Pestalozzi had no training or special qualifications as a teacher. He failed successively as a theologian, a lawyer and a farmer. In 1775, himself desperately poor, he turned his farm at Neuhof into an orphan asylum but in 1780 a combination of lack of funds and the desertion of most of the children caused him to abandon the experiment. He next tried his hand at writing. A volume of aphorisms on the value of education, 1780, was succeeded by *Lienhard und Gertrud* (4 vols., 1781–7), which was a kind of romance with an educational motif. For the ten years from 1787 he returned to farming; but his passion for educational advance did not pass without notice. He corresponded with Fellenberg, the pioneer of agricultural institutes, and with Fichte (244) who remarked on the coincidence of his ideas with those of Kant (226).

In 1798 Pestalozzi opened a second orphan asylum at Stans, where he had eighty pupils, several of whom he trained as pupil-teachers. One year later he was appointed to a primary school by the Swiss government at Burgdorf and it was here that 'How Gertrude teaches her Children' was produced. The title is misleading, because the series of letters deals rather with the results than with the methods of teaching, and Gertrude herself does not appear. It is nevertheless an exhaustive exposition of Pestalozzi's principles with especial emphasis on the three R's. The most important and forward-looking of his ideas, which he stressed continually in practice as well as precept, was that the true method of education is to develop the child, not to train him as one trains a dog. The pupil must be regarded as more important than the subject and the 'whole man' must be developed.

In 1805 Pestalozzi opened his last school at Yverdun. Although, perhaps because, this school attracted visitors from all over Europe, Pestalozzi seems to have felt himself less at home in this school than in its unsuccessful predecessors.

It has been well said that he became a Swiss curiosity, visited by tourists as they visited a glacier. His influence has been felt throughout the world and he is commemorated in the Pestalozzi villages where the children of war fugitives are cared for. Not less important than the institution of such ideas was his pungent criticism of the absence of standards in the recruitment of teachers. The miserable pay and wretched conditions attracted 'corrupt artisans, discharged soldiers, degraded students, and, in general, persons of questionable morality and education'. Mr Squeers affords ample evidence that such conditions were not abolished by Pestalozzi's efforts: but he pointed the way.

259

THE LAST NATURAL PHILOSOPHER

THOMAS YOUNG (1773–1829). On the Theory of Light and Colours. *In:* Philosophical Transactions of the Royal Society. *London, 1802*

Young was the last of the natural philosophers who could know all that was to be known. He was the perfector of the wave theory of light, he expounded the mechanism of vision, stated the laws of blood circulation, introduced the modern conceptions of 'energy' and 'work done', evolved a sound theory of tides, and helped to decipher the hieroglyphics of the Rosetta Stone.

[12]

II. *The Bakerian Lecture. On the Theory of Light and Colours. By* Thomas Young, *M. D. F. R. S. Professor of Natural Philosophy in the Royal Institution.*

Read November 12, 1801.

ALTHOUGH the invention of plausible hypotheses, independent of any connection with experimental observations, can be of very little use in the promotion of natural knowledge; yet the discovery of simple and uniform principles, by which a great number of apparently heterogeneous phenomena are reduced to coherent and universal laws, must ever be allowed to be of considerable importance towards the improvement of the human intellect.

The object of the present dissertation is not so much to propose any opinions which are absolutely new, as to refer some theories, which have been already advanced, to their original inventors, to support them by additional evidence, and to apply them to a great number of diversified facts, which have hitherto been buried in obscurity. Nor is it absolutely necessary in this instance to produce a single new experiment; for of experiments there is already an ample store, which are so much the more unexceptionable, as they must have been conducted without the least partiality for the system by which they will be explained; yet some facts, hitherto unobserved, will be brought forwards, in order to show the perfect agreement of that system with the multifarious phenomena of nature.

This Bakerian Lecture delivered in November 1801 is an epoch-making contribution to the theory of light in all its phases. Hooke (147), Huygens (154) and above all Newton (172) had discussed the nature of light in the seventeenth century. Huygens propounded the wave theory in 1690, whereas Newton was predominantly in favour of a corpuscular theory, despite the part etheric undulations played in his explanation of certain phenomena. Though criticized by Euler (196) and some others, the corpuscular theory held the field almost throughout the eighteenth century; but Young, in this and two subsequent papers printed in the *Philosophical Transactions*,

July 1802, and his Bakerian Lecture, November 1803, based himself firmly on the theory that 'radiant light consists of undulations of the luminous ether': a theory that held the field until the latter-day notions of Planck (391) and J. J. Thomson (386).

Young's experimental proofs were often deceptively simple. He admitted light into a darkened room through two pin-holes, so that the beams overlapped on a white screen. At the point of overlapping white light changed to a band of brilliant colours. This, said Young, was caused by the interference of similar waves from the two sources of light, the gap between the pin-holes being such that the crest of one wave coincided with the crest of another. This made it possible to measure the minute length of the waves—something like one fifty-thousandth part of an inch.

260*

THE METRIC SYSTEM

JEAN BAPTISTE JOSEPH DELAMBRE (1749–1822). Base du Système Métrique Décimal. 3 vols. *Paris: Baudouin for Garnery, 1806–10*

For many centuries there were no general standards of measurement: every trade and craft had its own peculiar units and they differed even in various regions of the same country. Since the development of international trade in the Middle Ages this chaotic situation had become more and more tiresome, but all efforts towards standardization were strongly resisted by vested interests.

The earliest books to advocate a universal system were Stevin's *De Thiende*, 1585 (99) and Mouton's *Observationes Diametrorum Solis et Lunae apparentium*, Lyons, 1670, which proposed to adopt as a standard the length of an arc of one minute of a great circle of the earth, with decimal subdivisions. Huygens (154) and others had proposed to use the length of a pendulum beating one second, or one-third of this length, as a unit. These proposals had to be rejected as they were not sufficiently precise; the length of the pendulum would differ from place to place and the meridian arc would vary at different latitudes.

We owe the introduction of an international metric system to the French Revolution. In 1790 the Académie des Sciences, at the request of Talleyrand, set up a commission to consider the question; among its members were J. C. Borda, Lagrange, Laplace (252), G. Monge and Condorcet (246). In 1791 they reported that the fundamental unit of length should be derived from a dimension of the earth: it should be the ten-millionth part of a quadrant of the earth's meridian extending between Dunkirk and Barcelona. As this distance was already approximately known, a provisional metre was at once adopted. The new unit of weight was to be the gramme: the weight of one cubic centimetre of water at 4° C.

The Constituent Assembly set up a general commission of weights and measures to carry these proposals into effect and in 1795 a law was passed introducing the metric system into France with provisional standards. The astronomers Jean Baptiste Joseph Delambre and Pierre

Francois André Mechain (1744–1805) were charged with the task of measuring accurately the newly adopted length along the meridian arc between Dunkirk and Barcelona. Owing to the disturbances of the revolutionary period their work was much impeded, but in 1799 their measurement was completed. The above work—'Basis of the Metric Decimal System'—embodies their report. The length of a metre (equalling 39·37 English inches) was marked on a platinum bar, and the unit of weight was also constructed of platinum, being the weight of a cubic decimetre, or litre, of pure water at its maximum density. These original bars remained the basic standards until 1875 and are still preserved in Paris.

The metric system was gradually accepted by most nations—with the notable exceptions of England and (for weights and measures) the United States; but optional use was legalized in 1864 (England) and 1866 (U.S.A.) and its general adoption in England was proposed in 1965. After meetings of an international commission in 1872 there was set up in 1875 the International Bureau of Weights and Measures. It is now situated near Sèvres and has since remained the international centre for all questions of standards. New units made from a bar of platinum alloyed with 10 per cent iridium were constructed, copies of which were distributed to the various participating countries. In 1921 its scope was extended to include the problems of electrical units based essentially on the metric system—ampère, volt (see 255), ohm (see 289)—and in 1927 photometric units were added.

261

THE ATOMIC THEORY

JOHN DALTON (1766–1844). A New System of Chemical Philosophy. Part I. *Manchester: Printed for R. Bickerstaff, London, 1808;* Part II, *Ibidem, 1810.* Vol. 2, Part I. *Manchester: Printed for G. Wilson, London, 1827*

The idea that matter is composed of ultimate, indestructible particles was very ancient in Greece. In Lucretius's detailed exposition (87) it survived through many centuries, though Aristotle's (38) continuum theory of matter generally prevailed. Atomism was revived by the seventeenth-century physicists, to whom it provided a fruitful view of the universe which mathematics and experiment seemed to confirm. Dalton reconstructed Newton's (161) speculations on the structure of matter, and, applying them in a new form to chemistry, gave Lavoisier's reformation of that science (238) a deeper significance.

Dalton, a Quaker, was the son of a poor weaver and was himself a teacher. He was an active member of the Manchester Literary and Philosophical Society, to which he read his first paper in October 1794, describing colour-blindness for the first time. In 1799 he contributed the first of a series of lectures supplementing his *Meterological Observations and Essays*, 1793. That book and the supplementary papers read to the Society not only laid the foundations of modern meteorology but one of them, entitled 'On the Absorption of Gases by Water and other Liquids', read in October 1803, published in 1805, declared that the invariable principles he had observed to govern the combination of elemental substances in the formation of compounds were explicable only by postulating a definite atomic weight for each element.

This contention he expounded in his *New System*. It involved the view that each of Lavoisier's *éléments* is composed of atoms all alike, and supported Lavoisier's notion of compounds of doublets, triplets, quadruplets, etc., of atoms, the composition of each being constant. The identity of each atom was established by its particular weight, which could be determined experimentally for each element, taking the weight of the hydrogen atom, the lightest, as equal to one. Thus Dalton found the oxygen atom to weigh 6·5 times as much as the hydrogen atom, etc. Hence the problem of chemical composition was that of determining how many atoms, and of which kinds, entered into the unit, later known as the molecule, of each compound substance. This problem dominated nineteenth-century chemistry.

In Dalton's 'Absorption of Gases' is a list of twenty-one atomic weights, which there is reason to suppose were added between the reading of the paper in 1803 and its publication two years later. He permitted Dr Thomas Thomson to insert in the third edition of his *System of Chemistry* (1807, vol. III, p. 424) a short account of the theory; but Dalton's own full-length statement, including the first periodic table of the elements, appeared in 1808 and 1810 in the first two parts of *A New System*. By the time the third part appeared in 1827 the theory had borne such widespread fruit that Dalton's own conclusions were almost all out-of-date.

This is typical of Dalton's indifference to the conclusions of others. He disputed Davy's discovery of the elemental nature of chlorine, sodium and potassium, and Gay-Lussac's discoveries on combining volumes, which, in fact, handsomely complemented his own law of combining weights.

BIBLIOGRAPHY: Complete lists of Dalton's scientific publications are contained in a memoir of Dalton contributed by Angus Smith to the *Memoirs of the Literary & Philosophical Society of Manchester*, vol. XIII of 2nd ser. (London, 1856); and in Lonsdale's *Worthies of Cumberland: John Dalton* (London, 1874).

262

THE DAWN OF EVOLUTION

JEAN BAPTISTE LAMARCK (1744–1829). Philosophie Zoologique. 2 vols. *Paris: Dentu, printed for the Author, 1809*

The 'Zoological Philosophy' of Lamarck is a classic in the literature of evolutionary theory. The concept of an evolutionary development of the universe is as old as Empedocles and Lucretius (87). In later centuries it was bedevilled by theological preconceptions. Hutton (247) had been the first to give a scientific basis to geology by demonstrating that changes in the inorganic world were the result of natural forces and not of a series of supernatural cataclysms. Lamarck observed that in the organic world also the interaction of natural forces was an adequate cause and explanation of the vastly more complicated phenomena of the variation of species.

Taking the whole of organic life in one broad view he demonstrated the possibility of ranging all living forms in a single series, starting with the lowest and simplest and progressing to the highest and most complicated. The idea itself was as old as Aristotle (38); what was new was Lamarck's suggestion that this scale corresponds to an order of historical development of the higher forms. This he did by tracing the progression in the reverse direction and observing the gradual changing, simplification and ultimate disappearance of the features distinguishing the higher forms as each lower scale is reached. From this it followed that the history of development of the higher forms of life was a continual and continuous process of specialization with no gap or interruption at any stage.

This is a clear adumbration of the evolutionary theory; but when Lamarck attempted to outline the mechanism by which changes come about he was less successful. He suggested that the use of a part or an organ caused developments that were inheritable, founding this on the hypothesis that the most-used part attracted most nourishment. It was this prominent feature of Lamarck's theory that caused Darwin (344) initially to dismiss his views as 'veritable rubbish'; but in the 'Historical Sketch' prefaced to the third edition of *The Origin of Species* he makes handsome amends in the following words: 'He first did the eminent service of arousing attention to the probability of all change in the organic as well as in the inorganic world being the result of law, and not of miraculous interposition'.

Eminent disciples of Lamarck have included Oscar Hertwig, Samuel Butler and Bernard Shaw. The possibility of the inheritance of acquired characteristics is attractive to Marxists and was recently revived in Russia, with unfortunate results. It has now been abandoned.

263

THE FATHER OF AERIAL NAVIGATION

SIR GEORGE CAYLEY, Bart (1773–1857). On Aerial Navigation. *In:* A Journal of Natural Philosophy Chemistry and the Arts, edited by W. Nicholson, vols. 24–5. *London, 1809–10*

'The true inventor of the aeroplane and one of the most powerful geniuses in the history of aviation': these are the words used by the French historian Charles Dollfus to describe Sir George Cayley, a scholarly Yorkshire baronet who until recently was virtually ignored by historians of applied science.

Cayley, who lived and did most of his work at Brompton Hall, near Scarborough, first had his aeronautical imagination fired by the invention of the balloon in 1783 (see 229)—when he was ten—and his active concern with flying lasted until his death in 1857. In the year 1796 he made a helicopter model on the lines of that invented by Launoy and Bienvenu, a device he later improved and modified. Then, within a few years, with no previous workers to guide him or suggest the lines of approach, he arrived at a correct conception of the modern aeroplane, and so laid the secure foundations for all subsequent developments in aviation.

It was in the year 1799 that Cayley took his first and most decisive step towards inaugurating the concept of the modern aeroplane: the proper separation of the system of thrust from the system of lift. This was the crucial breakaway from the ornithopter tradition of previous centuries; it meant picturing the bird with its wings held rigid as if in gliding flight, and propelled by some form of auxiliary mechanism. Then, during the most fruitful decade of his life (1799–1809) Cayley made his basic experiments, which included testing both model and full-size gliders, and arrived at his mature conception of aircraft and aerodynamics. It was almost an accident that he gathered together his notes and published them. For it

was in Nicholson's *Journal* for November 1809, February 1810, and March 1810, that there appeared Cayley's triple paper 'On Aerial Navigation'. It is at once the first and the greatest classic of aviation history, and laid the foundations of the science of aerodynamics. Ironically, Cayley was persuaded into print by a spurious report that, at Vienna, Jacob Degen had flown briefly with wings, under his own unaided muscle-power.

Cayley had a supreme confidence in the ultimate success of the powered aeroplane, a confidence preserved throughout his life. It was charmingly summed up in one of his *obiter dicta*: 'An uninterrupted navigable ocean, that comes to the threshold of every man's door, ought not be to neglected as a source of human gratification and advantage'.

264
WAR UNDER WATER

ROBERT FULTON (1765–1815). Torpedo War and Submarine Explosions. *New York: William Elliot, 1810*

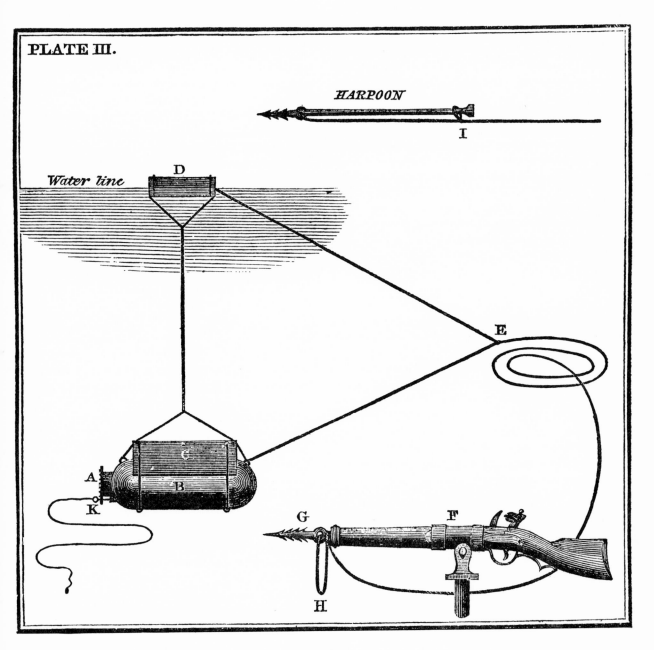

As early as 1797 Robert Fulton had been experimenting with torpedoes, mines and submarines. He envisaged a new and powerful arsenal of weapons which would serve as an equalizer between the small United States Navy and the much more powerful fleets of her European competitors: weapons which would put an end to naval blockades, ensure freedom of the seas and revolutionize naval warfare.

After the French Revolution he offered his new inventions to the French, who briefly tried out the submarine and the torpedo only to abandon them. The Fulton torpedo, it must be remembered, was not self-propelling: it had to be pushed. When the democratic experiment failed in France, Fulton crossed the Channel (1804) to help the British direct torpedo raids against Napoleon's flotilla at Boulogne. Two years later he returned to the United States, where he continued his researches in hopes of convincing the United States government of the utility of torpedo warfare. But his excessive enthusiasm for his invention militated against him. To the naval commanders it appeared that Fulton proposed replacing the fleet with torpedoes—and at that they drew the line.

In the years which led up to the War of 1812 Fulton gave a number of public exhibitions in his efforts to persuade Congress to support his experiments. In July 1807 he demonstrated the torpedo before a number of dignitaries in New York in an attempt to prove its potential as a defence for that city's harbour. The demonstration was only partially successful however. He failed in two out of three tries to sink the ship set up for the purpose and the new weapon became the object of some rather pointed mirth. In the 14 August issue of *Salmagundi* Washington Irving observed that 'all that was requisite to render the effect certain was that the enemy should enter into the project, or, in other words, be *agreeable to the measure*; so that, if the machine did not come to the ship, the ships should go to the machine, by which means. . . the success of the machine would be inevitable,—provided it struck fire'.

Fulton was not a man to be easily discouraged. Other demonstrations followed, with varying degrees of success, and though he won some converts—Thomas Jefferson, something of an inventor himself, among them—he still had to face the determined opposition of Commodore John Rogers and other influential navy men who feared that the new defensive weapon, like Jefferson's gunboats before it, would undermine the concept of an offensive blue-water fleet. Fulton's pamphlet *Torpedo War and Submarine Explosions* was written and published in 1810 in an effort to win Congressional support for further experimentation. He sent copies to all the members of the Congress, but they remained lukewarm to his proposals and pigeon-holed the motion that would have provided the necessary financial aid. Even during the British blockade of the War of 1812, use of the torpedo was limited to a series of semi-official adventures by men seeking rewards for sinking the enemy's ships. Spar and outrigger torpedoes were used in the Civil War: the Confederate ironclad *Albemarle* was sunk by one in the Roanoke River in 1864, and every American schoolboy knows Farragut's

order at Vicksburg, 'Damn the torpedoes! Full steam ahead!' But until the torpedo could propel itself and be steered it remained primarily a defensive weapon. Robert Whitehead solved the problem late in the century; but it was not until a hundred years after his death that Fulton's ideas did indeed revolutionize naval warfare.

265

HOMŒOPATHY

SAMUEL CHRISTIAN FRIEDRICH HAHNEMANN (1755–1843). Organon der rationellen Heilkunde. *Dresden: Arnold, 1810*

Hahnemann is a splendid example of a man hitting a target much higher than the one he aimed at and remaining largely unaware of the fact. He was the founder of homoeopathic medicine, and although this system is far more widely practised on the Continent than in Britain it is not so evidently superior to all others as to have replaced them. Moreover homoeopathy as now practised differs widely from Hahnemann's system, as expounded in his 'Method of Rational Healing'. His notion that all diseases are manifestations of either the itch, syphilis or fig-wart disease has been abandoned. His basic principle—the doctrine of similars—was as old as Hippocrates and occurs in the exact terminology used by him—*similia similibus curantur*—in a 1650 edition of the works of Paracelsus (110).

What is then left, and by what right is he included in the present august company? The answer is implicit in his life-story. The son of a porcelain painter at the Meissen factory, he was intended for an industrial career which was to include no more than elementary schooling. His teacher was so impressed with his intellectual promise that he undertook to continue his education free of charge. Later Hahnemann was entered as a medical student at Leipzig where he supported himself by translating English and French scientific works. He slept only every other night.

A rich patron from Transylvania engaged him as a librarian and general amanuensis, but as soon as he had saved enough money he returned to his medical studies and graduated in 1779. He was taken on as an assistant by the most fashionable doctor in Leipzig, and although he was very successful he was so appalled by the brutal hit-or-miss methods of medical practice at the time that he gave up his share in a prosperous practice to study the physiological effect of drugs.

Hahnemann was convinced that minute doses of drugs in greatly attenuated concentrations were efficacious cures. When modern practice is compared with the indiscriminate and massive prescriptions of his own day it will be seen how much closer we are to his views than to those of his contemporaries. Certainly his treatment showed that the *vis medicatrix naturae*, given a chance, with occasional and gentle assistance, often suffices to effect a cure. He gave great prominence to therapeutics, introduced many new specifics, but ignored the growing science of pathology. In his emphasis on the importance of studying the patient as a whole, he foreshadowed the psychosomatic component of modern medicine.

Alternately persecuted and ridiculed by fellow practitioners in his own country, Hahnemann was driven from one locality to another until finally, at the age of eighty, he married a rich young Frenchwoman, established himself in Paris and, according to Garrison, died a millionaire.

266

NORDIC PHILOLOGY

RASMUS KRISTIAN RASK (1787–1832). Vejledning til det Islandske eller gamle Nordiske Sprog. *Copenhagen: Printed for Schuboth by J. R. Thiele, 1811*

The 'Guide to the Icelandic or old Nordic Language' was the first of an important series of publications which qualify Rask as one of the founders of the modern science of language.

The interest that his writings aroused in the ancient Scandinavian tongues directed attention to their literature. He was the first to study the ancient Nordic languages systematically. He discovered the correspondence of consonant relations between the Indo-European languages, which led Jacob Grimm (281) to formulate the rules underlying the Germanic as well as the High-German sound-shifts. In 1818 Rask edited the first complete texts of the Eddas of Snorri (168) and Saemund and added modernized versions. During his journeys to Russia and Persia he collected valuable Avesta and Pali manuscripts which he gave to the Royal Library in Copenhagen of which he was librarian, and thereby promoted the study of the Asian branches of the Indo-European family of languages (see Jones, 235).

267

HISTORY v. MYTHOLOGY

BARTHOLD GEORG NIEBUHR (1776–1831). Römische Geschichte. 3 vols. *Berlin: Realschulbuchhandlung, 1811–12, 1832*

The son of a minor Danish official, Carsten Niebuhr (1733–1815), the importance of whose travels in the Middle East (1761–7) has only lately been appreciated, Niebuhr is the founder of modern, empirical and scientific history, and the publication of the first two volumes of his 'Roman History' (the third appeared posthumously) marked a turning-point from which historians have never looked back.

Niebuhr started as a banker like Grote (321). He worked first in the Danish and then from 1806 in the Prussian state banks, before he became a civil servant like Macaulay (328), Prussian envoy to the Vatican, 1816–23, and, in between, professor at the universities of Berlin and Bonn. He was thus almost the only German historian whose insight was deepened by experience of business, administration and international affairs.

Niebuhr established the principle, now universally adopted, of 'positive scepsis' (as Goethe happily termed it) which is that the systematic collection and critical assessment of the original sources must be the foundation of all historical writing. Gibbon (222) was in Niebuhr's opinion the only previous historian to have fulfilled these conditions; and his 'Roman History' was actually conceived as the first part, as it were, of Gibbon's great work. An enthusiastic anglophile like Montesquieu (197), and an admirer of Burke (239) Niebuhr tended to equate the Roman senate with the British parliament and the sturdy Roman farmers with the English yeomanry. His emphasis on institutions rather than individuals delimited the frontiers between fact and fable and finally separated real history from legendary tradition.

Niebuhr's excellence as an interpreter of sources and as the demolisher of the authority of Livy was unfortunately accompanied by severe literary shortcomings. His history, in the words of G. P. Gooch, 'is the most unreadable of historical classics' because, as Goethe recognized, it is not a Roman history but a 'critical dissertation on the writers who have transmitted Roman history'. The English translation by Thirlwall and Hare, 1828, and the French imitation by Michelet (324) in his *Histoire Romaine*, 1831, spread Niebuhr's fame over Europe, and 'all historians', in the words of Mommsen, 'so far as they are worthy of the name, are his pupils'. It was Mommsen himself who eventually wrote the classical *Römische Geschichte* (337★) on the foundations laid by Niebuhr.

268

HANSARD

THE PARLIAMENTARY DEBATES, from the year 1803 to the present time. *London: Printed by T. C. Hansard for Longman (and others), 1812*

The earliest accurate reports of the proceedings in Parliament are among the achievements of the ever industrious William Cobbett (294). The first series, which included the previous year, was published in 1804, and set a new standard for fidelity to the actual speeches. Like his predecessors, Cobbett was forced to make a patchwork from speakers' notes and newspaper reports, but, despite his own prejudices, he differed from them in his zeal to be accurate, whereas fine writing or party advocacy had earlier been the rule.

Cobbett's first printers were Cox and Baylis, but at the beginning of 1809 a new name appeared on the title-page, that of T. C. Hansard. Thomas Curson Hansard (1776–1833) was the eldest son of Luke Hansard (1752–1828), who had become a partner in the firm of John Hughs, printer to the House of Commons, in 1774. Luke was renowned for the accuracy and speed of his parliamentary printing, and eventually had to drop all other work (which had earned him the friendship and praise of Dr Johnson, Burke and Porson) while the House was sitting. Thomas, after working for some time for his father, set up in business on his own in 1803. He did well, and his father probably welcomed his return to an interest in parliamentary business, evinced by his taking on the *Debates* and Cobbett's other periodicals. But in 1810 a terrible blow fell: Cobbett published an article in his *Political Register* which attacked military flogging, and a prosecution for libel was brought against him by the government, in which Hansard was inculpated as printer. Both were found guilty: Cobbett was fined £1,000 and sentenced to two years imprisonment, and Thomas Hansard, to his father's misery and shame, to three months.

THE

Parliamentary Debates

FROM

THE YEAR

1803,

TO THE PRESENT TIME.

───────────

VOL. XXIII.

COMPRISING THE PERIOD

BETWEEN THE 5TH OF MAY AND THE CLOSE OF THE SESSION, JULY 30, 1812.

───────────

LONDON:

PRINTED BY T. C. HANSARD, PETERBOROUGH-COURT, FLEET-STREET:
FOR LONGMAN, HURST, REES, ORME, & BROWN; CRADOCK & JOY;
J. BOOKER; J. BOOTH; J. RICHARDSON; BLACK, PARRY, & CO.;
E. JEFFERY; J. HATCHARD; J. RIDGWAY; E. BUDD; J. RODWELL;
R. H. EVANS; AND T. C. HANSARD.

1812.

But good was come of this seeming disaster. After his release Thomas was able to pick up his business again and in 1812 he purchased *The Parliamentary Debates* from Cobbett, whose financial position had been badly damaged by his imprisonment. From then on the *Debates* formed a valuable extra asset to the Hansard family, in addition to the business still provided by the official printing required by Parliament. Thomas Hansard became one of the most learned and knowledgeable printers of his day; he was the author of *Typographia*, still the best and most reliable guide to printing practice of the time.

After Thomas Hansard's death the two branches of the business were reunited and remained closely attached to Parliament until the connexion ceased in 1895 (the name 'Hansard' was reintroduced on Parliamentary Reports in 1943). As a result of a famous law case in 1837, when the firm was prosecuted by J. J. Stockwell, who con-

sidered himself libelled by the official report of the Inspector of Prisons, 'published by order of the House', the printed parliamentary transactions and reports have since been protected by the same privilege as that accorded to Members' speeches. The relationship of Press to Parliament has been a pioneering one, but it has proved of great service to other parliamentary institutions, and 'Hansard' has served as a model for the parliamentary records of the world.

269

BROCKHAUS

FRIEDRICH ARNOLD BROCKHAUS (1772–1823). Conversations-Lexicon oder Hand-Wörterbuch für die gebildeten Stände. Vols. 1–4, *Amsterdam: Kunst- und Industrie-Comptoir, 1812–14*; vols. 5–10, *Altenburg and Leipzig: F. A. Brockhaus, 1815–19*

Just as the *Encyclopaedia Britannica* (218) has become the model of virtually every encyclopaedia in the English-speaking world, so all European dictionaries have followed, imitated, or adapted the principles on which Brockhaus's *Conversations-Lexicon* was constructed.

With the sure instinct of the great publisher, Friedrich Arnold Brockhaus in 1808 bought up for 1,800 talers the moribund encyclopaedia which Dr Renatus Gotthelf Löbel had edited from 1796 to his death in 1799 and which, rudderless and incomplete, had proved a dead loss to five successive publishers. Brockhaus realized its potentialities. He at once had the sixth and final volume compiled, added a two-volume supplement, and within two years sold the whole stock of 2,000 sets. He himself then edited the second to sixth editions—'Encyclopaedia or Dictionary for the Educated Classes'—which appeared between 1812 and 1819, calling them 'revised editions' so as not to lose any surviving goodwill attaching to the original publication. Each comprised ten volumes, each had to be reprinted, each printing numbering from 10,000 to 15,000 copies—an unheard-of success in those days. The imprints indicate Brockhaus's style and location in Amsterdam until 1814 and his removal to Altenburg in 1811 and Leipzig in 1817.

The absence of any legal copyright protection allowed at least half-a-dozen pirated and nakedly plagiarized editions to appear; but neither these rivals nor the ban imposed by the Austrian censorship could impede the uninterrupted growth of the work. Its high reputation was partly based on the careful choice of the contributors for even the most subordinate subject-matter—all of whom remained anonymous, as is still the case. Among them Jacob Burckhardt (347) and the Czech historian Palacky are, in retrospect, the most outstanding.

It throws an interesting sidelight on the attitude of the nineteenth-century reading public that an illustrated supplement, *Bilder-Atlas* (1844–9), was a huge success. By 1856 nearly four million sets had been issued and new editions came out until 1886. The demand for this illustrated supplement sharply contrasts with the repeated, costly failure of popular encyclopaedias which combined text and illustration. Neither the fifty copper-engravings of the *Deutsche Taschen-Encyklopädie* (4 vols., 1816–20) nor the 1,238 woodcuts of the *Bilder-Conversations-Lexicon* (4 vols., 1837–51) appealed to the public; both these enterprises had be to abandoned. It was as late as 1905 that an illustrated Brockhaus met with response and success.

The Brockhaus-type encyclopaedia soon found acceptance in other European countries besides Germany. The most important encyclopaedias compiled, translated and adapted in co-operation with the Leipzig firm were Lieber's *Encyclopaedia Americana* (1828–32), *Chambers's Encyclopaedia* (1860–8), Larousse's *Grand Dictionnaire Universel* (1864–76) and the huge *Entsiklopedicheskij Slovar* (43 vols., 1890–6), on which was based *Bolshaya Sovietskaya Entsiklopedia* (65 vols., 1926–47, and later editions). The latest edition of Brockhaus's dictionary, in 1928 renamed *Der Grosse Brockhaus*, appeared as the sixteenth edition in 1952–60.

Contrary to the prevalent English usage, Brockhaus has maintained the principle of a large number of entries, each comparatively short, instead of comprehensive summaries; the latest Brockhaus contains some 145,000 catchwords, compared with less than 40,000 in the current *Encyclopaedia Britannica*.

270★

BYRONISM

GEORGE GORDON NOEL BYRON, LORD BYRON (1788–1824). Childe Harold's Pilgrimage. *London: John Murray, 1812, 1816, 1818*

'I awoke one morning and found myself famous', Lord Byron entered in his diary on the publication of the first two cantos of *Childe Harold*. Certainly the failure of the then Cambridge undergraduate's jejune *Hours of Idleness*, 1807, had not prepared his publisher for this success: Murray had printed the usual 500 copies, at the time considered adequate for any book of verse. The edition was sold within three days, and Murray afterwards ventured to print 10,000 copies of each of the subsequent verse epics of his best-selling author—all of which, however, were snapped up by the public within weeks and had to be reprinted forthwith.

Byron did not exaggerate his fame. At home, he completely overshadowed his contemporaries, Wordsworth, Coleridge, Shelley, Keats, Blake. Walter Scott abandoned the writing of poetry, as he felt unequal to the younger rival in this field, and began the series of the *Waverley* novels (273). Abroad, Byron was, throughout the nineteenth century and beyond, considered the greatest English poet, inferior only to Shakespeare. Goethe, whose *Faust* (298) Byron tried to emulate with *Manfred*, 1817, immortalized him, in the second part of *Faust*, as Euphorion, the son of Faust and Helen of Troy, combining deepest thought and greatest beauty. 'Old Shakespeare' and Byron (followed by Heine and Béranger) were the favourite poets of the Iron Chancellor, Bismarck.

Byron's influence on the poetry of every foreign nation is incalculable. His debtors include—to name only a few outstanding examples—Chateaubriand, Alfred de Musset, Théophile Gautier and Victor Hugo in France; Heine and Lenau in Germany; Pushkin and Lermontov in Russia; Guerrazzi, Prati and Niccolini in Italy; Rivas, Larra and Espronceda in Spain; Almeida Garrett and Lemos in Portugal; and Azevedo in Brazil.

Mid-twentieth-century Englishmen find it almost impossible, and foreigners rather difficult, to understand this vogue of 'Byronism'. In any case, modern Englishmen would no doubt prefer *Don Juan* (1818–24) to *Childe Harold* and the other romantic verse epics and pseudo-metaphysical plays which swept Byron's contemporaries and near-contemporaries off their feet. But the huge, unfinished canvas of *Don Juan*, a veritable *comédie humaine*, is largely incomprehensible to foreigners, for the very reasons which maintain its appeal to at least a minority of English readers: the dazzling versification, the satirical allusions to Regency society, the empirical, typically English, approach to philosophical problems; Byron's whole 'Augustan' attitude, based on Dryden and Pope, despite its thin 'romantic' veneer.

For it was the very 'romanticism' of *Childe Harold* that established Byron and Byronism as a temporarily national and centennially international force in the western mind. What the whole of the nineteenth century admired most was the fascinating blend of aristocratic arrogance and revolutionary enthusiasm, sexual licentiousness and purity of love, glowing passion and deep melancholy, bitter irony and lachrymose sentimentality, exquisite dandyism and high personal courage. All these traits, and many more beside them, the public found in the mixture of realistic confession and stylized saga with which Byron expressed as well as veiled himself in the guise of Childe Harold, the Giaour, Lara, Conrad, Manfred, Don Juan and his other heroes. The Byronic combination of oriental enchantment and nature worship, pessimism and pantheism, stamped itself upon European civilization.

271

THE BIRTH OF SOCIALISM

ROBERT OWEN (1771–1858). A New View of Society. *London: Cadell and Davies, 1813–14*

The theory of socialism has a long and distinguished history, in which the two seminal figures are perhaps William Godwin (243) and the Marquis de Condorcet (246). Yet the first practical statement of socialist doctrine came not from a theorist but from one who based it on practical experiment.

Robert Owen became the manager of a cotton mill at the age of nineteen. He was brilliantly successful, not merely as a manager, but as an innovator, introducing the first imported cotton from America and improving the quality of the yarn. Before he was thirty he already had the experience, and the confidence born of it, to undertake his great experiment. He induced his partners to purchase New Lanark Mills near Glasgow, an old established factory with some of the poorest workers' quarters in the country. The hours were long and the workers themselves wretched and depraved. Owen improved their houses and the conditions of work; he opened a store where they could buy goods at little above cost price; and he restricted the sale of drink. His greatest success was in the education of workers' children. He was the founder of infant schools in Great Britain, and though anticipated by reformers abroad he seems to have been led to institute them from his own ideals of what education should be, and without any knowledge of foreign experiments. 'The Lanark Experiment' was a great success, and the mill ran at a profit; nevertheless Owen's partners were dissatisfied at the cost of his social schemes and he was forced to dissolve the partnership and form a new company, in which Jeremy Bentham (237) and William Allen, the Quaker philanthropist, were partners.

𝔄 𝔑𝔢𝔴 𝔙𝔦𝔢𝔴 𝔬𝔣 𝔖𝔬𝔠𝔦𝔢𝔱𝔶:

OR,

ESSAYS

ON THE PRINCIPLE OF THE

FORMATION OF THE HUMAN CHARACTER,

AND

THE APPLICATION OF THE PRINCIPLE

TO

PRACTICE.

" Any character, from the best to the worst, from the most ignorant to the most enlightened, may be given to any community, even to the world at large, by applying certain means; which are to a great extent at the command and under the controul, or easily made so, of those who possess the government of nations."

BY ONE OF HIS MAJESTY'S JUSTICES OF PEACE FOR
THE COUNTY OF LANARK.

London:
PRINTED FOR CADELL AND DAVIES, STRAND;
BY RICHARD TAYLOR AND CO., PRINTERS' COURT, SHOE LANE.

1813.

It was at this juncture that *A New View of Society* came out. In it Owen laid down the principles which had determined his experiment. Having no belief in any kind of religion, he had thought out a new system of beliefs for himself. The chief points were that man's character is made not by but for him and that it has been formed by circumstances over which he has no control. The prime necessity in the right formation of character is therefore to place him under proper physical, moral and social influences from the very beginning. These principles—the fundamental *irresponsibility* of man and the effect of good early influence—lie at the root of Owen's theories and his practice. New Lanark continued to show their efficacy, and it became a model community, much visited by the statesmen of Europe.

Owen now began to apply his principles to the nation as a whole, in the depth of the post-war depression, and in his evidence to the House of Commons Committee on the state of children in manufactories (1816) he recommended the introduction of community settlements with a common kitchen and dining rooms; families were to have private accommodation, but children from the age of three would be brought up by the community, their parents having reasonable access; the community would be supervised by a proper person; but its basis would be formed on work shared, and the profits of work equally divided. His plans were hailed with enthusiasm, but public confidence was shaken by his public admission of atheism, and his later experiments, in this country and at New Harmony, Indiana, were not a success. By 1846, a dozen years before his death, there was little to show for all Owen's energy and work; but the vitality of the word 'socialism', first coined by Owen about 1835, is testimony to the enduring value of his work.

BIBLIOGRAPHY: [W. Williams], *A Bibliography of Robert Owen, the Socialist, 1771–1858* (Aberystwyth, 1925).

272

OVERLAND TO THE PACIFIC

MERIWETHER LEWIS (1774–1809) and WILLIAM CLARK (1770–1838). History of the Expedition under the Command of Captains Lewis and Clark to the Pacific Ocean. 2 vols. *Philadelphia: Bradford and Inskeep; and Abraham H. Inskeep, New York, 1814*

Beyond the Missouri River there lay a vast and largely unexplored territory which bordered on the western reaches of the United States. Ceded by France to Spain in 1762 and then back to France in 1800 it was at this period visited only by some British and a few French trappers.

The importance of exploring this area had been evident to Thomas Jefferson as early as 1783, when he had proposed the project to George Rogers Clark; but it was not until twenty years later that Jefferson, then President of the United States, saw the realization of his idea. In a message which he sent to Congress in January 1803 he pointed out the importance of trade with the Indians of the region, a trade which would not only be lucrative in its own right but which would establish valuable ties with these tribes which, until then, were under the influence of British and French trappers. Relations between Britain and the United States were strained and in the event of war it would be essential to keep British influence from being used to send hordes of Indians on the warpath against the western settlements. Congress voted the appropriation.

As leader of the expedition Jefferson chose Meriwether Lewis, a scion of an old Virginia family who was both an accomplished amateur naturalist and an experienced army officer. Lewis, at this time, was serving as Secretary to the President and was intimately acquainted with Jefferson's hopes and expectations from the expedition. To prepare himself further for the detailed scientific note-taking which was expected of him, Lewis underwent a special course of instruction in Philadelphia, concentrating on scientific terminology and astronomy. For his companion in the expedition he selected William Clark, the younger brother of George Rogers Clark, and a man with a wide range of personal experience with Indians and frontier life.

The purchase of the Louisiana Territory from France in December 1803 greatly increased the importance of the expedition, which finally began its long journey to the headwaters of the Missouri in May of the following year. That year they wintered in the Mandan villages in the Dakotas and in the Spring pushed on west across the Rocky Mountains and then down the Columbia River to the Pacific Ocean. Returning by the same route nearly two-and-a-half years after they had set out they arrived back in St Louis in September 1806 to the amazed delight of the nation which had given them up for lost. Though unsuccessful in their attempt to find a transcontinental water route, they had demonstrated the feasibility of overland travel to the western coast, a feasibility which was greatly enhanced a few years later by the discovery of the South Pass across the Rockies.

The explorers had intended to publish the journal of their expedition shortly after they arrived home; but both found themselves involved in official duties which left no time for editorial work. Lewis was appointed Governor of the Louisiana Territory and Clark became Superintendent of Indian Affairs. The first account of the journey was *The Journal of Patrick Gass*, a sergeant in the party whose notes had been edited by a West Virginian schoolmaster, David McKeehan, and printed in Pittsburgh in 1807. A London edition followed in 1808, later American editions in 1808, 1810, and 1811 and a French translation in 1810. Meanwhile, before the editing of their own account had been completed, Lewis was murdered while travelling east through Tennessee (1809). On his death Clark asked Nicholas Biddle, a Philadelphia lawyer, to undertake editing the journals. However, before he had completed the job Biddle was elected to the Pennsylvania State Legislature and finding he had no more time for the work engaged Paul Allen to complete it. It was in the Lewis–Clark–Biddle–Allen form that the book was finally published in an edition of two thousand copies in February 1814, almost ten years after the historic expedition began its journey up the Missouri.

273

FICTION TEACHES HISTORY

WALTER SCOTT (1771–1832). Waverley; or 'Tis Sixty Years Since. 3 vols. *Edinburgh: Archibald Constable and Co., and Longman, London, 1814*

The first of the forty or so 'Waverley Novels' was the progenitor and has become the archetype of the historical novel throughout the world. At one blow Scott had established a new literary form; and the basic principles on which *Waverley* and all his subsequent novels were constructed have been disregarded only at the peril of artistic failure.

Scott recognized that the historical novel has to guard against lapsing into the improbabilities of the 'gothick' novel, of which Horace Walpole's *Castle of Otranto* (211) is a significant example, as well as against competing with the history books proper. He therefore wisely decided that the historical novel must be set against a factual background so as to enable the reader to relate the plot to the time and events in which it is supposed to take place, but not to overload it with documentary details which would only retard and probably obscure the imaginary narrative. Moreover, Scott deliberately assigned subordinate roles to known historic personalities, whose attested characters and actions often embarrass rather than stimulate the creative writer's imagination; he chose instead as his protagonists either heroes and heroines of his own invention or real but obscure people who could be made to fit the roles the author wished them to perform, without too obviously violating historic truth: Edward Waverley, the puppet hero of *Waverley*, and Jeanie Deans, the heroine of *The Heart of Midlothian* (modelled on the historic Helen Walker of Irongray), exemplify these two types of Scott's choosing.

It is only recently that attention has been drawn to one of Scott's most lovable traits: his understanding of, and compassion for, simple, humble, ordinary folk—the lower orders, as Scott would have called them. Characters such as Jeanie Deans and her Reuben Butler, the half-witted David Gellatley and Madge Wildfire, old Edie Ochiltree and a host of other lowly characters more than compensate for the insipidity of the nominal heroes. His recognition that their lives and characters were more original, and often more admirable, than those of their 'superiors' broke a rigid convention of fiction and prepared the way for the 'working-class hero'.

Walter Scott became the creator of the historical novel almost by accident. After having edited the ballads of the *Minstrelsy of the Scottish Border*, 1802–3, and while engaged on the verse epic *The Lay of the Last Minstrel*, 1805, he wrote down the first part of *Waverley*, mislaid the manuscript and rediscovered it by chance ten years later, just when Byron's success (270★) had decided him to give up a literary form in which his modesty made him feel inferior to the younger poet's brilliance. Within three weeks he completed *Waverley* and on 7 July 1814 the novel appeared, anonymously, in 3 volumes 12mo.

The success of all the 'Waverley Novels' was instantaneous, not only in England and Scotland but also in the

United States where pirated editions, and in Europe where German and French translations, swamped the market. George IV, since Charles I the first and only English monarch to appreciate literature—he was a great admirer of Jane Austen who dedicated *Emma* to him—created Scott a baronet (1820), and during his lifetime the first historical novels written on his model began to appear. Many of these, too, became best-sellers of national and even international fame: Fenimore Cooper's *The Last of the Mohicans*, Wilhelm Hauff's *Liechtenstein* (both 1826), Alessandro Manzoni's *I Promessi Sposi* (1827), Victor Hugo's *Notre Dame de Paris* (1831), to be followed later by Alexandre Dumas's *Les Trois Mousquetaires* (1844), W. M. Thackeray's *Henry Esmond* (1852), L. N. Tolstoy's *Voyna i mir* (1862–9), C. F. Meyer's *Jürg Jenatsch* (1876), J. P. Jacobsen's *Fru Marie Grubbe* (1876), Margaret Mitchell's *Gone with the Wind* (1936), to name only the most famous offspring of *Waverley*.

BIBLIOGRAPHY: G. Worthington, *A Bibliography of the Waverley Novels* (London, 1931).

274
STRATIFICATION

WILLIAM SMITH (1769–1839). *A Geological Map of England and Wales with Part of Scotland. 15 sheets. London: Cary, 1815*

William Smith was, for most of his active life, a civil engineer. Largely self-taught, even as a child at the village school he collected fossils. In 1793 he was entrusted with the survey for a canal in Somerset and subsequently with its construction. This started him on his lifelong hobby—the study of stratification. Thereafter, whether in the construction of canals, the inspection of coal-mines, or the interminable cross-country journeys on which he engaged to the tune of ten thousand miles a year—before the invention of railways—he lost no opportunity of noting the succession of the strata or of collecting geological specimens and the fossils embedded in the layers.

By 1799 Smith had classified the strata in chronological order by means of their fossil contents. He now got to work on his geological map, in the preparation of which he was encouraged by the Duke of Bedford, Arthur Young (214) and Sir Joseph Banks. The difficulty of finding a map as a suitable basis was overcome by William Cary, the learned philosophical instrument-maker and cartographer. He had a new map, 8½ feet high, specially engraved for Smith to work on. The finished map was submitted in 1815 to the Society of Arts who awarded Smith a premium of £50. 'The example of Smith's work convinced geologists that the strata in all parts of the Earth's crust belonged in a single common sequence—Cambrian, Ordovician, Silurian, Devonian and so on—and that this sequence was not merely a fact of geography, but reflected the temporal order in which the rocks had been laid down...the superposed strata were thus so many footholds in past time' (Toulmin and Goodfield, *The Discovery of Time*).

Smith's dating of the strata by means of the fossils found within them was not entirely new. Steno (151) had noted the association. But it was Smith who first planned and documented the association to 'identify the courses and continuity of the strata in their order of superposition'. This made palaeontology a fundamental part of geology. It was now beginning to emerge that geological time could no longer tolerate the shackles of biblical chronology. It was in the 'testimony of the rocks' and not in the Book of Genesis that the history of the earth must be sought.

275
COMPARATIVE GRAMMAR

FRANZ BOPP (1791–1867). *Über das Conjugationssystem der Sanskritsprache in Vergleichung mit jenem der griechischen, lateinischen, persischen und germanischen Sprache. Frankfurt am Main: Andreäische Buchhandlung, 1816*

Following up the discovery by Sir William Jones (235) of the kinship of the Indo-European languages, and building upon the recognition by Rask (266) of the phonetic agreements of the Germanic language group, Bopp in this, his first publication, proved the exact correspondence of the construction of the verb in five main branches of the Indo-European languages. He thereby established the science of comparative linguistics, 'à peu près comme Christophe Colomb a découvert l'Amérique en cherchant la route des Indes', to quote Antoine Meillet (1866–1936), the leading comparative philologist of modern times.

Bopp had obtained his knowledge of Sanskrit in the manuscript rooms of the Bibliothèque Nationale and the British Museum, and his book 'On the Conjugation System of Sanskrit compared with that of the Greek, Latin, Persian and Germanic Languages' secured for him the chair of oriental languages at Berlin University (1821–64). He later perceived that Lithuanian, Slav, Armenian, Celtic and Albanian, too, belonged to this same group of cognate languages, which in 1823 was given the misleading name 'Indo-Germanic' (still used in Germany, though nowhere else). Bopp's main work is his *Vergleichende Grammatik* ('Comparative Grammar', 1833–52); it was translated into French from the second (1857–61) and third, posthumous (1868–71) editions and thus gave international recognition to the results of Bopp's researches. When in 1915 and 1920 respectively the Hittite and Tokharic languages were discovered and recognized as Indo-European, Bopp's system was enlarged but not upset.

Bopp's importance lies in the fact that he was no mere grammarian but considered comparative philology to be an essential part of the history of civilization: out of their vocabulary he drew an accurate picture of the material and intellectual life of the earliest Indo-European people.

276

COMPARATIVE ANATOMY

GEORGES LEOPOLD DAGOBERT CUVIER (1769–1832). Le Règne Animal distribué d'après son Organisation. 4 vols. *Paris: Deterville, 1817*

LE

RÈGNE ANIMAL,

DISTRIBUÉ

D'APRÈS SON ORGANISATION.

INTRODUCTION.

DE L'HISTOIRE NATURELLE ET DE SES MÉTHODES
EN GÉNÉRAL.

PEU de personnes se faisant une idée juste de l'histoire naturelle, il nous a paru nécessaire de commencer notre ouvrage, en définissant bien l'objet que cette science se propose, et en établissant des limites rigoureuses entre elle et les sciences qui l'avoisinent..

Dans notre langue et dans la plupart des autres, le mot NATURE signifie : tantôt, les propriétés qu'un être tient de naissance, par opposition à celle qu'il peut devoir à l'art; tantôt, l'ensemble des êtres qui composent l'univers; tantôt enfin, les lois qui régissent ces êtres.

TOME I.   I

Cuvier is a curious example of great ability as a natural historian coupled with serious shortcomings as a natural philosopher.

His powers of observation, description and classification were considerable and provided indispensable data for further investigation. By this means, notably in 'The Animal Kingdom', he laid the foundations of comparative anatomy, just as in 'Researches on Fossil Remains', 1812, he had advanced the science of palaeontology. On the other hand, his geological theories (for example, that the extinction of certain species and the irregularity of certain formations of strata were due to a series of supernatural interventions—the latest of which was Noah's flood—succeeded by re-creations) were the more disastrously misleading because the weight of his authority caused them to be widely accepted. Nevertheless in the geological field also posterity is his debtor; for the exactitude of his observations was of service to Lyell, who showed that the disturbances were easily explicable on grounds of uniformity, and to Darwin (344), who adduced the evidence of fossils in support of the theory of evolution. The material provided by Cuvier gave opportunity for greater theorists to produce better answers.

It is in his classification of the animal kingdom into four main groups, Vertebrata, Mollusca, Articulata and Radiata, that he so notably succeeded in giving a lead that has been followed by all his successors. In contradiction to the current view that the structure of an animal determined its functions and habits Cuvier held that an animal's structure was due to its functions and habits. Stomachs are required by mobile creatures: plants do not have stomachs. A carnivore needs sharp teeth, powerful jaws, claws, etc.: a herbivore has flat teeth and hooves.

This kind of distinction is a commonplace today, but Cuvier was the first to apply such analyses and comparisons to the entire animal kingdom. He also saw that this homogeneity in an individual should enable a competent naturalist to reconstruct a complete animal from any significant part of its anatomy.

277

THE DISTRIBUTION OF WEALTH

DAVID RICARDO (1772–1823). The Principles of Political Economy and Taxation. *London: John Murray, 1817*

Ricardo was born in London; his father was a Dutch Jew who had settled in England and had become a considerable figure on the Stock Exchange. In 1793 he became a member of the Church of England, was left to himself, and, by the time he was twenty-five, had made a fortune.

He now began to interest himself in scientific and mathematical studies, but after reading *The Wealth of Nations* (221) he decided to devote himself to political economy. His first essay in this field, a proof of the devaluation of the bank notes, attracted some notice, and he made the acquaintance of James Mill who did much to spread his reputation abroad. In 1815 he published another tract on the Corn Laws, in which 'Ricardo's Theory of Rent' (which in fact he did not invent) was laid down. Two years later the famous *Principles* appeared, and in 1819 Ricardo retired from business and was elected to Parliament. At first diffident, he later became the House's acknowledged expert on economic affairs, and had a considerable share in swinging opinion towards free trade. He died untimely, and his friends established a lectureship in political economy as a memorial to him.

The fundamental ground-work of the *Principles* is based on the theory that, given free competition in trade, the exchange value of commodities will be determined by the amount of labour expended in production: not a wholly original thesis, nor one capable of absolute expression, but one which was given new force by the theory of distribution with which Ricardo reinforced it.

This has been summarized thus: 'the demand for food determines the margin of cultivation; this margin determines rent; the amount necessary to maintain the labourer determines wages; the difference between the amount produced by a given quantity of labour determines profit'. Ricardo also developed Adam Smith's theory of taxes as a part of the theory of distribution. A tax is not always paid by those on whom it is levied; a correct taxation policy will always depend on a correct estimate of the indirect and ultimate effects of every form of tax.

Ricardo was, in a sense, the first 'scientific' economist. Lacking Smith's warmth of sympathy for humanity and for the labourer in particular, Ricardo saw the study of economics as a pure science whose abstractions were capable of quasi-mathematical proof. Although his theorems remain hypothetical, his deductive methods have proved of great use in the elementary analysis of economic problems, and in the subjects which are capable of his rigid analysis, currency and banking, it has proved of lasting value.

278

THE SOLAR SPECTRUM

(a) JOSEPH VON FRAUNHOFER (1787–1826). Bestimmung des Brechungs- und Farbenzerstreuungsvermögens verschiedene Glasarten. In: Denkschriften der Königlichen Academie der Wissenschaften. *Munich*, *1817*

(b) GUSTAV KIRCHHOFF (1824–87). Untersuchungen über das Sonnenspectrum. In: Abhandlungen der Königlichen Akademie der Wissenschaften zu Berlin. *Berlin, 1862*

Newton (172) in 1672 had investigated the spectrum of coloured light formed when a beam passes through a glass prism. In 1753 Thomas Melvill used the prism with flames of various sources and noted variations in the range of colours. In 1802, when describing his new process for measuring the refraction of light, W. H. Wollaston reported the occurrence of dark lines in the solar spectrum but regarded them as simply natural dividing lines between the colours.

Fraunhofer, originally not a scientist but a practising optician, concentrated on these dark lines, and the title of his paper describes the method and purpose of his investigations: 'Definition of the Capacity of Refraction and Colour-diffusion of various kinds of Glass'. Fraunhofer substituted a grating for the prism and devised innumerable different forms of grating for special purposes. By these means he was enabled to measure the wavelengths of dark spectra to a considerable degree of accuracy. His achievements justify describing him as the founder of astrophysics. He charted several hundreds of the dark lines, which have been known as 'Fraunhofer lines' ever since; but their meaning remained a mystery.

A series of delicate experiments by Kirchhoff ('Investigation of the Solar Spectrum'), partly in conjunction with Bunsen, besides solving this mystery, went much further and created the new science of spectroscopy. Sodium was the substance most frequently used in experiments

with the spectrum, due to its volatility. Kirchhoff found that by exposing in the flame of a Bunsen burner a platinum wire dipped in salt he obtained in the spectrum the characteristic bright yellow lines of sodium superimposed on the spectrum of platinum. By repeating the process and introducing vaporized sodium between the incandescent wire and the screen, the yellow lines were replaced by dark lines.

With great ingenuity he repeated the experiment with sunlight and got the same result. The fact that the dark lines were produced when a beam of light from an incandescent element passed through the same substance at a lower temperature suggested that this was due to absorption. In the solar spectrum, for example, the dark lines were caused by absorption in the gases of the sun's atmosphere. Further experiments showed that every glowing vapour produced a spectrum peculiar to itself and thereby made chemical analysis possible on a scale and with a degree of accuracy previously unknown. More than this, it brought, so to speak, the stellar universe into the laboratory and showed that the basic materials of the universe are everywhere the same.

The perfection of the spectroscope has made possible other great forward strides. In 1861, by means of spectrum analysis, Kirchhoff and Bunsen discovered two new elements—caesium and rubidium. Three other new elements, thallium, indium and gallium were discovered during the next twenty years by the same means, which were also used by Rayleigh and Ramsay in identifying helium, neon, argon, krypton and xenon.

Planck (391) is on record as attributing to Kirchhoff the first step on the road to the Quantum Theory.

279

THE PHILOSOPHY OF PESSIMISM

ARTHUR SCHOPENHAUER (1778–1860). Die Welt als Wille und Vorstellung. 3 vols. *Leipzig: Brockhaus, 1819*

Schopenhauer was the child of well-to-do but incompatible parents whose quarrels were probably responsible for his restless and uncertain temperament. His mother was a successful romantic novelist. A broken education eventually brought him to the University of Göttingen where he first met the most important influence on his life and thought—the philosophy of Kant (226). In 1811 he moved to Berlin where he studied classics under Wolf (248) and philosophy under Fichte (244) and Schleiermacher. To the last two he developed an antipathy which alienated him from contemporary philosophical thought and made him lonely and depressed.

Schopenhauer moved to Dresden and it was there that he wrote his most famous book 'The World as Will and Idea'. The notions which had been forming in his mind about man's nature and destiny now found expression, and the conviction that scientific explanation could never do more than systematize and classify the appearances which we call reality led him to assert that it is the will and the passions which are the real determinants of all intellectual life: '*Wollen ist Ursein*', said Schelling—the will is primal being. Kant's principal difficulty, the existence of matter apart from our knowledge of it, is expressed by the very inadequacy of our knowledge: it is the cosmic will, an uncontrollable force superior to human will, which, in the individual will, can only be broken by leading a negative 'good life', in chastity, voluntary poverty, fasting and self-denial. The result is nothingness, and the aim of the saint is non-existence.

Die

Welt

als

Wille und Vorstellung:

vier Bücher,

nebst einem Anhange,

der die

Kritik der Kantischen Philosophie

enthält,

von

Arthur Schopenhauer.

Ob nicht Natur zuletzt sich doch ergründe?
Göthe.

Leipzig:
F. A. Brockhaus.
1819.

Schopenhauer's book made little initial impact; so little in fact that he quarrelled with his publisher, suspecting him of deliberate treachery. But by slow degrees his reputation grew. In 1844 a second edition of *Die Welt als Wille* appeared and he began to acquire disciples and public recognition. He was studied by Wagner (333) and Nietzsche (370), both of whom paid tribute to the influence he had on them; and Herbert Spencer did much to spread the knowledge of his theories. Yet his pessimistic denial of the identity of change and progress has proved more acceptable to the modern mind than to the obstinate optimism of the Victorians.

280

THE STETHOSCOPE

Réné Théophile Hyacinthe Laënnec (1781–1826). Traité de l'Auscultation Médiate. 2 vols. *Paris: J. A. Brosson & J. S. Chaudé, 1819*

The stethoscope is as familiar a symbol of the modern physician as was the urine-glass of his medieval predecessor. It was invented by the French physician R. T. H. Laënnec and is described in his 'Treatise on Mediate Auscultation'.

During his early career, Laënnec, a pupil of Corvisart, Napoleon's physician, and indirectly under the influence of Morgagni (206), studied morbid anatomy and sought a more effective method of diagnosis. It had been known for a very long time that strange sounds could be heard in the chests of certain sick people. Laënnec also knew of Auenbrugger's epoch-making discovery of percussion (*Inventum Novum*, 1761) which enabled doctors to determine whether the thoracic organs were normal or diseased by tapping the thorax. One day in 1816, observing some children tapping a hollow wooden log at one end and listening to the transmitted sound at the other, Laënnec conceived the idea of the stethoscope. Originally he used simply a roll of stiff paper, but soon he constructed a tube of cedar wood about one foot long. Applying it to the chest of the patient he listened to the amplified sounds of the heart and chest generally. This simple invention effected the greatest advance in physical diagnosis between Auenbrugger and the discovery of X-rays (see 380) and other modern instruments of diagnostic precision.

A true follower of Hippocrates (55) and Sydenham (159), Laënnec applied himself to observation of his cases at the bedside. Remarkable as his invention was, what he did with it was even more important. While listening to the movements of the heart and lungs, he learned to understand the significance of the various sounds, for which he created a terminology. In the enlarged second edition of his book (1826) he gives not only the physical signs, but the whole pathology, diagnosis and treatment of the diseases of the chest and heart. He virtually created the modern science of the respiratory organs and their diseases. His brilliant descriptions of bronchitis, pneumonia, gangrene and oedema of the lungs, emphysema, tuberculosis, cancer of the lung and other diseases, have in many respects remained unsurpassed until today.

Unlike Auenbrugger's, Laënnec's discovery was very quickly recognized and accepted. Nineteen editions were published between 1819 and 1839 in French, English, German and Italian; there was an American edition. The English translation of 1821 was by John Forbes who in 1824 also translated Auenbrugger.

BIBLIOGRAPHY: Henry R. Viets, 'Some editions of Laënnec's work on Mediate Auscultation'. In: *Boston Medical and Surgical Journal*, vol. 195, no. 5 (Boston, Mass., 1926).

281

THE HISTORY OF LANGUAGE

JACOB GRIMM (1785–1863). Deutsche Grammatik.
4 vols. *Göttingen: Dieterich, 1819–37*

Jacob Grimm and his brother Wilhelm (1786–1859) are
best known to the general public as the author-collectors
of the *Kinder- und Hausmärchen* (3 vols., 1812–22), but
these 'fairy tales' form only a small part of their activities.
Their real importance lies in the fact that they—and
especially Jacob, the greater of the two—created, almost
out of nothing, the scientific study of German and
Germanic mythology, philology, poetry and law, mostly
in the years 1806–29 when Jacob was a badly paid library-
assistant in Cassel.

His 'German Grammar' is in fact a 'Germanic
Grammar', tracing the development of this branch of
the Indo-European language family, whose relationship
Sir William Jones (235) had discovered and Rask (266)
and Bopp (275) further clarified. Grimm now explained
the differences of the Germanic languages from their
sister tongues and within themselves by showing the
determinable regularity of hitherto unnoticed or inexplicable phenomena such as the gradation and modification of vowels. He laid down the rules governing strong
and weak nouns and verbs; and he formulated what has
become known as 'Grimm's law', the sound-shift of
certain consonants which constitutes the main distinction
between High German and all other Germanic languages
(Wasser—water, machen—make, Pfund—pound, etc.).

Jacob Grimm also advocated the abolition of capital
letters in modern German (in which he failed) and the
use of roman types for all scientific publications (in
which he succeeded). The brothers' most ambitious
undertaking was the *Deutsches Wörterbuch* (from 1852)
which has been completed only more than a century
later, but was the model for the Oxford English
Dictionary (371).

282

ELECTRO-MAGNETISM

HANS CHRISTIAN OERSTED (1770–1851). Experimenta circa Effectum Conflictus Electrici in Acum
Magneticam. *Copenhagen: Schultz, for the Author, 1820*

In 'Experiments and Observations on Electricity', first
published in London, 1751, Benjamin Franklin (199*)
stated his theory that the nature of lightning is electrical.
In 1752, with his kite experiments he proved it and was on
the way to demonstrating the identity of all forms of
electricity. In 1760, however, J. H. van Swiden dismissed
the possibility of an affinity between electricity and
magnetism (*De Attractione*, Leiden). In 1802, on the other
hand, Adam Walker in the second edition of his *A System
of Familiar Philosophy* (first edition, 1799), among many
striking opinions on the monistic nature of electricity,
light and heat, declared categorically 'I think we have
infinite data in favour of an electro-magnetic fluid'.

Oersted, the son of an impoverished apothecary in
Rudkjöping, in 1812 discussed in his *Ansicht der chemischen
Naturgesetze* ('View of the Natural Laws of Chemistry')
the identity of chemical and electrical forces. He was an
enthusiastic follower of the *Naturphilosophie* school in
Germany, whose main object was the unification of
physical forces, thus producing a monistic theory of the
universe. It was to further this purpose that Oersted sought
in actual phenomena the electro-magnetic identity of
which he had already convinced himself on metaphysical
grounds.

It was after lecturing to students in his own rooms in
the Noerragade, Copenhagen, in 1819 or 1820 that he
invited a few of them to stay on to witness an experiment
—the possible deflection of a compass-needle by an
adjacent electric current. The experiment was successful;
but only just; and Oersted repeated it many times before
venturing on 21 July to proclaim the identity of magnetism and electricity in this four-page paper entitled 'Experiments relative to the Effect of the Contiguity of Electricity to a Magnetic Needle'.

The results were as important as they were widespread.
Oersted's paper was within the year reprinted in England,
France, Germany, Italy and Denmark. In 1823 Ronalds
and in 1833 Gauss and Weber constructed the first practical electric telegraphs. Faraday's momentous experiments
(309) with the sequels by Clerk Maxwell (355), Hertz
(377) and others bore further witness to its significance.

283

THE STATE AS PERFECT ORGANIZATION

GEORG WILHELM FRIEDRICH HEGEL (1770–1831).
Grundlinien der Philosophie des Rechts. *Berlin:
Nicolaische Buchhandlung, 1821*

The life of Hegel was spent in the relative calm of an
academic career. Relative, because he lived through one
of the most tempestuous epochs of modern times and also
because, although the external details of his life were
uneventful, his prodigious intellectual activity and enormous appetite for knowledge were anything but calm.

His early education gave little indication of this,
although it was in his schooldays that he began the series
of alphabetically arranged extracts and notes, from newspaper cuttings to original treatises on morals and mathematics, which formed the ore from which he refined his
own all-embracing systems. It was not until he left
Tübingen University in 1793 that his real progress began.
His early friendship with Hölderlin and Schelling had
given a revolutionary cast to his views, but when, through
the former, he obtained a post as tutor at Frankfurt, his
passion for order and organization began to assert itself.
He read Gibbon (222), Hume (194) and Montesquieu
(197) and his distaste for abstraction led him to formulate
the theory of systematic connexions, rejecting discussion
of church, state and law as abstract entities. His political
views also were expressed in an attack on the disorganized
state of Württemberg.

In 1801 Hegel moved to Jena, where his friend
Schelling had succeeded Fichte (244). Despite his gradual

divergence from Schelling, they worked together until the latter left in 1803. From then on until Napoleon's invasion in 1806, Hegel was on his own. There followed a brief period of disturbance until in 1808 he became rector of the Aegidien-Gymnasium at Nuremberg. Here he married, and here appeared the *Wissenschaft der Logik*, the first statement of his fully developed system, which earned him international fame. In 1818 the climax of his life was achieved when he was offered the chair of philosophy at Berlin. In 1821 'The Outline of the Philosophy of Right' appeared, in which his final system of a sociology of the perfectly organized state, such as an ideal Prussia might be, was laid down. He rejected the idealistic aspirations of the reformers, their vague assertions of individual freedom being, in his judgement, trifling compared with the all-important concept of government. His influence was now at its height, and he achieved an importance far beyond the limits of his professional position. The revolution of 1830 was a severe blow to him and in the next year he died, a victim of the great cholera epidemic.

An account of the growth of his opinions is necessary to achieve some grasp of his system, because it is notoriously difficult to compress. As all institutions and abstractions are attitudes of consciousness to reality, so all can be viewed in six aspects: consciousness, self-consciousness, reason, spirit (*Geist*—a typically Hegelian concept), religion and absolute knowledge. Hegel denies the pure idealism of Fichte, and shows that the perfect idea is an indissoluble part of existence as a whole, and that reality must be seen as permanently fluid. Both from a logical and psychological point of view, the universe is a continuing process, not static or capable of definition. It was Hegel's object to ascertain the method of its progress. In his philosophy of the mind he sets out the means of apprehension: the subjective (psychology), the objective (moral and political philosophy) and the absolute mind (the philosophy of art, religion and logic). The *Grundlinien* deals with the second, and is a complete system, in which the concept of a sociology dominated by the idea of the State is laid down. It turns away from the apparent chaos of the democratic advocates of individual right in favour of an overwhelming sense that liberty cannot exist apart from order, and that the vital connexion of all parts of the body politic is the source of all good. As the family is, without contract, the instinctive realization of the moral life, so, equally without contract, the State is the fullest expression of the moral spirit, where interdependence is combined with free will. The State is the perfection of man as a finite entity, whence the spirit moves into the absolute existence of art, religion and philosophy.

Taken apart from the rest of his system, Hegel's political philosophy has been much misrepresented by totalitarian propagandists. He was, however, one of the most profound and influential thinkers of the nineteenth century. Theology, philosophy, political theory, all have been radically influenced by his system; Strauss (300), Baur (322), Bradley, Kierkegaard (314), Marx (326, 359), Lenin (392), all came under his spell, and his indirect influence has been limitless.

284

THE GOTHIC REVIVAL

(a) AUGUSTUS CHARLES PUGIN (1762–1832). Specimens of Gothic Architecture. 3 parts. *London: For J. Taylor, A. Pugin and J. Britton, 1821–3*

(b) AUGUSTUS WELBY NORTHMORE PUGIN (1812–52). Contrasts; or a Parallel between the Noble Edifices of the fourteenth and fifteenth Centuries and similar Buildings of the Present Day. *London, printed for the Author, 1836*

Augustus Charles Pugin was a Frenchman by birth who settled in London, and established a considerable practice not as an architect but as an architectural draughtsman. He had a number of pupils who achieved distinction as practising architects, notably his son Augustus Welby Pugin. Augustus Charles was preoccupied for many years with the preparation and execution of a large series of drawings of Gothic buildings in England, which were engraved and published as *Specimens of Gothic Architecture*. They were almost, if not quite, the first accurate drawings of medieval buildings to be published, and their influence cannot be overestimated. Hitherto the principles of classical architecture had been paramount. The Roman textbook of Vitruvius (26), amplified by the Renaissance theorists, had seemed to provide the be-all and end-all of architectural theory. The latter half of the eighteenth century had seen an increasing restiveness, an anxiety to seek for a new style, whether in Greek, medieval or oriental buildings, but the aspirants had been frustrated by the absence of any theoretical documents. The rediscovery of Greek architecture, which answered another craving, that for simplicity, had some vogue. Of the three the least seriously considered, because apparently least 'theoretical', was the Gothic style; it was reserved for merely fashionable and frivolous constructions.

On to this confused scene Pugin's work burst with the force of a thunderclap. His detailed drawings demonstrated beyond doubt that the absence of any known architectural theory in medieval times was no inhibition to a formidable architectural competence, and he rediscovered the solution to a number of structural problems which had actually been lost in the long dominance of classical models.

Augustus Welby Pugin in his short life devoted himself to the practical demonstration of what his father's drawings revealed in theory. His early years were spent in his father's office, making the measured drawings for his father's books. In 1827 he designed medieval furniture for Windsor Castle, and began to establish a regular practice. He early realized, as William Morris (367) was to demonstrate even more convincingly, the importance of craftsmanship, and in his work on the detail of Barry's Houses of Parliament (1837–43) a great deal of the credit was due to the thoroughness with which he trained his masons and carvers. Many of his later works were spoiled, to his grief, by his clients' refusal to acknowledge this factor: they adopted plaster shams for his carefully designed decorations. A convert to Roman Catholicism, he was employed to design a number of churches after the Emancipation Bill, mostly on a painfully small budget.

Contrasts illustrates Augustus Welby's teaching in a particularly striking form. Written in eloquent, learned and lively prose, his lessons were forcibly driven home by the illustrations, which he etched himself. Here the ancient and modern styles were shown on facing pages; a visual demonstration which reflected directly on the shoddy work of his own time.

A whole century's architecture was to be influenced by the practical and theoretical expositions of the Pugins, father and son. It is to be seen in monuments as diverse as the Mont St Michel, the Nikolauskirche in Hamburg, Milan Cathedral and St Pancras Station in London.

285

CARNOT'S CYCLE

NICOLAS-LEONARD SADI CARNOT (1796–1832). Réflexions sur la Puissance Motrice deu Feu. *Paris: Bachelier, 1824*

Carnot's genius was extinguished at the age of thirty-six in a cholera epidemic. During his short life he published only this one book 'Reflections on the Motive Force of Fire'. Using the fallible analogy of a water-wheel and the language of the caloric theory the book was essentially an attempt to calculate the mechanical equivalent of heat; Carnot devised the type of apparatus afterwards used by J. P. Joule to produce exact figures in 1841. His work led directly to the enunciation of the theory of the conservation of energy by Helmholtz in 1847 (323). In fact, in a reprint of the *Réflexions* in 1878 Carnot's brother included the contents of some notebooks which showed that Carnot himself had formulated this theory, which is now the first law of thermodynamics.

The second law of thermodynamics is also implicit in Carnot's treatise. Work is done only when heat passes from a hotter to a colder body. It follows that when an equilibrium of temperature is reached work ceases. Rudolf Clausius, in Berlin, expressed this tendency by what he called entropy, the entropy of a system being 'the measure of the unavailability of its thermal energy for conversion into mechanical work'.

Carnot's ideas were elaborated by another French engineer, C. B. E. Clapeyron (1799–1864) in the *Journal de l'École Polytechnique*, 1832, and were later developed by J. P. Joule and Lord Kelvin. His researches led also to the absolute scale of temperature.

286

CRITICAL MODERN HISTORY

LEOPOLD RANKE (1795–1886). Zur Kritik neuerer Geschichtschreiber. *Leipzig & Berlin: G. Reimer, 1824*

Ranke first applied to medieval and modern history the critical principles which Niebuhr (267) had established for ancient history. He thereby set up novel standards of

scholarship which have since become accepted by historians of every nation who are not shackled by the straitjacket of a narrow dogma. Ranke expounded these rules in the essay here cited, which forms an appendix to his first book, the 'Histories of the Germanic Peoples from 1494 to 1514' (1824).

His 'Examination of Modern Historians' takes its departure from Guicciardini, who had hitherto been regarded as the chief authority on the period. Without belittling 'one of the great historical productions which we have', Ranke deprives the *Historia d'Italia* (85) of its claim to being a primary source and shows the extent to which Guicciardini was dependent on other writers and, even more important, how much his outlook is coloured by his own private life, professional career and party prejudices. In other words, Ranke tries to assess the value of a source through the explanation of the character of its author.

The preface to the 'Histories' contains the famous passage in which Ranke rejects the task historians had formerly assigned to themselves, of being the judges of the past and the teachers of their contemporaries; instead he proclaims as his aim 'merely to show how things actually were'. This striving for impartiality and reliance on the best original sources was allied with Ranke's conviction that all history is universal history. All his writings on Prussian, German, English, French and other national histories were conceived in this spirit, which finds its consummate expression in 'The Papacy in the sixteenth and seventeenth centuries' (1834–6). It led him at the age of eighty-five to embark on a universal history which at his death had reached, in seven volumes, the middle of the eleventh century.

Ranke's immense influence spread not so much through his lectures (he was professor at Berlin University from 1834 until he went blind in 1871, but he is reported to have been an indifferent speaker) as through his massive writings (his collected works comprise 54 volumes (1867–90)) and above all through his seminar, in which he trained generations of disciples in the critical use of original documents and the unbiased approach to every age and nation.

287

APOGEE OF MEDIEVAL SCHOLARSHIP

MONUMENTA GERMANIAE HISTORICA. *Hanover: Hahn, 1826 to date*

'The Monuments of German History' is a vast collection —still unfinished—of the written sources of medieval German history; it includes annals and chronicles, charters and laws, letters and pamphlets, poems and 'antiquities', from the fourth century onwards. Its international importance derives from the fact that its editors developed methods of painstaking scholarship and technical perfection which have made the *Monumenta* the yardstick by which critical editions of source material have since been measured everywhere.

The initiator of the enterprise was the statesman, Karl Freiherr vom Stein (1757–1831), the reformer of the

MONVMENTA

GERMANIAE

HISTORICA

INDE AB ANNO CHRISTI QVINGENTESIMO
VSQVE AD ANNVM MILLESIMVM
ET QVINGENTESIMVM

AVSPICIIS

SOCIETATIS APERIENDIS FONTIBVS

RERVM GERMANICARVM MEDII AEVI

EDIDIT

GEORGIVS HEINRICVS PERTZ

SERENISSIMI BRITANNIARVM ET HANNOVERAE REGIS TABVLARIVS.

SCRIPTORVM

TOMVS I.

HANNOVERAE

IMPENSIS BIBLIOPOLII AVLICI HAHNIANI

MDCCCXXVI.

Prussian state after the collapse of 1806. An unbiased knowledge of the past, he believed, would reawaken the old virtues of manly self-reliance and popular self-government and thus serve best the cause of German nationhood. The purpose of the 'Society for Germany's Ancient History' which Stein founded in 1819—with Goethe (298) and the brothers Grimm (281) among its sponsors—was to publish the authentic sources, and the first volume which appeared in 1826 bore the motto, chosen by Stein, 'Sanctus amor patriae dat animum'. Stein was exceedingly lucky in enlisting as his first editor the young Hanoverian, Georg Heinrich Pertz (1795–1876), who judiciously started his researches in the Vatican archives with the help of the Prussian envoy, Niebuhr (267), and in the Bibliothèque Nationale, where Thierry paved his way. He also gained access to the British Museum and to numerous private English libraries through his two marriages with well-connected English-women. English was the language spoken in Pertz's home, and he saw to it that all his children were born in England so as to become British subjects by birth. In 1836 Pertz recruited Ranke's greatest pupil, Georg Waitz, for the *Monumenta*; and after Pertz had become the director of the Royal Library in Berlin (1842), a regular school of 'Monumentists' came into being, who elaborated and perfected the editorial technique until it became an international model of accuracy, completeness and attention to the minutest details of textual criticism. It was quickly emulated in other European countries, belatedly (e.g. in the 'Rolls Series') in Great Britain.

Increasingly self-willed and idiosyncratic, Pertz was eventually forced by Ranke (286) and Mommsen (337★), perhaps his most brilliant single contributor, to retire in 1873. Although the *Monumenta* under the guidance of Waitz, 1875–86, now entered into its 'golden age', the previous sturdy independence was lost. The work was placed under the tutelage of the academies of Berlin, Munich and Vienna; and the unpleasant quarrels which followed Waitz's death (a day after Ranke's) and were renewed at every subsequent vacancy of the directorate resulted in the *Monumenta* gradually becoming a state institution under even stricter government control. The Monumentists almost ceased to be historians proper and contented themselves with being highly skilled technicians. The time of the unchallenged leadership of German medievalists in European historical science was past. In 1945 the *Monumenta* was saved from the general wreckage by the octogenarian Walter Goetz, whose un-blemished anti-Nazi record allowed him to win over the Allied occupation authorities for its re-establishment.

The history of the *Monumenta* reflects the development of the German intelligentsia from the romantic idealism of the generation of the 'war of liberation', through the liberal realism of the technical and industrial revolution of the mid-century and the nationalistic institutionalism of the Bismarckian and Wilhelmian empire, down to the national-socialist authoritarianism of Hitler's Third Reich.

288

THE MAMMALIAN OVUM

KARL ERNST VON BAER (1792–1876). (*a*) De Ovi Mammalium et Hominis Genesi. *Leipzig: Leopold Voss, 1827*; (*b*) Über Entwickelungsgeschichte der Thiere. 3 vols. *Königsberg: Bornträger, 1828–37*

Because the hen's egg is a conveniently large object the study of embryology is as ancient as Hippocrates (55) and Aristotle (38).

The notion that all animals come from eggs was pronounced by Harvey (127), and Reinier de Graaf (1641–73) proclaimed that the follicle named after him was really the mammalian egg. It remained for Baer to plot the course of ovulation and fertilization from its later stages back to the ovary and there to identify the minute cell which was the ovum. These discoveries were published in his first paper 'On the Mammalian Ovum and the Genesis of Man'.

In his more extensive work 'On the Embryology of Animals' Baer gathered together with great knowledge and scrupulous care all the known facts on embryology and followed in detail the development of the classical subject of embryological research, the hen's egg. He proceeded from this to study the embryological development of the vertebrates in general and subsequently to propose four basic principles which provided a sound basis for the foundation of a new branch of science.

289

MEASURING ELECTRICITY

GEORG SIMON OHM (1789–1854). Die Galvanische Kette mathematisch bearbeitet. *Berlin: T. H. Riemann, 1827*

The exact measurement of natural phenomena, though less generally attractive, is just as vital to science, pure and applied, as the record of their infinite variety.

In the field of electrical measurement Ohm was the great pioneer. Coulomb, in a series of seven papers to the *Académie des Sciences* between 1784 and 1789, had measured the attraction and repulsion at a distance of electrified bodies by means of his torsion balance, and he did important work on insulators. Ohm's great contribution—'The Galvanic Chain Mathematically Calculated' —was to measure the rate of current flow and the effects of resistance on the current. 'Ohm's law'—that the resistance of a given conductor is a constant independent of the voltage applied or the current flowing (that is, $C = E/R$, where C = current, E = electromotive force and R = resistance)—was arrived at theoretically by analogy with Fourier's heat measurements (1800–14).

Ohm's conclusions were either ignored or contradicted at the time. Faraday's researches (309) were completed without reference to his law and as late as 1883 Kelvin, in an address *On the Electrical Units of Measurement*, could still refer to the 'recent' date at which anything that could be called electric measurement had been introduced. He

$$\frac{du}{dx} = f \quad \text{und} \quad \frac{du'}{dx} = f',$$

wonach sich vorliegende Bedingungsgleichung in folgende verwandelt

$$\varkappa \, \omega \, f = \varkappa' \, \omega' \, f'.$$

Aus dieser und der eben aus den Spannungen hergeleiteten Gleichung $a + a' = f l + f' l'$ findet man nun die Werthe f und f' so:

$$f = \frac{(a + a') \, \varkappa' \, \omega'}{\varkappa' \, \omega' \, l + \varkappa \, \omega \, l'}$$

$$f' = \frac{(a + a') \, \varkappa \, \omega}{\varkappa' \, \omega' \, l + \varkappa \, \omega \, l'}$$

und mit Hülfe dieser Werthe findet man:

$$c' = c - a' + \frac{(a + a') \, (\varkappa' \, \omega' \, l - \varkappa \, \omega \, l)}{\varkappa' \, \omega' \, l + \varkappa \, \omega \, l'}.$$

Hieraus nun folgt zur Bestimmung der elektroskopischen Kraft der Kette in dem Theile P die Gleichung

was referring to the Paris Conference on standards of 1881 when, incidentally, the term *coulomb* was adopted for the practical unit of quantity and *ohm* for the unit of resistance. In point of fact both Coulomb and Ohm were proved to have been anticipated by Henry Cavendish when the papers of that secretive eighteenth-century recluse were published by Clerk Maxwell (355) in 1879.

290

BROWNIAN MOVEMENT

ROBERT BROWN (1773–1858). A Brief Account of Microscopical Observations on the Particles contained in the Pollen of Plants; and on the General Existence of Active Molecules in Organic and Inorganic Bodies. *Not Published.* [*London: Printed by Richard Taylor, 1828*]

Robert Brown, a Scottish botanist, first became widely known to the scientific world after his return with Captain Matthew Flinders in 1801 from their journey to Australia in H.M.S. *Investigator*. He returned with a collection of about four thousand botanical specimens, many of which were new to science. They were added to Sir Joseph Banks's great Herbarium, with which they passed in 1820 to the British Museum, when Brown became its first botanical curator.

Brown's name is commemorated in his discovery, the 'Brownian movement'. Plant cells had first been seen in the seventeenth century by Hooke (147), Leeuwenhoek (166), Grew and Malpighi, though none of these recognized them as independent living units of the vegetable world. But during the remainder of the seventeenth and eighteenth centuries the study of plant structure was neglected in favour of that of classification (see Linné, 192)

and the physiological workings of the plant as a whole (see Hales, 189). In the early nineteenth century, however, the study of plant cells was revived, notably in Germany by Treviranus and von Mohl, in Italy by Amici and in England by Brown.

In 1827 Brown, while making microscopical observations, saw that pollen grains of the herb *Clarkia pulchella*, while suspended in liquid, engaged in a continuous, haphazard, zig-zag movement. Surprised at what he saw, he continued similar experiments with other substances— including inanimate bodies such as minerals and smoke— and found that when the particles were very small, they all possessed this same motion. This movement was explained by Ramsay in 1879 as being due to bombardment by molecules, and this was experimentally proved in 1908 by Perrin, who was also able to calculate the weight of the molecule of water. In the twentieth century Exner and others were able with the help of photography and the ultramicroscope to investigate these processes in greater detail and the principle involved was further developed by Einstein (408). The idea that gases and liquids consist of molecules in rapid motion was not new, but it had remained largely speculative until it was scientifically proved and investigated in detail by Robert Brown and his followers.

Brown also made many other important contributions to botany; he rediscovered the nucleus, helped to introduce a natural system of plant classification based on that of de Jussieu, and was a pioneer in the study of the anatomy of fossil plants.

291

THE ENGLISH OF AMERICA

NOAH WEBSTER (1758–1843). An American Dictionary of the English Language. 2 vols. *New York: S. Converse, 1828*

This dictionary, which almost at once became, and has remained, the standard English dictionary in the United States, was the end-product of a stream of spelling books, grammars, readers and dictionaries which flowed from the pen of the industrious Noah Webster. Like so many of the American rebels he came from good English yeoman stock of seventeenth-century immigrants. After many years of teaching he became a lawyer, and his obvious gifts as a pedagogue and the sharpness of a legal brain were great assets to his activities as a lexicographer.

Webster was an ardent nationalist and he wanted to stress the political separation from Britain by the cultivation of a separate American language. He began with the publication of an elementary spelling book (1783), grammar (1784) and reader (1785), which were designed to inculcate in American children the characteristics of American usage, spoken and written. Under the influence of his friend Benjamin Franklin (199*) he turned his attention to 'a reformed mode of spelling'; and although he rejected the radical phonetic innovations proposed by Franklin, he went far enough to give many printed American words a distinctive appearance. This 'American' spelling appeared first in the *Compendious*

Dictionary of the English Language (1806) and was henceforth adopted by American printers.

Webster's great dictionary, all the 70,000 entries of which he wrote with his own hand, has been reprinted and brought up to date innumerable times. It suffered from the author's ignorance of the linguistic scholarship of his age—he had probably never heard of Rask (266), Grimm (281), or Bopp (275)—so that his philological and etymological notes were mostly valueless and sometimes ludicrous. On the other hand, the book marked a definite advance in modern lexicography, as it included many non-literary terms and paid great attention to the language actually spoken. Moreover, his definitions of the meaning of words were accurate and concise (Sir James Murray, editor of the *Oxford English Dictionary* (371), called him 'a born definer of words') and have for the greater part stood the test of time superbly well. In fact, Webster succeeded in breaking the fetters imposed upon American English by Dr Johnson (201), to the ultimate benefit of the living languages of both countries.

292
READING FOR THE BLIND

LOUIS BRAILLE (1809–1852). *Procédé pour écrire les Paroles, la Musique et le Plain-chant au Moyen de Points. Paris: [Institution Royale des Jeunes Aveugles], 1829*

Valentine Haüy (1745–1822), younger brother of the famous crystallographer, was the first to devise type that could be read by the blind. Characters slightly different in shape from ordinary italic were embossed on heavy paper to be read with the fingers. He founded the *Institut Royale des Jeunes Aveugles* in 1785 and seems actually to have succeeded in teaching some of his pupils not only to read by this method but to set and print the embossed type. His *Essai sur l'Éducation des Aveugles*, 1786, is an incunable of the method. The essay was translated into English by Thomas Blacklock, the blind poet, and included in an edition of his collected works in 1793.

The next experimenter was a Scot, James Gall of Edinburgh, who after long experiments in tangibility, devised an angular version of the sighted alphabet as being more easily recognizable by fingertip contact. He, like Haüy himself, and many of his successors, made the fundamental error, however, of approaching the problem from the angle of the sighted person and thus assuming that an adaptation of the conventional alphabet offered the best hope. Howe and Perkins in America, Taylor, Alston and Watts in England, and other philanthropists on the continent of Europe, pursued the same course.

The first to grasp the true essence of the problem seems to have been T. M. Lucas of Bristol. Taking his cue from stenographic systems of shorthand he devised an arbitrary set of characters representing sounds rather than letters and with them printed in embossed form the books of the Bible, Euclid and a chess-board. His first production was the New Testament, begun in 1837 and completed in 1851. J. H. Frere produced a similar system and developed an ingenious and cheap form of embossed

printing. His greatest boon to the blind, however, was his device of the 'return line' by which the lines are printed alternately from left to right and from right to left, the letters in the return lines being reversed. He also devised a cheap and effective form of stereotyping for embossed printing. His first production, the Book of Isaiah, appeared in 1843. The characters devised for these stenographic systems were more legible by the seeing eye than by the finger-tips. Only a person who was himself blind could solve the problem.

In 1821 the *Mercure Technologique* in Paris, commenting on a system of 'nocturnal writing' devised for the use of the armed forces by Charles Barbier, a former artillery officer, stated that the *Institut Royale* was experimenting with it for instructing young pupils. In Barbier's system letters and sounds were represented by groups of raised dots, ranging from two to twelve in a group.

Louis Braille, the twelve-year-old son of a harness maker, was a pupil at the school—one of the more brilliant of those 'blind beggars with a knowledge of geometry and Latin'. He was certainly among those who attempted to learn Barbier's system; but whereas Barbier found it easy to take in a group of twelve points with his eye, Braille found it much more difficult with his finger. It was virtually impossible as a method of writing.

When it was that Braille first started the complicated procedure of reducing the maximum of points to six is not known, but the principal of the Institute at the time, one Dr Pignier, recorded that the essentials of Braille's scheme were laid before him in 1825, when the young man was hardly sixteen years old.

The 32-page booklet—'Procedure for writing Words, Music and Plainsong by Means of Points'—was printed in the Institute in raised characters, the text using the normal alphabet, which some pupils had painstakingly trained their fingers to decipher. Braille also invented the stylo and frame still used by the blind for writing.

Thus Braille provided the blind with a complete alphabet, mathematical and musical notations, and a stenographic method of writing. Pignier, his first biographer, declared that his modification of the Barbier system 'was not merely an improvement, it was a new invention'.

The Braille system was not given an immediate welcome; it was only in 1854 that it was officially accepted by the Institute itself. But at an international congress in Paris in 1878 it was adopted throughout Europe. It is now in use virtually throughout the literate world.

A special aspect of the subject was approached by William Moon, who became totally blind in 1840 at the age of twenty-two. He was therefore especially aware of the problems of those who go blind comparatively late in life: the difficulty of learning a new alphabet, especially by the unaccustomed method of finger-tip contact. Profiting by his own knowledge of the normal alphabet he was able to devise characters based on it but simplified to facilitate touch reading. He adopted the return line system and added an embossed bracket at the end of each line leading to the line below. Moon's first production was *The Last Days of Polycarp*, issued 1 June 1847. His system is preferred to Braille by many and is widely used by those who become sightless late in life.

BIBLIOGRAPHY: Edmund C. Johnson's *Tangible Typography* (London, 1853), gives short accounts of all the principal systems to date with embossed type-specimens of most, including the earliest representation in England of Braille's system.

293

THE COPERNICUS OF GEOMETRY

(*a*) NICOLAI IVANOVITCH LOBATCHEWSKY (1793–1856). О Началахъ Геометріи. *In:* The Courier of the Imperial University of Kazan, Parts XXV, XXVII, XXVIII, February/March 1829–July/August 1830. *Printed at the University Press.*
(*b*) GEORG FRIEDRICH BERNHARD RIEMANN (1826–66). Ueber die Hypothesen, welch der Geometrie zu Grunde liegen. *In:* Abhandlungen der Königliche Gesellschaft der Wissenschaft zu Göttingen, vol. 13 (1867). *Göttingen: Dieterich, 1868*

It is now generally recognized that pure mathematics is neither true nor false in the same sense as physics but instead should be regarded simply as a self-consistent discipline which can be applied to different branches of science. This revolution in our conception of the nature of mathematics can be traced back to the explicit formulation of the first non-Euclidean geometries early in the nineteenth century.

The researches that culminated in the discovery of non-Euclidean geometry arose from unsuccessful attempts to *prove* the axiom of parallels in Euclidean geometry. This postulate asserts that through any point there can be drawn one and only one straight line parallel to a given straight line. Although this statement was not regarded as self-evident and its derivation from the other axioms of geometry was repeatedly sought, no one openly challenged it as an accepted truth of the universe until Lobatchewsky published the first non-Euclidean geometry. (We now know that Gauss (257) had already come to the same general conclusion as Lobatchewsky but he published nothing on the subject.) In Lobatchewsky's geometry an infinity of parallels can be drawn through a given point that never intersect a given straight line.

Nicolai Ivanovitch Lobatchewsky was born in Nizhni-Novgorod, Russia, and studied at the University of Kazan, where in 1827 he was appointed professor. His fundamental paper was read to his colleagues in Kazan in 1826 but he did not publish the results until 1829–30 when a series of five papers appeared in the Kazan University Courier, the first of which bore the title cited above, 'The Origins of Geometry'. He amplified his findings (still in Russian) in 1836–8 under the title 'New Elements of Geometry, with a Complete Theory of Parallels'. In 1840 he published a brief summary in Berlin under the title *Geometrische Untersuchungen zur Theorie der Parallellinien*.

Lobatchewsky's discovery was extended by the investigations of Georg Friedrich Riemann who was born at Hanover and studied under Gauss in Göttingen and later in Berlin. Returning to Göttingen in 1850, he chose for his *Habilitationsschrift* in 1854 (published in 1867) the problem of the foundations of geometry. This lecture threw a new light on geometry. He greatly extended the whole idea of what is meant by geometry, isolating the concept of measurement-relations ('metric') as fundamental. The concept, as generalized by Riemann, was a development of Gauss's theory of surfaces and was not restricted like the latter to two dimensions. The importance of this treatise is not confined to pure mathematics. Without it, Einstein (408) would not have been able to develop his general theory of relativity.

Riemann also did epoch-making work on the theory of functions and topology, and on the theory of prime numbers. He also made significant contributions to mathematical physics. His greatness as a mathematician is due to the power and generality of the new techniques and points of view which he introduced into different branches of the subject.

294

THE LAND

WILLIAM COBBETT (1762–1835). Rural Rides. *London: William Cobbett, 1830*

RURAL RIDES

IN THE COUNTIES OF

Surrey, Kent, Sussex, Hampshire, Wiltshire, Gloucestershire, Herefordshire, Worcestershire, Somersetshire, Oxfordshire, Berkshire, Essex, Suffolk, Norfolk, and Hertfordshire :

WITH

Economical and Political Observations relative to matters applicable to, and illustrated by, the State of those Counties respectively.

BY WILLIAM COBBETT,

LONDON:
PUBLISHED BY WILLIAM COBBETT, 183, FLEET STREET.
1830.

William Cobbett was the son of a small farmer at Farnham in Surrey where he spent most of his youth working on his father's farm. A sudden whim took him to London at the age of seventeen, when he enlisted in the army. His military career, during which he rose to the rank of sergeant-major, ended with an honourable discharge at his own request in 1791. The next year he married and went to the United States of America, where he first supported himself by teaching English to French emigrants; later he created a considerable stir by his attacks on the United States and France written under the name of 'Peter Porcupine' and his equally outspoken support of Great Britain.

By 1800 Cobbett had made America too hot to hold him, and he returned to England, to be hailed as the champion of order and the monarchy. He was soon in trouble again; he opposed the Peace at Amiens, attacked the government of Ireland, and in 1810 was imprisoned for an attack on military flogging. Through all this his pen remained busy. The parliamentary reports which he began in 1803, the *Parliamentary History* of the proceedings of both Houses up to that date (268), and a number of other works are a tribute to his industry. Moreover, every week, from January 1802 to his death, with very few exceptions, he published the *Weekly Political Register*, which was the platform from which his views were expounded for nearly thirty-four years. It bore early testimony to Cobbett's conversion to radicalism; in it appeared the famous article on flogging (hardly a week was missed during his two years in prison). In 1816, in the post-war depression, his militant support of the cause of reform led him to fear a second imprisonment, and he fled abroad, again to America.

On his return two years later he occupied himself with agricultural matters and continued to write. In 1821 a committee proposed certain remedies to alleviate the persistent agricultural depression. Cobbett disagreed with their conclusions, and 'made up his mind to see for himself, and to enforce by actual observation of rural conditions, the statements he had made in answer to the arguments of the landlords before the Agricultural Committee'. His method was to make a series of tours on horseback up and down the land, and to publish accounts of them in the *Register* (they were subsequently collected and published in the book here cited). The vividness and force of his writing, whether in describing the countryside or his encounters with those who worked in it, have made his work an enduring classic. In his accounts of the poverty caused by widespread enclosure he struck the first blow in the long struggle for improving the condition of labourers on the land, and the opinions he expresses in many ways anticipate the doctrine of the Young England group as led by Disraeli (319).

At the end of his life Cobbett fulfilled a long expressed ambition and became a member of the House of Commons. Here, after an uncertain start, he was listened to with respect on agricultural matters, and he ended a turbulent life relatively at peace with the world. His writings and reputation have lived after him; a grand centenary edition of the *Rides* was issued, and long after his political battles were won, the liveliness and sympathy of his descriptive writing have won him new readers.

295

POSITIVISM

AUGUSTE COMTE (1798–1857). Cours de Philosophie Positive. 6 vols. *Paris: Rouen Frères, 1830; Bachelier, 1835–42*

Comte was born in Montpellier. In 1826 he began in Paris the lectures on positivist philosophy, which, interrupted by a brief attack of insanity, were concluded in 1830. They brought him some measure of fame, and some employment; and their publication, expanded into six volumes as 'A Course of Positivist Philosophy', increased

COURS

DE

PHILOSOPHIE POSITIVE,

PAR M. AUGUSTE COMTE,

ANCIEN ÉLÈVE DE L'ÉCOLE POLYTECHNIQUE, RÉPÉTITEUR D'ANALYSE TRANSCENDANTE ET DE
MÉCANIQUE RATIONNELLE A LADITE ÉCOLE.

TOME PREMIER,

CONTENANT

LES PRÉLIMINAIRES GÉNÉRAUX ET LA PHILOSOPHIE
MATHÉMATIQUE.

PARIS,

BACHELIER, LIBRAIRE POUR LES MATHÉMATIQUES,
QUAI DES AUGUSTINS, N° 55.

1830

his reputation. But in the preface to his last volume Comte gratuitously offended those who had appointed him to his position as examiner to the École Polytechnique, and he was dismissed. At this juncture he was offered help, much as Hume had helped Rousseau, by J. S. Mill (345), and for the last nine years of his life Comte was dependent on subscriptions raised for him by Littré and other friends.

In 1848, moved by the revolutionary fervour which swept Europe, Comte founded the Positivist Society in the hope that it might come to exercise the same sort of control over events as the Jacobin Club in 1789. In this he was disappointed; but there grew up around him a group of sympathizers, whom Comte, by now dogmatic in his views, formed into a sort of church. In 1857 he died, leaving thirteen executors to continue his teaching.

The encyclopaedic system of Positivism has its roots in

a new theory of knowledge. The essence of this lies in the 'Law of the Three States' of the progress of knowledge. According to this, knowledge passes through three phases: the Theological State, when it supposes phenomena to exist by their own will or by that of some external supernatural being; the Metaphysical State, when the will is due to some abstract force residing in but existing independently of the object; and the final or Positive State, when the explanation of an individual phenomenon is to be seen by reference to other more general phenomena. The next step consists in the correct relation and balancing of science. Knowledge divides into practical and theoretical knowledge, and theoretical into concrete and abstract. Abstract science can be ordered into a hierarchy in which the first comprehends and adds to the truths of each succeeding science. Thus the sciences may be grouped in the following order: mathematics, astronomy, physics, chemistry, biology, sociology.

Comte's major work is devoted to the last and most neglected of these, and attempts to show that the facts of society are as reducible to general laws as other phenomena. Its history is parallel with the progress of knowledge. In the Middle Ages, feeling was subordinate to intellect; then the balance was reversed; finally, the balance of the two will be achieved by Positivism in the form of a religion, whereby feeling and intellect are perfectly adjusted in submission to the concept of Humanity, past, present and future, which is the Great Being. It is in fact a complete utilitarian system, in which all human actions and institutions form an arch, with an artificial Great Being as the keystone.

The remarkable achievement of Comte, all argument about the validity of his theories aside, is the construction of a system which embraces all human activity and knowledge. Having performed this great and real service to thought, he almost sacrifices any claim to gratitude by the invention of a system of control which is jejune and retrograde. None the less, his attempt to link up all science, to relate its development to the progress of society, and to combine it with a system of improvement with humanity in place of an external supreme being, is still one of the major documents of secular philosophy.

296
THE BATTLE FOR REFORM

THE EXTRAORDINARY BLACK BOOK. By the Original Editor [i.e. John Wade]. *London: Effingham Wilson, 1831*

At the turn of the eighteenth century both Houses of Parliament were largely composed of aristocrats and landowners. The growth of industry, vastly accelerated by the needs of the Napoleonic wars, had shaken the traditional agrarian communities, and with them the old structure of class dependence. When the war was over, the financial burden it left, coupled with the government's attempts to re-establish the old system by the introduction of restrictive measures designed to protect the agricultural classes by increasing the price of food, caused widespread unemployment. Near-starving factory workmen—the Luddites—wandered about the country smashing the machinery which they wrongly regarded as the immediate cause of their misfortunes.

The government still remained blind to the real causes of discontent, and in addition to the Corn Laws introduced the still more short-sighted Enclosure Bills, in a further effort to support home food supplies. In 1817 an attempt was made on the life of the Prince Regent, and the Habeas Corpus Act was suspended. William Cobbett (294), the most influential spokesman of Reform, had left the country in order to avoid arbitrary imprisonment, and in 1819 an armed clash came. A vast Reform meeting was held in Manchester; troops were ordered to disperse it, and arrest the agitators; six people were killed and many injured. The 'Manchester Massacre' gave a great impetus to the Reform movement. The government met it with the 'Six Acts' for its further repression. The country seemed poised on the brink of revolution.

The root of the matter lay in the unequal electoral representation in Parliament. Densely populated industrial areas remained without representation while the 'rotten boroughs' returned one or more members representing a minute electorate. Disinterested members of both parties had been pressing for Reform since the eighteenth century, but it was not until 1821 that the Whig party, in opposition, began the concerted drive which resulted in the passing of the Reform Bill of 1832. If the government at home was repressive, so were the foreign governments with whom the country was linked in Metternich's Grand Alliance. Castlereagh and Canning withdrew Britain from the Alliance, and removed one of the Reform agitators' principal grounds of complaint. The movement had powerful supporters: Burdett, Cartwright, Bentham, Brougham and Russell, and a first-rate organizer in Francis Place, the tailor of Charing Cross. Gradually a number of progressive measures, notably the Catholic Emancipation Bill (1829), were passed. On 26 June 1830 George IV died, a bare month before revolution broke out all over Europe. William IV came to the throne, saved from its immediate effects by the Castlereagh–Canning foreign policy, but at a time when discontent and unrest were rife as never before.

Finally the ultra-conservatives under Wellington were ousted, and the Whigs under Grey took office. The year 1831 passed in their redoubled efforts to force through the Reform Bill. Defeated in Committee after the second reading, they appealed to the country and were returned with a vast majority. The Bill was through the Commons by September, but was rejected after the second reading by the Lords next May. The government again resigned, but the Tories were unable to form a government, and William, thoroughly alarmed, put pressure on the peers; on 4 June 1832 the Reform Bill became law. One hundred and forty-three seats were set free to be bestowed on the industrial areas. At one blow power had passed from the traditional landowners.

The effect of this cannot be exaggerated. All Europe, liberal or reactionary, was watching the constitutional struggle with strained attention. The principles of monarchy and democracy alike were at stake. To foreign observers it seemed impossible that both could survive, but it is a tribute to the tenacity and flexibility of both sides that they did, and the next reign was to show Europe how both could be combined in a progressive state.

The long struggle was conducted through a mass of printed matter, which the press, just beginning its own industrial revolution, strove to provide. The 'Bible of the Reformers' was the *Black Book*, a massive compendium of all the abuses, electoral, ecclesiastical, legal, which they sought to abolish. It was first published in 1820 and passed through edition after edition, continually augmented with new arguments, new reports of abuses and new statistics. The edition cited here was the most influential, coming as it did on the eve of the Reform Bill (1832). For the *Black Book* was above all a practical document, and its emphasis on the need to have practical as well as equitable representation lies at the root of parliamentary democracy.

297
THE PHILOSOPHY OF WAR

KARL VON CLAUSEWITZ (1780–1831). Vom Kriege. 3 vols. *Berlin: Ferdinand Dümmler, 1832–4*

These thousand pages of 'On Warfare' occupy a unique position among military writings of any age and nation.

Vom Kriege.

Hinterlassenes Werk

des

Generals Carl von Clausewitz.

Erster Theil.

Berlin,
bei Ferdinand Dümmler.

1832.

The book is less a manual of strategy and tactics, although it incorporates the lessons learned from the French revolutionary and Napoleonic wars, than a general inquiry into the interdependence of politics and warfare and the

principles governing either or both. War, Clausewitz maintained, must always be regarded 'as a political instrument'; for war, his most famous aphorism runs, 'is nothing but politics continued by different means'. Consequently, he scorns the notion of 'the harmful influence of politics upon the conduct of war', since blame, or praise, must be attached to politics itself. If the course of politics is sound, political influence on the conduct of war can only be advantageous: 'The French revolutionary victories over twenty years resulted mainly from the faulty politics of the opposing governments'.

His basic conception, that military decisions must always be subordinate to political considerations, is buttressed by the emphasis laid on morals and morale as the decisive factors in war. He therefore condemns all rigid blue-prints for campaigns and battles, defines strategy as 'a perpetual alternation and combination of attack and defence', and implies the then startling proposition that there are no bad soldiers but only bad officers.

Clausewitz took an active part in all the continental campaigns between 1793 and 1815 as an officer in Prussian and, 1812–14, Russian services. He worked with Scharnhorst and Gneisenau for the reform of the Prussian army and from 1818 to 1830 was the head of the Berlin military academy, the forerunner of the Prussian general staff. His book *Vom Kriege* grew out of a series of 'aphorisms' jotted down in 1816–18 which formed the basis of his lectures at the academy. After his death from cholera during the Polish campaign, in which he served as chief of staff to Gneisenau, who succumbed to the same disease, the book was published by his widow and won immediate recognition as the most profound exposition of the philosophy of war—a place that has never been disputed.

298
THE FAUST LEGEND

JOHANN WOLFGANG VON GOETHE (1749–1832). Faust. Eine Tragödie. *Stuttgart & Tübingen: Cotta, 1834*

If Goethe may justly be called the last representative of the renaissance ideal of the *uomo universale*, his *Faust* embodies the sum total of his poetical growth. He worked on it intermittently from 1773 when he was the leading genius of the Storm and Stress movement, through his classicist period when, from 1800, Schiller encouraged him to proceed with the second part, to his final creative years from 1825 when he infused the last scenes with deep religious mysticism as well as the realism of practical and social problems.

Goethe called his play a tragedy; in fact, it is rather a comedy in the sense of Dante's *Divina Commedia* (8), as it ends with the ultimate salvation of the hero. This happy outcome was the result of a long development of the Faust theme. The original Georg Faust, who lived from about 1480 to about 1540, was a necromancer of (deservedly) bad reputation, who even during his lifetime occupied popular imagination as a powerful magician to whom evil spirits were ministering. These fables, augmented by lurid descriptions of his horrible end, were put into writing about 1575 and published by the Frankfurt printer Johann Spiess under the title of *Historia von D. Joh. Fausten*, 1587, as an awful warning against the dire consequences of fruitless theological speculation and dabbling in witchcraft.

The booklet was a huge success, and innumerable reprints, adaptations and popular versions kept the Faust story alive for two hundred years. An English translation of the Spiess book reached Christopher Marlowe, who transformed the crude material into the magnificent *Tragicall History of D. Faustus* (written 1588–9, performed 1592, printed 1604). English actors brought the tragedy to Germany, where in the course of time it degenerated into a farcical puppet show. The turning-point in the evolution of Faust came with Lessing's fragments of a Faust play published in 1759 and, posthumously, 1784. Lessing (213), the keen rationalist, transformed the bogeyman of Christian orthodoxy into a fearless searcher after truth whose thirst for knowledge deserved salvation rather than damnation.

These heterogeneous sources were the raw materials out of which the greatest German poet created successively *Faust: Ein Fragment* (1790), *Faust: Erster Teil* (1808), the Helena *Zwischenspiel* (1827), *Faust: Zweiter Teil* (completed in January 1832, published posthumously 1832). A combined text appeared in 1834. Byron's *Manfred* (1817) is the first of a long list of 'Faustian' plays, novels and musical compositions of which there may be mentioned Heine's *Tanzpoem* (1847), Gounod's opera (1859), Paul Valéry's *Mon Faust* (1946) and Thomas Mann's novel (1948).

While Goethe the poet, the playwright, the novelist has found his secure place side by side with the greatest—Dante, Shakespeare, Voltaire—Goethe the scientist has been unduly neglected. Three of his many researches in the fields of biology, optics, anatomy, geology, etc. deserve special mention. He was a pioneer of plant morphology; he is the only physicist to have drawn up an independent theory of colours in opposition to Newton's chromatics; and his discovery in 1784 of the intermaxillary bone in the human skull proved the homology of man and the vertebrates which has become the basis of all evolutionary theory.

The English man of letters, George Henry Lewes, wrote the first standard *Life of Goethe* (1855); the English Nobel Prize winner, Sir Charles Sherrington, established the importance of *Goethe on Nature and on Science* (2nd ed. 1949).

299
THE UGLY DUCKLING

Hans Christian Andersen (1805–75). Eventyr fortalte for Børn. 2 vols. *Copenhagen: Printed by Bianco Luno & Schneider for C. A. Reitzel, [1835]–1837*

The tales of Hans Christian Andersen are unique. Unlike Perrault's and Grimm's (281) his stories were original inventions. They are of two kinds. The *Eventyr* are fairy tales of supernatural creatures and fantastic happenings;

the *Historie* are stories of everyday people and occurrences. To the fashioning of both he brought his own childlike imagination and a creative faculty and originality strangely lacking in his other writings. Over and

Eventyr,

fortalte for Børn

af

H. C. Andersen.

Kjøbenhavn.
Forlagt af Universitets-Boghandler C. A. Reitzel.
Trykt hos Bianco Luno & Schneider.
1837.

above their intrinsic merit Andersen's stories signalized a new and fundamentally different approach to the writing of books for children. Mawkishness, didacticism, and moral proselytizing were totally abjured and he was the harbinger of a new era in this genre.

Success at home was slow. 'Fairy Tales related for Children', published in parts from 1835 at 4½d. apiece and collected in 1837, were regarded by the author himself as mere bagatelles thrown off by a dubious kind of sleight of hand in the intervals of establishing himself as a greater poet than Oehlenschläger and a greater dramatist than Heiberg. To the end of his life he regarded them at best with tolerance and refused to admit that his international reputation rested on them. Most of the leading critics treated them contemptuously, regarding them as yet further evidence of the incapacity of an author of whom they had no great opinion in any case.

Between 1838 and 1848 Andersen turned out several more volumes of tales, frequently accepting books instead of money in payment. Although these collections included 'What the Moon Saw' and such little masterpieces as 'The Little Mermaid', 'The Tin Soldier' and 'The Tinder Box', it was not until 1843/4 that the appearance of 'The Ugly Duckling' swept them into general favour. H. C. Oersted the scientist (282) and Thorvaldsen the sculptor, were enthusiastic admirers of the tales, matinée readings of them were given in the Royal Theatre at Copenhagen; but it was their swiftly achieved success abroad that first brought them to local notice.

They were widely read in Sweden, all of them were translated into German almost as soon as they appeared, and Vilhelm Pedersen's famous illustrations were commissioned by a German publisher.

The first English translations appeared in 1846—four different collections by different translators and from different publishers.

BIBLIOGRAPHY: B. F. Nielsen, *H. C. Andersen. Bibliografi* (Copenhagen, 1942).

300

'JESUS WITHOUT THE MYTHS'

DAVID FRIEDRICH STRAUSS (1808–74). Das Leben Jesu kritisch bearbeitet. 2 vols. *Tübingen: C. F. Osiander, 1835–6*

The publication of 'The Life of Jesus Critically Considered' aroused a storm of controversy; its revolutionary thesis and content were violently attacked, and wrenched out of context. It is important therefore to consider it in context, in the light of Strauss's development. No account of this is possible without mentioning F. C. Baur (322), founder of the Tübingen School of biblical criticism. Strauss was educated at the evangelical seminary at Blaubeuren, where Baur was then a master. From there, like Baur, he went on to Tübingen University in 1825; he too became interested in the philosophy of Hegel (283) and Schleiermacher, and in 1830 resigned his first post in order to study under them in Berlin. Hegel had died before he arrived, but Schleiermacher's lectures on the life of Jesus and Strauss's conversations with Hegel's followers finally determined the path of his theological views—an exclusively analytical and critical path, almost without religious feeling, philosophy or historical sympathy—which did not materially change for the rest of his life. In 1832 he returned to Tübingen as a lecturer, but after the publication of the *Leben Jesu* lost his post and was removed to a secondary school.

Strauss's principal objective was to explode not only the traditional orthodox view of the Gospel accounts of the life of Jesus, but also earlier rationalistic views, notably those of H. S. Reimarus. He maintained with unyielding vigour the theory (which has no basis in fact) that the Christ of the Gospels, excepting the barest scraps of personal history, was the unintentional creation of the early Christian Messianic expectations. The miracles, to which he applied the severest and narrowest criteria, were thus largely dismissed as fiction, and his view of the relation of the human to the divine was jejune. Strauss had expected the onslaught his work received, and published answers to his critics in 1838. In the third edition of the *Leben* he modified his position considerably, but withdrew these concessions in the fourth edition (1840), which was translated into English by George Eliot, as her first publication.

The controversy having cost him a promised chair of theology at Zürich, Strauss abandoned the subject for twenty years, and made a name for himself by a series of valuable biographies. But in 1864 he returned to the subject of the life of Christ, and published a series of works mainly dealing with the limits of belief. These, especially the last, *Der Alte und der neue Glaube*, 1872, showed that he had not modified his early position, and they aroused almost as much controversy. His always narrow viewpoint seemed if anything narrower: he now saw the history of Christianity as the continuous disintegration of belief, and seemed almost to be abandoning religion for materialism. Yet there can be no doubt that Strauss's scepticism, strongly argued if on a limited plane, had a valuable effect in puncturing the complacency of contemporary theologians.

301

THE PHILOSOPHY OF SPEECH

KARL WILHELM VON HUMBOLDT (1767–1835). Über die Verschiedenheit des Menschlichen Sprachbaues. *Berlin: Druckerei des Königlichen Akademie der Wissenschaften, 1836*

Humboldt was a scion of a wealthy family of the minor Pomeranian aristocracy. He became a diplomatist and a statesman who played an important part in the final coalition against Napoleon. He introduced the Pestalozzi system of education (258) into Germany and was largely responsible for the foundation of the University of Berlin.

Although necessarily something of a dilettante in scholarship he was a serious student of philology. For his researches into the Basque language, for example, he made extensive visits to the French and Spanish Basque districts, studying the language in remote villages and with local philologians, and consulted rare manuscripts in the Spanish royal library. He planned the compilation of a Basque–Spanish dictionary based on these studies. Instead, after twenty years of study he produced 'Researches into the Early Inhabitants of Spain by the help of the Basque language', 1821, in which he already attempted to trace a connexion between the character and evolution of the Basque peoples and the style and content of their language.

Eventually he turned to the study of the ancient Kawi language of Java. This work remained only a fragment when Humboldt died; but he had completed a lengthy foreword on 'The Heterogeneity of Human Language and its Influence upon the Intellectual Development of Mankind', which was edited by his younger brother, Alexander, the great traveller and naturalist (320★), and published posthumously.

In this, his philological testament, Humboldt attempts the classification of peoples according to language. More important than the classification itself was the corollary to it, which seemed to Humboldt to imply that the development of individual languages is affected by physiology, ethnography, history, geography, political and religious relationships, and that stages in the cultural development of peoples leave strongly marked traces in their languages. In the words of A. H. Sayce, a great philologist of our own day: 'This essay first clearly laid down that the character and structure of a language expresses the inner life and knowledge of the speakers, and that languages must differ from one another in the same way and to the same degree as those who use them . . . What Humboldt terms the inner form of the language is just that mode of denoting the relations between the part of a sentence which reflects the manner in which a particular body of men regards the world about them.'

302
TRAVELLERS' GUIDES

(a) JOHN MURRAY III (1808–92). Hand-Book for Travellers on the Continent: being a Guide through Holland, Belgium, Prussia and Northern Germany and along the Rhine, from Holland to Switzerland. *London: John Murray, 1836*
(b) KARL BAEDEKER (1801–89). Rheinreise von Basel bis Düsseldorf. Sechste verbesserte und vermehrte Auflage der Klein'schen Rheinreise, bearbeitet von K. Baedeker. *Coblenz: Baedeker, 1849*

Marianna Starke, at the suggestion of the publisher John Murray II, cast her second book on Italy in the form of a guide-book. Published in 1820, with the title *Travels on the Continent*, it was the forerunner of the modern guide-book; but it had no progeny. In 1836, however,

Λ.

HAND-BOOK

FOR

TRAVELLERS ON THE CONTINENT:

BEING A GUIDE THROUGH

HOLLAND, BELGIUM, PRUSSIA,

AND

NORTHERN GERMANY,

AND

𝔄long the 𝔯hine, from 𝔥olland to 𝔖witzerland.

CONTAINING

DESCRIPTIONS OF THE PRINCIPAL CITIES, THEIR MUSEUMS, PICTURE GALLERIES, &c.;—THE GREAT HIGH ROADS;—AND THE MOST INTERESTING AND PICTURESQUE DISTRICTS;

ALSO

Directions for Travellers; and Hints for Tours.

WITH AN INDEX MAP.

LONDON:
JOHN MURRAY AND SON, ALBEMARLE-STREET.
———
MDCCCXXXVI.

as a sequel to many years' personal exploration of northern and central Europe, John Murray III issued his first *Hand-Book*. It was an immediate success and was quickly followed by others on South Germany, Switzerland and France, all written by Murray himself. Possibly the most famous of the long Murray series was Richard Ford's *Handbook to Spain*, 1845, a literary work in its own right.

In 1832 Karl Baedeker took over the firm of F. Röhling, one of whose publications was a guide to the River Rhine by a certain Professor Klein (first published 1832). In 1835 Baedeker issued a slightly improved edition and in each of the following editions (1839, 1843 and 1846) more changes were introduced until in 1849 the sixth edition assumed the now familiar form and carried Baedeker's name as editor for the first time ('The Rhine from Basle to Düsseldorf. Sixth improved and enlarged edition of Klein's Rhine Guide, revised by Karl Baedeker'). Before this date Baedeker had compiled and published four other handbooks—Belgium (1839), Holland (1839), Germany (1842) and Switzerland (1844) and some of these had been reprinted: but none of them had the characteristic Baedeker format.

Baedeker frequently made graceful acknowledgements to Murray's pioneer efforts. In his guide to Holland, for example, he referred to 'the most outstanding traveller's handbook ever published' which he had taken as his model—Murray's volume of 1836; and similar acknowledgements appeared in the German and the Swiss handbooks of 1842 and 1851. In the 1850s Baedeker paid Murray an even more striking, though apparently less welcome, compliment by adopting the red cover and general format of the Murray Guides, which caused Murray to adopt the since familiar blue.

The Murray–Baedeker formula was designed for those increasingly numerous travellers who could not depend on a courier or a *cicerone* to make all their arrangements. Its precise guidance about hotels, restaurants and tipping, the arrangement of pictures in a museum or gallery, and the right side-door for finding the sacristan, makes the many out-of-print volumes out-of-date in such details; yet the mass of accurate information they contained, combined with the sparing intrusion of contemporary aesthetic judgements, makes the well-worn red and blue volumes steady and reliable friends to many a traveller today.

303
ADAM AND EVE WERE BLACK?

JAMES COWLES PRICHARD (1786–1848). Researches into the Physical History of Mankind. Third edition, 5 vols. *London: Sherwood, Gilbert & Piper, J. & A. Arch, 1836–47*

Prichard's vast researches were directed to 'the physical diversities which characterise different races of men'. They began with his M.D. thesis at Edinburgh, entitled *De Humani Generis Varietate*, which he expanded in 1813 into the first edition of the *Researches*. He concluded that the human race was originally dark-skinned and that the whiteness of the white man developed under the influence

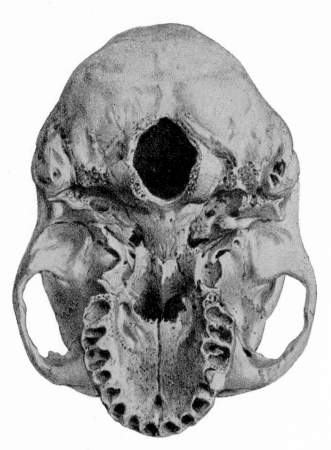
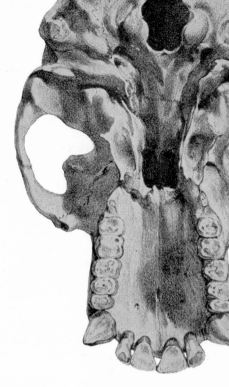

ESQUIMAUX   (NO. 303)   ORANG, OR SIMIA SATYRUS

of civilization. His conclusion that 'all human races are of one species and one family' was added to the greatly enlarged second edition of the *Researches*, 1836, in which the original emphasis on the development of white races from a dark-skinned ancestor was rather played down.

It is the third edition of the book that represents Prichard's positive contribution, as it includes all that was known about the various races of mankind, thus forming a synthesis upon which modern ethnological research has been based.

Prichard spent most of his life as a physician in Bristol. In 1835 he published his *Treatise on Insanity*, describing for the first time 'moral' insanity as now recognized in English law; for half a century it remained the standard work on the subject.

Carlyle wrote his *French Revolution* as a secular 'tract for the times' and as a warning for his compatriots of the frightful consequences of materialism, utilitarianism and democracy. Scottish puritanism and German romanticism were his lodestars; 'History is the essence of innumerable biographies' was his historical creed. The result is not a work of scholarship but a prose epic, teeming with colourful scenes of dramatic events and imaginative portraits of the leading revolutionaries. The book at once captured the English-speaking world, and has, outside France, moulded popular conception of the French Revolution down to the present day.

304

THE DRAMATIZED REVOLUTION

THOMAS CARLYLE (1795–1881). The French Revolution. 3 vols. *London: James Fraser, 1837*

Of the three great political upheavals which have altered the face of the world—the American, French and Russian Revolutions—only the French Revolution has stimulated literary masterpieces which, in turn, have made their impact, direct and indirect, upon millions of readers who would have, and have, left unread the productions of dispassionate scholarship. They are Carlyle's book and the 'History of the French Revolution' by Michelet (324).

305

THE TOLPUDDLE MARTYRS

GEORGE LOVELESS (1797–1874). The Victims of Whiggery; being a Statement of the Persecutions experienced by the Dorchester Labourers. *London: Effingham Wilson (and others), [1837]*

The ancient and complicated history of Trade Unionism in Great Britain is recorded in the standard work of that name by Sidney and Beatrice Webb (revised ed., 1920).

In October 1833 Robert Owen (271) outlined to the Congress of Owenite Societies an intention to form a nation-wide association of working men. In January 1834 the Grand National Consolidated Trades Union was formed. Its immediate success, both in the affiliation of existing associations and in the encouragement of new branches, led to massive retaliation by employers and by the government—largely synonymous terms.

Very soon after the formation of the 'Grand National' it was invited to send delegates to a group of agricultural labourers headed by George and James Loveless at Tolpuddle in Dorset to advise in the formation of a 'Friendly Society'. The local farmers took alarm and induced the magistrates to issue a pronouncement that membership of the Society would be treated as an offence liable to a penalty of seven years transportation. The Lovelesses and four other labourers were arrested, and although no charge was brought against them, nor evidence offered of anything more serious than the performing of initiation ceremonies (i.e. 'administering an unlawful oath') they were given the full sentence.

The Whigs under Melbourne openly approved the sentence in the House of Commons, apparently with no sense of the storm of protest it was to arouse. In fact, this was precisely the kind of test case that the 'Grand National' was seeking, and the blatant nature of the whole proceeding could not have been better to their purpose had they devised it. The entire organization was concentrated on a national protest against this travesty of justice, and infinitely greater concentration of effort between the various Unions resulted. Over a quarter of a million signatures were secured to a petition for remission of the sentences and a gigantic procession of some thirty thousand people marched to present it. The 'London Dorchester Committee' was formed to keep the protest alive.

In 1836 continual agitation caused the sentences to be remitted, but it was not until 1838 that five of the six men got back to England. They had struck a blow from which the opposition to trades unionism never recovered and the 'Tolpuddle Martyrs' are saints in the trade union hagiology.

306
THE PENNY POST

ROWLAND HILL (1795–1879). (a) Post Office Reform; its Importance and Practicability. *London: Privately printed, by W. Clowes and Sons, 1837*; (b) Third Report from the Select Committee on Postage...*Ordered, by The House of Commons, to be Printed, 13 August 1838*

The penny post inaugurated and administered by Rowland Hill required the adoption of four novel principles: (1) prepayment of postage, (2) payment by weight instead of by the number of sheets, (3) the use of envelopes, (4) the use of adhesive stamps on letters. Prior to this reform, for example, the use of an envelope would have been a novelty to most letter-writers and entailed double postage.

Hill's privately printed pamphlet of 1837, publicly issued in a revised edition in the same year, coincided with official concern at the decline in postal revenue. Hill declared that the high cost of postal distribution was largely due to complicated post office arrangements, most of which would be avoided if postal charges were made

uniform, irrespective of distance, and were collected in advance. A charge of one penny for each half-ounce weight of postal packages would, he contended, show a profit of two hundred per cent on the cost of distribution.

After the publication of Hill's pamphlet, Robert Wallace, a Member of Parliament, and a postal reformer of longer standing than Hill, moved for a Committee to examine the plan. Wallace was made Chairman and much evidence was taken, not least from Rowland Hill and from the Postmaster General, who steadfastly opposed him. The Committee's Report was favourable, with the notable exception that they recommended a basic charge of twopence. Spring Rice, the Chancellor of the Exchequer, surprised everybody by both accepting the Report in general and rejecting the twopenny in favour of the penny minimum.

This became law in August 1839 and well over two thousand designs for envelopes and stamps were received; one designer alone, Charles Whiting, submitted about a hundred of them. None of these was in fact adopted. Instead Henry Corbould was commissioned to adapt the portrait made for Queen Victoria's accession medal by William Wyon, engraver at the Royal Mint, and this was engraved by Charles Heath with the assistance of his son, Frederick. The background was from a stock design of the printers, Perkins, Bacon & Sketch. It had been in use for several years in the production of bank notes and securities. This was the famous, and still deservedly admired, 'Penny Black'.

In December 1839 a uniform postage fee of fourpence was introduced. This period ended on 10 January 1840, after which date the minimum charge became one penny for a packet weighing not more than half an ounce and prepayment became compulsory, which meant the presentation of letters for franking at post offices.

On 6 May 1840 covers and stamps were first issued, and the reform proved an immediate and brilliant success. In 1840 the number of letters posted totalled 169,000,000, more than double the number in 1839. Net revenue, however, fell alarmingly and was not fully restored for thirty-five years.

Hill's idea that covers would be advisable—'the little bags called envelopes'—to replace the wafered folded sheet formerly in use, also produced innumerable designs, the most acceptable being one designed by William Mulready. In practice, however, it was soon found that no special form of envelope was necessary. The first envelope with an embossed stamp was issued in 1841.

307
THE CELL AS THE BASIS OF LIFE

(a) MATTHIAS JACOB SCHLEIDEN (1804–81). Beiträge zur Phytogenesis. *In:* Archiv für Anatomische Physiologie und Wissenschaftliche Medizin, edited by J. Müller. *Berlin: Veit, 1838*
(b) THEODOR SCHWANN (1810–82). Mikroskopische Untersuchungen über die Übereinstimmung in der

Struktur und dem Wachsthum der Thiere und Pflanzen. *Berlin: Sander'schen Buchhandlung (G. E. Reimer), 1839*
(c) RUDOLF VIRCHOW (1821–1902). Die Cellular-pathologie. *Berlin: August Hirschwald, 1858*

Among the observations recorded in Hooke's *Micrographia* (147) is the cellular nature of plant construction. Malpighi, in 1671 and 1674, laid before the Royal Society two papers. On 7 December 1671, the date of the presentation of Malpighi's first paper, Nehemiah Grew laid a printed copy of his *The Anatomy of Vegetables Begun* (title-page dated 1672) before the Society. Both Grew and Malpighi had observed with the microscope the cellular construction of the woody parts of plants and thence constructed a rough working hypothesis of a cellular theory of plant life.

Robert Brown (290) was the first microscopist to revive the cell concept in the nineteenth century. After him Schleiden, in his 'Contributions to Phytogenesis', taking the embryonic cell as his starting-point proceeded to attempt a reconstruction of the development of the cell. He went seriously astray in this but he insisted on the independence of the cell and presented for the first time the notion that a plant, for example, is a community of cells.

Schwann, a much more accurate and better trained observer than Schleiden, took the latter's investigation one vital step further by declaring in his 'Microscopical Investigations into Conformities in the Structure and Growth of Animals and Plants' that the cell was the universal unit of life throughout the animal and vegetable kingdom.

Virchow was the first to state the now universally accepted axiom 'Omnis cellula a cellula'. 'Wo eine Zelle entsteht, da muß eine Zelle vorausgegangen sein' he writes 'ebenso wie das Tier nur aus dem Tiere, die Pflanze nur aus der Pflanze entstehen kann' (Where a cell originates it must have been preceded by another cell, just as animals are produced only by other animals and plants by other plants). His object in his 'Cellular Pathology' was to relate the Schleiden–Schwann theory to his own field of pathology, a field to which he made contributions of prime importance. He was the founder (1847) of the Archive for pathological anatomy universally quoted as 'Virchow's *Archiv*'.

308
THE GREAT EXPERIMENTER

MICHAEL FARADAY (1791–1867). Experimental Researches in Electricity. Reprinted from the Philosophical Transactions of 1831–1838. 3 vols. *London: Richard and John Edward Taylor, 1839, 1844, 1855*

Faraday was both one of the greatest physicists of the nineteenth century and one of the finest experimenters of all time. His principal contributions were made in advancing our knowledge of the nature and potentialities of electricity.

Faraday pursued some suggestions of Wollaston based upon Oersted's discovery that a magnetic needle was deflected by an electric current (282), and in 1821 showed that a current-carrying wire would rotate round a magnetic pole, or a pole round a current-carrying wire. This is the principle of the electric motor. Faraday long sought the opposite effect, that is the production of electricity by magnetism, and finally discovered in 1831 that when a wire moved with respect to a magnetic pole a current flowed in it. This was the principle of the dynamo and of the transformer, and with it Faraday opened his great series of investigations into electricity.

Faraday himself however was interested in these experiments only as a stage in his investigation of the phenomena of electromagnetism, by which he finally succeeded in demonstrating the identity of all forms of electricity however produced, whether by friction machines, voltaic piles, electric fish, lightning discharges or by any other means. He also showed that in electrolysis the quantity of chemical action is directly proportionate to the quantity of electricity used. Finally he enunciated his theory of 'lines' or 'tubes' of magnetic force which was the starting point for the revolutionary theories of Clerk Maxwell (355) and later of Einstein (408).

Although his discovery of the electric motor and the dynamo was almost entirely incidental to his theoretical discoveries, it laid the foundation of the modern electrical industry—electric light and power, telephony, wireless telegraphy, television, etc.—by providing for the production of continuous mechanical motion from an electrical source, and vice versa.

In a paper on the condensation of chlorine he was the first to demonstrate that all gases are vaporized liquids with low boiling points; he discovered benzol and coined a whole new terminology—electrolyte, electrolyze, cathode, anode and ion. Helmholtz, in the Faraday Lecture for 1881, pointed out that Faraday had trembled on the brink of discovering the electron theory of matter.

309
THE ICE AGE

JEAN LOUIS RODOLPHE AGASSIZ (1807–73). Études sur les Glaciers (A volume of text and an atlas of plates). *Neuchâtel: for the Author, and sold by Jent & Gassman, Soleure, 1840*

Jean Louis Rodolphe Agassiz, a Swiss naturalist, was appointed in 1848 professor of zoology at Harvard University where he founded the Museum of Comparative Zoology and became one of the greatest teachers of biology and natural sciences of the nineteenth century.

His 'Studies on Glaciers' is one of his most influential books. Together with Charpentier and other companions he built a hut on the Agar glacier and made extensive observations on the glaciers near Chamonix and the great moraines of the Rhone valley, investigating their action on the formation of land masses. The Huttonians (see 247) had already suggested that glaciers could act as carriers of rock. Agassiz came to the conclusion that certain smooth rock faces above the present level of glaciers and on the lower southern slopes of the Jura

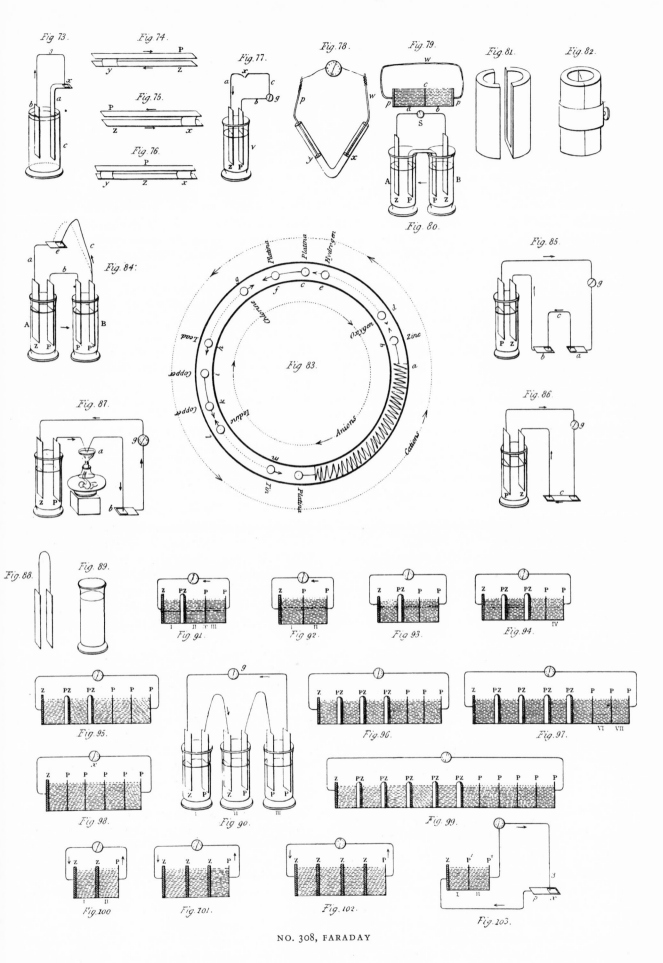

NO. 308, FARADAY

mountains could not have been worn into their present shape by water (as had been suggested) but only by ice moving over them, although they were far removed from the present paths of the glaciers. He became convinced, therefore, that glaciers, now only to be found in the higher valleys, must once have covered the whole of north-west Switzerland and that the moraines and erratic boulders scattered in the plain of Switzerland and on the lower slopes of the Jura mountains must have been distributed there by great masses of land-ice. This contradicted the views then variously held that these rocks had been brought there by water, as believed by the 'Neptunists', by floating ice, or by explosions.

Agassiz visited England, where he discovered similar phenomena in the north, in Scotland and in Ireland. He now extended his hypothesis and stated his conviction that the earth had once suffered a great fall of temperature resulting in the formation of an enormous ice-sheet covering the greater part of Europe as far south as the Mediterranean and the Atlas mountains, North Asia and North America. He named this geological period the Ice Age, following a suggestion of his German colleague Schimper.

At first his views met with much opposition, but gradually they found acceptance, particularly in England by Buckland and eventually by Charles Lyell, and there is today a very large literature on the subject. Thus Agassiz's observations were the beginning of modern glacial geology.

Agassiz also wrote a classic book on fossil fishes (1834–44)—in which the number of named species of fossil fish was raised to well over one thousand, and which gave a great impetus to the study of extinct life in general—and an important work on the natural history of Brazil. He was himself throughout his life a catastrophist and a natural theologist, convinced that there was abundant evidence for 'the direct intervention of a supreme intelligence in the plan of creation'. Ironically his many important discoveries provided much material for men such as Darwin (344) and Lyell, while his conservative philosophical assumptions led him to resist dogmatically the great changes in the interpretation of nature that they were bringing about.

310

ORGANIC CHEMISTRY

JUSTUS LIEBIG (1803–1873). (a) Die Organische Chemie in ihrer Anwendung auf Agricultur und Physiologie. *Brunswick: Friedrich Vieweg, 1840; (b)* Die Organische Chemie in ihrer Anwendung auf Physiologie und Pathologie. *Brunswick: Friedrich Vieweg, 1842*

An extended series of papers by Liebig and his friend Friedrich Wöhler (1800–82), notably their investigation of oil of bitter almonds and other compounds containing benzoyl, created what Berzelius called 'the dawn of a new day in vegetable [i.e. organic] chemistry'. Indeed modern views on the molecular structure and chemical constitution of organic compounds lead straight back to the 'twin constellation' represented by Liebig's two volumes.

In applied science Liebig's influence was more immediate and spectacular. In 1840 ((a) above—'Organic Chemistry as applied to Agriculture and Physiology') he asserted with his customary passionate conviction that only the mineral elements of the soil were essential to plant health and growth. Humus he derided. We now know that in this he was wrong: and fanatics have even gone to the other extreme, decrying all use of the artificial fertilizers that Liebig advocated. But his insistence on the importance of artificial fertilizers was vital to a solution of the problem posed by Malthus (251).

In 1842 ((b) above—'Organic Chemistry as applied to Physiology and Pathology') he carried his chemical investigations into the realm of animal physiology. He showed, like Lavoisier (238), that animal heat is not innate, but the result of combustion; introduced the concept of metabolism (*Stoffwechsel*); and classified animal foodstuffs as fats, carbohydrates and proteins according to their function. He thus became the founder of the modern science of nutrition. Liebig was also a great teacher of chemistry. He outlined the principles upon which modern teaching is based and was largely responsible for the institution and equipment of special laboratories for the purpose.

311

NATIONALISM AND ECONOMICS

FRIEDRICH LIST (1789–1846). Das Nationale System der Politischen Oekonomie. *Stuttgart & Tübingen: J. G. Cotta, 1841*

List, though entirely self-educated, became professor of administration and politics at the university of Tübingen in 1817. He was dismissed in 1820 for his advocacy of a German Customs Union. As a democratic deputy of the Wurttemberg Diet he tried to put through administrative reforms, but in 1822 he was sentenced to imprisonment for his subversive provocation. He escaped to Alsace and visited France and England, returning to finish his sentence in 1824; he was then released on condition that he emigrated to America.

He remained there for seven years, during which time the strongly nationalist views in politics and economics for which he is remembered were developed, under the influence of Alexander Hamilton's writings (234). In 1830, financially independent, he returned to Germany as United States Consul at Leipzig. He became an ardent partisan of national union; as its economic basis he urged once again the establishment of a German Customs Union and of a comprehensive railway system. The creation of the former in the *Zollverein* (1833) was largely due to his enthusiastic advocacy of the abolition of internal tariffs. Disappointed in his hopes of obtaining a secure position, he finally committed suicide.

Despite the influence of Alexander Hamilton, the seeds of 'The National System of Political Economy' are to be found in the romantic theories of Adam Müller (1779–1829). From him List derived his opposition to Adam Smith (221) and the principle of free-trade. He denied Smith's parallel between the economic good of the individual and the state, and saw in Smith's 'free trade' un-principled private advantage to the detriment of the state. To List, the nation was a separate unit standing between the concepts of the individual and humanity as a whole; its unity consisting of common language, tradi-tions, culture and constitution. It followed that its wealth lay not in the capacity for commercial international ex-change, as Smith held, but in the development of its own economic and productive resources. Thus, the good of the national economy must override that of the individual.

From this followed List's theory of industrial politics, which was based on an alternating pattern of free trade and controls determined always by the final good of the state, one generation being prepared to sacrifice its own material prosperity for the benefit of the next; the im-mediate gains by exchange to be offset by long-term gains in productivity. These views coincided so exactly with the reawakening of German nationalism that List's book caused a great sensation when it was published, and it remained for seventy years the theoretic gospel of the advocates of protectionist tariffs in Germany, Britain and the United States.

312

TRACT NINETY

JOHN HENRY NEWMAN (1801–90). Remarks on Cer-tain Passages in the Thirty-nine Articles. (Tracts for the Times no. 90.) *London: J. G. F. & J. Rivington and J. H. Parker, 1841*

Newman's long life spanned the major crisis of Christi-anity in England in the nineteenth century, and with almost every part of it he had been deeply involved. He had gone up to Oxford in 1817, an evangelical Calvinistic Low Churchman, and this he remained throughout the period (1822–32) of his fellowship at Oriel. But latterly he began to detach himself from the Low Church party, and when he returned from a long journey in the Mediterranean (during which he wrote 'Lead, Kindly Light') he joined with Pusey, Rose and Froude in what was to become the Oxford Movement.

Newman was not in fact present at the meeting in Rose's rectory of the High Church clergy, who then resolved to fight for 'the apostolic succession and the integrity of the prayer-book', and it was on his own initiative that a few weeks later he founded the *Tracts for the Times* which he edited till 1841. Their importance is shown by the fact that what we now call the Oxford Movement was then usually called 'Tractarian'. His aim was to secure for the Church of England a definite basis of doctrine and discipline, in case either of disestablishment or of a decision by High Churchmen to quit the establish-ment; an eventuality which was thought not impossible in view of the government's recent high-handed dealings with the established Church of Ireland. Newman's writ-ing was supplemented by his immensely popular Sunday afternoon sermons; but it was about this time that he began to doubt whether the Anglican position was really tenable. His doubts were reinforced by reading an article by Wiseman which seemed to indicate that St Augustine had acknowledged an immanent authority in the Church, apart from that derived from the teaching of antiquity.

Newman continued as a High Church contro-versialist until, in Tract Ninety, he found a means of expressing his doubts. He put out, as a sort of specimen charge to test the tenability of all Catholic doctrine within the Church of England, a detailed examination of the Thirty-nine Articles, suggesting that their nega-tions were directed not against authorized Catholic belief, but only against popular errors and exaggerations. Although this notion was not wholly new, its pub-lication at that particular time caused great alarm and

No. 90.]   [*Price 1s.*

TRACTS FOR THE TIMES.

REMARKS ON CERTAIN PASSAGES IN THE THIRTY-NINE ARTICLES.

CONTENTS.

VOL. VI.—90.   B

indignation in Oxford, and at the request of the Bishop of Oxford, the publication of the Tracts came to an end. In 1842 Newman withdrew to nearby Littlemore, and in 1843 resigned his living. After another two years of painful self-searching, during which he wrote an essay on the development of Christian doctrine through which he sought to reconcile himself to the elaborate creed and practical system of the Roman Church, he was finally received into the Roman Catholic Church.

The rest of his career is another story. His early, un-happy, neglected years in the Roman Church culminated in the controversy with Charles Kingsley which produced the *Apologia pro Vita sua*, from which time on his integrity was wholly vindicated, and his position both as a human being and as a member of the Roman Catholic Church became a great deal easier. Even at the end of his life, when the value both of his work and of his magnetic personality were belatedly acknowledged by his elevation to the College of Cardinals, he never quite regained the authority which he had wielded in the thirties. The work Newman did then, as carried on by Pusey and the other Tractarians, did far more to shape the development of the Church of England in modern times than anything he could do for Rome.

313
SANITARY REFORM

EDWIN CHADWICK (1800–90). Report to Her Majesty's Principal Secretary of State for the Home Department, from the Poor Law Commissioners, on an Inquiry into the Sanitary Conditions of the Labouring Population of Great Britain. *London: Her Majesty's Stationery Office, 1842*

In 1830 Chadwick, while training to be a barrister, became literary secretary to Bentham (237), who was then writing his *Constitutional Code*. Many of its principles were embodied in the new Poor Law of 1834, which emerged from the Report of a Commission to which Chadwick had been appointed in 1832. In the following year he joined the Factory Commission and was largely responsible for the Factory Act which resulted.

In 1838 a serious outbreak of disease in Whitechapel prompted Chadwick, as Secretary of the Poor Law Commissioners, to appoint Dr Southwood Smith and two other medical men to report on it. What they found so shocked the country that similar reports were called for from other industrial centres. The sequel was the issue of the staggering document cited above. In its own words 'More filth, worse physical suffering and moral disorder than Howard describes [224] are to be found among the cellar population of the working people of Liverpool, Manchester, or Leeds, and in large portions of the metropolis'. No wonder Engels (see 326) quoted freely from it in his 'Conditions of the Working Classes in England', 1845.

Nominally the work of the Commissioners, the Report was in fact drawn up by Chadwick; and it is one of the most important documents in the history of the first half of the nineteenth century. Its recommendations included for the first time national responsibility for drainage, cleaning of streets, paving, light and water supply, and a national health and burial service. The Health Board of 1848, the Local Government Board of 1871 and today's Ministry of Health (1919) are all directly traceable to Chadwick's report.

G. M. Young, in *Victorian England*, has pointed out that Chadwick's influence with the Commission was responsible for the introduction into the British constitution of 'the Benthamite formula—inquiry, legislation, execution, inspection and report'.

A *Supplementary Report* was issued in 1843.

314
THE PROPHET OF EXISTENTIALISM

SØREN AABYE KIERKEGAARD (1813–55). Enten–Eller. *Copenhagen: E. A. Reitzel, 1843*

Kierkegaard was born in Copenhagen and died there after a life much misunderstood by his countrymen. His complicated nature was profoundly influenced by his father, a stern religious determinist, convinced of his own guilt, who inflicted his principles on his son's education. In obedience to his father's wishes he entered the University of Copenhagen as a theology student in 1830. There he changed his subject for philosophy and literature, and although he finally took his theological examination in 1840, he never took orders. He remained a

Enten — Eller.

Et Livs-Fragment

udgivet

af

Victor Eremita.

———

Første Deel.

'perpetual student', living on his ample patrimony, of which through his extravagance there was little left when he died. His habits of life were eccentric, notably in his treatment of his fiancée, breaking off their engagement on idealist grounds which seemed open to considerable misconception. By the time of his death Kierkegaard had achieved a certain literary influence, but his philosophy had made little impact (it was a handicap that he wrote in Danish: it was long before he was translated).

Enten—Eller ('Either—Or') was written before he was twenty-nine. It is a curious bundle of papers, essays, semi-dialogues and notes, seemingly ill-assorted, but in fact dialectically arranged. Originally published under a variety of pseudonyms (all recognizable) the chief advantage of this method seems to have been to give

Kierkegaard the opportunity of letting different sides of his mind converse as individuals with each other, in a semi-Socratic fashion. Without disclosing his real beliefs, he confronted his readers with a choice of different possibilities. Educated as a Hegelian (283), he attacked Hegel's system of interpreting life as a synthesis of ideas. Adopting what he called an 'aesthetic attitude' he held that this consisted in balancing possibilities, and that in matters religious and ethical it was up to the individual to make his choice. Choice, as the title of his work suggests, was at the root of Kierkegaard's theory. There can be no system of existence, only a system of ideas. From this he develops his thesis of 'Existence' (since taken up by the modern Existentialists), in which human beings considered as subjects not objects are the only real existence: their reflective as opposed to active nature being focused on the 'acts' of making perpetual decisions.

In his religious works, notably 'Stages on Life's Way', Kierkegaard again sees the progress of religion as a pattern of decisions and conflicts, and the history of Christianity mainly as a process of deterioration from the radical categories of the New Testament. To him there was only God, infinitely great, and the individual man, infinitely small, and the demands which each made of the other were irreconcilable. To the comfortable religiosity of the nineteenth century this was intolerable, and Kierkegaard was bitterly attacked as well as misunderstood. More recently his contrast between categorical Christianity and speculative philosophy has found some accord with the 'dialectical theology' of Karl Barth, and his 'existential' thinking has been further developed by Heidegger and Jaspers. As a thinker, Kierkegaard had to wait for the twentieth century to find his audience; he is now generally considered to be, however eccentric, one of the most important Christian philosophers.

315

ART RECONSIDERED

JOHN RUSKIN (1819–1900). Modern Painters. By a Graduate of Oxford. 5 vols. *London: Smith, Elder & Co., 1843–60*

It is a little difficult now to understand the dominance exercised by Ruskin upon two whole generations, first in forming the artistic taste of the second half of the nineteenth century and secondly in advocating that particularly English form of Utopian socialism which came into being at the same time. Ruskin began writing early and, when he died, books he had written thirty or forty years earlier were still among the best-sellers. His popularity, then, is incontrovertible: what caused it?

He was an only child, and his parents were possessively devoted to him. His upbringing was carefully supervised, although his formal education, both at school and the university, was desultorily pursued; and from early youth he began to develop those studies of nature, art and literature which were to combine with unequalled intensity in his writings. He published his first poem, 'On Skiddaw and Derwent Water', in 1830, and three essays from his pen appeared in the *Magazine of Natural History* in 1834; but his earliest major work was *Modern Painters*, of which the first volume, containing the celebrated defence of Turner, appeared anonymously in 1843. *Modern Painters* was to occupy Ruskin for another seventeen years, spanning the whole period of his writing on art, but none of the subsequent volumes achieved quite the sensational impact of the first.

Many critics were unfavourable, and a number of painters, including Turner himself, were unenthusiastic. There could be, however, no doubt of its success. His parents were delighted, and characteristically took him to the Alps to study the formation of mountains and 'Truth' in art. The second volume, a survey of Italian art which demands special notice as one of the direct causes of the foundation of the Pre-Raphaelite Brotherhood, appeared in 1846, followed in quick succession by *The Seven Lamps of Architecture* and *The Stones of Venice*, both of which, with their obsession with the function and aesthetics of architecture, over and beyond its history and practice, again proved a revolutionary success. In 1851 Ruskin put his name to *Modern Painters*. The fourth volume (1856) was devoted to a favourite Ruskinian subject, mountain scenery and its formation. Both here and in the last volume, the illustrations are beautifully engraved—Ruskin took an infinity of pains with the quality of the workmanship—often after his own exquisite drawings, which he thought of as merely diagrams but which are now valued as some of the most original watercolours ever executed. The fifth volume appeared in 1860, eliciting from Dante Gabriel Rossetti the gibe that its subjects would be Old Masters before Ruskin had finished.

But Ruskin *had* finished; not merely *Modern Painters*, but also his writings on art, although as Slade Professor of Art at Oxford he continued to preach the doctrines he had laid down. The next thirty years were to be devoted to expounding his equally dogmatic opinions on sociology, industry, education and religion; and just as he had earlier succeeded in waking the dormant aesthetic conscience of the public, so now he woke its social conscience. He was read and loved by the working classes from whom he seemed so distant, and the many 'Ruskin Societies', formed to put his social thinking into practice, bore witness to it. Yet, in the end, Ruskin is remembered chiefly as the great champion of art; if he found the artist a tradesman, it was he who gave the word its new meaning.

BIBLIOGRAPHY: E. T. Cook and A. D. O. Wedderburn, in vol. XXXVIII and throughout their library edition of Ruskin's works, 39 vols. (London & New York, 1903–12).

316

ASEPSIS AND ANTISEPSIS

(a) OLIVER WENDELL HOLMES (1809–94). On the Contagiousness of Puerperal Fever. *In:* The New England Quarterly Journal of Medicine and Surgery. *Boston, 1843*

(b) IGNAZ PHILIPP SEMMELWEISS (1818–65). Höchst wichtige Erfahrungen über die Aetiologie der Gebäranstalten Epidemischen Puerperalfieber. *In:* Zeitschrift der Kaiserliche Königliche Gesellsch. der Aerzte in Wien. *Vienna, 1847–9;* (b2) Die Aetiologie, der Begriff und die Prophylaxis des Kindbettfiebers. *Pest, Vienna & Leipzig: C. A Hartleben, 1861*

(c) JOSEPH LISTER (1827–1912). On a new Method of treating Compound Fracture, Abscess, &c. With Observations on the Conditions of Suppuration. *In:* The Lancet, *London, 1867.* (Six papers at various dates from 16 March to 21 September.)

Priority and impact are not always combined in the same pronouncement. Holmes declared in 1843 that puerperal fever was contagious, that before attending women in childbed doctors who have been performing post-mortem dissections or who have treated cases of puerperal fever should wash their hands in calcium chloride and change their clothes. This made no impact at all except to arouse the wrathful contempt of all orthodox obstetricians. Holmes was the first to acknowledge the priority of Alexander Gordon of Aberdeen, who in 1795 had come to precisely the same conclusion in his *Treatise on the Epidemic Puerperal Fever of Aberdeen.*

Semmelweiss, an Austro-Hungarian, was totally unaware of Holmes's paper when he analysed the probable cause of the endemic nature of puerperal fever in the maternity hospital in Vienna. He observed that the mortality was much higher in the ward attended by students than in the one attended only by midwives.

After attending a post mortem on a colleague who died from bloodpoisoning contracted from a wound while dissecting a cadaver, Semmelweiss observed that the symptoms and bodily effects were identical to those in puerperal fever: he recognized that this was a septicaemia brought into the maternity wards from the dissecting rooms. He decreed, like Holmes, the washing of hands in calcium chloride solution before the examination of childbed cases—(b) 'Experiences of the highest importance in the Etiology of the Epidemic of Puerperal Fever in Maternity Hospitals'—with the result that the mortality was reduced by five-sixths.

The publication of Semmelweiss's papers in 1847–9 was met by ridicule, opposition and veritable persecution to a degree that compelled him to leave Vienna for Budapest, where he produced his great book, (b2) 'The Etiology of the Onset and Prophylaxis of Childbed Fever'. He developed acute persecution mania and died insane. Despite the support of a faithful few, Semmelweiss's aseptic precautions hardly survived him.

Lister approached the question *de novo* in the attempt to reduce the tragic rate of 45 per cent mortality in cases of compound fractures. The fashionable term 'laudable pus'

was suspect to him. He was familiar with Pasteur's (336) conclusions, and he guessed that suppuration, like decomposition, was caused by minute airborne organisms. He used carbolic acid to destroy the organisms and within three years amputation mortality had fallen by almost two-thirds.

In the eighties and nineties a return was made to the asepsis of Semmelweiss as against Lister's antisepsis. Von Bergmann introduced steam sterilization of dressings in 1886 and W. S. Halsted introduced rubber gloves in 1890.

317

THE KINDERGARTEN

FRIEDRICH WILHELM AUGUST FROEBEL (1782–1852). Mutter- und Kose-Lieder. Dichtung und Bilder zur Pflege des Kindheitslebens. *Blankenburg bei Rudolstadt: Die Anstalt zur Pflege des Beschäftigungstriebes der Kindheit und Jugend,* [1844]

Froebel may be not unjustly described as a crank. He was absent-minded, improvident, theatrical, eccentric, convinced of his own infallibility and steeped in metaphysical and mystical notions. But he loved children and by devising the kindergarten, in which very young children are instructed through the medium of games and recreation, he conferred a lasting benefit on humanity.

He was born in a Thuringian village where his father was pastor, lost his mother almost at birth, was neglected by his stepmother, was sent to his father's brother, pastor at Stadtilm, and went to school there. A dreamy and fanciful boy, he was treated as a dunce, and this unquestionably made a lasting impression on him as an example of inadequacy in the teacher.

Before entering the teaching profession himself, in a model school at Frankfurt in 1805, Froebel was, by turns, a forester, architect, soldier, and museum attendant. In 1808 he became tutor to three boys and obtained the consent of their parents to take them to Pestalozzi's Institute at Yverdun (258) where he and they remained for two years. In 1811 he published a 'Treatise on Sphericity', in which obscure metaphysical notions frequently degenerate into something perilously near nonsense. It is important, however, because Froebel's later ideas on infant education were based on the mystique that the sphere is the prototype of unity in all things and that all the different shapes assumed by material objects have an occult and spiritual significance.

In 1816 he opened a school of his own at Griesheim, but soon moved to Keilhau. Pestalozzian methods were used, but by 1826 he had attracted only fifty pupils and these were never enough to support his two army colleagues and a relation, all of whom had married and joined the educational community. The school had to be closed for lack of support in 1829. In 1831 he tried two more schools in Switzerland, and the Government of Berne entrusted him with refresher courses for schoolmasters and made him the director of an orphan asylum at Burgdorf, where Pestalozzi had laboured thirty years earlier. In 1837 he was back in the district where he was born and opened his first infant school at Blankenburg. It was here that he instituted his Kindergarten. He ran a weekly journal, *Sonntagsblatt* (1837–40), to propagate his ideas and published, at his own expense, the charming 'Fondling Songs for Mothers' with the motto 'Come, let us bring life to our children!'

Froebel's basic principle was to teach the children by means of instructive games. Each child had his own chair and his own acknowledged place at the common play-table. His interest was immediately aroused by participation in a game and he was supplied with a variety of familiar objects—balls of coloured wool, matchsticks, wooden bricks, strips of coloured paper, etc.—with which he was encouraged to make patterns and constructions to his own design. The attention awakened by these activities was enlarged by persuading the children to answer a series of questions carefully framed to rationalize these pursuits and relate them to their everyday lives. All this was outlined in the book, and music, songs and games were added.

In 1851 the Prussian Government suppressed the Kindergartens which Froebel had created in increasing numbers, as 'atheistic and demagogic', and the unavailing fight against this obscurantism undermined his health. He died very suddenly in 1852: the year in which the *Oxford Dictionary* records the acceptance of kindergarten as an English word.

The Baronin von Marenholtz-Bülow, who had lent him her castle at Marienthal for a school, was responsible for the Froebel stand at the Educational Exhibition of the Society of Arts in London in 1854. It attracted so much attention that in the following year she produced the first book in English on the system, *Woman's Educational Mission*; and in 1859 she was influential in founding the first Kindergarten in Belgium and in having Froebel's book translated into French. Her *Erinnerungen an F. Froebel* is a charming portrait of this unfortunate, lovable man.

with a camera, were first made public as late as 1841, in his son Isidore's brochure—*Historique de la Découverte improprement nommée Daguerréotype.*

Arago, himself a chemist and a member of the Chamber of Deputies, made a brief pronouncement on Daguerre's process in the Chamber on 7 January 1839, and in the following August printed the full text of his report thereon made to a joint session of the Chamber of Deputies and the Academy of Sciences. The first publication by Daguerre himself (he was a painter by profession), is the monograph cited above—'History and Description of the Daguerréotype Process'.

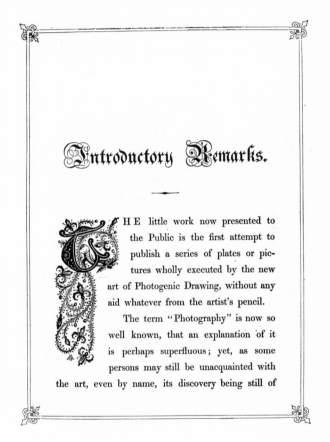

PHOTOGRAPHY

318

(a) WILLIAM HENRY FOX TALBOT (1800–77). The Pencil of Nature. *London: Longman, Brown, Green and Longman, 1844–[6]*

(b) LOUIS JACQUES MANDÉ DAGUERRE (1787–1851). Historique et Description des Procédés du Daguerréotype et du Diorama. *Paris: Alphonse Giroux & Cie, ou se fabriquent les Appareils; Delloye, Libraire, 1839*

There had been earlier discoveries of the actinic effect of sunlight on silver compounds but the first successful attempts to produce images by this means were described in a paper by Thomas Wedgwood in 1802 (*Journal of the Royal Institute*, I, 170). He tried to reproduce camera obscura effects but the light was too dim. The outlines of leaves, some silhouettes and other objects exposed on suitably impregnated paper were reproduced. J. N. Niepce's experiments of 1822 and 1824, when he unquestionably took at least one successful photograph

Fox Talbot, a physicist, contributed a paper to the Royal Society on 31 January 1839, describing pictures taken by him as early as 1835 but with no details of his process. These latter were first disclosed in February and March 1839. *The Pencil of Nature*, originally issued in parts—and confusingly given the date of the first part when published in volume form—contains a full account of his process, which he patented, and twenty-four actual photographs taken by means of it.

Priority of discovery will be argued till doomsday by the respective supporters of Niepce, Daguerre and Fox Talbot. The Englishman was unquestionably the inventor of the negative/positive process which has completely superseded the French invention.

319

ENGLAND'S 'TWO NATIONS'

BENJAMIN DISRAELI (1804–81). Sybil, or the Two Nations. 3 vols. *London: Henry Colburn, 1845*

The passing of the Reform Bill (see 296) had put an end to the immediate causes of the unrest resulting from the profound change in the structure of British society which had begun at the end of the eighteenth century. It could not arrest the change itself, nor was it a total panacea for all the social injustice which it brought about. The ever-increasing development of industry, and the egotistic pursuit of wealth by the new middle classes which succeeded the short-sighted attempts of the old landed aristocracy to maintain their privileges, continued to vitiate the harmony of British political life.

Disraeli, with his Jewish ancestry and the genius which was peculiarly his own, was the one man in Parliament who stood apart in perfect detachment from the interests involved. His novel *Vivian Grey*, published when he was twenty-two, introduced him to the world of politics and of society, and his wide travels and further writings (notably the *Vindication of the British Constitution*) had qualified him for the task to which he set himself when he finally entered Parliament in 1837. His quality was soon apparent: breadth of view, insight, foresight are all necessary qualifications in a statesman, but it was Disraeli's imagination—romantic, perceptive, interpretative, judicial, at times almost divining—which was the driving force, sometimes taking complete control of the other faculties, sometimes acting almost in defiance of common prudence. When he spoke against the injurious treatment of Ireland, when he made his impassioned defence of the Chartists, he did his career no good; but his prescience was justified by subsequent events.

In these early days, this political genius led him to open a determined campaign against the traditional positions of the party he had chosen. He founded the 'Young England' group as the instrument of his views; to it he attracted young and brilliant men from all sections of the Tory party, whose only bond was dissatisfaction with the current policy; and he thus sharpened the lack of sympathy between himself and Peel, the Prime Minister.

Disraeli drove his point home to the reading public in two novels. The first was *Coningsby, or, The New Generation*, 1844, which put the political problem. Following up his pamphlet on the constitution, he showed that for generations before the passing of the Reform Bill the authority of the crown and the liberties of the people had been absorbed by an oligarchy which had itself become fossilized and inert. The point was one which Cobbett (294), who could hardly have been otherwise more different from Disraeli, would have approved. Still more would he have agreed with the thesis of *Sybil*. Disraeli, with the other 'Young Englanders', had visited the factory districts, and he had seen for himself the dreadful conditions there. The novel was a shattering indictment of the social relations of rich and poor: the agricultural labourer, abandoned by the neglectful landowners and the factory workers, was forced to live in unimaginable squalor through the blind craving for material prosperity of the new industrialists.

Thus the social and economic policy of the Young England party and the concept of a nation divided into 'Two Nations', the rich and the poor, were enforced by the startling, vivid description of industrial suffering which derived from Disraeli's own observation. His prophetic criticism aroused the conscience of the country, and started the movement towards social reform which has been the mainstay of 'Tory Democracy' ever since.

320*

THE UNIVERSE SURVEYED

FRIEDRICH HEINRICH ALEXANDER, BARON VON HUMBOLDT (1769–1859). Kosmos, Entwurf einer Physischen Weltbeschreibung. 4 vols. text, and atlas. *Stuttgart & Tübingen: Cotta, 1845–62*

Alexander von Humboldt produced in his 'Cosmos' one of the last really comprehensive physical surveys ever to be attempted.

Born in Berlin as the son of a Chamberlain to the King of Prussia, he was destined for a career in government service, but during his student days in Frankfurt-on-the-Oder, Göttingen and Freiburg he discovered his bent for science. He undertook several scientific voyages, in which he was encouraged by Georg Forster, Cook's companion, whom he had visited in London in 1790. After a period as director of mines at Freiberg, Humboldt set out in 1799 with the French naturalist Aimé Bonpland on a voyage to explore South America. He visited Venezuela, Ecuador, Peru and Mexico and returned in 1804. In 1829 there followed a journey to the Ural, the Altai mountains and the Caspian Sea, at the suggestion of the Russian Minister of Finance who wished him to report whether the newly found platinum deposits in the Ural mountains could be used for silver coinage. Humboldt discovered diamonds in the Ural and brought back much botanical, zoological, geological and astronomical information. His later years were spent in various diplomatic missions and at the Berlin court.

For twenty years Humboldt was occupied in composing, in collaboration with Cuvier (276), Latreille, Gay-Lussac and others, his monumental account of South America. The first part was entitled *Voyages aux Régions Equinoxiales du Nouveau Continent fait en 1799–1804*, which serves usually to describe the whole work; thirty large volumes were published between 1805 and 1834, but even then it remained uncompleted.

But it was *Kosmos*—'The Cosmos, Outline of a Description of the Physical World'—based on lectures delivered at the Berlin Singakademie in 1828–9, which Humboldt really considered as his life work. The last of the five volumes was published posthumously from his notes. In his own words it was meant 'to represent in one work the whole material world, everything we know today of the phenomena in the celestial spaces and of life on earth, from the nebulae to the geography of mosses on granite rocks...it is meant to describe a chapter in the intellectual development of mankind (the knowledge of nature)'. The book contains a complete survey of the physical sciences and their relation to each other. Though Humboldt was convinced that techno-logical knowledge was essential for the progress of man-kind and that scientific education was therefore vital for the growth of both power and prosperity of a nation, he believed that humanistic studies were equally important and that a balance between the two must be maintained. Volume II contains a history of geographical and scientific discoveries and then goes on to discuss art and poetry, attempting to find a connecting link between imagina-tion and scientific studies.

Humboldt's scientific and other achievements cover an enormous field. He laid the foundation of modern physical geography, meteorology and geography of plants. He investigated the connexions between geogra-phy, climate, distribution of plants, animals and mineral resources and the economics of countries. He studied plant life in its environmental conditions, collecting no less than sixty thousand specimens, many of them new species. While comparing the distribution of plant fami-lies with the mean annual temperatures of the regions concerned, he conceived the idea of isothermal lines, which connect points of the same temperature on a chart. In geology he demonstrated that volcanoes follow certain lines corresponding to large subterranean fissures, a com-

pletely new conception. While in South America he made measurements of the intensity of the terrestrial magnetic field; the resulting discovery that it decreases from the Pole to the Equator Humboldt regarded as the most important result of his American voyage. It made possible the important investigations of Gauss (257) in this field. By sending guano from South America to Europe for chemical investigation as a potential fertilizer he initiated its eventual export to Europe on a large scale, and he discovered curare being used as an arrow-poison by the Indians—now a valuable drug in medical practice. Humboldt was a proponent of international scientific co-operation and his suggestion of the establishment of a line of meteorological stations across northern Asia marks an important step towards modern methods of weather forecasting; the International Geophysical Years go back to Humboldt's ideas. He first described scientifically the languages and cultures of the South American peoples and studied the distribution and densities of populations and the influences of natural and economic conditions on social and political life.

Humboldt's fame was international; apart from the current off the coast of Peru being called after him, his name has been given to many other places in the world.

Although *Kosmos* is by no means a book of popular science, it had a great success. The first edition of volume I was sold out within two months; it was immediately translated into most European languages; and by 1852, eighty thousand copies had been sold.

BIBLIOGRAPHY: Julius Löwenberg, *Alexander von Humboldt. Bibliographische Übersicht seiner Werke* (Stutt-gart, 1960).

321

THE GLORY THAT WAS GREECE

GEORGE GROTE (1794-1871). A History of Greece. 12 vols. *London: John Murray, 1846-56*

Although as biased as Macaulay's *History of England* (328) and less scholarly than Mommsen's 'Roman History' (337*), Grote's *History of Greece* can be bracketed with these two works. Like them, it was received with uni-versal acclamation, was translated into French and German, shaped the European conception of its subject-matter throughout the nineteenth century, and still merits respect as a monument of industrious Victorian scholar-ship.

Grote's background largely explains the initial success as well as the final supersession of his book. The scion of a family of prosperous bankers, who originally came from Bremen, Grote joined the paternal firm, moved in the circle of radical reformers such as David Ricardo (277), James Mill and Jeremy Bentham (237), represented the City of London in Parliament, 1832-41, helped to establish the University of London (of which he later, 1862, became Vice-Chancellor) and could afford to retire from business in 1843 in order to devote himself entirely to the writing of the *History of Greece*. Thus he brought to his task the self-assurance of a Victorian businessman, untroubled by any doubt about the supreme merits of democracy and progress; and he naïvely adopted the middle-class ideals of his period as yardsticks for measuring the civilization of ancient Greece. The *History* is, in fact, a paean in praise of political liberty, and he glorified the Athenian democracy as fervently as he misrepresented the despotism of the 'barbarian', Alexander the Great. Grote gave penetrating sketches of Greek intellectual life, and his enthusiasm for 'the noble, the good and the beautiful' deeply influenced political and educational thought. But he completely neglected the social and economic factors, and this failure to see history in the round eventually killed the book, the last reprint of which appeared in 1888.

was responsible for the revolution in thought which persuaded some Christians to depart from the earlier Judaism, and thus originated a controversy that persisted until the two groups drew together in one Catholic Church in the second century.

The fallacy of Baur's position lay in his false premise that the controversy ran so deep and lasted so long; in fact, the cataclysmic fall of Jerusalem in A.D. 70 put an end to a strife which had never been as bitter as Baur believed. But the idea of applying any criterion, even that of Hegelian theory, which was untinctured by theological *parti pris* was wholly original. If biblical criticism has been revolutionized in the last century, Baur's work was the germ of the revolution.

322

MODERN BIBLICAL CRITICISM

FERDINAND CHRISTIAN BAUR (1792–1860). Kritische Untersuchungen über die Kanonischen Evangelien. *Tübingen: L. F. Fues, 1847*

The Tübingen school of theological and biblical criticism dominated all New Testament studies in the nineteenth century, and, if its matter is now largely superseded, its method has remained to exercise the most profound influence on all modern theological writing.

The founder, and for thirty-four years the dominant figure, of the school was F. C. Baur. He was educated at the seminary of Blaubeuren, whence in 1809 he proceeded to Tübingen University, by tradition a centre of New Testament scholarship. Baur's early works followed the traditional views, but on his return to Blaubeuren in 1817 the originality of his mind found freer rein, and his first important book, on the 'Ancient Nature Religion' (1824–5), showed the depth of his philosophical studies. Its learning was widely acknowledged, and in 1826 he returned to Tübingen as professor of theology, remaining there for the rest of his life.

Baur's first publications after his return are indicative of the course his biblical criticism was to follow: between 1831 and 1837 his works included studies of Manichaeanism, Apollonius of Tyana and the Christian Gnosis, and *Über das Christliche im Platonismus*, 1837. By now Baur had come under the spell of Hegel's (283) comprehensive philosophy of history, and the change of view is apparent in an article of 1831 on a subject closely related to his other studies; the controversy which he detected between the Universal or Pauline party and the Petrine Jewish party in the early Corinthian Church. From the year 1835 Baur proceeded to apply the Hegelian historical criteria to various sections of the New Testament and thus to reorientate New Testament criticism.

In 1847 his greatest and most influential work, the *Kritische Untersuchungen*—'Critical Enquiries into the Canonical Gospels'—confirmed this reorientation. Baur held that Christianity evolved from Judaism and that the Gospel of Matthew was the nearest to a lost, contemporary 'Petrine' evangel. Paul, in his view,

323

THE CONSERVATION OF ENERGY

HERMANN HELMHOLTZ (1821–94). Über die Erhaltung der Kraft. *Berlin: G. Reimer, 1847*

This short paper of twenty-eight pages, 'On the Conservation of Energy', is the first comprehensive statement of the first law of thermodynamics: that all modes of energy, heat, light, electricity, and all chemical phenomena, are capable of transformation from one to the other but are indestructible and cannot be created.

Benjamin Thompson, Count Rumford, the American-born scientist largely responsible for the foundation of the Royal Institution and the founder of the Royal Society's Rumford Medal, was the first to challenge successfully the accepted theory that heat was the manifestation of an imponderable fluid called 'caloric'. He declared, and gave experimental proof before the Royal Society in 1798, that heat was a mode of motion. Rumford was, in fact, conspicuous in his day for what was considered his old-fashioned theory of heat. He harked back to the seventeenth-century views of Bacon, Locke and Newton in opposition to the fashionable modern theory of caloric, which, indeed, worked very well, especially in chemistry.

Sadi Carnot (285), in 1824, approached very close to the principle of the conservation of energy and his brother found among his papers an almost explicit statement of it, although Carnot had actually used the caloric theory in his researches. J. R. Mayer in *Liebig's Annalen*, 1842, demonstrated its application in physiological processes, but his paper made little impression until it was reprinted as a polemic in 1867. J. P. Joule made a manuscript translation of Mayer's thesis for his own use, and, in a series of papers in the *Philosophical Magazine*, 1840–3, provided experimental proof of the mechanical equivalent of heat for physical phenomena. Joule was, in 1843, twenty-four years of age. A scientific electrical unit of measurement is named after him.

Helmholtz was twenty-six years old in 1847 when he published his historic paper. He was an army surgeon living in barracks in Potsdam at the time. He was familiar with Joule's papers, but not with Mayer's, which was the cause of bitter controversy in later years. Helmholtz's experiments ranged over the entire field of physical energy without finding a single exception to the rule and he propounded his conviction that the law of the conservation of energy is of universal application. Einstein's researches (408) have somewhat modified his conclusions. The second law of thermodynamics, which is concerned with the ultimate dissipation of energy, was established by Rudolf Clausius and William Thomson, 1850–2. They reconciled the first and second laws. Einstein showed that mass and energy *together* are conserved in the universe, but that one could be transformed into the other as in the hydrogen bomb (see 422). This, however, has not affected the second law, which simply states that in any closed system the availability of the energy decreases with the passage of time, which involves the running down of the solar system.

Über

die Erhaltung der Kraft,

eine physikalische Abhandlung,

vorgetragen in der Sitzung der physikalischen Gesellschaft zu Berlin
am 23sten Juli 1847

von

Dr. H. Helmholtz.

B e r l i n,
Druck und Verlag von G. Reimer
1847.

The practical uses of the two laws of thermodynamics became evident within a very few years. Not only did they provide the engineer with a reliable basic principle for the construction of heat engines, but William Thomson's theory of an absolute scale of temperature led to his porous plug experiments, with Joule, which have ultimately led to the liquefaction of all known gases. A by-product was Dewar's vacuum flask.

Helmholtz invented the ophthalmoscope in 1851 and made fundamental contributions to physiology, electricity and acoustics.

324

THE IDEALIZED REVOLUTION

JULES MICHELET (1798–1874). Histoire de la Révolution Française. 7 vols. *Paris: Chamerot, 1847–53*

During the same years when Macaulay (328) was fixing the Whig image of the Glorious Revolution in the minds of the English public, Michelet was giving to the French radicals the most colourful and fervent justification of the French Revolution. Ten years after Carlyle (304) had painted it in lurid colours as the twilight of the gods, Michelet hailed it as the birth of a new age. Michelet was a sounder historian than the Scot—he based his *Histoire Romaine*, 1831, on Niebuhr (267), and the section of his *Histoire de France*, 1833–67, dealing with the Middle Ages is an outstanding example of romantic historiography. From 1840, if not earlier, Michelet turned an outspoken anti-clerical; his violent attacks on the Jesuits, the Church of Rome and Christianity itself cost him his professorial chairs under Guizot as well as Napoleon III, who also ejected him from the state archives.

In all his writings Michelet came very near the fulfilment of his ideal, namely that history should be 'la résurrection de la vie intégrale'. His 'History of the French Revolution' is a sustained panegyric of radical democracy: 'from the first page to the last', he said, 'there is only one hero—the people'. Neither his openly anti-clerical and anti-royalist partisanship nor his many inaccuracies can detract from the grandiose narrative which has secured the book a permanent place in French literature such as none of his successors has attained.

325

THE STONE AGE

JACQUES BOUCHER DE CRÈVECŒUR DE PERTHES (1788–1868). Antiquités Celtiques et Antédiluviennes. 3 vols. *Paris: Treuttel & Würtz (and others), 1847–64*

In the face of growing geological evidence it was necessary by the early nineteenth century to abandon Archbishop Ussher's biblical chronology, which had fixed the date of the creation as 4004 B.C. It was recognized that many fossiliferous deposits, including the gravels of the Paris basin which contained the bones of large extinct mammals, were far more ancient than that. As regards *man*, however, there was a general reluctance to allow him a greater antiquity. Cuvier (276) died convinced that man had been created about six thousand years ago.

Various claims had been made of human artefacts being found in conjunction with the bones of the great extinct mammals, both in Britain and on the Continent; but they attracted little attention until Boucher de Perthes, a French customs official and minor literary figure, began, in 1847, to publish the details of his discoveries in the fossiliferous deposits at Abbeville in northern France. In 'Celtic and Antediluvian Antiquities' he claimed to have found flint implements in the same deposits and in close conjunction with the bones of mammoth and other fossil mammals. For Boucher these finds proved that man had been a contemporary of the mammoth, and was therefore of far greater antiquity than had been supposed. Such a view was regarded by the orthodox as ridiculous, or much more seriously, impious. It jeopardized Cuvier's theory of a catastrophic destruction of the extinct European fauna before the creation of man. Buckland's universal flood was preferred to explain these discoveries, postulating a mixing of two separate deposits by the action of flood waters. Both Darwin (344) and Lyell are on record as ridiculing Boucher's claim when it was first made.

The evidence was mounting up, however, and in 1854 at Amiens a Dr Rigollet, at first violently opposed to Boucher, confirmed his findings. More important, similar discoveries were made in England, pointing to the same conclusion. In 1859—that *annus mirabilis*—it was a party headed by Lyell and Prestwich, another geologist, and including a palaeontologist, an archaeologist and an anatomist, which visited Abbeville and unhesitatingly endorsed Boucher's views.

Unfortunately for Boucher his enthusiasm led him to include in his work descriptions and pictures of numerous flints that were almost certainly natural products and not artefacts at all. Worse, from 1861 on he was the victim of a hoax—the workmen began 'salting' the excavation pits with flint hand-axes and even human bones. But in spite of all this Boucher de Perthes had established beyond doubt that man had been a contemporary of the mammoth; 'he had', Darwin wrote to Lyell, 'done for man something like what Agassiz [309] has done for glaciers'.

326

WORKERS OF THE WORLD, UNITE!

KARL MARX (1818–83) and FRIEDRICH ENGELS (1820–95). Manifest der Kommunistischen Partei. *London: J. E. Burghard, 1848*

'Admitted by every serious student of society to be one of the outstanding political documents of all time'—to quote the late Harold Laski—the 'Manifesto of the Communist Party' outlined the main positions of Marxism as a theory of history, a criticism of Socialist doctrine and a programme of revolutionary action.

It was commissioned by the second congress of the Communist League, a largely German body of revolutionary exiles, which met in London in November–December 1847. The Communist League's hall was in Great Windmill Street, W., in an upper part of what is now the Red Lion public house. Engels had already drafted a question-and-answer *Principles of Communism* (it did not come to light till 1913) but he now wrote to Marx: 'I believe we had better drop the catechism form and call the thing *Communist Manifesto*'. Meeting in Brussels, the two friends worked jointly on the 'Manifesto's' text; the manuscript reached London at the beginning of February 1848 and was promptly produced in pamphlet form by a German printer in Bishopsgate; thus bulk supplies began to arrive on the Continent just

as the first wave of the revolutions of 1848 broke over France and Germany.

The revolutionary upsurge in Europe owed nothing to the 'Manifesto'; but the panic-stricken authorities found its subversive sentiments a good excuse for action against its authors. Marx and his wife were arrested and expelled from Belgium. Later the *Neue Rheinische Zeitung*, Marx's principal organ of expression, was suppressed in Cologne, the final issue being defiantly printed in red, and Marx himself was expelled in turn from Germany and France. He then emigrated to England ('the most important landmark in his career' as E. H. Carr put it), where he spent the rest of his life—much of it in the reading room of the British Museum. He is buried in Highgate cemetery in London.

Engels himself later expounded the 'fundamental proposition' of the 'Manifesto' as follows: 'in every historical epoch the prevailing mode of economic production and exchange, and the social organisation necessarily following from it, form the basis upon which is built up, and from which alone can be explained, the political and intellectual history of that epoch'. Human history has thus been one of class struggles, evolving to the point where the oppressed class (the proletariat) cannot free itself from the rule of the exploiting class (the bourgeoisie) without 'once and for all emancipating society at large'. Hence the classic passage: 'The proletarians have nothing to lose but their chains. They have a world to win. Workers of the World, Unite!'

French and Polish translations of the 'Manifesto' speedily followed the German original. In 1850 the first, very stilted, English translation appeared in the *Red Republican* of George Julian Harney, the Chartist (it disclosed that the authors were 'Citizens Charles Marx and Frederic Engels'). The first Russian translation, by Bakunin, was issued by Herzen's *Kolokol* Press in Geneva in 1869; and a second, by Plekhanov, with a preface by the authors, appeared in 1882. Of exceptional importance was the authorized English translation of 1888 (by Samuel Moore, translator of Marx's *Das Kapital*, 359), the only translation personally edited and annotated by Engels, although he edited and prefaced a German text published in London in 1890.

BIBLIOGRAPHY: M. Rubel, *Bibliographie des Œuvres de Karl Marx avec en appendice un Répertoire des œuvres de Friedrich Engels* (Paris, 1956); Bert Andréas, *Le Manifeste Communiste de Marx et Engels: Histoire et Bibliographie, 1848–1918* (Milan, 1963).

327

FRONTIER LIFE

FRANCIS PARKMAN (1823–93). The California and Oregon Trail: being Sketches of Praerie and Rocky Mountain Life. *New York & London: George P. Putnam, 1849*

The consuming interest of Francis Parkman was not the West, nor is *The California and Oregon Trail* about either California or Oregon. Indeed it is only incidentally about the Oregon Trail. The twenty-two-year-old Parkman, just graduated from Harvard, undertook his westward journey in part to restore his failing health and in part to learn more about Indian life in its natural state, information which he hoped would be useful in writing the history he planned of the conflict between the French and the British in North America. He was thwarted on both counts: he returned broken in health, a virtual invalid, and the knowledge gained of the western plains Indians can have served him but slightly in writing about the Iroquois, Algonquins, and Hurons of the north-east. The unexpected result was the history Parkman never intended to write; though it is somewhat misleading to call this book history, for it is in fact one part history and two parts travel narrative and adventure story.

The route which Parkman and his companion Quincy Adams Shaw travelled took them from New York to St Louis, then north along the Missouri to Independence Landing where they began their overland journey across what are now the States of Kansas and Nebraska to the North Platte River which they followed to Fort Laramie. It was here that Parkman went to join a band of Sioux (whom he prefers to call Dakotas) living and travelling with them in the 'Black Hills' (i.e. the Laramie Mountains). This is the portion of the narrative which is not only the most vivid but also of greatest historical value. There are many and better accounts of life among the settlers of the West; but Parkman has given us a unique picture of life in a Sioux village before it was changed and eventually destroyed by contact with the white man. The journey home took the travellers south along the eastern slopes of the Rocky Mountains and eventually to the Arkansas River and then east along the Santa Fé Trail to what is now Kansas City. They had travelled less than a third of the Oregon Trail and had never reached the point at which that route branches north to Oregon.

Having returned home too ill to undertake writing his account of their journey, Parkman dictated it to Shaw. The first publication was serialized, beginning in February 1847 in irregular monthly episodes in the *Knickerbocker Magazine* under the title 'The Oregon Trail, or A Summer's Journey Out of Bounds'. By what Parkman called 'a sly trick' the publisher of the first book edition changed the title to *The California and Oregon Trail, Being Sketches of Praerie and Rocky Mountain Life*, hoping to capitalize on public interest in the California gold rush. The deception was successful and the first edition of one thousand copies, with engravings by F. O. C. Darley who had illustrated works by Cooper and Irving, sold out in a month. It was issued both as one volume in cloth and in two parts in paper wrappers.

Competition from the almost instantaneous flood of accounts of the California gold fields slowed sale of the second edition. To stimulate business the publishers, in 1852, transposed the title and half-title for the third edition which appeared as *Praerie and Rocky Mountain Life, or, the California and Oregon Trail*. Eventually, when the Boston firm of Little, Brown, publishers of Parkman's histories, decided to reissue the work in 1872 with a new preface by the author, Parkman insisted on a return to the original title, *The Oregon Trail*, by

which this classic of Western Americana has subsequently been known.

328

THE WHIG INTERPRETATION OF HISTORY

THOMAS BABINGTON MACAULAY (1800–59). History of England from the Accession of James II. 5 vols. *London: Longman, 1849–61*

The first historical work deliberately designed to outsell the best-selling novel of the day, Macaulay's book immediately fulfilled its author's aspiration. His colourful style and stirring power of description secured for the *History* a success such as no historical work in the English language has had since Gibbon (222). Each volume sold about one hundred and fifty thousand copies within a month of its publication, and the numerous reprints and translations into almost every literary language have perpetuated Macaulay's ideas almost to this day.

Macaulay (from 1857 Lord Macaulay) brought to his great work qualifications such as hardly any other historian ever possessed. He had established his reputation with a brilliant essay on Milton written in 1825 for the *Edinburgh Review*, to which he continued for two decades to contribute *Critical and Historical Essays* (collected edition in 3 vols., 1843). He was called to the Bar in 1826, became a Whig M.P. in 1830, served on the Supreme Council of India 1834–8 (where he was instrumental in unifying the system of higher education and the criminal law), was again M.P. in 1839–47 and 1852–6 and a member of two Whig governments (Secretary of War, 1839–41; Paymaster of the Forces, 1846–7). He sponsored and carried the Copyright Bill of 1842 (which remained in force until 1911), and still found time for writing poetry such as *Lays of Ancient Rome* (1842).

In 1839 Macaulay turned to the writing of the *History*, embodying in it his vast administrative experience as well as his political prejudices. The hero of the book is William III, and its aim the justification of the 'Glorious Revolution' which, by the mid-nineteenth century had, in Macaulay's opinion, produced 'the most enlightened generation of the most enlightened people that ever existed'. The continuation of the *History*, which breaks off in 1702, by Macaulay's nephew, George Macaulay Trevelyan (1876–1962), is free of the errors and bias of Macaulay's book, which cannot now safely be used without the *Commentary* by Sir Charles Firth (1938).

329

A LANDMARK IN TEXTUAL CRITICISM

KARL LACHMANN (1793–1851). In T. Lucretii Cari De Rerum Natura Libros Commentarius. *Berlin: Georg Reimer, 1850*

Lucretius has been fortunate in his editors. In the sixteenth century, Denys Lambin devoted years of patient and sympathetic work to the preparation of his *editio major* (87), one of the greatest achievements of Renaissance humanist scholarship. Lachmann's edition occupies the same position in nineteenth-century scholarship; it is the masterpiece of the great German school of philology which owed its inception to Wolf (248) and it was Lachmann's final, and perhaps finest, work.

Karl Lachmann was born at Brunswick. He was a student at the universities of Leipzig and Göttingen, and in 1816 he obtained a post in the University of Königsberg, becoming professor of classical philology in 1818. Here the foundation of his strict critical methods, and of his reputation, were laid. New members of the university staff were expected to produce some published work to inaugurate their tenure; Lachmann produced two, an edition of Propertius and a thesis on the original text of the *Nibelungennot*, which indicated the path he was to follow. Here, in periodical articles, and most of all in his 'Selection from the High German Poets of the Thirteenth Century' (1820), he established the rules of textual criticism and the metrical and phonetic principles of Middle High German in a scientific manner which was far in advance of his contemporaries.

In 1825 Lachmann moved to Berlin, becoming a regular professor in 1827. Here he continued his work on German texts with editions of Walther von der Vogelweide and Wolfram von Eschenbach; nor did he neglect the classics, publishing editions of Catullus and other Latin poets, of the 'Institutes' of Gaius, and of the Agrimensores. He also applied the critical experience gained from his knowledge of the medieval German poets to the *Iliad*, which he considered to have been once sixteen separate lays, conflated and interpolated at a later date. This view, although no longer accepted, has had considerable influence on Homeric criticism. Between 1831 and 1842 he brought to fruition a work of biblical criticism first projected by Bentley (see 178): a text of the New Testament based on the most ancient Eastern manuscripts, using the consensus of the oldest Western texts where the oriental authorities differ. This valuable work finally superseded the *textus receptus* sponsored by Erasmus (46). Lachmann's edition of Lessing (213), published 1838–40, is the first example of the works of a modern author treated with the philological apparatus hitherto reserved for classical and medieval writers.

But his lasting reputation rests on the edition of Lucretius which occupied the last six years of his life. His brilliant assessment of the relative values of the surviving manuscripts set a new standard in the analysis of corrupt and 'difficult' texts, by concentrating conjecture on the actual readings. Lachmann was no mechanical editor, content to record and select according to a preconceived formula. He had as deep an understanding of his author as Lambin, four centuries before, and it is this combination which made his edition famous. It was indeed, as Munro, who produced the next major edition, pointed out, 'a work which will be a landmark for scholars as long as the Latin language continues to be studied'.

BIBLIOGRAPHY: Cosmo Gordon, *A Bibliography of Lucretius* (London, 1961).

330

THE EARTH'S ROTATION DEMONSTRATED

JEAN BERNARD LÉON FOUCAULT (1819–68). Sur Divers Signes Sensibles du Mouvement Diurne de la Terre. *In:* Comptes rendus des Séances de l'Académie des Sciences. *Paris, 1851*

Although the rotation of the earth had been accepted since Copernicus (70), it was Foucault who first demonstrated it by experiment.

His early experiments were private, but Louis Napoleon (later Napoleon III) became so interested that he arranged for them to be repeated publicly. This was a splendid affair which took place in the Pantheon in 1851 before a fashionable audience. A heavy metal ball was suspended from the dome on a wire 220 feet long; beneath the ball was a table 12 feet in diameter covered with sand on which the ball could leave a mark. This is known as 'Foucault's pendulum'. It soon became apparent that the plane in which the pendulum was swinging moved in a clockwise direction and in about thirty-two hours the plane of vibration had completed a full circuit. Mathematical calculations made it possible to apply the results of this experiment to the rotation of the earth. The audience in the Pantheon was greatly impressed; some ladies fainted with excitement, while other spectators maintained that they could feel the earth move beneath them.

In his optical studies Foucault provided, in collaboration with Hippolyte Louis Fizeau, a convincing proof for the wave theory of light, which by the mid-nineteenth century had become widely accepted. By using rotating mirrors he proved that light travelled more rapidly through air than through water. This demolished the opposite view put forward by Descartes (129) in support of the corpuscular theory. Foucault is also remembered for his method of giving the reflectors of optical instruments a spheroid or parabolic form, and his name is attached to several electrical devices. He invented the gyroscope, which has been used in modern navigation as a stabilizer, and has led to the possibility of the automatic pilot in aviation.

331

THE FIRST INTERNATIONAL EXHIBITION

GREAT EXHIBITION OF THE WORKS OF INDUSTRY OF ALL NATIONS OF 1851. Report by the Juries. *London: Printed for the Royal Commission by William Clowes & Sons, 1852*

On 30 June 1849 Prince Albert addressed to the Society of Arts, as its President, a proposal that a committee of investigation be appointed to examine the possibility of organizing an international exhibition of industry in

FIG. 5

FIG 1

FIG 2.

FIG 3

FIG 4

DAY & SON, LITHRS TO THE QUEEN

NO. 331, GREAT EXHIBITION

London. The notion was opposed from many influential quarters at almost every stage, but the single-minded and unwearying purpose of the Prince Consort was at last brought to fruition in 1851.

Not the least interesting feature of the Exhibition was the design of the building itself and the techniques of prefabrication employed in it. Joseph Paxton, the Duke of Devonshire's gardener, based his design on that of a massive glasshouse he had constructed at Chatsworth with the express purpose of growing and inducing to flower a tropical water-lily. His design, roughly sketched on a sheet of blotting-paper, was accepted after more than two hundred others had been rejected.

Despite pessimism on every feature of the enterprise, from the insecurity of the huge glass structure to the certainty of financial disaster, the success of the exhibition was unprecedented. Exhibitors numbered seventeen thousand, of whom six thousand five hundred were foreign and over five hundred colonials. The attendance topped six million, the takings were £423,792 and the surplus was about £170,000.

The total effect of 'The Great Exhibition' was considerable, if incalculable. It is well summed up by R. H. Mottram in *Early Victorian England*: 'It symbolized the solid gains of early Victorian enterprise, cheap production, and easy communication, and a visitor looking back over the alarms of 1848, the misery of the early forties, the sack of Bristol in 1831, the fearful disasters of 1825, might well see in it also the realization of hopes which a few years before would have seemed too visionary for men to contemplate. It was the first International Exhibition and has had many successors in all parts of the world.'

Paxton's great structure was successfully dismantled and re-erected at Sydenham as 'The Crystal Palace'. It was destroyed by fire in 1936.

332

THE NOVEL AS PROPAGANDA

HARRIET BEECHER STOWE (1811–96). Uncle Tom's Cabin. 2 vols. *Boston: John P. Jewett; Cleveland: Jewett, Proctor & Worthington, 1852*

For Harriet Beecher Stowe, as for many others attached to the abolitionist cause, the battle against slavery was a God-ordained crusade to cleanse the United States of an evil offensive to humanity and to the Christian religion. The daughter, sister, wife and mother of New England clergymen (her brother, Henry Ward Beecher, was a prominent moral crusader), her life was spent in an atmosphere of Calvinist righteousness which, in mid-nineteenth-century America, was thoroughly imbued with abolitionist sentiment.

As a young woman of twenty-one, Harriet Beecher moved with her father's family to Cincinnati where, for the next eighteen years, she lived across the Ohio River from the slave state of Kentucky. It was here that her personal impressions of slavery were formed and by the time she returned to her native New England with her husband, Calvin Stowe, her sympathies were firmly attached to the anti-slavery cause.

Shortly after the Stowes had established their new household in Brunswick, Maine, the United States Congress passed the Fugitive Slave Act (1850), placing in the hands of the Federal authorities the power of apprehending escaped slaves and imposing heavy penalties on any official found derelict in this duty. A wave of anger and indignation swept New England. Harriet's brother, Edward, preached against the new law from his pulpit and, while she was on a visit to him in New York, urged her to use her pen in the abolitionist cause. By this time she had already had some small success as an author of pieces for magazines and annuals, some of which had been collected in a small volume entitled *The Mayflower*, 1843.

On 9 March 1851 she wrote to Gamaliel Bailey, editor of the abolitionist newspaper *The National Era*, proposing a serialized story embodying a series of sketches showing the evils of life under slavery. Bailey accepted and in April Harriet sent him the first instalment of *Uncle Tom's Cabin; or, Life Among the Lowly*. The serial, which began in the 5 June issue of the paper, was originally intended to run only three months, but it soon became apparent that it was assuming much broader dimensions. Inspired by religious zeal, its author wrote with great speed, producing instalment after weekly instalment, and finally bringing the story to a close in the issue of 1 April 1852. For the entire series Bailey paid her three hundred dollars.

Even before the conclusion of the serial the Boston publisher John P. Jewett had expressed an interest in publishing *Uncle Tom's Cabin* in book form. The two volumes, issued both in brown cloth and paper wrappers, appeared on 20 March 1852, two instalments before the conclusion of the serial in *The National Era*. The first printing of five thousand copies was exhausted in a few days and a second printing of the same size, indicated by 'tenth thousand' on the title-page, was completely disposed of before the end of March. The sale of the book was indeed phenomenal. By August Harriet had received $10,000 in royalties. Printing after printing was called for as the publishers tried to keep pace with the public demand. Before the summer was out sales had topped the hundred thousand mark, and within a year, the three hundred thousand mark—and that only the American sale. In England the book was hardly less successful than in America. Beside the authorized edition published by Thomas Bosworth more than twenty pirated London editions appeared in 1852, one of them, issued in thirteen weekly parts, with illustrations by George Cruikshank. It was translated into twenty-five languages, ranging from Armenian and Bengali at one end of the alphabet to Wallachian and Welsh at the other.

In the emotion-charged atmosphere of mid-nineteenth-century America *Uncle Tom's Cabin* exploded like a bombshell. To those engaged in fighting slavery it appeared as an indictment of all the evils inherent in the system they opposed; to the pro-slavery forces it was a slanderous attack on 'the Southern way of life'. Dramatized versions, exaggerating the cruelties depicted in the novel, appeared almost immediately on the stage adding to the righteous indignation, whether aimed at slavery or at the book's author, which swept the country. Whatever its weaknesses as a literary work—structural looseness and excess of sentiment among them—the social impact of *Uncle Tom's Cabin* on the United States was greater than that of any book before or since.

333

MUSIC DRAMA

RICHARD WAGNER (1813–83). (*a*) Oper und Drama. 3 vols. *Leipzig: J. J. Weber, 1852*; (*b*) Drei Operndichtungen [Der Fliegende Holländer, Tannhäuser, Lohengrin], nebst einer Mittheilung an seine Freunde als Vorwort. *Leipzig: Breitkopf & Härtel, 1852*

Wagner's philosophy is fustian, his literary style is appalling, and his 'poetry' is often preposterous. His adoption as a kind of posthumous member of the Nazi party is sufficient condemnation of his politics. As a musician, however, he was among the masters. A vast knowledge of the subject formed the basis for a revolutionary technique of opera which welded music and words into a synthesis never before attempted.

The two works above listed are complementary. The first of them—'Opera and Drama'—is the more important and lengthy of the two. In it Wagner is concerned with the past history of opera and its relation to the music of the future. It is divided into three parts, the first an historical survey of music in relation to drama with notable references to the supremacy of Mozart. There follows a disquisition on the nature of dramatic art and of theatrical presentation. The third part deals with 'Poetry and Music in the Drama of the Future'. In it he treats with great learning and knowledge of the necessity for an organic relation between drama and music. The controlling factor must be the drama itself; all else, words, gesture, costumes, scenery and music itself are its subordinate, component parts.

In the second work—'Three Opera Poems, with a Communication to his Friends as a Foreword'—he relates the theories expressed in 'Opera and Drama' to his own work. It is curious that he should have chosen to attach this foreword to the libretti of three operas none of which clearly exemplifies theories first embodied in the *Ring* cycle, begun in 1853 and completed in 1874.

334

QUATERNIONS

SIR WILLIAM ROWAN HAMILTON (1805–65). Lectures on Quaternions. *Dublin: Hodges and Smith; London: Whittaker; Cambridge: Macmillan, 1853*

Sir William Rowan Hamilton, the Irish mathematician, was a child prodigy whose youthful promise was fulfilled by his scientific achievements in later life. At the age of thirteen he knew as many languages, including Sanskrit and Syriac, and the study of Newton's *Arithmetica Universalis* inspired him with an early interest in mathematics. While still an undergraduate, Hamilton was made professor of astronomy in Dublin and later became Astronomer Royal for Ireland and President of the Royal Irish Academy.

The achievement in pure mathematics for which he is now best remembered is the invention of quaternions, a linear algebra of rotations in space of three dimensions. Quaternions were the first non-commutative number system to be investigated in detail, and Hamilton's discovery that a consistent and useful system of algebra could be constructed without obeisance to the commutative law of multiplication was comparable in importance to the invention of non-Euclidean geometry (see 293). Quaternions led to vector analysis, and were eventually superseded by the latter, which has become of the greatest importance in mathematical physics and was developed by G. F. B. Riemann and E. B. Christoffel into tensor analysis. This made possible the creation of the general theory of relativity (see 408).

Hamilton did important work on optics—he predicted conical refraction of light, afterwards verified experimentally—and above all in dynamics. In the latter field his discoveries were at first disregarded, but they have since been recognized as highly important for the theory of wave mechanics and particles. He left an enormous collection of manuscripts, now in Trinity College, Dublin, full of original mathematical discoveries.

335

HITLER'S FRENCH MENTOR

JOSEPH-ARTHUR COMTE DE GOBINEAU (1816–82). Essai sur l'Inégalité des Races Humaines. 4 vols. *Paris: Firmin Didot; Hanover: Rumpler, 1853–5*

The French diplomatist and man of letters, Gobineau, has, through the 'Essay on the Inequality of the Human Races'—his one excursion into the realms of anthropology and sociology—exerted an influence upon European thought and action which is quite disproportionate to its scholarly insignificance and inconsequential argumentation.

The men of the Action Française, Lenin (392), Mussolini, and Hitler (415) were, at one remove, the disciples and propagandists of Gobineau's most outrageous ideas. Gobineau's racial theories were based on a complete misunderstanding of the positivism of Comte (295) and the researches of Prichard (303) into the physiological differences of the various human races. Fortified by the innate arrogance of a scion of an *ancien régime* family and by his observations as an envoy in the Near and Middle East, he championed the theory, since entirely disproved, that 'race' is a permanent and immutable phenomenon, and he proclaimed the unchallengeable superiority of the white race over all others. Within the white race, Gobineau assigned the supreme position to the 'nordic'—or as he fatuously called them 'aryan'—

peoples who, thanks to their praiseworthy qualities of hardiness and lust for power, are predestined to rule the rest of mankind.

This farrago of biological nonsense, wishful romanticism and imperialistic dreams was lapped up eagerly by French and German intellectuals. The German enthusiasm for Gobineau—the German translation of the *Essai*

ESSAI
SUR L'INÉGALITÉ
DES
RACES HUMAINES,

PAR

M. A. DE GOBINEAU,

PREMIER SECRÉTAIRE DE LA LÉGATION DE FRANCE EN SUISSE,
MEMBRE DE LA SOCIÉTÉ ASIATIQUE DE PARIS.

TOME PREMIER.

PARIS,
LIBRAIRIE DE FIRMIN DIDOT FRÈRES,
RUE JACOB, 56.
HANOVRE.—RUMPLER, LIBRAIRE-ÉDITEUR.

1853.

went through several editions—is the less comprehensible in that Gobineau thought very poorly of the 'German race', which he considered a mixture of Celts and Slavs with hardly any pure 'nordic' blood. But there was enough substance in Gobineau's book to provide nourishment for the growth of pan-germanism and national self-adulation, and seemingly to justify anti-semitic and anti-slav excesses. Hence derived the 'superman' and the glorious 'blond beast' of Nietzsche (370) and the germanomania and anti-semitism of Wagner (333), which reached their nadir in *Die Grundlagen des 19. Jahrhunderts* (1899) by Wagner's English-born son-in-law, Houston Stewart Chamberlain. He in turn inspired Alfred Rosenberg's *Mythos des 20. Jahrhunderts* (1930) from which Hitler and his henchmen imbibed the 'scientific' arguments of their racialist programme.

In France, the sociologist Georges Sorel and the publicist Maurice Barrès became the apostles of Gobineau. Sorel's *Réflexions sur la Violence* (1908) indicates by its very title the aspect of Gobineau's work that appealed most to a section of his compatriots. The chauvinism, anti-semitism and fascism of the Action Française were largely due to the application of Gobineau's ideas to French conditions, while Sorel was the most influential single theoretical teacher of both Mussolini and Lenin.

336
BACTERIOLOGY

LOUIS PASTEUR (1822–95). (*a*) Recherches sur la Dissymétrie Moléculaire des Produits Organiques Naturels. *In:* Comptes rendus de l'Académie des Sciences. *Paris, 1853; (b)* Expériences relatives aux Générations dites Spontanées. *Ibidem, Paris, 1860* (four papers); (*c*) Mémoire sur les Corpuscules Organisés qui existent dans l'Atmosphère. *In:* Annales des Sciences Naturelles (Partie Zoologique). *Paris, 1861; (d)* Recherches sur la Putrefaction. *In:* Comptes rendus de l'Académie des Sciences. *Paris, 1863; (e)* Sur les Maladies Virulentes, et en particulier sur la Maladie appelée vulgairement Choléra des Poules. *Ibidem, Paris, 1880* (two papers)

It is impossible to select a single scientific paper or book to represent adequately the work of Pasteur. This is due less to the recondite nature of his discoveries than to their variety and ramification. Yet all of them are interconnected.

His earliest paper gave the first scientific explanation of isomerism, a term coined by Berzelius to describe his discovery that two or more compounds of identical composition may display totally different properties. The effects of Pasteur's discoveries in this connexion have been far-reaching in chemistry both theoretically and practically, notably in the work of van't Hoff and Lebel on chemistry in space. They are detailed in (*a*) 'Researches on Molecular Asymmetry in Natural Organic Substances'. Indeed it was the existence of asymmetric molecules that he discovered.

While engaged in these experiments Pasteur found that when molecules were brought into contact with a certain mould only the right-handed molecules were destroyed. This led him to the investigation of fermentation. In 1860 he had completed a series of careful but simple 'Experiments relative to so-called Spontaneous Generation', which he proved to be a myth: (*b*) above.

When his conclusions were called in question by Pouchet, who claimed to have repeated his experiments with totally dissimilar results, Pasteur reported in 1861, in (*c*) 'Notes on the Organized Corpuscles existing in the Atmosphere', further experiments which demonstrated beyond dispute that fermentation is caused by the action of minute living organisms and that if these are excluded or killed fermentation does not occur. This enabled him to explain to brewers and vintners the cause and prevention of sourness in their products. The heating process that he recommended was the earliest form of 'pasteurization'. He went further and concluded (*d*) that putrefaction was also caused by living organisms: an observation that prompted the experiments of Lister and led to modern asepsis (see 316).

In 1865 Davaine was the first to associate a disease,

anthrax, with a specific germ, and in 1876 Koch (366) obtained pure cultures of the anthrax bacillus, explained its life-history and laid down the principles upon which modern bacteriology is based.

In 1880 Pasteur ((e) above—'On Virulent Diseases and in particular on the Disease popularly called Chicken-cholera') prepared a culture of bacteria from the head of a cock that had died from this disease. He discovered that an inoculation of attenuated virus afforded protection against the disease, and later in the same year, with two colleagues, he performed a similarly successful experiment with anthrax. Possibly best known of all is his application of this principle to the cure of hydrophobia in 1885.

Pasteur was the recipient of innumerable honours. His greatest memorial is the Pasteur Institute in Paris.

337*

HISTORY DEMYTHOLOGIZED

THEODOR MOMMSEN (1817–1903). Römische Geschichte. 3 vols., 1854–6; final edition, 1856–7; vol. 5, 1885. *Berlin: Weidmann*

Mommsen and Grote (321) largely determined the concept of ancient history during the second half of the nineteenth century; but whereas Grote's book is now completely superseded, Mommsen's 'Roman History' is still not only the most brilliant production of German historiography but in many respects unsurpassed as a work of scholarship. The whole of Roman studies after the death of Niebuhr (267) is essentially connected with his name, and together with Ranke (286) Mommsen marks the high tide of German influence upon international historical scholarship.

With his 'Roman History' Mommsen 'wanted to bring down the ancients from their fantastic pedestal into the real world'. In this ambition he succeeded, to the delight of a wide international public, who could soon read the book in translation in every standard language, and to the consternation of his German colleagues who abused him as a journalistic hack. The 'Roman History' grew out of the suggestion of a publisher who was fascinated by a popular lecture given by Mommsen at Leipzig. As a lifelong Radical, Mommsen was a fervent advocate of a strong and centralized government that would champion the peasants and workmen, such as he believed at the time to find in the Second Empire of Napoleon III: hence his admiration for Caesar and his denigration of the 'Corporal' Pompey and the 'pettifogger' Cicero. Caustic comments and asides such as these, of course, enhanced the appeal of the book; but its lasting value is based on Mommsen's incomparable mastery of every aspect of ancient civilization.

Mommsen was the founder of the scientific study of Roman epigraphy (*Corpus Inscriptionum Latinarum*, 1863 ff.) and numismatics, and one of the first to recognize the importance of the new-found papyri. He originated the *Thesaurus Linguae Latinae*, 1894 ff., designed to supersede that of Robert Estienne (62). His editorship of the

Auctores Antiquissimi, 1882–98, in the *Monumenta Germaniae Historica* (287) showed him as an outstanding textual critic. And his *Römisches Staatsrecht* (3 vols., 1871–5, 1888) and *Römisches Strafrecht* (1899) proved that the political historian was equally at home in constitutional and criminal law—the 'Constitutional Law' perhaps being Mommsen's greatest work. In 1902 he was awarded the Nobel prize for literature.

Besides his prodigious literary output and his duties as professor successively in Leipzig (1848), Zürich (1852), Breslau (1854) and Berlin (1858), Mommsen took an active part in the political life of Germany: as a revolutionary in 1848, as a Radical deputy of the Prussian Diet (1863–6, 1873–9) and the German Reichstag (1881–4), and as a pungent contributor to left-wing journals. He was an opponent of Bismarck and unremittingly fought anti-semitism, colonialism and protectionism, often reinforcing his arguments with pertinent examples drawn from his unrivalled knowledge of Roman history.

338

THE GOSPEL OF MATERIALISM

FRIEDRICH KARL CHRISTIAN LUDWIG BÜCHNER (1824–99). Kraft und Stoff. *Frankfurt am Main: Meidinger, 1855*

Berkeley (176) denied the existence of matter. Büchner declared that nothing else existed.

It was not, however, the idealist philosophy of Berkeley that the materialist school was concerned to oppose so much as the application of vitalistic ideas to scientific problems. The vitalistic view of creation, of which Paracelsus (110) and Helmont (135) were notable exponents, is that all substances, whether organic or inorganic, are actuated by a vital spark or force which is the cause of growth and which determines their form. This viewpoint is evident in the monadism of Leibniz (177), and it influenced Schelling, Kant (226) and Goethe (298). The opposite view, that all natural phenomena are explicable by the action of purely mechanical forces, was accepted by Newton (161) and Descartes (129). Helmholtz in one of his essays explains that 'For the vitalist physician the essential part of the vital processes did not depend on natural forces which act according to fixed laws...He thought to be face to face with something soul-like which had to be met by a thinker, a philosopher, a man of spirit...'

It will be seen that this leads directly to the creation of a gap between the organic and the inorganic worlds, with man as an exceptional being with a mind and a soul the existence of which are inexplicable on a purely materialistic basis of reasoning. Lavoisier (238) made an important assault on what has been called the philosophy of gaps when he explained the processes of respiration, nutrition and the generation of natural heat as part of a combustion process.

Analysis of organic compounds in the human body and their resolution into chemical products, accompanied by the study of metabolism and its accompanying phenomena leading eventually to the artificial synthesis of organic substances in the laboratory—urea in 1828 and hippuric acid in 1842, both by Liebig's (310) colleague Friedrich Wöhler—fostered a school of thought that went to the other extreme. They declared that all the phenomena of the functioning of the human body were explicable on purely materialistic lines and that it was only a question of time before this fact would be experimentally demonstrable.

Büchner was not only one of the earliest, he was also the most uncompromising representative of this school. The thesis pursued in his 'Force and Matter' is that thought is as much an emanation of the brain as bile is an emanation of the liver. The mind and the spirit are products of an animal organism in the same way as motion is a product of a steam-engine.

The outcry provoked by the book compelled Büchner to resign his lectureship at Tübingen. But he had many disciples, Dühring and Haeckel among them, and he still occupies an honoured place in the hierarchy of free thought.

339

THE SUEZ CANAL

FERDINAND MARIE DE LESSEPS (1805–94). Percement de l'Isthme de Suez. *Paris: Henri Plon, 1855*

Ferdinand de Lesseps, who came of ancient French stock, was a diplomat by profession. In 1832 his ship was in quarantine while he was on his way to take up the post of vice-consul in Alexandria. To relieve the tedium he was sent several books by the French consul-general, one of which was the report drawn up by J.-B. Lepère for Napoleon on the possibility of re-opening the canal connecting the Mediterranean with the Red Sea by way of the Nile. His father had previously been consul-general, and Mehemet Ali, the Sultan's Viceroy, was greatly beholden to him. In 1849, as French envoy to Rome, Ferdinand was shabbily treated by the new 'revolutionary' government and in consequence resigned from government service. In 1854 he sought and received from Said Pasha, the son and successor of Mehemet Ali, a concession authorizing his scheme for the construction of a canal across the Isthmus of Suez.

De Lesseps was not deterred by either political or practical objections to the project; but capital had to be raised to finance it. In this treatise of nearly three hundred pages, with maps—'The Piercing of the Isthmus of Suez'—he set out the whole case for the canal and his proposed method of building it. He secured the support of Napoleon III and raised a capital of two hundred million francs. Construction was begun in 1859 and completed ten years later. Palmerston had opposed the whole scheme as inimical to British interests, and not a single share was taken up by British investors; but in 1875 Disraeli, in a dazzling secret coup assisted by the Rothschilds, bought for Britain the shares originally subscribed for by the Khedive Ismail.

At the age of seventy-four De Lesseps undertook to construct a canal in Panama, but the magnitude of the

PERCEMENT

DE

L'ISTHME DE SUEZ

EXPOSÉ ET DOCUMENTS OFFICIELS

PAR

M. FERDINAND DE LESSEPS

MINISTRE PLÉNIPOTENTIAIRE.

Aperire terram gentibus.

PARIS

HENRI PLON, ÉDITEUR,

RUE GARANCIÈRE, 8.

1855

task was too great for him. Failure cost him not only his fortune but his great reputation with his countrymen. He died a poor and disappointed man.

340

THE POET OF DEMOCRACY

WALT WHITMAN (1819–92). Leaves of Grass. *Brooklyn, New York: [printed by Rome Brothers], 1855*

It would not have surprised Walt Whitman to find *Leaves of Grass* included in a catalogue of the great printed works of man. Indeed, from its very first publication in 1855 he had complete confidence in the greatness of both the book and its author. This superabundance of ego, which exudes from every page of Whitman's writings, has offended some readers and infuriated a number of critics, but it has also proved a powerful magnet for others who have seen that the poet's song of himself was also of themselves—and of mankind. He writes

It is you talking just as much as myself—I act as the
tongue of you.
It was tied in your mouth—in mine it begins to be
loosened.

Always the champion of the common man, Whitman is both the poet and the prophet of democracy. The whole of *Leaves of Grass* is imbued with the spirit of brother-hood and a pride in the democracy of the young American nation. In a sense, it is America's second Declaration of Independence: that of 1776 was political, this of 1855 intellectual. As the preface to the first edition puts it, the poems are saturated 'with a vehemence of pride and audacity of freedom necessary to loosen the mind of still-to-be-formed America from the folds, the superstitions, and all the long, tenacious, and stifling anti-democratic authorities of Asiatic and European past'. To the young nation, only just becoming aware of an individual liter-ary identity distinct from its European origins, Whit-man's message and his outspoken confidence came at the decisive moment.

Though only one unit in a substantial body of writing, *Leaves of Grass* was Whitman's favourite child. From the time of its original publication, in a slim quarto volume containing twelve poems and a long prose preface, until the year of his death, he continued revising and enlarging it. The second edition, published in Brooklyn in 1856, contains thirty-five poems and is stamped in gilt on the backstrip with a quotation from a letter which Emerson had written to the author, 'I greet you at the beginning of a great career'. The third edition, which bears the imprint, 'Boston, Thayer and Eldridge, Year 85 of the States, 1860–61', includes one hundred and fifty-seven poems of which one hundred and twenty-two are new. By the time of the so-called 'Deathbed Edition' (Phila-delphia, 1891–2), the last to be supervised by Whitman, the total had reached two hundred and ninety-five.

If Whitman's reputation has fluctuated over the years and his position among, if indeed not at the head of, the list of great American poets was not assured until some time after his death, there was never any doubt of the matter in his own mind. 'I know I am deathless', he wrote. 'Whether I come to my own today or in ten thousand or ten million years, I can cheerfully take it now, or with equal cheerfulness I can wait.' Time has vindicated his conviction.

341
CHRISTIANITY AND EXPLORATION IN AFRICA

DAVID LIVINGSTONE (1813–73). Missionary Travels and Researches in South Africa. *London: John Murray, 1857*

David Livingstone, perhaps the greatest of the African explorers, was of Scottish birth and originally graduated in medicine at Glasgow University. He became a mis-sionary and was sent to South Africa by the London Missionary Society in 1840. From then onwards his life was devoted to the exploration of central Africa. Although a missionary—and even in later life after he had severed his connexion with the Missionary Society and acted in the service of the British Government, the idea of a Christian mission was always in his mind—he regarded himself more as a pioneer explorer opening up the country for others.

Livingstone's services to African geography during thirty years are almost unequalled; he covered about a third of the continent from the Cape to the Equator and from the Atlantic to the Indian Ocean. He made three great expeditions; in 1853–6 (described in this book), 1858–64 and 1865–73, of which the first and third are the most important. During these years he explored vast regions of central Africa, many of which had never been seen by white men before.

He first discovered the Zambesi River at Secheke and followed it northwards, eventually reaching the west coast of Africa at Luanda, Angola, and the east coast at Quelimane, Mozambique. In 1855 he discovered the great falls of the Zambesi and named them the Victoria Falls. He explored the Zambesi, Shire and Ruyuma rivers and found the salt lake Chilwa and Lake Nyasa.

Livingstone's last voyage was undertaken to investi-gate the watershed of central Africa and to find the true source of the Nile, which he believed must lie farther south than Baker (357) and Speke had supposed. He explored Lake Tanganyika and proved conclusively that the Rusizi River runs into and not out of it. Livingstone had suffered great hardships on many of his journeys and several times suffered from fevers. He now fell ill again, and died at Ilala on the south shore of Lake Bangweolo.

During his travels Livingstone was appalled at what he saw of the terrible effects of the slave trade (mainly carried on by Arabs) on African life. He followed the principles of Wilberforce (232 b) and became a protago-nist in the fight to abolish slavery. The geographical results of his journeys were of supreme importance, and made it possible to fill in great stretches of the maps of Central Africa which hitherto had been blank.

Livingstone, as one of the great characters of the nine-teenth century, embodying all the virtues of the Victorian age, is often remembered more for his qualities as a man than for his achievements as an explorer. Born with no social advantages, it was his courage and boldness of con-ception, his deep religious feeling and his great powers of endurance that carried him through the trials and hardships of a dedicated life and eventually gained him the honour of burial in Westminster Abbey.

BIBLIOGRAPHY: Margaret Elizabeth Appleyard, *Dr David Livingstone. A Bibliography* (Capetown, 1949).

342
NEANDERTHAL MAN

JOHANN CARL FUHLROTT (1804–77) and H. SCHAAFFHAUSEN. Menschliche Überreste aus einer Felsengrotte des Düsselthals. *In*: Verhandlungen der Naturhistorischer Vereins der Preussische Rheinlande und Westphalens. Two parts. *Bonn, 1857, 1859*

In 1856 quarrymen working in the Neanderthal between Düsseldorf and Elberfeld unearthed a number of bones in a limestone grotto. Part of a skull and some long bones eventually reached Johann Carl Fuhlrott, a schoolmaster at the college in Elberfeld. He immediately recognized the importance of the find, but was not able to save any more bones from what was, in all probability, a whole skeleton. He sent a cast of the cranium to Schaaffhausen at Bonn University, who was at once convinced that they were human, and that the extraordinary skull was not a pathological specimen but had belonged to a normal individual of some ancient race of man which differed considerably from all modern races. This opinion Fuhlrott presented early in 1857 to the Natural History Society in Bonn, and later in the same year he compiled a fuller account of the find prepared in conjunction with Schaaffhausen: 'Human Remains from a Grotto in Düsselthal'.

For a long time the antiquity of the bones was suspect. Virchow (307c) and others were convinced that the strange skull was that of an idiot, but some, especially in England, gladly accepted the find as practical evidence of human evolution. Busk translated a paper by Schaaffhausen on the subject from Müller's *Archiv*, 1858, with the title 'On the Crania of the Most Ancient Races of Man' (*Natural History Review*, 1861) of which Huxley made much in *Man's Place in Nature*, 1863. Acceptance however was still slow in many quarters although further finds, in 1864 at Gibraltar and in 1866 at La Naulette, increased the evidence for an extinct beetle-browed race. It was not until 1886 that Neanderthal-type remains were unearthed with a rigorous scientific precision that left no doubt as to the antiquity and normality of 'Neanderthal man'.

343

THE LADY WITH THE LAMP

FLORENCE NIGHTINGALE (1820–1910). Notes on Matters affecting the Health, Efficiency, and Hospital Administration of the British Army. *London: Harrison, 1858*

On 16 November 1856 Lord Panmure, the Secretary for War, called on Miss Nightingale. When he left three hours later she not only had his promise of the appointment of a Royal Commission on the Army, but she had imposed her own Chairman, Sidney Herbert, and her own Secretary, Dr T. Graham Balfour. The Royal Warrant for the Commission, however, was not issued until 5 May 1857.

It had been agreed between Miss Nightingale and Lord Panmure that she was to prepare a report of her own experiences of hospital life. This would be placed at the disposal of the Commission but would not be generally published if army medical and sanitary affairs were properly reformed as a sequel to the inquiry.

It is this remarkable document that is here under consideration. It is a large volume of over eight hundred pages and the whole was compiled and printed within nine months of Florence Nightingale's first meeting with Panmure.

There is not a grievance, nor a defect of the system (or lack of it), nor a remedy that is overlooked. An introduction deals with army health in earlier campaigns. The first six chapters are concerned with the ghastly medical

history of the Crimean War. This is followed by extensive and detailed recommendations on hospital organization. The rest of the book ranges far and wide over matters of army life, from sanitary requirements to the pay of private soldiers.

Because the Royal Commission produced results, this massive report was not generally issued, but circulated

NOTES ON MATTERS

AFFECTING THE

HEALTH, EFFICIENCY, AND HOSPITAL ADMINISTRATION

OF THE

BRITISH ARMY,

FOUNDED CHIEFLY ON THE EXPERIENCE OF THE LATE WAR.

BY

FLORENCE NIGHTINGALE.

Presented by request to the Secretary of State for War.

LONDON:
PRINTED BY HARRISON AND SONS, ST. MARTIN'S LANE, W.C.
1858.

only to a few friends and people of influence. Yet its existence was not only responsible for the setting up of the Royal Commission but also for the nature of most of its recommendations. The reforms thus instituted, moreover, spread far beyond the confines of the British Army and have revolutionized hospital practice throughout the world.

BIBLIOGRAPHY: W. J. Bishop and S. Goldie, *A Bio-bibliography of Florence Nightingale* (1962).

344

THE THEORY OF EVOLUTION

(*a*) CHARLES DARWIN (1809–82) and ALFRED RUSSEL WALLACE (1823–1913). On the Tendency of Species to Form Varieties; and on the Perpetuation of Varieties and Species by Natural Selection. *In:* Journal of the Proceedings of the Linnean Society. *London, 1858*

(b) CHARLES DARWIN. On the Origin of Species by Means of Natural Selection. *London: John Murray, 1859*

To the third edition of *The Origin of Species*, 1861, Darwin added a short history of the theory. He begins with Lamarck, 1809 (262) and mentions St Hilaire, Dean Herbert, Patrick Matthew, Herbert Spencer and Huxley as among those who had suspected or speculated on an evolutionary theory of creation. To these might be added Hutton (247), Erasmus Darwin—Charles's grandfather—Playfair, and Lyell among many more. Lyell is a very special case, for although he was extremely sceptical about the mutability of species and was known for his strong opposition to the theories of Lamarck, and although he was still suspicious of the evidence for organic progression as late as 1851, his influence on Darwin was incalculable.

When the *Beagle* expedition sailed in 1831 Henslow presented Darwin with the first volume of Lyell's *Principles of Geology*, which had been published in 1830, with the strong injunction that he should 'on no account accept the views therein advocated'. Lyell had established once and for all the uniformitarian theory of geology, which dispensed with the notion of supernatural intervention. The second volume of Lyell's book reached Darwin in Montevideo and his constant references to the enormous influence on his thinking of this great work are typified by a letter from him to Leonard Horner saying 'I always feel as if my books came half out of Lyell's brain'. Both Haeckel and Huxley regarded the *Origin* as a necessary corollary to Lyell's *Principles*.

Darwin, indeed, was intent upon carrying Lyell's demonstration of the uniformity of natural causes over into the organic world. The outstanding difficulty was to discover the means by which the infinite variety of living organisms could have been produced within the limits of geological time. In accomplishing this Darwin not only drew an entirely new picture of the workings of organic nature; he revolutionized our methods of thinking and our outlook on the natural order of things. The recognition that constant change is the order of the universe had been finally established and a vast step forward in the uniformity of nature had been taken.

The scientific-cum-theological dogma of the immutability of species had been proof against sceptics, from Lucretius to Lamarck, who guessed at what Darwin was the first to prove. From being an *a priori* anticipation the theory of evolution became with Darwin an interpretation of nature and eventually a causal theory affecting every department of scientific research. This is what is essential in Darwin's contribution. The modifications due to the rediscovery of Mendel's investigations by Bateson (356), Weissman's germ-plasm hypothesis, and the changed interpretation of 'natural selection' as the basic cause of evolutionary change do not diminish Darwin's eminence as a pioneer.

In June 1858 Darwin received a letter from Wallace, then in the Malay Archipelago, which, in Darwin's own words, 'contained exactly the same theories as mine...If Wallace had my manuscript sketch written in 1842, he could not have made a better abstract...Even his terms stand as heads of my chapters.' It was clear that Wallace had been thinking along the same lines as Darwin, though without his wealth of observed evidence.

Lyell and Hooker suggested simultaneous publication of Wallace's paper and passages from Darwin's unpublished monograph, together with an extract from his letter to Asa Gray, written in 1857, in which he outlined the theory. This constituted the joint paper presented before the Linnean Society.

345

LIBERTY AND THE INDIVIDUAL

JOHN STUART MILL (1806–73). On Liberty. *London: John W. Parker, 1859*

One of the notable features of the last years of the East India Company was that it should, for forty years, have enjoyed the devoted service and loyalty of James Mill (1773–1836), historian and political philosopher, and of his still more famous son, John Stuart Mill.

James had already achieved a considerable reputation as a writer before he entered the Company's service in 1819; during this time, he had become the devoted friend and ally of Bentham (237) and also of Ricardo (277). He was one of the advocates of utilitarianism, notably in his articles for the fifth edition of the *Encyclopaedia Britannica* (218) and his major philosophical work, *Elements of Political Economy*, followed up Ricardo's views and laid the foundations of the 'philosophic radicalism' which became the gospel of liberal politicians in the midnineteenth century. He educated his son himself, and his régime, as recorded by John Stuart Mill in his *Autobiography*, has excited universal astonishment. At the age of three the boy could read Greek; by the time he was eight he was reading Plato and Herodotus and an incredible quantity of historical writing; at twelve he had embarked on Aristotle's works on logic, Adam Smith and Ricardo. It says worlds for his intellectual strength that he survived this intimidating course, and that when in 1822 he followed his father to the India Office, he was not overshadowed by him.

Not surprisingly, in 1826 he underwent a mental crisis, an inevitable reaction against his father's unemotional and remote idealism, his almost inhuman philanthropy. He saw himself becoming an 'intellectual machine', and he came to realize that to pursue the public good without considering the individual, to work for rather than with men, was to neglect a large part of human activity. The French Revolution of 1830 and the passing of the Reform Bill (see 296) filled him with enthusiasm: his crisis was over, and he resumed his earlier activities with renewed energy. His writings in the next fifteen years reflect his new convictions, which underlie perhaps his best-known work, the *Principles of Political Economy*, 1848. In 1851 he married, and his wife, a most exceptional woman, provided the stimulus which led him to his great essay *On Liberty*.

Before it was published, Mill had to pass through another crisis. In 1857 it fell to him to prepare the defence of the East India Company's conduct of the government of India when the transfer of its powers was proposed; and when, despite his eloquent presentation of the facts—and his own convictions—this was carried, he retired from the Company's service. Almost immediately afterwards his wife died, and when *On Liberty* appeared Mill could only dedicate it to her in the most touching language. He found some respite from his grief in active political work. He published a book on parliamentary reform and energetically supported the cause of the North in the American Civil War, believing and helping to make others realize that the abolition of slavery was the issue at stake. In 1865 he became Member of Parliament for Westminster, and, being no mere party politician, his speeches were heard with a new respect in the House. In 1868 he retired, with some relief, and spent his last years in the cottage at Avignon which his wife and he had bought.

'Mill on Liberty' remains his most widely read book. It represents the final stage in the growth of Utilitarian doctrine, and its central point is one which had escaped both Mill's father and Bentham. Mill realized that the 'greatest good' of the community is inseparable from the liberty of the individual. Hitherto, liberty had always been considered relative, in relation to tyranny or oppression: Mill extended tyranny to include a custom-ridden majority, and declared that 'the sole end for which mankind is justified in interfering with liberty of action is self-protection'. Characteristically, he put this into practice: his electoral defeat in 1868 was largely due to his support of Bradlaugh. Many of Mill's ideas are now the commonplaces of democracy. His arguments for freedom of every kind of thought or speech have never been improved on. He was the first to recognize the tendency of a democratically elected majority to tyrannize over a minority, and his warning against it has a contemporary ring: 'We can never be sure that the opinion we are endeavouring to stifle is a false opinion; and, if we were sure, stifling it would be an evil still'.

346

SELF-HELP

SAMUEL SMILES (1812–1904). Self-Help, with Illustrations of Character and Conduct. *London: John Murray, 1859*

Samuel Smiles, author, businessman, journalist and social reformer, is the epitome of that energetic probity which characterizes the best side of Victorian society. He was the eldest of eleven children and his mother's courage and resource in supporting her family after the death of her husband in 1832 are exemplary of those characteristics later to be belauded by her eldest child in his voluminous writings.

Smiles graduated in medicine from Edinburgh University in 1832, and set up practice in his native Haddington but, dissatisfied with his limited success as a doctor, he sold up and after a brief tour abroad answered an advertisement for a post on the *Leeds Times*. He became

Editor in 1838 and had a share in the radical politics of the forties. He also became interested in railways and it was at the opening of the North Midland line in 1840 that he met George Stephenson. The eventual sequel to this meeting was twofold. After a short period as a freelance writer, having resigned his editorship in 1842, he took up secretarial work to two railway companies and in 1857 he produced a prodigiously successful biography of George Stephenson. This was the precursor of a whole series of biographies, mostly of inventors and technocrats, of which the virtues of industry and manly rectitude were the *leitmotivs*.

He now became a frequent lecturer on similar themes at mechanics' institutes and before mutual improvement societies and in 1859 his publisher, John Murray, issued the first of the innumerable editions of *Self-Help*. Its success was immediate and then unequalled: twenty thousand copies were sold in the first year, fifty-five thousand by 1864 and two hundred and seventy thousand by the end of the century. It was translated into almost every foreign language, but the proof of its success which most delighted Smiles was the number of letters attesting its usefulness which he received from artisans—the class to whom it was directed—all over the world. In 1871 Smiles retired, to give himself up to writing and travel. He published a series of studies on the Huguenots and more biographies of self-taught and successful men; his last was a biography of Josiah Wedgwood. His autobiography was published after his death at the age of ninety-two; but his own life was perhaps the best testimony to the efficacy of the principles he had taught for so long.

347

RENAISSANCE CIVILIZATION

JAKOB BURCKHARDT (1818–97). Die Cultur der Renaissance in Italien. *Basle: Schweighauser, 1860*

'The most penetrating and subtle treatise on the history of civilization', in Lord Acton's words, 'a mere essay', as Burckhardt himself called it, 'The Civilization of the Renaissance in Italy' has, for more than a century, determined the general conception of thirteenth- to fifteenth-century Italy.

Burckhardt, a native of Basle where he spent nearly all his life, received his scholarly training in Ranke's (286) seminar at Berlin, where a casual aside of the master's impressed him deeply: 'Develop the sense of the interesting in history'. Having obtained the modest competency of the chair of history at Zurich (1855) and Basle universities (1858–93), he declined the call to become Ranke's successor in Berlin (1871). Outstanding among his writings are, besides the books on Italian art and civilization, 'The Age of Constantine the Great', 1853, in which he reinterpreted Gibbon (see 222), and the two posthumously published books, 'Greek Cultural History', 1892–1902, which destroyed the idealized picture presented by Grote (see 321), and 'Reflections on History', 1905, which ranks among the most penetrating, and deeply pessimistic, observations of the principles underlying human behaviour.

The terms 'restauratio' or 'restitutio' had been applied by fourteenth-century Italian humanists to the revival of ancient languages and literatures, that of 'rinascita' by Ghiberti and Vasari (88) to the new blossoming of art and architecture. In the eighteenth century Voltaire (202) and Gibbon first saw the Italian civilization of the fourteenth to sixteenth centuries as an entity and as a determining factor in the whole course of European history. Michelet (324) in 1855 first used the term 'renaissance' for this period as an historical epoch in its own right. Burckhardt, an admirer of both Voltaire and Gibbon, supplied the final synthesis.

The chapter headings show the main trend of Burckhardt's argument as well as the scope of his subject-matter. 'The state as a work of art' contrasts the monarchies of the tyrants and dynasts with the republics of Venice and Florence, 'The development of the individual'

der Renaissance, 1868, a curiously misnamed history of renaissance architecture.

Modern historical research has revealed the weaknesses of Burckhardt's picture: his obliteration of the medieval roots of the Renaissance, especially of the Carolingian and Anglo-French 'renaissances' of the ninth and twelfth centuries respectively; his identification of the Renaissance with the 'modern world'; his over-sharp antithesis of despotic and popular forms of government; and, of course, his dependence on the contemporary state of historical knowledge. In fact, the whole concept of the Renaissance as Burckhardt saw it has been called in doubt—although at least the Italians are unlikely ever to abandon it. However, as in the case of other great historians, such as Gibbon, Ranke (286), Macaulay (328), no criticism of details can detract from the powerful spell which Burckhardt's book has exercised upon such widely different writers as Ruskin (315), Nietzsche (370) and Gobineau (335), as well as upon innumerable lovers of the most magnificent period of European history.

Die Cultur der Renaissance

in Italien.

Ein Versuch

von

Jacob Burckhardt.

Basel,

Druck und Verlag der Schweighauser'schen Verlagsbuchhandlung.

1860.

and 'The discovery of the world and Man', emphasize the optimism and amorality of the age, 'The revival of classical antiquity' sketches the importance of the humanists in the fields of education and culture, 'Society and festivities' and 'Morals and religion' deal with the outward and spiritual manifestations of public and private life as, for instance, embodied in Castiglione's 'The Courtier' (59). Burckhardt deliberately omitted architecture and the arts, which he had already dealt with in his Cicerone, 1855, or was later to treat in his Geschichte

348

'SEPTEM CONTRA CHRISTUM'

FREDERICK TEMPLE, ROWLAND WILLIAMS,
BADEN POWELL, HENRY BRISTOW WILSON,
CHARLES WYCLIFFE GOODWIN,
MARK PATTISON and BENJAMIN JOWETT.
Essays and Reviews. London: John W. Parker, 1860

The sources of disquiet about the literal truth of the Bible went far beyond the pages of the book which was the immediate cause of the outburst in 1860. The first of these distant causes was the series of scientific discoveries, beginning with the publication in 1830 of Lyell's Principles of Geology and reaching a climax with The Origin of Species in 1859 (344) which began to shake the general confidence of clergy and laity alike in the literal infallibility of Holy Writ. It was not, indeed, so much the 'new' science itself as the popular ignorance of it which caused so much alarm and misunderstanding. Utilitarianism was an adversary that could be understood: Evolution was not.

The second source was more disturbing. The new critical attitude to the text of the Bible associated with the University of Tübingen and especially with the names of Baur (322) and Strauss (300) seemed like an attack in the rear; not from scientific agnostics but by Protestant Christian theologians. 'I cannot but think', wrote Bishop Blomfield in the aftermath of the Tractarian Movement (see 312), 'that we have more to apprehend from the theology of Germany than from that of Rome.' Again, it was not so much the works of Strauss and Renan (352), which stressed the humanity of Christ and belittled the divine and the miraculous, as the new scientific textual analysis of the authorship of the Pentateuch and the Pauline epistles, that now caused alarm. The average cleric lacked the equipment to deal with such antagonists.

But all these were outside the Church of England, and it was thus with a double force that Essays and Reviews, when it became generally known, struck clergy and laity. Not only did the book subscribe to the modern non-literal concept of the Bible text, but, far worse, the authors were with one exception beneficed clergy, and the majority came from the sanctuary of Oxford. At first, it is true, the book seemed unlikely to achieve notoriety. The authors, although acknowledging a common aim, imprudently failed to read each others' contributions, and so did not realize the damaging effect of the collection as a whole; their own modest ambition was to strike a blow against undue reticence on disputed scriptural topics. Jowett, in particular, writing on interpretation, made their position clear. His thesis was that 'Scripture had one meaning—the meaning which it had to the prophet or evangelist who uttered or wrote it'. His rule 'Interpret the Scripture like any other book' became the war-cry of the attackers.

Essays and Reviews might well have escaped wide public notice, had it not been for an article by Frederic Harrison in the *Westminster Review* welcoming (from a Positivist standpoint) such a 'broadminded' collection. Bishop Wilberforce, who had reviewed *The Origin of Species* the year before, published a rejoinder in the *Quarterly*, but later in the year had the worst of a heated exchange with Huxley at the meeting of the British Association at Oxford. By now the fat was in the fire. In February 1861 the bishops met at Fulham and condemned the book. As a result, prosecutions in the Court of Arches were brought against two of the writers, Williams and Wilson. They were found guilty; but the decision was reversed by the Judicial Committee of the Privy Council under Lord Westbury, who was said to have 'dismissed Hell with costs'. This further embittered Church opposition, and *Essays and Reviews* was finally condemned by Convocation.

The immediate effect was the realization that legal sanctions could not be invoked by the Church of England for theological offences. The long-term effect, however, was the acceptance by the Church of much of what the essayists had advocated.

social control was exercised through men (patriarchy). Herodotus describes such a system among the Lycians, where the mother-wife was the directing element of the household and was joined only from time to time by one or more husbands in more or less inconstant unions. Similar systems were in force later in Sparta, and when Bachofen discovered that they also existed among some primitive races in India, Africa and America in his own time, he concluded that a matriarchal stage preceded the patriarchal one in the social development of all peoples.

From this premise Bachofen developed a whole evolutionary system. He maintained that feminine rule was not the earliest stage of social organization but arose as a reform superseding a still earlier stage of promiscuity (*hetärismus*). He attributed this development to the cult of female deities and to woman's fundamental religiosity, since he believed that in these early periods religious attitudes were largely responsible for the formation of social structures.

This evolutionary sequence—hetaerism, matriarchy, patriarchy—is not now accepted, nor is Bachofen's theory that the acceptance of matrilinear descent implies a matriarchate, i.e. a society controlled by women; and some of his thought has traces of Germanic mysticism. Nevertheless, Bachofen is an important figure in the history of ethnology inasmuch as he was the first to direct attention to matrilinear descent as a problem. Furthermore, by connecting social structure with religious practice and by studying classical culture in its entirety—including its crudities, which classicists of his time preferred to overlook—he developed general principles which have remained valid for investigating early cultures. His observations on woman's social position influenced Marxist doctrine and helped eventually to lead to a complete change of view in sociological study and law.

Bachofen published two other studies, partly bearing on these problems: *Versuch über Gräbersymbolik der Alten*, 1859, and *Antiquarische Briefe vornehmlich zur Kenntniss der älteren Verwandtschaftebegriffe*, 1881–6.

349
MATRIARCHAL SOCIETY

JOHANN JAKOB BACHOFEN (1815–87). Das Mutterrecht. Eine Untersuchung über die Gynaikokratie der alten Welt nach ihrer religiösen und rechtlichen Natur. *Stuttgart: Krais & Hoffmann, 1861*

Boucher de Perthes (325) had opened up new vistas of ethnological research. Bachofen, a Swiss professor of Roman law and later a judge at Basle, set a new trend, which approached the investigation of early man from a sociological and historico-legal standpoint, in his book 'Matriarchal Law, an Investigation of the Gynaecocracy of the Ancient World in its Religious and Legal Significance'. He was a lawyer and a philologist, and also a student of ancient mythology.

He traced descent through female lines (matrilineally) in certain groups of men in classical antiquity even where

350
THE RED CROSS

JEAN HENRI DUNANT (1828–1910). Un Souvenir de Solférino. *Ne se vend pas, Genève: Imprimerie Jules-Guillaume Fick, 1862*

Dunant, a Swiss philanthropist, must have been aware of Florence Nightingale's (343) work in the Crimea, for it was what he read of the treatment of the sick and wounded in that war that drove him to the seat of the war in Italy between the French and the Austrians in 1859. He was present at the battle of Solferino, where the casualties were appalling, totalling nearly 40,000 on both sides. The treatment of the wounded was worse than callous: it was virtually non-existent.

Dunant's account of the state of affairs, disarmingly entitled 'A Souvenir of Solferino', produced almost immediate results. An unofficial international conference met in Geneva in October 1863, and in the following year the Swiss Government called an official conference at which the Geneva Convention was drawn up and signed on 22 August 1864.

This provided for the humane treatment of the sick and the wounded, and the proper treatment of prisoners of war and the civilian population. After hesitation on the part of some governments, including the British, and as the result of subsequent conferences, the Convention as it now stands was signed in 1906 by the governments of every civilized country in the world.

Dunant was the first recipient of the Nobel Peace Prize in 1901.

351

THE GETTYSBURG ADDRESS

ABRAHAM LINCOLN (1809–65). *The Gettysburg Solemnities. Dedication of The National Cemetery at Gettysburg, Pennsylvania, November 19, 1863, with the Oration of Hon. Edward Everett, Speech of President Lincoln, &c., &c., &c. Published at the Washington[D.C.] Chronicle Office, 1863*

The *Washington Chronicle* of 18–21 November 1863 reported extensively on this ceremony and included a verbatim text of 'Edward Everett's Great Oration' (Everett, who had been Governor of, and later Senator from, Massachusetts, was the most famous American orator of his time). On the fourth day it noted in passing that the President had also made a speech, but gave no details.

When it came to the separate publication on 22 November, Everett's 'Oration' was reprinted from the standing type, but Lincoln's speech had still to be set up. It was tucked away as a final paragraph on page 16 of the pamphlet. It was similarly treated when the meanly produced leaflet was replaced by a forty-eight-page booklet published by Baker and Goodwin of New York in the same year, considered until recently to be the first printing of the Gettysburg Address.

Everett's speech, every word of which is now forgotten, lasted two hours. Lincoln's address, composed on the train on the way to Gettysburg and written down, according to tradition, on scratch-paper and the backs of envelopes, comprised ten sentences and took only a few minutes to deliver. From the first words—'Four score and seven years ago'—to the last—'that government of the people, by the people, and for the people, shall not perish from the earth'—it is immortal, one of the supreme utterances of the principles of democratic freedom.

352

THE HISTORICAL CHRIST

ERNEST RENAN (1823–92). *La Vie de Jésus. Paris: Michel Lévy, 1863*

Renan's mother wanted him to become a priest and his early studies were directed to this end. Indeed he took the

first steps to the priesthood in 1844, but his studies had already raised grave doubts of the historical truth of the Scriptures and he refused to proceed beyond the acceptance of minor orders.

He studied intensively the languages of the Bible and filled a number of minor academic positions, frequently encountering difficulties because of the heterodoxy and outspokenness of his religious opinions. Memoirs on semitic languages and on the study of Greek in the Middle Ages were crowned by the Académie in 1848 and 1849 but do not seem to have been published. Renan's first book, published in 1852, was, in fact, *Averroes et l'Averroïsme* (see 24) which earned him a doctorate of letters. In 1862 he was appointed to his first important post as professor of Hebrew and Chaldean at the Collège de France. The heterodoxy of his first lecture on 21 February caused his suspension five days later. The chair was abolished in 1864 and Renan was offered 'compensation' as Assistant-Director of the manuscript department of the Bibliothèque Nationale. This post he indignantly refused and henceforth earned his livelihood independently.

Meanwhile he had published his 'Life of Jesus', which had an immediate and resounding success both at home

VIE

DE JÉSUS

PAR

ERNEST RENAN

MEMBRE DE L'INSTITUT

PARIS

MICHEL LÉVY FRÈRES, LIBRAIRES ÉDITEURS

RUE VIVIENNE, 2 BIS, ET BOULEVARD DES ITALIENS, 15

A LA LIBRAIRIE NOUVELLE

1863

Tous droits réservés

and abroad. In six months sixty thousand copies of the French edition had been sold and edition succeeded edition. Renan regarded the book as the first of a series on the 'Origins of Christianity', which he continued with

'The Apostles' (1866), 'Saint Paul' (1869), 'The Anti-Christ' (1873), 'The Gospels' (1877), 'The Christian Church' (1879) and 'Marcus Aurelius' (1881) but none of these emulated the success of the 'Life of Jesus'. It is not because of its scholarship that the book had such an immediate and abiding success—indeed scholarship has frequently been denied it. This is unjust, for Renan was a considerable scholar and apart from his own linguistic studies, he was familiar with the work of the Tübingen school (see 322) and had praised at length Strauss's *Das Leben Jesu* (300). Immediate success was partly a *succès de scandale* but this would not have kept the book alive. It is Renan's approach to the subject and his beautiful prose that gave it lasting eminence.

Renan's theory of history was based on personalities, and in reconstructing it he endeavoured always to penetrate and to expound the psychology of the leading characters. Indeed, in 1845 he wrote, but never published, an essay on the psychology of Jesus; and in the 'Life' he created what remains a figure of his own imagination. It is a pastoral idyll with the central figure a gentle, albeit oracular visionary, his power to work miracles a part of his unique personality—the son of man, but not the Son of God.

Christianity to Renan was a religion like any other, with its own mythology. He agreed with Baur that it was originally a form of Judaism, that Jesus was a Jewish Messiah, and that it was Paul, the fanatic and missionary, who was the principal architect of Christian dogma.

Renan perhaps would not himself have chosen the 'Life' as his masterpiece and indeed it is more than a little unfair to his genius to detach it, as later readers have done, from the sequels that make up the *Histoire des Origines du Christianisme*. In this great work it seems clear that the audience he has found was the one he sought: the general reading public rather than the limited coterie of scholars; and there is no doubt of the fact or the degree of his success.

353*

EXPERIMENTAL MEDICINE

Claude Bernard (1813–78). Introduction à l'Étude de la Médecine Expérimentale. *Paris: J. B. Baillière, 1865*

In the mid-nineteenth century the Collège de France, through its professors François Magendie (1783–1855) and Claude Bernard, established a high reputation for research in scientific medicine. Through careful, ingenious and systematic animal experimentation Magendie, and even more Bernard, made major discoveries concerning nervous physiology, the mechanisms of poisoning and the physiology of digestion.

The 'Introduction to the Study of Experimental Medicine' was intended as an apologia for such study, as well as an exhortation to it. Here Bernard presented his own personal analysis of scientific method in a manner which earned him commendation from the philosophers of science: he was an ardent but by no means an uncritical devotee of experiment, while re-

maining keenly appreciative of the role of hypothesis. His discussion of method is illustrated by examples drawn from his own researches, such as led to his discovery of the role of the pancreatic juice in digestion, the glycogenic function of the liver, the mechanism of curare and carbon monoxide poisoning, the production of artificial diabetes, and so on. One sentence may sum up Bernard's own philosophy: 'In living bodies, as in inorganic bodies, laws are immutable and the phenomena governed by these laws are bound to the conditions on which they exist, by a necessary and absolute determinism.'

Bernard's researches were first described in technical papers and collections of his lectures, but the *Introduction* was an important didactic work which biologists of the last hundred years have found of great interest and value. It has appeared in many French editions, and was first published in English translation in 1927 at the instigation of the distinguished American physiologist and biochemist L. J. Henderson. This translation has been several times reprinted.

BIBLIOGRAPHY: G. Malloizel, *L'Œuvre de Claude Bernard* (Paris, 1881).

354

ALICE IN WONDERLAND

Lewis Carroll [i.e. Charles Lutwidge Dodgson] (1832–98). Alice's Adventures in Wonderland. With forty-two illustrations by John Tenniel. *London: Macmillan, 1865*

Alice's Adventures in Wonderland and its hardly less famous sequel *Through the Looking Glass* (1872), although ostensibly written for children (in particular, for one child, Alice Liddell, afterwards Hargreaves) are unique among 'juveniles' in appealing equally if not more strongly to adults. Written by an Oxford don, a clergyman, and a professional mathematician, they abound in characters—the White Knight, the Red Queen, the Mad Hatter, Humpty Dumpty—who are part of everybody's mental furniture. And the philosophic profundity of scores, if not hundreds, of these characters' observations, long household words wherever English is spoken, gains mightily from the delicious fantasy of their setting.

The first edition, familiarly known to book-collectors as 'the 1865 Alice', was printed at the Oxford University Press. This edition was at the last moment cancelled by the author, for whom Macmillan's were publishing 'on commission' (i.e. as agent, not sponsors) because of what was considered the poor printing of Sir John Tenniel's almost equally famous illustrations. The few early copies sent out were recalled; seemingly with fair success, since less than a score are known to survive today. The book was then reprinted, by Clay, with the title-page re-dated 1866, and this constitutes the first regularly published edition.

Dodgson thriftily sold 500 copies of the suppressed 1865 printing for publication, with suitably altered title-page, by Appleton's of New York in 1866.

BIBLIOGRAPHY: *The Lewis Carroll Handbook* by Williams, Madan and Green (London, 1962); William H. Bond, 'The Publication of "Alice's Adventures in Wonderland"', In: *Harvard Library Bulletin*, vol. x, no. 3 (Cambridge, Mass., 1956).

355
LIGHT AS A FORM OF ELECTRICITY

JAMES CLERK MAXWELL (1831–79). A Dynamical Theory of the Electromagnetic Field. *In:* Philosophical Transactions of the Royal Society. *London, 1865*

Faraday (309) had both derived electricity from magnetism and obtained magnetism from electricity; in 1845 he had also shown how electricity could act upon light. And always he pondered deeply upon the mechanisms involved in these new phenomena and the laws governing them. In particular, Faraday had abandoned the notion of 'action at a distance' for the concept of the 'fields of force' surrounding bodies by which they act upon one another electromagnetically. But Faraday was a conceptual, not a mathematical thinker.

Clerk Maxwell, who may well be judged the greatest theoretical physicist of the nineteenth century, was happy to acknowledge his debt to Faraday; for what he did was to construct the *mathematical* theory of the field. By 1855, when a Fellow of Trinity College, Cambridge, Maxwell had read a paper on 'Faraday's Lines of Force' to the Cambridge Philosophical Society. The subject remained one of his chief preoccupations until 1864, when the present paper, containing his dynamical theory of the field, was presented to the Royal Society. In this the consideration of 'mechanical models' representing the interplay and movement of electromagnetic forces on the field, which Maxwell had pursued in earlier papers, was abandoned: the developed field-theory, expressed in twenty equations, was purely and elegantly mathematical.

It was one of its consequences that an electromagnetic disturbance, or wave, should travel through space with the speed of light, a circumstance impelling Maxwell to define light as an electromagnetic phenomenon (*A Treatise on Electricity and Magnetism* was published in 1873). When electromagnetic waves were first investigated experimentally by Hertz (377) they were found, indeed, to display optical properties such as reflexion, refraction and interference.

A generation later Einstein's (408) work on relativity was founded directly upon Maxwell's electromagnetic theory; it was this that led him to equate Faraday with Galileo (113, 128, 130) and Maxwell with Newton (161). Like Newton, too, Maxwell made important contributions to optics and other branches of physics, most notably to the kinetic theory of gases, where his work combined ingenious experimentation with great mathematical depth.

356
GENETICS

(*a*) GREGOR JOHANN MENDEL (1822–84). Versuche über Pflanzen-Hybriden. *In:* Verhandlungen des Naturforschenden Vereins zu Brünn, IV Band, 1865. *Brünn, 1866*
(*b*) WILLIAM BATESON (1861–1926). Mendel's Principles of Heredity. *Cambridge University Press, 1909*

Versuche über Pflanzen-Hybriden.
Von
Gregor Mendel.

(Vorgelegt in den Sitzungen vom 8. Februar und 8. März 1865.)

Einleitende Bemerkungen.

Künstliche Befruchtungen, welche an Zierpflanzen desshalb vorgenommen wurden, um neue Farben-Varianten zu erzielen, waren die Veranlassung zu den Versuchen, die her besprochen werden sollen. Die auffallende Regelmässigkeit, mit welcher dieselben Hybridformen immer wiederkehrten, so oft die Befruchtung zwischen gleichen Arten geschah, gab die Anregung zu weiteren Experimenten, deren Aufgabe es war, die Entwicklung der Hybriden in ihren Nachkommen zu verfolgen.

Dieser Aufgabe haben sorgfältige Beobachter, wie Kölreuter, Gärtner, Herbert, Lecocq, Wichura u. a. einen Theil ihres Lebens mit unermüdlicher Ausdauer geopfert. Namentlich hat Gärtner in seinem Werke „die Bastarderzeugung im Pflanzenreiche" sehr schätzbare Beobachtungen niedergelegt, und in neuester Zeit wurden von Wichura gründliche Untersuchungen über die Bastarde der Weiden veröffentlicht. Wenn es noch nicht gelungen ist, ein allgemein giltiges Gesetz für die Bildung und Entwicklung der Hybriden aufzustellen, so kann das Niemanden Wunder nehmen, der den Umfang der Aufgabe kennt und die Schwierigkeiten zu würdigen weiss, mit denen Versuche dieser Art zu kämpfen haben. Eine endgiltige Entscheidung kann erst dann erfolgen, bis Detail-Versuche aus den verschiedensten Pflanzen-Familien vorliegen. Wer die Ar-

1*

In the history of what is now called genetics there is a curious cleavage between experiments in the garden and in the laboratory.

Richard Bradley, in *New Improvements of Planting*, etc., 1717, gives the earliest record known of artificial cross-fertilization. This was a hybrid produced by Thomas Fairchild, a Chelsea nurseryman, who crossed carnations with sweet williams. In 1819 and 1822 the Royal Prussian Academy vainly offered a prize for a satisfactory answer to the question whether hybrid fertilization of plants occurs in nature. In 1830 the Dutch Academy in Haarlem offered a similar prize which was won in 1837 by K. F. Gärtner (1772–1850), a doctor of medicine in Calw. He published the full results of his myriad experiments in 1849—*Versuche und Beobachtungen über die Bastardenzeugung*. This great work established once and for all the sexuality of plants—hitherto strongly contested (see 165). He also unquestionably had an inkling of the laws governing the variation in the offspring resulting from hybridization. Charles Naudin, in a report to the Paris Académie des Sciences in 1864, came very close indeed to formulating these laws.

In March 1900 there appeared in the *Berichte der Deutschen Botanischen Gesellschaft* a paper by Hugo de Vries, professor of botany at Amsterdam, setting forth certain experiments in the hybridization of plants and the unexpected results that had ensued. In April Carl Correns, Director of the Imperial Institute of Biology in Berlin, reported similar experiments of his own. But it eventually transpired that these experiments had been anticipated by a monk, Father Gregor, working in an obscure Bohemian monastery.

The son of a peasant, born Johann Mendel, he entered the monastery at Brünn in 1843 and after being ordained priest in 1847 was released to study mathematics and natural science in Vienna from 1851 to 1853. Thereafter returning to Brünn, he resumed the life of a monk and taught natural science in the local high school. He pursued his hobby of plant breeding in the monastery garden and set himself to discover the effects of cross-fertilization. Wisely or fortunately Mendel chose for the subjects of his experiments plants of strong contrast. Thus he crossed tall with dwarf sweet peas and bred from their stock. Instead of producing, as might have been anticipated on *a priori* reasoning, a plant of intermediate height, all the offspring were at least as tall as the tall parent. The seeds of the tall hybrids, however, produced a surprisingly different generation of which three-quarters were tall and one-quarter dwarf. All the dwarfs and one-third of the talls bred true; two-thirds of the talls behaved exactly like the second generation.

From this and other much more elaborate and extensive experiments Mendel concluded that the characteristics of dwarfness and tallness existed in the sex-cells, or gametes, and that tallness is dominant over dwarfness. The gamete of each parent contributed either the tall factor (T) or the dwarf (D). Crossing true-breeding T's and D's produced all T's because where the T factor is present it dominates D. In the second generation the possible combinations are TT, TD, DT, DD. Thus at either end are true-breeds, while the two mixed crosses repeat the differentiation process. Mendel found this hereditary process uniform in a variety of factors—colour, shape of seeds, etc.

A variety of circumstances contributed to prevent wide knowledge and appreciation of this discovery, which has revolutionized the science of biology. First is the obscurity of publication of Mendel's 'Investigations of Plant Hybrids' in the journal of a small-town society of amateur naturalists. Mendel had first sent his paper to Nägeli, the great Swiss naturalist, who discouraged further experiments and pooh-poohed those already completed because they conflicted with preconceived notions of his own. Furthermore Mendel himself derived what appeared to be contradictory results from experiments with hawkweeds. Finally, when he became head of his monastery he abandoned his experiments in favour of a reactionary campaign against official tax-policies.

Curiously enough, in 1881 W. O. Focke in his *Pflanzenmischlinge* had remarked on Mendel's belief that he had discovered the laws governing hybridization. It was this note that called the attention of Correns to the fact that he had been anticipated. William Bateson read the newly discovered paper and recognized immediately its relevance to the unsolved problem expounded in his *Materials for the Study of Variation*, 1894 (the book by which he was represented at Earls Court). Variation is the cause of the evolution of species; but what causes variation, and how does it happen? Bateson was convinced that species do not evolve as the result of the accumulation of innumerable small changes. His view was that variations occur suddenly and discontinuously. Mendel's paper gave him the clue that he was seeking.

Even in 1900, however, the ideas put forward by Mendel were sharply contested. Bateson was among his foremost champions. In 1902 he published *Mendel's Principles of Heredity—a Defence*, and in his 1909 volume he included a translation of the original paper. Simultaneously with L. Cuénot in France he extended the principle to animals. He became virtually the founder of the modern study of heredity and variation for which he adopted the term 'genetics'. Further development of Mendelian principles has extended far beyond pure science to everyday life where 'results obtained in the flower-pot, the milk bottle and the breeding pan' have been placed on an exact scientific basis.

357

THE SOURCE OF THE NILE

SAMUEL WHITE BAKER (1821–93). The Albert N'yanza, Great Basin of the Nile, and Exploration of the Nile Sources. 2 vols. *London: Macmillan, 1866*

Little was known in ancient times about the origin of the Nile, but Ptolemy (18*), living in Alexandria in the second century, thought that the White Nile came from high snow-covered mountains in Central Africa (called Mountains of the Moon) and passed through two lakes. A little more knowledge was added by Portuguese explorers in Ethiopia in the fifteenth and sixteenth centuries, but not much real progress was made until the travels of James Bruce in 1770. Further journeys were undertaken by Turkish and German travellers in the first half of the nineteenth century, but the solution of the problem is due to the explorations of Richard Burton, J. A. Grant, J. H. Speke, David Livingstone (341) and Sir Samuel Baker.

Baker had travelled extensively in the Near East between 1856 and 1860, and in 1861 he set out, accompanied by his Hungarian wife, on a journey to discover the source of the White Nile. He spent some time in the Sudan, and in February 1863 at Gondokro he met Speke and Grant on their return from an expedition undertaken with the same purpose during which they had reached Lake Victoria. They told Baker of some rumours they had heard of another great lake farther to the west. Baker then continued his journey, and after many adventures he first saw the great lake on 14 March 1864, and named it Albert N'yanza (Lake Albert). He discovered also the Murchison Falls, but could not explore the whole of the lake which he believed to be rather larger than it actually is.

With this discovery an answer had been found to the age-old question of the origin of the Nile; even though further problems remained to be solved by the later explorations of General George Gordon, Colonel Charles Chaille-Long, and H. M. Stanley, so that by 1890 all the main features of the Nile basin were known.

Baker was much honoured on his return. In 1869 he went back to Africa, at the request of the Khedive Ismail, in command of an expedition to suppress the slave trade in the equatorial regions of the Nile and to open the way for trade. He was made Governor-General of these regions and remained there until 1873 when he was succeeded by General Gordon. After that he undertook further travels in India, Japan, the Rocky Mountains, etc. Baker was a man in the great imperial tradition of the Victorian age. He published many books on his various journeys and big-game hunting trips, and these books were some of the first to bring to Europe a picture of Africa as it really was.

358
'WE HAVE NO CONSTITUTION, WE HAVE BAGEHOT'

WALTER BAGEHOT (1826–77). The English Constitution. *London: Chapman and Hall, 1867*

This classic account of that most elusive and least codified of entities, the Constitution of England, has never lost its popularity, and shows signs of being elevated from the rank of first-class handbook to a place with DeTocqueville as one of the most important texts in political literature.

Bagehot was the son of a Somerset banker, and his uneventful career might be taken as the epitome of the life of a Victorian gentleman. Born in comfortable circumstances and blessed with great intelligence, he did not combine the two to make a fortune or a career in politics, but, without dissociating himself from the family business (he remained its agent in London and was an underwriter at Lloyd's) or from the world of affairs, he remained a spectator, and an exponent, a lucid, eloquent, informed and penetrating recorder, of the sources of the English economy (*Lombard Street*, 1873) and, in the present work, of the constitution.

It was perhaps originally due to his early association with *The Economist* (he married the first editor's daughter in 1858, and was editor himself from 1860 to his death) that Bagehot owed his introduction to the sources of power, and it was from this deep experience of the real working of political machinery in this country that he wrote. He showed how the close co-operation between executive government and legislature established by the cabinet system is the effective part of the English Constitution and the real centre of power—or was so at least until quite recently. Some measure of the importance of what might seem at first sight an insular topic—the practical working of one nation's constitution—can be gained from the number of times it has been translated. Bagehot's work is of more than English importance: it is the great defence of empirical as against theoretical politics.

359
THE NEW RELIGION

KARL MARX (1818–83). Das Kapital. Kritik der Politischen Oekonomie, vol. I. *Hamburg: Otto Meissner, 1867*

Only this first volume of Marx's magnum opus appeared in his lifetime, though in a letter to his friend Dr Kugelmann in the autumn of 1866, when he was working over the manuscript, he described a four-book three-volume work on lines identical with those edited after his death by Friedrich Engels (see 326). Thus vol. I is the 'Critical Analysis of Capitalist Production' including the central concept of surplus-value; vol. II (1885) discusses the process of circulation of capital; vol. III (1894) the process of capitalist production as a whole. Marx's fourth section, on the history of economic theory, exists only in the form of a book, edited from his voluminous notes by Karl Kautsky, entitled *Theorien über den Mehrwert* ('Theories of Surplus-Value'), 3 vols., 1905–10.

Das Kapital.

Kritik der politischen Oekonomie.

Von

Karl Marx.

Erster Band.
Buch I. Der Produktionsprocess des Kapitals.

Das Recht der Uebersetzung wird vorbehalten.

Hamburg
Verlag von Otto Meissner.
1867.

New-York: L. W. Schmidt. 24 Barclay-Street.

Marx himself modestly described *Das Kapital* as a continuation of his *Zur Kritik der Politischen Oekonomie*, 1859. It was in fact the summation of his quarter of a century's economic studies, mostly in the Reading Room of the British Museum. The *Athenaeum* reviewer of the first English translation (1887) later wrote: 'Under the guise of a critical analysis of capital, Karl Marx's work is principally a polemic against capitalists and the capitalist mode of production, and it is this polemical tone which is its chief charm'. The historical-polemical passages, with their formidable documentation from British official sources, have remained memorable; and, as Marx (a chronic furunculosis victim) wrote to Engels while the volume was still in the press, 'I hope the bourgeoisie will remember my carbuncles all the rest of their lives'.

Carbuncles, financial embarrassment and political pre-occupations of many kinds hampered Marx's work on *Das Kapital*, which he would never have completed but for the material and moral support of Engels. At 2 a.m. on 16 August 1867, when he had just corrected the final proofs, Marx wrote to 'Dear Fred' that the first volume was finished 'thanks to *you* alone. Without your self-sacrifice for me I could never possibly have done the enormous work...The £15 received with best thanks'.

By an odd quirk of history the first foreign translation of *Das Kapital* to appear was the Russian, which Peters-burgers found in their bookshops early in April 1872. Giving his imprimatur, the censor, one Skuratov, had written 'few people in Russia will read it, and still fewer will understand it'. He was wrong: the edition of three thousand sold out quickly; and in 1880 Marx was writing to his friend F. A. Sorge that 'our success is still greater in Russia, where *Kapital* is read and appreciated more than anywhere else'.

The first French translation, issued in 10-centime parts in 1872–5, was substantially revised by Marx himself; and these revisions were taken into account when at length the first English translation, by Samuel Moore and Edward Aveling, appeared in London, in 1887, four years after Marx's death, under the editorship of Engels. Aveling was the husband of Marx's youngest daughter, Eleanor, and Moore an old friend, an unwilling business-man (like Engels), who later turned to the law and ended as a magistrate in Nigeria.

BIBLIOGRAPHY: See 326.

360*

NATURAL RIGHTS

OTTO VON GIERKE (1841–1921). Das Deutsche Genossenschaftsrecht. 4 vols. *Berlin: Weidmann, 1868–1913*

Otto von Gierke was born at Stettin, the son of a town commissioner who later became Prussian Minister of Agriculture. He was educated at Heidelberg and Berlin, making a special study of jurisprudence and law. In 1867 he became a lecturer at the University of Berlin, and after serving in the Franco-Prussian War returned to Berlin as professor. He moved to Breslau the next year, to Heidelberg in 1884, and returned to Berlin in 1887 where he remained for the rest of his life, being rector of the university from 1902 to 1903.

The book which was to be his life work began while he was still a student, and the first volume was published within a year of his first appointment. His subject was the construction and development of social groups and human associations in relation to legal and ethical theory; a study for which the involved history of Germany pro-vided admirable matter. But 'The German Law of Associations', as Maitland translated it, is an inadequate title. Gierke's first two volumes gave exhaustive treat-ment to the growth of associations and corporations in Germany, but his theme widened in the last two volumes to provide a history of the theory of the State and Cor-poration from the ancient world to modern times. This part of Gierke's work provides the only connected and critical account of the general theory of human society—the theory of politics, of constitutional law, and of the law of associations—which was developed by the great school of Natural Law. This is the theory of the ideal or natural law of human society, and of the ideal or natural rights of man. It is a theory which we have followed from Hooker, Althusius (whose work Gierke revived) and Grotius to Milton, Hobbes, Locke and Rousseau; from Spinoza and Leibniz to Vico and Beccaria, Fichte and Kant.

We have seen it enforced in practice in the Declaration of Independence (220) and the French Revolution. To all this Gierke's immense work forms the summa; to it he brought a vast learning and an originality of treat-ment based on his own conception of the organic group —tribe, city or nation—which have given his subject-matter a new dimension.

361

AMERICAN FREE-THOUGHT

ROBERT G. INGERSOLL (1833–99). An Oration on the Gods. *Peoria, Illinois: Transcript Book and Job Printers, 1872*

James A. Garfield dubbed him 'Royal Bob'; the opposi-tion press preferred such labels as 'Sly Bob' or 'Pagan Bob', but by whatever appellation Robert G. Ingersoll was as well known to the America of his time as any figure on the national scene.

His great oratorical powers had raised him from modest beginnings as a trial lawyer in Peoria, Illinois, to the attorney-generalship of his State (1867–9). His friends claimed he could have gone on to even greater heights and would surely have been Governor except for his unorthodox religious views. Yet while Ingersoll never attained high political office for himself he came to be regarded nationally as the big voice of the Republican Party. At the Republican National Convention of 1876 in Cincinnati he was selected to make the nominating speech for James G. Blaine as the Party's candidate for President, and though Blaine's bid for the nomination was unsuccessful Ingersoll's speech was the high point of the convention. It brought him national fame, which he enlarged while campaigning for the election of the successful nominee, Rutherford B. Hayes. For the next two decades he remained one of the Republican Party's most sought-after and effective spokesmen.

His success as a trial lawyer contributed to his fame, and

in some cases to his notoriety, as well as to his prosperity. But his legal career and his political activities constituted only a portion of his public life. He used his ability as a public speaker in the lecture hall as well as the courtroom and the political rostrum. In an age alive with the Darwinian controversy Ingersoll was a rationalist and a free-thinker who believed that the salvation of humanity was to be found in science, not in religion. Applying to himself the term 'agnostic' almost as soon as Professor Huxley coined it, he mounted the platform to propagate his views. Wherever he went he drew large crowds. Even those scandalized at his ideas came to hear and wonder at the 'great agnostic'.

His first published lecture, *An Oration on the Gods*, appeared in 1872 and was followed in the ensuing years by others in which he continued his attack on the basis of Christian orthodoxy. Among these are *Some Mistakes of Moses*, 1789, *What Must We Do To Be Saved*, 1880, *About the Holy Bible*, 1894, *Why I am an Agnostic*, 1896, *Superstition*, 1898 and *The Devil*, 1899, as well as a number of lectures on literary, historical, and scientific figures.

The mark which Ingersoll left upon his age does not derive from any one of these publications alone but rather from the combined effect of his printed and spoken word. He was a great propagandist of the rationalist and scientific view of the relation of man to the universe and he helped to popularize and lend an aura of respectability to ideas which previously had gained little acceptance outside intellectual circles.

362*

HOMERIC TROY

HEINRICH SCHLIEMANN (1822-90). Trojanische Alterthümer. *Leipzig: F. A. Brockhaus, 1874*

The story of Schliemann is one of the most extraordinary in the history of archaeology, and not the least remarkable feature of it is the fact that although he was the least systematic of excavators, his supreme good luck laid the foundation of modern systematic archaeology.

Heinrich Schliemann, the son of a pastor in Mecklenburg, became successively grocer's apprentice, cabin boy and accountant, and finally established a big import-export business in Russia which allowed him from 1863 to devote himself entirely to his ambition to prove the reality of the Homeric epics. After travels in America, China, Japan and India, he took his fortune to Greece. The first result of his visits to the Homeric sites was a book, *Ithaka, der Peloponnes und Troja* (1869), in which he suggested two theories: that Hissarlik was the real site of Troy, and that the Atreid tombs seen by Pausanias at Mycenae lay within the citadel. Both theories he subsequently proved to be true.

In 1870 Schliemann started work at Hissarlik and by 1873, at the lowest stratum, he laid bare vast fortifications destroyed by fire and discovered a treasure of gold

jewellery. He was convinced that this was Homeric Troy, and published his discoveries first in reports to *The Times* of London, then in 'Trojan Antiquities', which had a popular success unequalled by any previous archaeological work. What Schliemann had in fact discovered is now known to be a pre-Achaean city, long preceding the Homeric city; but he had proved his initial thesis: here was the real site of Troy.

In 1874 he began work at Mycenae, and here too his excavations were, again by good luck, successful beyond all expectations. After discovering a slab platform which

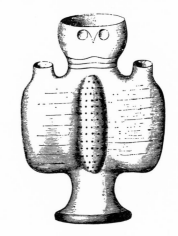

TROJANISCHE ALTERTHÜMER.

BERICHT
ÜBER
DIE AUSGRABUNGEN IN TROJA.
VON
DR. HEINRICH SCHLIEMANN.

LEIPZIG:
IN COMMISSION BEI F. A. BROCKHAUS.
1874.

he took to be the original ground level, he persisted in the seemingly unfruitful task of excavating down to the bedrock and there lighted on the six great shaft graves and the vast treasure of gold, silver and bronze and fine stone and ivory objects, which is still the greatest of all archaeological finds.

By now Schliemann was world famous; he had married a Greek lady who was the chief collaborator in his excavations, and his house became the centre of Athenian society. His later digs were not—they could hardly be—so successful, but in association with a trained archaeologist, Dörpfeld, he laid bare the citadel of Tiryns, a complete Mycenaean palace; and the Greek Archaeological Society continued his work at Mycenae with notable results. He was planning further work at Hissarlik when he was suddenly taken ill and died on Boxing Day, 1890. In his will he left money for Dörpfeld to continue his work on Troy, who by clearing away the debris of previous excavations discovered the great walls of the sixth stratum. These Schliemann had thought to be Lydian, but Dörpfeld was able to prove them contemporary with Mycenae. This was Homer's Troy, if it ever existed: a triumphant conclusion to Schliemann's life-work.

363

CHRISTIAN SCIENCE

MARY BAKER GLOVER (EDDY) (1821–1910). Science and Health. Boston [Mass.]: Christian Scientist Publishing Company, 1875

Commentators on Mary Baker Eddy almost without exception have been either in the camp of her apologists or in that of her detractors. As the numerous studies of her life, her writings, and the movement which she founded testify, she has proved a difficult figure to view with objectivity and she remains among the most controversial in this volume.

Born of old New England yeoman stock, her youth was spent in an atmosphere of pious Protestantism, but an atmosphere which was also alive with the mystical concepts of the Transcendentalist movement, spiritualism and mesmerism. Her health was frail even from childhood and she was subject to seizures of hysteria, relief from which had been sought through mesmeric treatment. Certainly in her early life she suffered more than the common lot of unhappiness and insecurity. Her first marriage, to George Washington Glover in December 1843, ended with the death of her husband in July of the following year. A chronic invalid without visible means of support, she was thrown on the charity of her family, living by turns with her father and her married sister Abigail. Her second marriage, to Dr Daniel Patterson in 1853, was an unhappy one punctuated by long periods of separation and eventually terminated by divorce on grounds of desertion, at which time she resumed the name of Glover.

In 1862 her search for health led her to consult Dr Phineas Parkhurst Quimby, of Portland, Maine, a faith healer to whom, after three weeks under his care, she wrote in a letter published 7 November 1862 in the Portland Courier, that he 'speaks as a man never spoke and heals as a man never healed since Christ'. She became a disciple of Quimby's methods and, with one of his manuscripts as a text, began teaching his system of healing.

In spite of her high fees, which she claimed were sanctioned by Divine Providence—her first students paid $100 for twelve lectures and the price thereafter was raised to $300 and the number of lectures eventually cut from twelve to seven—her venture flourished. Gradually her own methods superseded Quimby's and his name disappeared from her lectures. During this time she was at work on the manuscript of Science and Health. Several attempts to find a publisher for it failed and it was finally brought out in an edition of one thousand copies, the cost of which was paid by two of her students. The title she claimed to have received by divine inspiration, but more likely it derives from 'The Science of Health', the name which Quimby applied to his system of healing.

The essence of Mary Baker Eddy's philosophy is that the Eternal Mind is the source of all being, that the duality of mind and matter is an error. There is no matter and, hence, 'disease is caused by the mind alone'. Science is

SCIENCE

AND

HEALTH.

BY

MARY BAKER GLOVER.

———

BOSTON:
CHRISTIAN SCIENTIST PUBLISHING COMPANY.
1875.

the wisdom of the Eternal Mind as revealed through Jesus Christ: hence 'Christian Science'. What began as a system of faith healing had by now evolved into a religious philosophy. Mary Baker Eddy was an uneducated woman, ignorant of the meaning of the philosophical terms she used so freely and as faulty in her logic as in her syntax. To confuse matters further the first edition of Science and Health is a jungle of typographical errors, the most blatant of which are pointed out in an errata slip which apparently was not inserted until a number of copies had been issued. Much rarer than the first edition is the second or so-called 'Noah's Ark' edition, of which two hundred copies were hastily printed in 1878. It consists of two chapters from the original plus three new ones, the most interesting of which is that on mesmerism. In the third edition (1881) the author added a chapter on demonology. The textual changes in these and later editions provide a formidable task for any editor who might undertake to provide a definitive text.

In spite of the mechanical faults of her book and the

controversial nature of many of her teachings, Mary Baker Eddy was far ahead of her time in the emphasis she placed upon positive thinking, a force which modern psychology was belated in recognizing. The movement which has grown out of her teachings has had an influence in the world far beyond the size of its membership.

364
THE PATHOLOGY OF CRIME

CESARE LOMBROSO (1836–1909). L'Uomo Delinquente. *Milan: Ulrico Hoepli, 1876*

Lombroso was one of the first professional academic criminologists. Born in Verona of a Jewish family, he studied biology and chemistry at Padua, Vienna and Paris. In 1862 he was appointed professor at Pavia, which he left to gain practical experience as director of a lunatic asylum at Pesaro. He then became professor of psychiatry and forensic medicine at Turin. He remained at Turin for the rest of his life, finally becoming professor of criminal anthropology, a chair created for him.

Lombroso was the leader of an influential school of criminologists, who derived the basis of their theories from Comte (295). They maintained that criminals are more often found to suffer from physical, nervous and mental abnormalities than non-criminals, and that these abnormalities are either inherited or the result of physical degeneration. This reference of mental phenomena to purely physical and biological causes follows Comtian theory, and like it requires forcing and exaggeration of the evidence. The fallacies involved were revealed in Lombroso's later *Genio e Follia*, 1864, in which he unsuccessfully attempted to show that genius was also a form of degeneration akin to madness.

Nevertheless, 'Criminal Man' was a revolutionary work which not only caused a considerable stir when it first came out but had a practical effect which was wholly beneficial. The division which it indicated between the congenital criminal and those who were tempted to crime by circumstances has had a lasting effect on penal theory. Again, by connecting the treatment of crime with the treatment of insanity, Lombroso initiated a branch of psychiatric research which has cast new light on problems, such as criminal responsibility, which lie at the root of human society. In 1899 Lombroso published in French a résumé of his earlier work, *Le Crime, causes et remèdes*, which reinforced these views and established him as a pioneer of the medical treatment of criminals.

365
THE TELEPHONE

ALEXANDER GRAHAM BELL (1847–1922). Researches in Telephony. *In*: Proceedings of the American Academy of Arts and Sciences. *Boston [Mass.], 1877*

Bell was born in Edinburgh, emigrated with his family to Canada in 1870, and became an American citizen in 1874. His grandfather and his father taught elocution and voice production. Bell himself devoted his life to the amelioration of the lot of people born deaf. As part of his studies he attempted various methods of conveying sounds to the deaf. In 1874, while experimenting with a tuned system of telegraphy, and also studying the path of sound waves in the human ear, he combined the two investigations and worked out the theory of the telephone.

Telephones were already in existence. Philip Reis perfected the first of them in 1861, but it remained little more than a toy. He failed, in fact, in the primary object, which was to produce intelligible speech at the receiving end. This seems to have been due to his use of an interrupted transmission current which seriously affected the quality of reception.

Bell surmounted this obstacle by the use of what he termed an 'undulating' current. Even so he succeeded only after long and discouraging experiment and he produced three telephones before he felt equal to a public demonstration in 1876. The first intelligible sentences exchanged over the telephone were transmitted from one room to another in the same house between Bell and an assistant. They were 'Do you understand what I say?' 'Yes; I understand you perfectly'. In the same month, March 1876, Bell took out his first patent which, although frequently and bitterly contested, was consistently upheld by the courts. In April 1877 Bell's system was installed between New York and Boston as the first public telephone service. His name is still commemorated in the nation-wide telephone service of the United States.

Nevertheless Bell's telephone and those of his rivals, Elisha Gray and Thomas Edison among them, were not commercially satisfactory, the transmission system leaving much to be desired. It was not until 1878, when David Edward Hughes (another Anglo-American, who had invented in 1854 what was virtually the teleprinter), devised the microphone, that telephony became feasible for general communication. He communicated the details of his invention to the Royal Society in May 1878. Lüdtge, a German inventor, patented a similar device in January 1878. Hughes did not take out a patent. It is interesting that he discovered the principle on which the microphone is based by accident, when experimenting with a Bell telephone.

A microphone is an instrument by means of which variations in sound produce corresponding changes in electrical resistance, so that an electrical current passing along a wire is made to vary its wave in height, length and intensity in exact correspondence with the inducing sounds. Moreover the microphone translates the electrical variations back into sound with similar fidelity. The importance of this instrument in modern society needs no emphasis.

Owing to the caution of the British Postmaster General and to the litigious inclinations of some patentees, a telephone service was not instituted in England until 1881 and was then confined to a five-mile radius from the centre of London. Long-distance trunk lines were installed in 1884. The General Post Office began to take over the service in 1907.

366

THE LIFE-HISTORY OF BACTERIA

ROBERT KOCH (1843–1910). (*a*) Untersuchungen über Bacterien. v. Die Aetiologie der Milzbrand-Krankheit. vi. Verfahren zur Untersuchung, zum Conserviren und Photographiren der Bacterien. *In*: Cohn, Beiträge zur Biologie der Pflanzen. *Breslau, 1877*; (*b*) Untersuchungen über die Aetiologie der Wundinfektionskrankheiten. *Leipzig: F. C. W. Vogel, 1878*; (*c*) Die Aetiologie der Tuberculose. *In*: Berliner Klinische Wochenschrift. *Berlin, 1882*

The contributions of Koch to the germ theory of disease are of major importance and run parallel with those of Pasteur (336).

C. J. Davaine, a doctor in Paris, in 1865, had reported in the *Comptes rendus* the first identification of a specific micro-organism as the cause of a disease. This was the anthrax bacillus. Koch, a provincial doctor in Posen, followed up Davaine's discovery and in the fifth of a series of 'Investigations into Bacteria' in course of publication in Cohn's *Beiträge*, he became the first to describe the complete life-history of a micro-organism, 'The Etiology of Anthrax ((*a*), v).

In the following paper—'Experiences in attempting the Preservation and Photography of Bacteria' ((*a*) vi)— he detailed his methods of growing bacterial cultures in gelatine solutions and of differential staining with the aniline dyes discovered by W. H. Perkin in 1856. These two papers form the basis of modern bacteriological practice—indeed of the very science itself.

In 1878, in 'Investigations into the Etiology of Wound Infections', (*b*) above, he carried the proof of the bacteriological cause of diseases a considerable stage further, tracing the course of six different diseases due to the infection of wounds and producing cultures of the causative organisms through several generations. In 1882, tracing 'The Etiology of Tuberculosis', (*c*), he isolated the tubercle bacillus.

Koch was awarded the Nobel Prize for Medicine in 1905.

367

APPLIED ART

WILLIAM MORRIS (1834–96). (*a*) The Decorative Arts, their Relation to Modern Life and Progress. *London: Ellis & White [1878]*; (*b*) Some Hints on Pattern-Designing. *London: Longmans, 1899*

'Poet, artist, manufacturer, and socialist, author of *The Earthly Paradise*: this terse unimpassioned entry in the *Fasti Britannici* sums up the life and work of a very remarkable man.' These are the opening words of the standard biography of Morris by J. W. Mackail.

No man's life was ever more completely interwoven with his work than Morris's. This conclusion emerges ever more strongly in the pages of Mackail. The toy suit of armour in which he bestrode his Shetland pony as a

child, the fact that he had read all the Waverley Novels before he was seven and his insatiable eight-year-old appetite for the interiors of old churches all show a precocious inclination towards the interests that dominated his later life. At Marlborough, we are told, he showed a passionate interest in the ancient monuments of the district—Pewsey, Silbury, Avebury and the Roman villas at Kennet—and he used to claim that before he went up to Oxford he knew all that there was to know about English gothic.

At Oxford began his lifelong friendship with Burne-Jones. When he came down in 1856 he entered the office of G. E. Street as an architectural pupil and issued the first number of the *Oxford and Cambridge Magazine*. Rossetti became a contributor and persuaded Morris to take up painting.

Morris was married to Jane Burden in 1859 and he commissioned a former fellow pupil in Street's office, Philip Webb, to build him a house on Bexley Heath.

SOME HINTS ON PATTERN-DESIGNING. A LECTURE DELIVERED BY WILLIAM MORRIS AT THE WORKING MEN'S COLLEGE, LONDON, ON DECEMBER 10, 1881.

By the word pattern-design, of which I have undertaken to speak to you to-night, I mean the ornamentation of a surface by work that is not imitative or historical, at any rate, not principally or essentially so. Such work is often, not literally flat, for it may be carving or moulded work in plaster or pottery; but whatever material relief it may have is given to it for the sake of beauty & richness, and not for the sake of imitation, or to tell a fact directly; so that people have called this art ornamental art, though indeed all real art is ornamental.

Now, before we go further, we may as well ask ourselves what reason or right this so-called ornamental art has to existence? We might answer the question shortly by saying that it seems clear that mankind has hitherto determined to have it even at the cost of a good deal of labour & trouble: an answer good enough to satisfy our consciences that we are not necessarily wasting our time in meeting here to consider it; but we may furthermore try to get at the reasons that have forced men in the mass always to expect to have what to some of them doubtless seems an absurd superfluity of life.

b   1

They agreed that the architect's job should not end with the shell that was the house itself but should include interior decorating and furnishing. Out of the difficulties in finding materials of the high standards that they insisted on eventually arose the founding of the firm of Morris & Co. in 1861, in which Webb, Burne-Jones and Rossetti were among the partners. After a number of vicissitudes, it prospered and to its original activities was added the tapestry industry which Morris founded at Merton. At the same time, Morris wrote poetry on an heroic scale, *The Earthly Paradise*, 1868–70, being perhaps his best-known work. In the seventies and eighties he was in the vanguard of the socialist movement, and *News from Nowhere*, his most widely read prose work, was first published in the socialist magazine, *Commonweal*. At length, Morris's idealism clashed with the policy of the other members, and in 1889 his connexion with the movement ceased.

The final years of Morris's life, however, saw the last and in many ways the most fruitful of his experiments, the Kelmscott Press. With undiminished energy, he demanded and got the finest ink and paper, commissioned special types, enlisted Burne-Jones and others to design the illustrations, and issued a series of books, perfect in their way, both in design and in the quality of the printing, of which the last and most magnificent, the Kelmscott Chaucer, was published only a few weeks before his death.

His *Hints on Pattern-Designing* summarizes succinctly views which would apply equally well to any branch of applied art: the principles behind them were given in full in *The Decorative Arts*, an address originally delivered to the Trades' Guild of Learning in 1877.

Walter Crane, writing not long after Morris's death, saw clearly the magnitude of his influence. 'The secret of Morris's great influence in the revival was no doubt to be attributed to his way of personally mastering the working details and handling of each craft he took up, as well as to his power of inspiring his helpers and followers. The demand for the acknowledgement of the personality of each responsible craftsman in a co-operative work was new, and it had a direct bearing on the social and economic conditions of artistic production. The principle, too, of regarding the material, object, method and purpose of a work as essential conditions of its artistic expression, the form and character of which must always be controlled by such conditions, had never been so emphatically stated …if it has not turned all British craftsmen into artists or all British artists into craftsmen, it has done not a little to expand and socialize the idea of art, and (perhaps it is not too much to say) has made the tasteful English house with its furniture and decorations a model for the civilized world.'

BIBLIOGRAPHY: H. Buxton Forman, *The Books of William Morris described* (London, 1897).

368

PRUSSIAN CHAUVINISM

HEINRICH VON TREITSCHKE (1834–96). Deutsche Geschichte im neunzehnten Jahrhundert. 5 vols. *Leipzig: Hirzel, 1879–94*

It is symptomatic of the spiritual degeneration of the German middle classes in the Bismarckian empire, which shrewd observers such as Burckhardt (347) and Nietzsche (370) noticed soon after the Franco-German war of 1870–1, that the impartial cosmopolitan Ranke (286) was in 1886 succeeded in the sinecure office of Prussian Historiographer Royal by the violent chauvinist Treitschke.

Treitschke was the son of a Saxon general of Czech ancestry (the family name was originally spelt Třčk), but his early espousal of the cause of Prussia as the leader towards German unity, and his blind admiration of Bismarck as the strong man of blood and iron, made him break with his family, abandon his professorship in the anti-Prussian grand-duchy of Baden and devote his life to the journalistic, poetical and academic idolization of the aggrandizement of Prussia for which Bismarck suitably rewarded the 'herald of the empire'.

Treitschke's 'German History in the Nineteenth Century' (which in fact ends before the outbreak of the revolution of 1848) represents the height of the Prussian interpretation of history. Never before or since have the Prussian contempt for all non-Prussian Germans, above all the despised Austrians; the hatred of the 'hereditary enemy', France, and the 'nation of shopkeepers', England; the rage against democracy, socialism, pacifism and parliamentary government; and virulent anti-semitism, found as brilliant an outlet as in Treitschke's books, pamphlets and lectures. For, with all his faults, Treitschke was an incomparable master of the spoken and written word; and the broad sweep of his vision embraced every aspect of political, cultural and economic life. Although never taken seriously by his academic fellow-historians, Treitschke exerted an immense influence, wholly detrimental, upon the German bourgeoisie of the Wilhelmian era who uncritically applauded his worship of militarism, reaction and power-politics.

369

LIBERAL IMPERIALISM

JOHN ROBERT SEELEY (1834–95). The Expansion of England. *London: Macmillan, 1883*

Seeley, from 1869 Regius Professor of History at Cambridge, delivered these sixteen lectures as an answer to 'the question how history should be taught'. After nearly a century his main arguments are still valid and his main prognostications have proved correct; only his Victorian terminology has dated.

Seeley ridiculed the division of English history according to the reigns of 'dim' monarchs (still prevalent in many school books); he stigmatized 'the error of confounding the history of England with the history of Parliament' (given a fresh stimulus by the late Lewis Namier); he demanded a 'single conception' of English history, namely 'that the European policy and the colonial policy are but different aspects of the same great national development'; he maintained that North America and India are integral parts of English history and that France lost both these continents because of her 'European entanglements'. He predicted that the United States of America, Russia and a 'federal union' centred on Britain would be the dominant powers of the future, beside which France and Germany would be relegated to 'second-class' states. He unhesitatingly called English rule in India 'a good specimen of a bad political system' and, although he correctly described India as a 'territory of many nations and many languages', he clearly foresaw that, 'if there could arise in India a nationality movement', England would have to withdraw 'at once', and 'a national government might be more beneficial because more congenial'.

Seeley's profound reflexions on the magnitude, the responsibilities and the obligations of empire-building did not prevent the book from being perverted into the bible of those 'bombastic' imperialists upon whom Seeley directed his sharpest strictures. Further injustice has been done to him by the isolation of his remark that 'we seem, as it were, to have conquered and peopled half the world in a fit of absence of mind'. Read in their proper context the words introduce Seeley's attack on the 'indifference' of the Little Englanders towards world affairs, on their refusal to regard history as the school of statesmanship, and on their reluctance to face the greatest problem confronting England: 'how to give a moral unity' to the vast empire or, as we should now say, the Commonwealth of Nations.

370

THE SUPERMAN

FRIEDRICH WILHELM NIETZSCHE (1844–1900). Also sprach Zarathustra. Ein Buch für Alle und Keinen. Parts 1–3, *Chemnitz: E. Schmeitzner, 1883–4*; part 4, *Leipzig: Naumann, 1891*

Friedrich Wilhelm Nietzsche, son of a Saxon pastor, studied classical philology and was appointed professor in Basle before he had taken his doctor's degree (1869). He resigned in 1879 for reasons of health and in 1889 became incurably insane.

In his youth he was a disciple of Schopenhauer (279) but his intimate friendship with Wagner (333) was a decisive feature in Nietzsche's development, although the bitter hatred that later arose between them, in the words of Ernest Newman, 'poisoned his pen as the thing itself had once poisoned his soul'. His principal work during the Wagner period, 1868–78, was *Die Geburt der Tragödie aus dem Geist der Musik*, 1872. In this he adopted a tragico-pessimistic conception of Greek civilization, like Burckhardt (347) but contrary to Grote (321). This started his career as a critic of modern civilization based on disgust with imperial Germany, Christianity, bourgeois ethics, and so on.

Nietzsche was also a poet, as much perhaps a poet and critic as a philosopher. It is, moreover, the critical or destructive aspect of his philosophy that has made a significant mark on the mind of sophisticated man. He emphasized the important part in all spheres of human thought and activity played by self-deception, illusion and prejudice, and it is his stark insistence on the necessity to recognize and ruthlessly to uproot these sinister and treasured falsities that has made him appear unsympathetic. In this main aspect of his outlook and in its reception, similarities with Freud (389) are plainly observable.

Unsympathetic also was his emphasis on the here and now as opposed to the hereafter, his glorification of heroism and power and his impatience with the accepted Christian virtues of selflessness, suffering and charity.

Also sprach Zarathustra.

—◆—

Ein Buch

für

Alle und Keinen.

Von

Friedrich Nietzsche.

—◆—◆—◆—

Chemnitz 1883.

Verlag von Ernst Schmeitzner.

	St. Petersburg	
Paris	H. Schmitzdorff	Turin
W. Fischbacher	(C. Roettger.)	(Florenz, Rom.)
33 Rue de Seine.	Kais. Hof-Buchhandlung.	Hermann Loescher
	5 Newsky Prospekt.	via di Po 19.
New-York		London
E. Steiger & Co.		Williams & Norgate
25 Park Place.		14 Henrietta Street,
		Covent Garden.

'Thus Spake Zarathustra' glorifies the Übermensch (superman). It is a long philosophical prose poem and the most widely known of his works. He did not complete what was intended to be his masterpiece, *Der Wille zur Macht* ('The Will to Power'), conceived in 1883.

Much of Nietzsche's work has never been properly published and much was suppressed and partly destroyed by his sister and evil genius, Elisabeth Förster-Nietzsche (1846–1935), the custodian of the Nietzsche-Archiv in Weimar. She was a rabid German nationalist and anti-semite, and her numerous publications on her brother have been a major obstacle to any correct assessment of Nietzsche's philosophy. Being totally antipathetic to his anti-Christian and anti-nationalistic beliefs she was a dangerously unsuitable editor for the writings of the man who is credited with coining the term 'a good European' (*guter Europäer*).

Nietzsche's influence in Germany, where the false glosses introduced by his sister were even further debased, was bad. In England his influence on the Shavian coterie, responsible for the earliest English translations, was temporary. His greatest influence has been in France, where Charles Andler produced the standard biography (6 vols., 1920–31).

371
O.E.D.

JAMES MURRAY (1837–1915), HENRY BRADLEY (1845–1923), WILLIAM A. CRAIGIE (1867–1957), C. T. ONIONS (1873–1963), Editors. A New [from 1895, The Oxford] English Dictionary on Historical Principles. 11 vols. *Oxford: at the Clarendon Press, 1884–1928; supplement 1933*

The *N.E.D.*, as it was originally cited, or the *O.E.D.*, as it is now known, is the greatest treasure-house of any language in the world, unrivalled for its comprehensiveness and ease of consultation as well as for its reliability and scholarship.

This vast enterprise was initiated in 1857 by the Philological Society (founded in 1842) which, under the direction of a Cambridge man, Dr Richard Chenevix Trench (1807–86; from 1856 to 1863 Dean of Westminster, thereafter Archbishop of Dublin), worked out full details and appointed as its first editor the brilliant young philologist, Herbert Coleridge (1830–61), nephew of the poet.

After his untimely death, Frederick James Furnivall (1825–1910), the Society's secretary, carried on the work. As a means of strengthening the 'historical principles' he founded the Early English Text Society (1864), the Chaucer Society (1868), the Ballad Society, the New Shakspere Society (1873) and the Wiclif Society (1881), and he maintained his active interest in the Dictionary (as well as in Browning, rowing and sculling) until the day of his death.

After negotiations with the publishing firm of Macmillan in 1876 had come to nothing, the Oxford University Press became interested in the undertaking and in 1879 an agreement was signed by the Delegates. Murray (knighted in 1908), at the time assistant master at Mill Hill School, gave the Dictionary its final shape, and in 1884 brought out the first instalment. Nearly half the whole work (7,207 pages out of a total of 15,487) was done by him. After the editorial office had been transferred to Oxford (1885), Murray was supported successively and jointly by the assistant editors Bradley (from 1885), Craigie (from 1897; knighted in 1928) and Onions (from 1914).

The 'corrected reissue' of the main work has been supplemented by various smaller offspring: *The Shorter Oxford Dictionary*, *The Concise Oxford Dictionary of Current English*, *The Oxford Illustrated Dictionary*, and the *Pocket*, *Little* and *School* Dictionaries, each serving a different public but all of them worthy of their progenitor.

372
D.N.B.

THE DICTIONARY OF NATIONAL BIOGRAPHY, 63 vols. *London: Smith, Elder & Co., 1885–1900*

On the completion of the *D.N.B.*, the editors proudly stated that 'this is the outcome of private enterprise and the handiwork of private citizens', whereas similar works abroad were sponsored by learned institutions and subsidized by the national exchequers.

In fact, the *D.N.B.* owed its inception to that adventurous publisher, George Smith (1824–1901), who in 1882 proposed an English counterpart of the *Biographie Universelle*, the latest edition of which, in forty volumes, had appeared in Paris in 1843–63. On the advice of his friend Leslie Stephen (1832–1904; knighted in 1902), he abandoned this plan in favour of a collection of national, British biographies. Stephen was appointed the first editor (until 1891); he was succeeded by Sidney Lee (1859–1926; knighted in 1911), who, in 1900, completed the work, which comprises about 30,000 lives.

It was followed by two supplements (1902 and 1912, 3 volumes each) and, after the Smith family had presented it to the University of Oxford in 1917, continued as *The Twentieth-Century D.N.B.*, issuing supplements at about ten-yearly intervals, together with *The Concise D.N.B.* in two volumes (the first containing the biographies to 1900, the second those of people who died in or after 1901). The Institute of Historical Research, London University, currently publishes amendments and corrections to the *D.N.B.* which, like that other great enterprise of co-operative British scholarship, the *Oxford English Dictionary* (371), is an essential and indispensable work of reference in every library in the world.

373
THE SALVATION ARMY

GENERAL BOOTH (1829–1912). In Darkest England and the Way Out. *London: International Headquarters of the Salvation Army*, [1890]

William Booth started life as a pawnbroker's assistant in Nottingham. After coming to London in 1849 he became an itinerant revivalist preacher. In 1865 he started a 'Christian Mission' in Whitechapel. In 1878 he founded, almost by accident, the Salvation Army (whose centenary was inaccurately commemorated by the British Post Office in 1965).

His passionate preoccupation with the submerged tenth was not confined to their spiritual welfare; he was determined to relieve their physical misery as well. In 1890, the same year that Stanley published *In Darkest Africa*, Booth published *In Darkest England*. In this book he analysed the causes of pauperism and vice of the period, and proposed a remedy by ten expedients. These included land settlement, emigration, rescue work among prostitutes and at the prison-gate, the poor man's bank, and the poor man's lawyer. Money was liberally subscribed and a large part of the scheme was carried through.

The book was largely 'ghosted' by W. T. Stead, who was associated with Booth's son in a sensational frontal attack on the recruitment of young children for brothels. Booth's biographer, Harold Begbie, stresses his lack of learning and says that 'in everything intellectual he was an obscurantist of the most pronounced type'. Begbie does not conceal, either, Booth's compromises with the mammon of unrighteousness. 'He never appeared before these people except as a prophet of God', he writes, 'but the urgent need of their money for his emigration scheme, his farm colonies, his shelters, and his halls, induced him to tone down the thunders of Sinai to the *piano* note of a somewhat chaffing and good-natured admonition.'

This should not detract from 'General' Booth's achievement in developing, from an obscure mission hall in the East End of London, a world-wide organization complete with military ranks and uniforms: an organization which has earned virtually universal respect and affection. Booth's colossal self-confidence, his burning sense of injustice coupled with unswerving devotion to his purpose, and his deep sympathy with the unfortunate, made of him an evangelist and an organizer of the first order.

374

THE GOLDEN BOUGH

JAMES GEORGE FRAZER (1854–1941). The Golden Bough: a Study in Comparative Religion. 2 vols. *London: Macmillan, 1890*

It is strange that anthropology—the study of man— should be of so little general appeal to the layman. E. B. Tylor, the author of *Primitive Culture*, 1871, a most provocative study of one aspect of the subject, lamented the fact that anthropology was little more than 'a derided byway'. Frazer was in fact attracted to the subject by reading Tylor's book. In 1888 William Robertson Smith, as editor of the ninth edition of the *Encyclopaedia Britannica* (218) induced Frazer to contribute the articles on 'Taboo' and 'Totemism'. These two tribal practices Frazer regarded as half-religious, half-social phenomena —the 'clean' and 'unclean' conception leading to sacrificial practices. He was especially attracted to tracing the connexion of these ideas with the mysteries associated with the shrine of Diana at Lake Nemi and the riddle of the King of the Wood, whom he conceived as a totemistic figure. The explanation of these Arician Mysteries led him to study their origins and to find comparisons and parallels in other and more primitive religious systems.

The result of these wider studies was *The Golden Bough*. First published in two volumes in 1890, edition succeeded edition in continually enlarged form—a second edition in three volumes in 1900, a third edition beginning in 1911 and extending to thirteen volumes by 1936.

The constant reprinting of the great work itself and the widespread popularity of an abridged edition in one volume—now available also as a paperback—has brought very close to reality Tylor's hope that the time would come when anthropology would be a handmaid of government.

BIBLIOGRAPHY: T. Besterman, *A Bibliography of Sir James George Frazer* (London, 1934).

375

REVOLUTION IN THE THEATRE

HENRIK IBSEN (1828–1906). Hedda Gabler. *Copenhagen: Gyldendal, 1890*

Ibsen was the son of a merchant who inherited a mixed ancestry of Danish, German and Scottish, but no Norwegian blood. When Ibsen was eight years old his father went bankrupt and grinding poverty darkened the boy's early years. Apprenticed to an apothecary, he expressed his inner anguish in a series of gloomy poems. In 1850, by the generosity of a friend, he published, under a pseudonym, a blank verse tragedy, *Catilina*, which attracted no attention. He then started to earn a precarious living as a free-lance journalist. In 1851 he was appointed 'stagepoet' and became virtually the manager of a small theatre in Bergen, and in 1857 director of the National Theatre in Oslo.

Ibsen now tried his hand at romantic drama. He wrote seven more plays before eventually finding his true métier with 'Love's Comedy', 1862, but neither this nor any of his other early plays found any general response. At last, in 1864, he won a travelling scholarship and went to Rome, where he wrote *Brand*, 1866, and *Peer Gynt*, 1867. These earned him an official 'poet's pension', and his plays, especially *Brand*, began to achieve a wide circulation among readers. Apart from brief visits to Norway in 1874 and 1885, he lived in Dresden and Munich until 1891 when he settled down for the rest of his life in Norway.

It is virtually impossible to select any one play as 'typical' of Ibsen's outlook. His own favourite, 'Emperor and Galilean', 1873, would certainly not be generally acceptable; but to choose between his attacks on social corruption, such as 'Pillars of Society', 1877, or 'An Enemy of the People', 1882, and his critical studies of the subjection of women, such as 'A Doll's House', 1879, or 'The Wild Duck', 1884, is not easy. 'Hedda Gabler', 1890, has been selected here as possibly his most frequently performed play in the modern theatre.

Ibsen's influence on the whole course of modern drama may be indicated by the inclusion of his plays in the repertoire of every *avant-garde* theatre of his day—the Théâtre Libre, Paris, 1887, Die Freie Bühne in Berlin, 1887, and The Independent Theatre in London, 1891— and although on every occasion that they were produced audience reaction was largely a mixture of protest and bewilderment, Ibsen's revolutionary technique has now become firmly established—indeed, slightly old-fashioned. As to the social message of his plays, it should be remembered that his purpose was analytic rather than didactic. He was concerned with the exploration of social problems rather than with moral preaching.

Bibliographically it must be noted that the above edition was briefly preceded by one consisting of twelve copies only printed in London in Norwegian, suggested and supervised by Edmund Gosse, under a well-intentioned illusion that this was necessary for copyright protection. 'The Master Builder', 1892, and 'John Gabriel Borkman', 1896, were similarly treated.

FIG. 6.

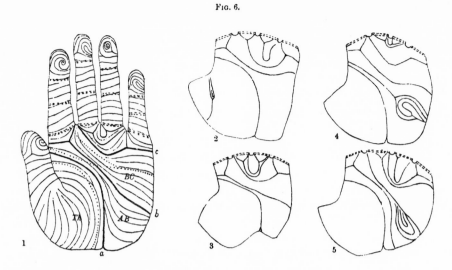

Systems of Ridges, and the Creases in the Palm.

376

FINGER-PRINTS AND CRIMINOLOGY

FRANCIS GALTON (1822–1911). *Finger Prints. London: Macmillan, 1892*

The earliest modern use of finger-prints as a means of identification was by Thomas Bewick, the engraver. His thumbprint appears on receipts for the first edition of his Aesop in 1818.

In 1823 J. E. Purkinje contributed a paper to the Transactions of the University of Breslau in which he remarked on the importance of finger-prints and their patterns; but the notion, for example in Garrison-Morton's *Medical Bibliography*, that he suggested using them as a means of identification is erroneous. It was in a letter to *Nature*, 28 October 1880, 'On the Skin-furrows of the Hand', that Sir Henry Faulds first made such a suggestion in print. On 25 November W. J. Herschel in the same journal reported his use of the handprints of Hindu natives on contracts from 1858 onwards. Before he left India in 1878 he had instituted a primitive system of criminal identification by means of finger-prints. He was also aware of the persistence of the patterns.

Galton, a cousin of Charles Darwin (344) and the originator of eugenic studies, was greatly interested by Herschel's letter as indicating a possible form of anthropometric classification. On 27 November 1890 he read a paper to the Royal Society, which was printed in its *Transactions*, on 'The Patterns of Thumb and Finger Marks'. He borrowed and exhibited for the occasion one of Herschel's contracts. In May 1891 Galton contributed to the *Proceedings of the Royal Society* 'A Method of indexing Finger-Marks' and in August of the same year he wrote for *The Nineteenth Century* a popular account of the subject under the title 'Identification by Finger-Tips'.

In 1892, in his book *Finger Prints*, Galton gathered together all these earlier studies and recorded other experiments, illustrated from photographs and drawings. The outcome of this was the appointment in 1899 of a Royal Commission which came out in favour of the adoption of the system by the British police forces.

E. R. Henry had reported to the Commission his own use of the system as Inspector-General of Police in Bengal, and in 1900 he published *Classification and Uses of Finger Prints*, on which the system now used throughout the world is based. Henry was a Police Commissioner at Scotland Yard from 1903 to 1918.

Galton also made important contributions to the study of heredity and genetics, and although he exaggerated the importance of statistics his insistence on the necessity for exact measurements in biology is of great significance.

377

THE THEORY OF WIRELESS TELEGRAPHY

HEINRICH RUDOLF HERTZ (1857–94). *Untersuchungen über die Ausbreitung der Elektrischen Kraft. Leipzig: Johann Ambrosius, 1892*

Experimental proof by Hertz of the Faraday–Maxwell hypothesis that electrical waves can be projected through space (see 309, 355) was begun in 1887, eight years after Maxwell's death.

The two main requirements were (a) a method of producing the waves, supposing that they existed, and (b) a method of detecting them once they were produced. Hertz found the first problem easy to solve. He used the oscillatory discharge of a condenser. Detection was much more difficult, because there then existed no means of detecting currents alternating at the high speed of these waves. Hertz in fact used an effect as old as the discovery of electricity itself—the electric spark.

By inducing the waves to produce an electric spark at a distance, with no apparent connexion between the oscillator and the spark gap, and by moving the sparking apparatus so that the length of the spark varied, he proved beyond question the passage of electric waves through space. The distance was no greater than the length of Hertz's laboratory at Kiel, but the fact of projection had been scientifically determined. J. J. Thomson (386) described the results as 'one of the most marvellous triumphs of experimental skill'. The experiments were reported periodically from 1887 onwards in the *Annalen der Physik und Chemie* and are gathered together in the above volume. The title of the English translation, published in 1893, with a preface by Kelvin, is expressive of its contents—'Electric Waves, being Researches on the Propagation of Electric Action with Finite Velocity through Space'. G. F. Fitzgerald had already announced Hertz's first results in his address to the British Association in Bath in 1888.

David Hughes, while at work on perfecting his microphone (see 365) had arrived at similar conclusions. In 1880 he gave a demonstration lasting three hours before the President, Spottiswood, and the Honorary Secretaries of the Royal Society, Huxley and Stokes; but they were unable to accept his contention that the results were due to wave action and discouraged him from contributing a paper to the Society.

Hertz was first encouraged to investigate the Maxwellian hypothesis by Helmholtz (323), his senior professor in Berlin. In the course of this work he induced cathode rays to pass through metals. His colleague, Philipp Lenard, inserted a metal plate in a vacuum tube and found that it acted as a 'window' through which the rays could escape. It is said to have been with such a tube given him by Lenard that Röntgen (380) discovered X-rays.

378

THE ELECTRON THEORY

HENDRIK ANTOON LORENTZ (1853–1928). (a) La Théorie Electromagnétique de Maxwell, et son Application aux Corps Mouvants. *Leiden: E. J. Brill, 1893;* (b) Versuch einer Theorie der Electrischen und Optischen Erscheinungen in Bewegten Körpern. *Leiden: E. J. Brill, 1895*

In 1729 James Bradley, later Astronomer Royal, reported to the Royal Society that in observing any fixed star it was necessary to point the telescope not directly at the star but a little in advance of it. This he called the angle of aberration. The fact reported by Bradley was repeatedly confirmed and the angle of aberration was accounted for by the movement of the earth through the ether—the medium by which light waves are conveyed. If the luminiferous ether is a medium through which the earth moves without disturbing it, it would seem to follow that a beam of light reaching the earth from the direction towards

which the earth itself is moving should reach it faster than one from an opposite direction.

In August 1881 Albert Abraham Michelson (see 408) described, in the *American Journal of Science*, a new interferometer which he had devised with the express purpose of measuring these relative speeds with minute accuracy. Any form of clock hitherto invented, however accurate, would necessarily be subject to a margin of error greater than the time difference in question. Michelson's instrument was planned to measure the relative speeds of lightwaves moving at right angles to each other. In August 1887, in the same journal, in collaboration with Edward Williams Morley, he reported the almost completely negative results of their experiments.

The dilemma appeared inescapable until Lorentz found the solution, which he announced in two papers: (a) 'The Electromagnetic Theory of Maxwell and its Application to Moving Bodies', and (b) 'An Attempted Theory of Electrical and Optical Appearances in Moving Bodies'. In these papers Lorentz assumed the electrical nature of matter and stated that all electrical particles become shortened when in motion along the direction in which the ether drifts. Thus one arm of Michelson's interferometer would be just sufficiently shorter than the other to reduce the time necessary for light to traverse it and thus to make that time coincident with that of the beam in the transverse arm of the instrument. In 1905 Einstein propounded a special, limited theory of relativity with the express purpose of clarifying the aberration problem, to which end he adopted Lorentz's theory.

The further importance of the earlier paper is that coincidentally with J. J. Thomson (386) Lorentz had hit upon the electron theory of matter. Whetham (*A History of Science*, 3rd edition 1942, page 389) has ably summed up their respective contributions in a sentence: 'While Thomson explained electricity in terms of matter, Lorentz expressed matter in terms of electricity'. This is exemplified by Thomson's preference, as late as 1907, for the term 'corpuscle' over 'electron', which Lorentz adopted from the physicist Johnstone Stoney who had coined it in 1891 with reference to Maxwell's theory of light (355). Lorentz was a Nobel Laureate in 1902.

379

THE AMERICAN FRONTIER

FREDRICK JACKSON TURNER (1861–1932). The Significance of the Frontier in American History. *In:* Proceedings of the State Historical Society of Wisconsin. *Madison, Wis., 1894*

This brief address, given by the professor of history at the University of Wisconsin to the American Historical Association during the Chicago World Fair on 12 July 1893, initiated a novel interpretation of the course of American history.

Turner, himself a native of the young state of Wisconsin, discarded the facile view, entertained by nationalist Americans, that the United States owed its growth to the fight for religious freedom and against British tyranny. Instead, he put forward the theory that the un-interrupted search for 'free land' and its corollary, the constantly moving 'frontier', 'with its new opportunities, its continuous touch with the simplicity of primitive society, furnish the forces dominating American character'. The trader, the rancher, the farmer, the missionary, the soldier, they all contributed to 'this perennial re-birth, this fluidity of American life'; the necessity of setting up, again and again, new forms of administrative, judicial and governmental institutions made the 'frontier' a sort of political laboratory of democracy. In short, Turner—to quote the *Dictionary of American Biography*— 'regarded the frontier less as a place than as a continuous process sweeping the continent'.

What to Turner was a bold hypothesis, which he later tried to underpin with a wealth of detailed studies (col-lected in *The Frontier in American History*, 1920), became in the hands of lesser men a fixed dogma. Thus Turner was made to appear as one of those *terrible simplificateurs* when the term 'frontier' had been taken out of serious academic discussion and, charged with emotional undertones, be-came an integral part of American folklore and journalistic mythology. Its latest manifestation was the slogan of the 'new frontier' adopted by the Kennedy administration in 1961.

Röntgen himself appears to have been more interested in the purely scientific nature of the rays. Because they were unlike other and more familiar rays that emerged from the cathode terminal of the tube, and because he could not identify their origin, he named them 'X-rays', by which name the 'Röntgen–Strahlen' are still known in England.

Their importance in surgery, medicine and metallurgy is well known. Incomparably the most important aspect of Röntgen's experiments, however, is his discovery of matter in a new form, which has completely revolu-tionized the study of chemistry and physics. Laue and the Braggs (406) have used the X-rays to show us the atomic structure of crystals. Moseley (407) has reconstructed the periodic table of the elements. Becquerel (393) was directly inspired by Röntgen's results to the investigation that discovered radio-activity. Finally J. J. Thomson (386) enunciated the electron theory as a result of investi-gating the nature of the X-rays.

Röntgen was not the first to find photographic plates fogged by proximity to electrical discharges. He was the first to investigate the cause and to emerge with the explanation. This won him the first award of the Nobel Prize for Physics in 1901 and made him world famous.

380

X-RAYS

WILHELM CONRAD RÖNTGEN (1845–1923). Ueber eine Neue Art von Strahlen. *In:* Sitzungsberichte der Physikalisch-medicinischen Gesellschaft zu Würzburg. Two parts. *Würzburg, 1895–6*

The history of the discovery of X-rays begins in the seventeenth century with Otto von Guericke's vacuum pump. Heinrich Geissler, a glass-blower in the laboratory at Bonn University in the mid-nineteenth century, per-fected a form of 'vacuum' tube with platinum terminals sealed in the ends which permitted the passage of an electric current through the rarefied gas in the tube.

It was while experimenting with forms of the Geissler tube devised by Philipp Lenard and William Crookes that Röntgen, at the time professor at Würzburg Uni-versity, noticed that a paper screen coated with barium platinocyanide lying on a table had become fluorescent. He traced the cause of this phenomenon to the tube, despite the fact that it was enclosed in a light-tight black cardboard box.

Röntgen expounded in these two papers—'A New Kind of Ray'—his experiments with the comparative penetrative powers of this form of radiation. He found that although human flesh is translucent to it, bone is opaque, and photographic plates are affected by it. Indeed at the second of the two sittings in which he announced his discovery he persuaded a member of his audience, his colleague, Professor Albert von Kölliker, the famous anatomist, to permit the photographing of his hand by X-rays. Amid tremendous enthusiasm the result was exhibited and later circulated.

381

ZIONISM

THEODOR HERZL (1860–1904). Der Judenstaat, Ver-such einer Modernen Lösung der Judenfrage. *Leipzig & Vienna: M. Breitenstein, 1896*

Ever since the Jewish State was abolished by the Romans in A.D. 70, the Jews, in all countries to which they dis-persed, prayed for the restoration of their native land. Many remained in Palestine, though they were almost wiped out by the Arab invasions and during the Crusades, and many pious Jews made pilgrimages thither from the Middle Ages onwards.

The real impetus to regain their country and to reconstitute their State did not come until the mid-nineteenth century, when a new political solution was advocated by a number of politicians and thinkers, both Jewish and non-Jewish. It was Herzl's book which really crystallized the idea of a national home for the Jews. Two conceptions had prevailed hitherto: either that of the ghetto, presupposing an unbridgeable gulf between Jews and Gentiles, or that of assimilation, which meant a com-plete acceptance by the Jews of their environment leading eventually to their becoming part of the people among whom they lived. Herzl took a different view. By his work he transformed the Jewish people from a passive community into a positive political force.

Theodor Herzl was born in Buda-Pest, but his out-look, like that of all central European Jews, was essentially German. He was the Paris correspondent of the *Neue Freie Presse* in Vienna, the leading liberal newspaper in Austria, and while in Paris he was deeply influenced by the Dreyfus case and the effects of the pogroms in Russia during the eighties. He came to the conclusion that any new relationship between the Jews and other peoples could be established only if the Jews organized themselves and acted as a people. His book advocated the establishment of a State of their own. He originally conceived this simply as a progressive and advanced State, not necessarily in Palestine or even using Hebrew as its language; but he gradually accepted the idea that Palestine was the true and natural home of the Jews.

In consequence of the publication of his book—'The Jewish State, An Attempt at a Modern Solution of the Jewish Question'—a congress was held at Basle in 1897 attended by two hundred and six delegates from all parts of the world and here the Zionist organization was founded. The movement became world-wide.

During the First World War two Jews of Polish origin, Dr Chaim Weizmann and Naham Sokoloff, approached British politicians on the problem. This resulted in the historic 'Balfour Declaration' of 2 November 1917, in which Lord Balfour, then Prime Minister, promised support for the establishment of a Jewish national home in Palestine. Later all the allied nations agreed to it in principle; but the political complications were formidable and Arab objections persistent, so that it was not until 14 May 1948 that the State of Israel was finally established.

That a Jewish State was created in Palestine within fifty years of his death was due to the vision and the practical methods of Herzl, expressed in his manifesto of 1896.

382

PRACTICAL WIRELESS TELEGRAPHY

GUGLIELMO MARCONI (1874–1937). Provisional Specification. Improvements in Transmitting Electrical Impulses and Signals. *London, 2 June 1896*

The experiments of Hertz (377) were confined to the laboratory. Moreover he would appear never to have used waves of less than thirty centimetres long. Shorter wavelengths, together with refinement in transmitting and receiving apparatus, were needed to make wireless telegraphy commercially possible.

Oliver Lodge, in 1894, demonstrated at the Royal Institution an apparatus capable of transmitting and receiving signals over a distance of 150 yards. Hughes, however, claims to have more than trebled this distance at an earlier date (see 377). In 1895 A. Popoff erected antennae in his receiving circuit at Kronstadt and in the same year he demonstrated in St Petersburg an apparatus very similar to the one invented by Marconi, with one striking exception.

Popoff regarded the necessary perfecting factor as a more powerful generator of vibrations. Marconi, on the other hand, who so far as is known had proceeded without knowledge of Popoff's work, concentrated on the receiving end and the improvement of the detector, or 'coherer'. In this he confessedly followed Lodge, who, in his turn, had produced an improved form of the instrument devised by E. Branly in 1891. This was indispensable to the successful exploitation of the Hertzian experiments. The basic principle—the electrical be-

haviour of a bad contact—was discovered by Hughes and was incorporated in the microphone which he described in a paper to the Royal Society in 1878 (see 365). Branly rediscovered the principle, Lodge improved it, and Marconi made it commercially practicable.

Marconi's first successful experiments were made in Bologna. He came to London and in July 1898 was granted a patent based on the specification described above. In the same month the Wireless Telegraph Company was formed after exhaustive tests by the General Post Office. These culminated in the first successful transatlantic communication of 1901.

383

THE CINEMATOGRAPH

AUGUSTE (1862–1954) and LOUIS LUMIÈRE (1864–1948). Notice sur le Cinématographe. *Lyons: Decléris for Lumière, 1897*

Cinematography is based upon persistence of vision—a phenomenon familiar to Lucretius (87). Fox Talbot (318), inventor of the first practical method of photography, foresaw the possibility of 'living pictures' in 1851, but no commercial process was possible until the perfection of photographic film by Eastman in 1889.

Friese-Greene, Evans and Paul in England, and Edison in the United States, were among those whose early efforts were rewarded with some degree of success; but the Lumière brothers appear to have been the first to produce a cinematograph machine with commercial possibilities. 'Machine' seems to be the best description of an apparatus that was both camera and projector. This prevented the flicker so prevalent in other early machines. They took out their first patent and gave their first public exhibition in 1895. This 1897 trade catalogue, 'An Account of the Cinematograph', appears to be the first public announcement of their invention. Some of the films listed in it were exhibited at the memorial exhibition in Paris in 1937 and were found to be in perfect condition.

The Lumières were professional photographers in Lyons. In 1893, at the International Photographic Exhibition in Geneva, they exhibited the first camera portrait photographed in colour.

384

FARTHEST NORTH

FRIDTJOF NANSEN (1861–1930). Fram øver Polhavet. *Christiania: H. Aschehoug, 1897*

'Farthest North' (the title given to the English translation of this book) is Nansen's own account of a remarkable achievement in polar exploration, every detail of which was worked out by Nansen himself and went absolutely according to plan.

Early whaling experience, and the traverse of Greenland on snow-shoes and sleighs in 1888-9, convinced him that arctic exploration was feasible on revolutionary lines. He convinced himself, against accepted opinion, that there was a regular ice-drift from Alaska to Greenland. He set himself to design a ship that, by its shape, would evade the crushing pressure of the ice. His idea was deliberately to allow the ship to be frozen into the ice-pack and then to drift across the Arctic region.

This ship, the *Fram*, four hundred tons and immensely strong, was built in a Scottish yard to Nansen's design, sailed from Norway in June 1893 and in the following September rode triumphantly above the ice at the appointed spot. In August 1896 she reached Norway once more.

Nansen, with one companion and three sledges drawn by huskies, had left the ship in March 1895 and within

FRAM
OVER POLHAVET

DEN NORSKE POLARFÆRD 1893–1896

AF

FRIDTJOF NANSEN

MED ET TILLÆG AF OTTO SVERDRUP

FØRSTE DEL

KRISTIANIA
H. ASCHEHOUG & CO.s FORLAG
1897

a few weeks reached the farthest north latitude yet attained by man (86°14'). Nansen had hoped to reach the Pole, but the condition of his dogs warned him to turn back. Wintering in Franz Josef Land from August 1895 to May 1896, in June they fell in with an expedition headed by Frederick Jackson—after whom Nansen named his winter quarters—and returned to Norway with him.

His great journey received world-wide acclaim and brought him many international honours. In his native land he was made professor of oceanography at Christiania where he concentrated on his favourite subject, the study of oceanic currents. He became involved in national politics and played a very active part in the

movement for Norwegian independence from Swedish rule, subsequently becoming his government's first plenipotentiary in London.

After the First World War Nansen entered international politics and under the League of Nations handled the complicated problems associated with the vast numbers of Russian refugees, devising the 'Nansen Passport' for those who had abandoned Russian nationality without acquiring any other. He was also instrumental in furthering Germany's entry into the League of Nations. He was awarded the Nobel Peace Prize in 1922.

385
CONDITIONED REFLEXES

IVAN PETROVITCH PAVLOV (1849–1936). Лекціи о Работѣ Главныхъ Пищеварительныхъ Железъ. *St Petersburg:* [*Kushnereff*], *1897*

Mouth-watering is a familiar experience and may be induced without the sight or smell of food. The sounds of a table being laid for lunch in another room may induce salivation in man, and the rattle of a dish in which its food is usually served will cause similar reaction in a dog.

By detailed analysis of such facts as these Pavlov made great contributions to our knowledge of the physiology of digestion in a series of lectures delivered in St Petersburg and published in the following year. In the course of these lectures he described the artificial stomach for dogs used by him to produce for the first time gastric juices uncontaminated by food. Further experiments led him to the conclusion that salivation and the flow of gastric juice ensuing upon the sight or smell of food was due to a reflex process. This simple form of reaction he called first a 'psychic', later an 'unconditioned', reflex. Reflex action was familiar to physiologists, but it had never been invoked to explain such a complicated process.

Pavlov now set himself to discover the far more complicated process involved in the evocation of gastric responses to stimuli other than food, for example the rattle of a familiar platter. This was in the nature of an acquired stimulus and as reflex action was induced by a particular condition or set of conditions he called it a 'conditioned' reflex. From a series of experiments increasingly detailed, and a tabulation of results increasingly exact, he found that virtually any natural phenomenon may be developed into a conditioned stimulus to produce the selected response—'The Activity of the Digestive Glands'. All that was necessary was to submit the animal to the selected stimulus at feeding time and the stimulus would eventually cause salivation in the absence of food.

The elaboration of these experiments and their extension to children demonstrated how great a proportion of human behaviour is explicable as a series of conditioned reflexes. Indeed some psychologists seem nowadays to believe that behaviour is all. Pavlov's results are, indeed, clearly complementary to those of Freud

(389) and many regard them as of more fundamental significance. Like Freud's, this was the work of one man and a completely new departure. Pavlov was awarded the Nobel Prize for Medicine in 1905.

386

CATHODE RAYS

JOSEPH JOHN THOMSON (1856–1940). (a) Cathode Rays. *In*: Philosophical Magazine. *London, 1897*; (b) The Discharge of Electricity through Gases. *New York: Scribner, 1898*; (c) On the Charge of Electricity carried by the Ions produced by Röntgen Rays. *In*: Philosophical Magazine. *London, 1898*; (d) Conduction of Electricity through Gases. *Cambridge University Press, 1903*

Cathode rays were first observed by Julius Plücker in 1859 (Poggendorff's *Annalen der Physik und Chemie*, 107). They are rays which are found in the neighbourhood of the point of exit of an electric current passing through a Geissler tube (see 380). These rays stimulated intense interest and experiment. Sir William Crookes greatly improved these discharge tubes and intensified the degree of rarefication of gases within them. The tube in this form is known as a Crookes tube. In 1879 (*Phil. Trans.* 170), Crookes declared his conviction that the cathode rays represented matter in a fourth, hitherto unobserved form. Unfortunately he made this suggestion unacceptable by describing particles that make up the cathode stream as of molecular proportions.

It was reserved for J. J. Thomson (knighted in 1908) to discover the true nature of the cathode rays. In April 1897 he gave a public demonstration at one of the Friday evening discourses at the Royal Institution in which he declared that cathode rays are composed of particles of sub-atomic proportions. At this stage, he had been unable to calculate the weight of the particles, but he had measured their rate of charge to mass. The ratio was large, so they must either have a big charge or a small mass. Thomson gave reasons for preferring the latter—from experiments performed by Lenard in particular.

If the charge could be calculated, then the mass could be found, since the ratio between the two was known. Thomson eventually succeeded in calculating the charge, by an ingenious adaptation of the 'dust counter' devised by C. T. R. Wilson (*Phil. Trans.* 189A). Thomson substituted for the dust particles counted by Wilson the cathode-ray particles. By observing variations in their fall in various electric fields he was able to calculate the electric charge on the particles. These experiments, later perfected by Millikan, led to the calculation of the mass of the electron as one eighteen-hundredth of a hydrogen atom, hitherto the lightest known object. Moreover the mass of these 'corpuscles', as Thomson called them, was constant, whatever their origin. That is to say that all forms of matter, no matter how varied their chemical composition, produced cathode rays of uniform make-up.

The reference to 'Röntgen rays' in (c) above indicates their identity with cathode rays. Although he still pre-

ferred as late as 1907 'corpuscle' to 'electron' to describe this ultimate particle, Thomson had provided experimental proof of the theoretical speculation of Lorentz (378). In doing so he had revolutionized the science of physics. The 'indestructible' atom was no more and it began to seem likely that the common constituent of all matter was a form of energy. Thomson's discovery opened up new fields of investigation in almost every branch of physics and initiated such departments as thermionics and photo-electricity. The four titles at the head of this entry indicate Thomson's intense and developing interest in this subject.

He was closely associated with Aston (412), his research assistant, in the discovery of isotopes of non-radioactive elements; and in 1913 he produced a massive work on *Positive Rays of Electricity* from which important contributions to chemical analysis by others besides Aston followed.

Thomson was President of the Royal Society from 1915 to 1920 and Nobel Prize Winner in Physics in 1906. He made of the Cavendish Laboratory at Cambridge the greatest experimental school in physics ever known and was succeeded there by his pupil Rutherford (411).

387

THE GARDEN CITY

EBENEZER HOWARD (1850–1928). To-Morrow: a Peaceful Path to Real Reform. *London: Swan, Sonnenschein, 1898*

Garden cities are the creation of one man, Ebenezer Howard. Town planning is as old as ancient Babylon. Garden villages, designed to house factory workers decently and close to their work, were built by Titus Salt—Saltaire, near Bradford, in 1856; by George Cadbury—Bournville, near Birmingham, 1879; and by W. H. Lever—Port Sunlight, near Birkenhead, 1888. Each of these is associated with a particular manufacturer and confined to his own employees. Moreover they are not self-contained and have no protective green belt.

Howard was a shorthand writer at the Law Courts in London. A nonconformist, as a result of sojourn in the United States he had come under the influence of Emerson, Lincoln, Lowell, and Whitman; and it is on record that his garden city plans were derived from reading Bellamy's *Looking Backward* in 1888. He determined that the most practical way to realize Bellamy's ideas in England was 'to build by private enterprise pervaded by public spirit an entirely new town, industrial, residential and agricultural'. This was the idea upon which he enlarged in the book published in 1898 and which he carried forward nine months later by the formation of a Garden City Association.

There can be little doubt that the project was both helped and hindered by the crankiness of some of its supporters. Howard himself was an Esperantist, teetotaller and non-smoker, with strong leanings towards vegetarianism. Nevertheless he was the inventor of a forerunner of the modern stenographic typewriter, and when in 1903 nearly four thousand acres came into the market at Letchworth, Hertfordshire, Howard, himself a poor man, was able to raise subscriptions totalling £155,000 or more to purchase the land with a view to building the first Garden City there.

In 1919 he acquired land at Welwyn, Hertfordshire, on which to build a second city. He was to live to see not

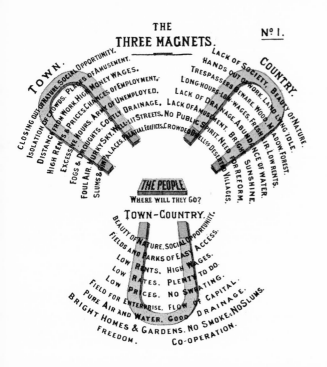

only the spread throughout the world of the movement he had started singlehanded, but the establishment of Town and Country Planning as a universally recognized obligation of government in the civilized world. Satellite towns, and the very latest suggestion of city-clusters, were well in the forefront of Howard's ideas.

388

TROPICAL MEDICINE

PATRICK MANSON (1844–1922). Tropical Diseases. London: Cassell, 1898

In 1866 Manson, who was born and educated in Aberdeenshire, took up a medical appointment in Formosa, moving shortly to Amoy, China, where he began the study of tropical diseases which was to become his main interest in life. He found little but ignorance and an almost total lack of interest in tropical medicine in the profession. An exception was a detailed report by Timothy Lewis, a medical officer in India, on a thread-like worm he had found in human blood which he named Filaria sanguinis hominis.

In 1876 Manson sought and found this worm in the blood of his Chinese patients suffering from elephantoid

diseases. Controlled and detailed experiments and observations on his devoted servants disclosed that the parasites appear in the blood much more rarely during the hours of daylight than at night, which coincided with the feeding times of a domestic mosquito, now identified as Culex fatigans. Manson believed that filarial disease was found only where this insect was active. Although this belief later proved erroneous, it was a fortunate error, for it encouraged an assumption that Filaria spent part of its life in the body of the mosquito, which was responsible for the spread of infection. This he succeeded in proving. He had demonstrated for the first time that insects could be carriers of disease.

When Surgeon-Major Ronald Ross (1857–1932) met Manson while on leave from India in 1894, the latter had become a consultant in London. Ross was a poet, novelist and playwright and did not take his profession seriously. Manson had by this time made up his mind that a mosquito would be found to be the carrier of malaria. He committed himself to this view in the British Medical Journal in December 1894 and he succeeded in firing the dilettante Surgeon-Major with enthusiasm for following up the project. In 1897 Ross contributed two papers to the British Medical Journal in which he described his observations of the malaria parasite in the abdomen of a 'dapple-winged' mosquito, now called anopheles, and in 1898 in the Lancet he proved conclusively that the infection was conveyed by anopheles in avian malaria. In 1901 G. B. Grassi published an elaborate monograph in which the transmission of human malaria by a similar process was fully worked out.

Manson campaigned tirelessly for better instruction in tropical diseases in the face of much opposition and ridicule. He was disparaged even by Ross in later years. In 1898 he published his great work, Tropical Diseases, and in 1899 was responsible for persuading Joseph Chamberlain, then Secretary of State for the Colonies, to institute the London School of Tropical Medicine.

The conquest of yellow fever and sleeping sickness together with all the numerous maladies now known to be transmitted by fleas, bugs, lice, ticks and other insects originated with Manson's study of Filaria published in 1877. Equally important was his lifelong campaign for the proper equipment of tropical medical services, which fully earned him the title of 'Father of Tropical Medicine'.

389

PSYCHOANALYSIS

SIGMUND FREUD (1856–1939). Die Traumdeutung. Leipzig & Vienna: Deuticke, 1900

Freud qualified as a doctor in 1881. In 1883 he took the advice of Josef Breuer, a practising physician and a family friend, and began to specialize in neurology. In 1885 he went to Paris and studied under J. M. Charcot, the greatest neurologist of his day. One of the most impressive of Charcot's demonstrations was to induce the symptoms of hysteria in normal patients under hypnosis. This indicated clearly that hysteria was a mental affliction and not necessarily a symptom of organic disorder. After his return to Vienna Freud read a paper on the subject before the *Gesellschaft der Aertze* which was not treated with the seriousness it deserved.

In 1889 Freud went to Nancy to witness the experiments in hypnosis of Hippolyte Bernheim, whose work, like that of Charcot, he translated into German. These were experiments in post-hypnotic suggestion; and what impressed Freud most deeply was the reluctance of the subject to divulge the true reason for his actions. Only after persistent questioning were false reasons abandoned and the truth disclosed. Freud suggested to Breuer a joint study of the subject, combining Breuer's knowledge with that gleaned from Charcot and Bernheim. Breuer was a much older man but eventually his reluctance to resume interest in the subject was conquered by Freud's persistence. In January 1893 they published jointly a paper in the *Neurologisches Centralblatt* on the treatment of hysteria, which was followed in 1895 by *Studien über Hysterie*.

Very briefly, what they had done was to reverse Charcot's experiment. He induced hysteria in normal subjects under hypnosis—they used hypnosis to release hysterical patients from their affliction. Their experience was that patients who could be induced to recall the circumstances associated with the onset of hysteria would thus purge themselves of the disorder. For this reason they called their methods 'cathartic'.

Freud, however, had learned from Bernheim that subjects would be unlikely to know the reasons for their actions, because they were buried deep in what Freud called the 'unconscious mind'. Only by allowing the patient to talk at random was it possible eventually to unearth the true cause of the trouble. This was called 'free association'. It will be seen that not only had some of the essentials of what was to become psychoanalysis already emerged by 1895 but that a revolution in mental therapy had been adumbrated.

'Studies in Hysteria' made impact only in so far as its conclusions were fiercely contested by the medical profession: Krafft-Ebing, in 1896, in the chair at one of Freud's papers, described it as 'a scientific fairy-tale'. Yet bitter disappointment did not diminish Freud's enthusiasm. In 1894–5 he was already developing his theories of obsessional neuroses, which explained the remoteness of 'replacement ideas' as the covering up of painful experiences; and also the most controversial of all his theories, that the painful experiences were usually of sexual origin.

Although not published until 1900 'The Interpretation of Dreams' was virtually complete in all essentials at the beginning of 1896. Extending the wish-fulfilment nature of day-dreams to night-dreams, Freud differentiated the two kinds of wish: those in day-dreams being open and conscious, while the less pleasant subjects were repressed, to be released from the sub-conscious only in sleep when the censorship of consciousness is relaxed.

This is unquestionably Freud's greatest single work. It contains all the basic components of psychoanalytic

DIE

TRAUMDEUTUNG

VON

DR. SIGM. FREUD.

———

»FLECTERE SI NEQUEO SUPEROS, ACHERONTA MOVEBO.

——— ◄►► ———

LEIPZIG UND WIEN.
FRANZ DEUTICKE.
1900.

theory and practice: the erotic nature of dreams, the 'Oedipus complex', the libido, and the rest; all related to the background of the 'unconscious', later to be called the 'sub-conscious'.

390
LIBERAL PROTESTANTISM

ADOLF HARNACK (1851–1930). *Das Wesen des Christentums*. *Leipzig: J. C. Hinrichs, 1900*

These lectures on 'The Essence of Christianity' by the then professor of church history at Berlin University were received with an enthusiasm unparalleled for centuries in the field of religious pamphleteering. They proclaimed the fundamental concord of the tenets of the early Church as preserved in the non-Roman Churches with the religious aspirations, the intellectual climate and the social and economic morality of the twentieth century; and innumerable reprints and translations broadcast this message of liberal Protestantism all over the world.

Harnack (ennobled in 1914) won international fame as the leading student of the early Church with his monumental *Lehrbuch der Dogmengeschichte*, 3 vols., 1886–9, which has remained the indispensable 'Manual of the History of Dogma'; his *Geschichte der altchristlichen*

Literatur bis Eusebius, 3 vols., 1893–1904, which is as yet unsurpassed as a 'History of Christian Literature till Eusebius'; his *Mission und Ausbreitung des Christentums in den ersten drei Jahrhunderten* (1902; 4th edition, 2 vols., 1923) which explained the 'mission and expansion of Christianity before Constantine'; and his *Marcion* (1921; 2nd edition 1924) in which he elucidated the life and teaching of the gnostic arch-heretic.

Harnack's influence upon the intellectual life of Germany was enormous. He was a co-founder and for many years the president of the Evangelic-Social Congress (1890) which brought together theologians, politicians and economists interested in the problems of social welfare. He was an active member of the Prussian Academy of Sciences, through which he exerted great power over the universities—he wrote its history in the *Geschichte der kgl. Preussischen Akademie*, 3 vols., 1900. As director-general of the Prussian state library (1905–21) he initiated the work on the union catalogue of the German libraries as well as the international 'Catalogue of Incunabula' (*Gesamtkatalog der Wiegendrucke*). Through his friendship with the Emperor William II he originated, and became the first president of, the Kaiser-Wilhelm-Gesellschaft (1910/11), the holding organization of all German research institutes.

391

THE QUANTUM THEORY

MAX PLANCK (1858–1947). (*a*) Zur Theorie des Gesetzes der Energieverteilung im Normalspectrum. *In:* Verhandlungen der Deutschen Physikalischen Gesellschaft. *Leipzig, 1900;* (*b*) Ueber des Gesetzes der Energieverteilung im Normalspectrum. *In:* Annalen der Physik. *Leipzig, 1901*

Planck, in his Nobel Prize Address in 1920, gives a remarkable instance of the interconnexion between superficially unconnected investigations. He received the prize for his theory that energy is not continuous but is released in small, discrete, indivisible units which he called quanta; and his historical survey indicated that he was first attracted to the subject by a paper on the spectrum of radiant heat by Kirchhoff (278 *b*) whom, incidentally, he had succeeded at Berlin in 1889. When he began his investigations he used a series of resonators devised by Hertz (377), and he would have arrived at his conclusion much earlier if he had been less sceptical of the theories put forward by Lorentz (378).

Everybody knows that a certain minimum of power is necessary to work a machine and it had been assumed that with gradually increased power the output grows in smoothly continuous fashion. Planck found that this anticipated continuous progression was not borne out by the facts. In these two papers on 'The Law of Distribution of Energy in the Normal Spectrum' he explained that his resonators began to react only when a definite unit of energy was available, and that acceleration occurred in exact multiples of that unit: not continuously, but in a series of discrete gushes. This unit he called a *quantum* of energy.

Here was a revolutionary theory. It contradicted the mechanics of Newton (161) and the electromagnetics of Faraday (309) and Maxwell (355). Moreover it challenged the notion of the continuity of nature.

The quantum was found to be constant only in relation to a particular source of energy. If different forms of matter are classified in accordance with spectrum analysis, this is to rank them in order of the wavelength of light emitted by them. The quantum of energy necessary to evoke this radiation will vary accordingly, being smallest at the infra-red end of the spectrum and increasing as we pass to the ultra-violet.

The quantum theory has affected virtually every branch of physics. Its earliest and one of its most significant developments was Einstein's (see 408) application of the theory to what is known as the 'photo-electric effect'. If ultra-violet light or X-rays are passed through a gas, some of its atoms are broken up and electrons are emitted from it. A puzzling feature of this phenomenon is that neither the number nor the speed of the ejected electrons bears a direct relation to the intensity of the beam. Feeble radiation of high frequency may be much more effective than intense radiation at low frequency; but if the frequency of light is below a given figure no electrons will be ejected, however intense the beam. Above that figure the energy of the electrons depends on frequency and their number on intensity.

Einstein explained this by suggesting that the classical view that light is emitted in the form of continuous waves must be abandoned. The photo-electric effect could be explained only as an example of quantum action where the waves of light or X-rays are emitted in minute particles or bullets. It is the size of the bullet (the wavelength of the radiation) which determines the number of electrons ejected. It was for this, and not for the theory of relativity, that Einstein was awarded the Nobel Prize in 1921. Einstein's two fundamental papers on this subject are: 'Ueber einen die Erzeugung und Verwandlung des Lichtes betreffenden Heuristichen Gesichtspunkt' (in *Annalen der Physik*, Leipzig, 1905), and 'Zur Theorie der Lichterzeugung und Lichtabsorption' (*ibid.* 1906).

As with the theory of relativity, so with the quantum theory the classic hypothesis of the continuity of force still holds good not only in everyday life but in some spheres of scientific enquiry. Indeed Sir William Bragg (406 *b*) has said that scientists use the classical theory on Mondays, Wednesdays and Fridays and the quantum theory on Tuesdays, Thursdays and Saturdays—Sunday being a day of rest. Bragg likened this to the carpenter's changing his saw for a chisel.

Planck was the President of the Kaiser-Wilhelm-Gesellschaft from 1930 to 1937 but was deposed by the Nazis. After the Second World War the Gesellschaft was refounded under his name.

392

BOLSHEVISM

Vladimir Ilyich [Ulyanov] Lenin (1870–1924).
Что дѣлать? Наболѣвшіе вопросы нашего движенія. *Stuttgart: J. H. W. Dietz, 1902*

Written between the autumn of 1901 and February 1902, while Lenin and his wife, N. K. Krupskaya, were in exile in Munich (with Zürich the main centre of Russian revolutionary emigration at that time) 'What is to be done?' was the ideological keystone of the Bolshevik Party.

It was published, with the subtitle 'Burning Questions of Our Movement', by the official publishers of the German Social-Democratic Party, Dietz of Stuttgart.

Что дѣлать?

Наболѣвшіе вопросы нашего движенія

Н. ЛЕНИНА.

... „Партійная борьба придаетъ партіи силу и жизненность, величайшимъ доказательствомъ слабости партіи является ея расплывчатость и притупленіе рѣзко обозначенныхъ границъ, партія укрѣпляется тѣмъ, что очищаетъ себя“... (Изъ письма Лассаля къ Марксу отъ 24 іюня 1852 г.).

STUTTGART
Verlag von J. H. W. Dietz Nachf. (G. m. b. H.)
1902

The title-page bore the significant quotation from Lassalle: 'Party struggles give a party strength and life... A party becomes stronger by purging itself'. Of the book's first appearance Krupskaya wrote: 'Later the Mensheviks vehemently attacked *What is to be done?* but at this juncture the book captivated everyone, especially those more closely in touch with Russian work.' This was because it 'provided a plan for extensive revolutionary work. It pointed out definite jobs to be done.'

But though the book's appeal for better organization was of central importance, particularly in the haphazard Russian movement of those days, this was not separated from the general argument on the political necessity to build a strong, centralized party (a 'party of a new type'), fighting constantly for the purity of its doctrine, and led by professionals 'who shall devote to the revolution not only their spare evenings, but the whole of their lives'.

Lenin contended for conscious leadership as against reliance on 'spontaneous' reactions among the people and stressed the great value of a party newspaper as a collective organizer, drawing on the experience of the recently-founded *Iskra*: it was in no. 4 (May 1901) of that journal that Lenin, in an article headed 'Where to begin?', had sketched the ideas fully developed in 'What is to be done?'.

The book presented Lenin's most searching criticism of the 'economist' tendency; the view that the purely economic, trade union struggle was all that concerned the workers. On the contrary, he said, 'the workers can acquire class political consciousness *only from without*, that it is only outside of the economic struggle'. The revolutionary socialist's ideal, he added, 'should not be a trade union secretary, but a *tribune of the people*'.

393

RADIO-ACTIVITY

Henri Becquerel (1852–1908). Recherches sur une Propriété Nouvelle de la Matière...ou Radioactivité de la Matière. *Paris: Firmin-Didot, 1903*

Becquerel attended a session of the Académie des Sciences in Paris on 20 January 1896, when Jules Henri Poincaré exhibited a series of radiographs sent to him by Röntgen (380). He, like others, observed that the emission of X-rays from the cathode tube was accompanied by strong phosphorescence of the glass. He therefore suspected that other forms of induced phosphorescence might be accompanied by other and hitherto unknown rays.

In February 1896 Charles Henry reported to the Académie his discovery that phosphorescence could be induced in certain substances by exposure to sunlight. In the same month Becquerel reported that uranium was among those substances. Like all his other early papers on the subject, this appeared in the *Comptes rendus* and was entitled 'Sur les Radiations Invisibles émises par les Corps Phosphorescents'. In a second paper, 'Sur quelques Propriétés Nouvelles des Radiations Invisibles', he reported the astonishing fact that uranium was capable of fogging photographic plates even without previous exposure to sunlight and when the plates themselves were completely protected from ordinary light. In a third paper, March 1896, 'Sur les Radiations invisibles émises par les sels d'Uranium' Becquerel discarded phosphorescence completely and declared that the emanations from uranium constituted an entirely new and unsuspected property of matter, which in his seventh paper he named *radioactivité*. He also found that the uranium rays discharged a gold-leaf electroscope, which is still used as one method of detecting radio-activity.

Becquerel also discovered that the residue of pitch-blende, a natural uranium oxide, after the uranium had been extracted from it was about four times as radio-active as uranium itself. He therefore suggested to the Curies (394) the importance of further investigation of the ore, with the result that they discovered radium. He continued to work on the subject until 1903, in which year he collaborated with Pierre Curie in a paper, 'Action Physiologique des Rayons du Radium', which is the starting-point of the treatment of disease by radio-active substances. In that year he also published the above massive volume of some three hundred and sixty pages, 'Researches into a New Property of Matter, or Radio-activity in Matter', which is his definitive work, containing a chronological narrative of his investigations, his mature conclusions and a bibliography of two hundred and fourteen treatises on radio-activity, dating from his own first paper in 1896.

The rays emitted by uranium were named in his honour 'Becquerel' rays. They were later discovered to be a composite of three forms of emanation, distinguished by Rutherford (411) as alpha, beta and gamma rays and identified thus: alpha as helium nuclei, beta as electrons, and gamma as powerful X-rays. Becquerel shared with Madame Curie and her husband Pierre the Nobel Prize for Physics in 1903.

A considerable event in the life of this devoted couple was Marie Curie's appointment to a lectureship in physics at a girls' school in Seires. Her advancement in this post was dependent on her obtaining a Doctorate in Science, for which purpose she prepared the two theses listed above—'Researches on Radio-active Substances', and 'Propositions set by the Faculty'.

Pierre's Œuvres is a collection of all his papers on radio-activity.

The Curies shared a Nobel Prize for Physics with Becquerel in 1903 and Marie won it alone for Chemistry in 1911. The Curies's daughter Iréne, with her husband, Frédéric Joliot, won the Nobel Prize for Chemistry in 1935.

BIBLIOGRAPHY: For those concerned with bibliographical niceties it is unusually consoling to find that Gauthier-Villars borrowed from the musical world the practice of giving serial numbers to his publications. The two papers by Marie, listed above, were also printed in the Annales de Chimie et de Physique from September to November 1903 and offprints of this printing were made. The Thèses as described above bear the serial number 33566, the offprint is 33957 and the revised edition of 1904 is 35119.

394

THE DISCOVERY OF RADIUM

(a) MARIE SKLODOWSKA CURIE (1867–1934). Thèses présentées à la Faculté des Sciences de Paris pour obtenir le grade de Docteur ès Sciences Physiques. 1re. Thèse: Recherches sur les Substances Radio-actives. 2e. Thèse: Propositions données par la Faculté. Paris: Gauthier-Villars, 1903
(b) PIERRE CURIE (1859–1906). Œuvres. Paris: Gauthier-Villars, 1908

In 1896 Becquerel (393) had suggested to the Curies that the peculiarly powerful radio-active properties of pitch-blende would repay intensive examination. The wretched poverty in which they lived was frustrating, but the generous gift by the Austrian Government of a ton of pitchblende from the Joachimsthal mines made it possible for them to undertake the necessary experiments.

In a series of papers beginning in 1897 in the Comptes rendus they reported progress in their researches. First they isolated a new substance about three hundred times as active as radium. This they called polonium in honour of Marie's native Poland. A further examination of the residue of pitchblende after the removal of uranium and polonium disclosed residual radio-activity far greater than was possessed by either substance alone. To this material the name of radium was given. This was in 1898 and already Marie was able to estimate its probable atomic weight as 226·2. Although not yet isolated in its pure form, radium was found to be about two million times as radio-active as uranium. By 1902, from several tons of pitchblende the Curies had abstracted a single decigram of radium chloride.

395

POWERED FLIGHT

WILBUR (1867–1912) and ORVILLE WRIGHT (1871–1948). The Experiments of the Brothers Wright. In: Journal of the Aeronautical Society of Great Britain. London, 1904

The Wright brothers were the first men in history to make powered, sustained and controlled flights in an aeroplane (1903), and the first to build and fly a fully practical aeroplane (1905).

They began their serious aeronautical experiments in 1899 with the construction of a biplane kite whose wings could be helically twisted to present differing angles of incidence to the wind, and thus to provide a control in roll (lateral control). In 1900 they took their first full-size glider to Kitty Hawk, North Carolina, where they were to master the art of flight control in three seasons of glider flight. With their improved No. 3 glider of 1902 they had learnt to offset the troublesome drag caused by the twisting (warping) of the wings by use of a vertical rear rudder, and thus to establish the control which has been used ever since.

On 17 December 1903, with their first specially built powered machine, the Flyer, they made the first proper powered flights in history at the Kill Devil Hills, south of Kitty Hawk. The best of four 'flights' that day was of 59 seconds duration, during which the machine covered 852 feet over the ground, and a half mile through the air, as they flew into the wind.

The brothers wrote various accounts of these flights, but the earliest to have been printed is the one written by Orville for newspaper publication, and sent by him to Major Baden-Powell, the President of the Aeronautical

Society of Great Britain, by whom it was inserted in its 'Journal'. It was for this purpose that Orville sent over his piece, to correct the wildly misleading accounts circulating in the newspapers. 'On the morning of December 17th, between the hours of 10.30 o'clock and noon four flights were made, two by Mr Orville Wright, and two by Mr Wilbur Wright. The starts were all made from a point on the level, and about 200 feet west of our camp, which is located about a quarter of a mile north of the Kill Devil Sand Hill, in Dare County, North Carolina. The wind at the time of the flights had a velocity of twenty-seven miles an hour at 10 o'clock, and 24 miles an hour at noon, as recorded by the anemometer at the Kitty Hawk weather bureau station...The flights were directly against the wind. Each time the machine started from the level ground by its own power alone, with no assistance from gravity or any other sources whatever... Only those who are acquainted with practical aeronautics can appreciate the difficulties of attempting the first trials of a flying machine in a 25-mile gale. As winter was already well set in, we should have postponed our trials to a more favourable season, but for the fact that we were determined before returning home, to know whether the machine possessed sufficient power to fly, sufficient strength to withstand the shocks of landings, and sufficient capacity of control to make flight safe in boisterous winds, as well as in calm air. When these points had been definitely established, we at once packed our goods and returned home knowing that the age of the flying machine had come at last.'

The brothers then abandoned the North Carolina coast, and in 1904 and 1905 perfected their machines (the Flyers II and III) and their flight control at the Huffman Prairie near their home-town of Dayton, Ohio; with the III they could bank, turn and circle, and fly for over half-an-hour at a time.

After many frustrations, the first flights in public were made in 1908, with Wilbur flying in France, and Orville at Fort Myer, Washington. These flights revolutionized the primitive state of European aviation, and resulted in the true conquest of the air.

Their original machine of 1903 was lent by Orville Wright to the Science Museum in South Kensington in 1928; and the Museum recently gave it to the Smithsonian Institute in Washington, so that the brothers are now properly commemorated in the capital of their own country. A replica has replaced the original in the Science Museum in London.

396
BROADCASTING FORESHADOWED

JAMES AMBROSE FLEMING (1849–1945). On the Conversion of Electric Oscillations into Continuous Currents by means of a Vacuum Valve. *In:* Proceedings of the Royal Society. *London, 1905*

In 1884 William Henry Preece, an official of the British General Post Office, was shown an experiment by Thomas Edison. Of this experiment Preece gave what appears to be the first printed account in a paper entitled 'On a Peculiar Behaviour of Glow-Lamps when raised to high Incandescence' (*Proceedings of the Royal Society*, 1885, XXXVIII, pp. 219–30). What Edison had demonstrated was that if a metal plate is sealed into an electric light bulb and joined to the positive end of the filament a considerable current will pass. If the plate is joined to the negative terminal, however, no current will pass.

This was known as the 'Edison effect' and in 1890 Fleming, an electrical engineer who had worked with the Edison company in London and was now a professor at University College, began a careful study of this phenomenon in carbon filament lamps. In 1904 he was able to demonstrate that this occurred not only with electric waves but also with wireless waves. He thus introduced the basic principle of the modern wireless valve, which permits only unilateral conductivity.

The immense superiority of the Fleming thermionic valve to all previous detectors of wireless waves caused it to be widely used as an efficient and reliable detector; but it was not until Lee DeForest in America in 1907 perfected the 'grid' that wireless signals could be amplified to the degree necessary to make radio-telephony and broadcasting possible. DeForest published his results only in 1913, by which time other investigators had made use of his system.

397
A CLASSIC OF NEUROLOGY

CHARLES SCOTT SHERRINGTON (1857–1952). The Integrative Action of the Nervous System. *New Haven: Yale University Press, 1906*

Sir Charles Sherrington did much experimental work on all phases of reflex action and of the functions of the nervous system. He demonstrated that most reflexes are coordinated; that the nervous system functions as a whole, so that reflex action is not an isolated phenomenon; and that the true function of the nervous system is to integrate the organism, making it an individual whole, not just a collection of organs and cells.

Sherrington further analysed the mechanism of the interaction of nerve cells and their effect on behaviour. He explained that inhibitory or excitatory effects interact on the individual nerve cells and that two different physico-chemical processes account for these effects. The points of contact between nerve-cells, where the 'interaction of neurons' takes place, he called 'synapses'. He also proved the presence of sense organs in skeletal muscles, i.e. reactions caused by stimuli not from outside but originating within the body; and he analysed mass discharges of motor centres. These and other highly complicated problems were elucidated by Sherrington in various papers and are summed up in this book, which is recognized as a classic of modern neurology. The experiments on reflex action carried out by Pavlov (385) and by Sherrington provided a foundation for the objective treatment of human psychological problems, in particular the theory of behaviourism.

Sherrington was Waynflete professor of physiology at Oxford from 1913 to 1935, and President of the Royal Society; he received the Order of Merit and in 1932 the Nobel Prize for Medicine. He was a man of remarkably wide interests. His *Man on his Nature*, 1940, contains a monograph on mind and body; he wrote a brilliant book on Goethe as a natural scientist (2nd edition, 1949), published a volume of verses and a work on Fernel (68) containing a most scholarly exposition of sixteenth-century medicine; and he also found time to form a fine collection of early printed books.

BIBLIOGRAPHY: John F. Fulton, 'Bibliography of Sir Charles Sherrington'. In: *Obituary Notices of the Royal Society*, vol. 8 (London, 1952).

398
VOTES FOR WOMEN

FREDERICK WILLIAM (1871–1961) and EMMELINE (1867–1954) PETHICK LAWRENCE (Editors). Votes for Women. *London: The Reformer's Press, 1907–17*

The struggle for the emancipation of women in Great Britain is a movement virtually confined to the nineteenth century, despite bold forerunners like Mary Wollstonecraft (242). In the Reform Bill of 1832 the new franchise qualifications specifically included the word 'male' for the first time. Hitherto it had been tacitly assumed that women had no open part in national politics—the *Lysistrata* of Aristophanes notwithstanding.

John Stuart Mill (345) declared for women's suffrage in his election address at Westminster in 1885 and from that time forward a new bill was introduced into Parliament every few years to promote it. Although several of these bills passed their second reading they all failed because of the unreadiness of the government of the day to grant them further facilities.

In 1896 Mrs Henry Fawcett was instrumental in the amalgamation of a number of separate societies into the National Union of Women's Suffrage Societies; but it was not until the formation, in 1906, of the National Women's Social and Political Union by Mrs Pankhurst and her daughter Christabel that real progress began to be made. Immediately a more vigorous plan of campaign was instituted and already in 1906 two members of the new organization were imprisoned for refusing to pay fines for disturbances caused at public meetings. Strong financial and public support was enlisted, not merely from women—a Men's League for Women's Suffrage was formed in 1907—and the journal *Votes for Women* was started in 1907, and became the organ of the 'militants'.

In Mr Roy Jenkins's *Asquith* the onset of 'militancy' is said to date from October 1905, when Christabel Pankhurst and Annie Kenney wrecked Edward Grey's meeting in Manchester. It seems to have been adopted as a deliberate policy in 1908, including breaches of the law and acts of public violence. Hunger strikes were practised by those in prison, and the activities of the suffragettes,

as they were by now commonly called, became a major government preoccupation in the years immediately preceding the outbreak of the First World War. More bills were introduced during this period, all equally abortive, and the failure of the most promising was said to have been due to disgust with the 'militants'.

VOTES FOR WOMEN

EDITED BY

FREDERICK & EMMELINE PETHICK LAWRENCE.

. . ᛫ ᛫ ᛫

VOL. I.

October, 1907, to September, 1908.

—

London :

THE REFORMER'S PRESS,

4, CLEMENTS INN, W.C.

Further consideration of the question was set aside during the war, when no elections were held, although a Speaker's Committee in 1916 reported in favour of female suffrage. However, the enormous contribution made by women to the war effort as nurses, munition workers, even taxi-drivers, did more than all the earlier agitation to establish the right of women to some say in the government of the country, and a government bill in 1918 granting the vote to married women, women householders and women university graduates aged thirty or over was passed by an overwhelming majority, which enabled them to vote in the first post-war election. Finally, in 1928, all women over twenty-one were given the vote and placed on an equality with male voters.

399
THE BOY SCOUT MOVEMENT

ROBERT STEPHENSON SMYTH BADEN-POWELL (1857–1941). Scouting for Boys. Six parts. *London: Horace Cox, 1908*

Baden-Powell was the son of an Oxford don. His mother was descended collaterally from John Smith of Virginia and was a great-niece of Nelson. He was named after his godfather, Robert Stephenson the engineer.

As a subaltern in the 13th Hussars, Baden-Powell early showed an interest in reconnaissance and scouting and published a book on the subject in 1884. In 1899, when in command of the 5th Dragoon Guards, he published *Aids to Scouting*.

When he reviewed a national parade of the Boys' Brigade in 1904 he was much impressed with their bearing and efficiency, but deplored their small numbers. Sir William Smith, their commander, suggested that a new edition of *Aids to Scouting* written for boys might help. Baden-Powell was a great believer in practical experiment. All his previous books had been based on personal experience, so in 1907, before acting on Smith's suggestion, he organized a trial camp for boys from all walks of life at Brownsea Island. Its success was unmistakable, and he began at once to write *Scouting for Boys*.

CHAPTER I.

SCOUTCRAFT.

➤◦◦◦◅

NOTE FOR INSTRUCTOR.

The following is a suggestion for the distribution of the work for the first week. It is merely a suggestion and in no sense binding.

FIRST EVENING :
INDOORS.
Address the boys on " Scoutcraft," giving a summary of the whole scheme, as in this chapter, with demonstrations or lantern slides, etc.
Swear in the Scouts, form Patrols, and give shoulder knots.
FOLLOWING DAY :
MORNING AND AFTERNOON.
Practical work, outdoors if possible, as follows :—
Alternatives according to whether in town or country, indoors or out.
MORNING.
Parade, hoist Union Jack and salute it.
Scouting game : e.g., " Scout Meets Scout." (See page 53).
Practise salutes, secret signs, patrol calls, scouts' chorus, etc.
Practise drawing scout-signs on ground or walls with stick or chalk.
Tie knots.
Make ration bags, leather buttons, etc.

Before the series of fortnightly parts was half completed, troops were being formed all over the country. Thus, instead of revamping the Boys' Brigade, Baden-Powell started a new organization, which entirely eclipsed the Brigade.

By 1910 the movement had grown to such a size (over one hundred thousand) that Baden-Powell left the army to devote himself exclusively to the Boy Scouts; and in 1929, on the occasion of the third international 'Jamboree', as he called his Boy Scout rallies, Baden-Powell

was raised to the peerage. The organization became world-wide and has been extensively copied, or perverted, in police-states. Moreover, repugnant though their aims would have been to the founder of the movement, Komsomols and Hitler-Jugend also professed his aim of 'promoting good citizenship in the rising generation'.

400

FUTURISM

FILIPPO TOMMASO MARINETTI (1876–1944). Manifesto Futurista. *In:* Figaro (20 February). *Paris, 1909*

In all ages the young artist probably regards the creations of the Old Masters with mixed feelings. Appreciation of their mastery of the medium must be mingled with a despairing conviction that there remains nothing new to be said. The true creative urge, however, is not satisfied by imitativeness and new generations must find new idioms. Sometimes this has resulted from the discovery of new media—tempera, oil paints; sometimes from a fresh technical approach—impressionism, pointillism, fauvism. Perhaps only in modern times is the development of a whole new movement traceable to the printed word of one who was not himself an artist.

Marinetti, who was born in Alexandria, studied at the Sorbonne, and, although he also graduated in law at the University of Genoa, all his early writings are in French. He began his literary career as a champion of the French *décadence*. This is, perhaps, a not altogether surprising background to his increasing conviction that modern art should be representative of the unrest and uncertainty of the age. He was not alone in this. The surrealists, for example, acknowledge the great influence of Lautréamont's *Les Chants de Maldoror*, 1868–74.

But, long regarded as a tiresome, flippant and illegitimate intrusion into the field of aesthetics, the heritage of Marinetti's 'futurism', the earliest exposition of which is the *Manifesto* published in *Figaro*, and perhaps the most characteristic, his 'novel', 'Mafarka the Futurist', originally published in French in 1910, is clearly perceptible. Dadaism, surrealism, abstract painting, concrete music and blacksmith sculpture are some of the fields in which his impact is unmistakable. Doubtless much that is inferior and ephemeral has been fostered by inability to apply the new criteria expertly. Glibness has unquestionably sponsored some rubbish; and possibly in some quarters undue importance has been given to the movement as a whole. But already a new generation is giving it a proper perspective.

In 'Futurism and Fascism', 1924, Marinetti claimed that futurism had been fulfilled by Mussolini. He became a member of the Italian Academy in 1929, and was also a member of the National Council of Co-operatives.

401

THE FOURTH DIMENSION

HERMANN MINKOWSKI (1864–1909). *Raum und Zeit. In:* Jahresberichte der Deutschen Mathematiker-Vereinigung. *Leipzig, 1909*

In this paper, 'Space and Time', read by Minkowski in Cologne only a few months before his death, he introduced the notion that made possible the expansion of the relativity theory of Einstein (408) from its specific (1905) to its general form (1916).

The technical description of Minkowski's hypothesis is the four-dimensional space–time continuum.

The Michelson–Morley experiment, briefly outlined under Lorentz (378), was expected to show the rate of the earth's movement through the ether. The failure of this experiment was a serious blow to classical scientific theories because it cast doubts on the existence of the universal ether which had been a basic principle of, for example, the Newtonian theories of the universe.

In 1905 Einstein, while working as a clerk in the Patent Office at Berne, propounded his special theory of relativity in a paper on 'The Electro-dynamics of Moving Bodies' contributed to the *Annalen d. Physik* (Weil 9). In this paper he pointed out that the Michelson–Morley experiment was doomed to failure because it assumed the existence of a privileged observer of the universe independent of any relation with it. Any conceivable observer of natural phenomena must, however, be himself in motion within the universe, which made the measurement of speed dependent on the position of the measurer. Thus two railway trains passing one another in opposite directions have two different speeds—one the speed at which they pass each other and one the speed at which they pass a 'stationary' object. Therefore it was not merely impracticable to measure the earth's speed through space: the very formulation of the enquiry showed a complete misconception of the nature of the universe. Absolute space and time are not constituents of the real world but metaphysical concepts of the human mind.

Minkowski's space–time hypothesis was in effect a restatement of Einstein's basic principle in a form that greatly enhanced its plausibility and also introduced important new developments. Hitherto natural phenomena had been thought to occur in a space of three dimensions and to flow uniformly through time. Minkowski maintained that the separation of time and space is a false conception; that time is itself a dimension, comparable to length, breadth and height; and that therefore the true conception of reality was constituted by a space–time continuum possessing these four dimensions. This strongly reinforced Einstein's objections to absolute concepts and supported his view of the relativity of events in nature.

In the Minkowski–Einstein universe a geometry conceived in terms of space and not of flat surfaces is essential. Such a non-Euclidean geometry was originally worked out by Lobatchewsky and perfected by Riemann (293). No particle in a Euclidean universe moves at such a speed that no greater speed is conceivable. In Minkowski's universe this is not true. A finite figure of ultimate velocity must be found. This is now conceded to be the speed of light.

BIBLIOGRAPHY: Minkowski's paper was reprinted in separate form in 1909 as a tribute to him after his sudden and tragic death. It was also incorporated by Einstein with papers of his own and Lorentz in *Das Relativitätsprinzips*, Leipzig, 1913 ('The Principle of Relativity', London, 1923).

402

CHEMOTHERAPY

PAUL EHRLICH (1854–1915) and SAHACHIRO HATA (1873–1938). Die experimentelle Chemotherapie der Spirillosen. *Berlin: Springer, 1910*

In 1908 Ehrlich, the Director of the Institute of Serum Research at Frankfurt, shared the Nobel Prize for Medicine with Elie Metchnikoff, the eminent Russian biologist, for studies in immunity.

Only four years later Ehrlich was again among the select few being considered by the Nobel Prize committee, this time for his discovery of a powerful specific against syphilis. Very early in his scientific career Ehrlich had connexions with the dye industry which led him to undertake a series of intensive experiments on the differential staining of micro-organisms with aniline dyes, a method first developed by Robert Koch (366). Noting with increasing interest the way in which the bacteria took up the dye while the tissue section remained unaffected, he conceived his idea of a 'magic bullet'—a specific drug to seek out and destroy the invading organism without harming healthy tissue.

This was the basic concept of a great advance in treatment which came to be known as chemotherapy. The only such drug then known was quinine, a specific against the malaria parasite which was first isolated from cinchona bark in 1820. When Fritz Schaudinn in 1905 discovered the spirochaeta pallida, the organism coiled like a hair-spring which is responsible for syphilis, Ehrlich was presented with a target for his 'magic bullet'. Working with arsenical compounds, he and his Japanese laboratory assistant, Hata, carried out six hundred and five experiments before reaching the one compound which satisfied all requirements. This was the famous '606', later modified to eliminate some remaining side effects and renamed neo-salvarsan. The experiments and the discovery of the new compound are described in the book cited ('Experimental Chemotherapy of Spirochaetal Diseases').

This was the first chapter in the history of chemotherapy, later stages being marked by the discovery of prontosil and the brilliantly successful sulpha drugs, including the well-known 'M. & B. 693' which was to save the life of Winston Churchill at a critical point in the Second World War.

403

TIME AND MOTION STUDY

FREDERICK WINSLOW TAYLOR (1856–1915). The Principles of Scientific Management. *New York and London: Harper, 1911*

F. W. Taylor, an engineer in the Bethlehem Steel Works in Philadelphia, was the originator of what he called 'scientific management', now known as 'time and motion study'. His system was based on what he estimated to be a fair day's work and the best means of ensuring such a standard of production. He was interested in any factor that hindered or helped in attaining this end, and besides studying factory conditions and methods in great detail he was responsible for fundamental changes in machinery and machine tools.

The main lines of approach to increased efficiency were standardizing processes and machines, time and motion study, and payment by results, all of which have been welcomed in the U.S.S.R., where 'Stakhanovism' is virtually 'Taylorism' renamed, and in Germany, where the *Principles* was translated and achieved a wide circulation (thirty-one thousand copies sold by 1922). The adoption of his methods there contributed notably to the speedy recovery of German production after the First World War. His methods were anathema to trade unionists almost everywhere else.

Taylor's principal contribution to engineering was the development, with Maunsel White, of a new method of tempering tool steel which permitted metal-cutting at very high speeds.

404*

VITAMINS

FREDERICK GOWLAND HOPKINS (1861–1947). Feeding Experiments illustrating the Importance of Accessory Factors in Normal Dietaries. *In:* The Journal of Physiology. *Cambridge, 1912*

In the sixteenth century fruit-juices were carried on Dutch and British ships as a specific against scurvy, and in 1796 lemon juice and other antiscorbutics were made a compulsory issue for seamen in the Royal Navy. In 1880 N. Lunin showed that a synthetic milk diet inhibited the growth of animals. Little attention was paid to this discovery. In 1886 an official commission was sent to the Dutch East Indies to study beri-beri. Christiaan Eijkman, a bacteriologist, was in the party and when the main body returned home he remained as the director of a new pathological laboratory in Batavia.

In the chicken-run of this laboratory the birds were suddenly stricken by a disease with symptoms remarkably similar to those of beri-beri. Neither in the live birds nor in the corpses was any bacterium or parasite found to account for the disease. Just as suddenly as it had appeared the disease came to an end, and some of the sick hens even recovered. Suspicion was directed to food and it was found that the dates of the beginning and end of the out-break coincided almost exactly with the period during which the birds had been fed with rice from the hospital kitchen. The only discoverable difference between this and the rice usually fed to the birds was that the hospital rice was polished, thus removing the hulls. A control experiment produced the disease in fowls fed with the polished rice, while those which ate only unpolished rice remained healthy. Moreover sick birds recovered when put on the unpolished diet. Eijkman interpreted these phenomena as a kind of poisoning due to excess of carbohydrate in a rice diet which was counteracted by some neutralizing substance in the bran. He reported his conclusions in 1897 in a paper entitled *Eine Beri-ähnliche Krankeit der Hühner* ('A Sickness in Hens resembling Beri-beri').

It was reserved for Hopkins to produce the scientific explanation of these and other observations, all of which had been purely empirical, and to blaze the trail leading to vitamin therapy.

Starting life as an insurance clerk, subsequently a pupil in analytical chemistry, a mineralogist, and an assistant in Thomas Stephenson's forensic medicine laboratory at Guy's Hospital, Hopkins graduated extramurally at London University and began to study medicine in 1884. In 1894 he qualified and in 1898 joined the faculty of physiological chemistry at Cambridge. He eventually concentrated on research in nutrition and by 1907 was able to announce his discovery that full supplies of basal foodstuffs were insufficient for the survival of small animals. His experiments continued but were interrupted by a severe breakdown in health.

Hopkins was already convinced that certain 'accessory factors' were essential to the health and growth of animals, and on returning to work he discovered that rats who declined and died on what appeared adequate feeding throve when small quantities of milk were added to their diet. In 1912, in the paper cited, he made the pronouncement upon which all subsequent vitamin research is based: that 'accessory factors' are essential to nutrition. In 1913 McCollum and Davis demonstrated that the growth-factor in milk comprised a fat-soluble and a water-soluble substance—vitamins A and B. In 1914 Casimir Funk published a book with the title *Die Vitamine*, the name which has been generally adopted for these accessory food substances.

In 1929 Hopkins shared with Eijkman the Nobel Prize for Medicine. He was knighted in 1925, became President of the Royal Society in 1931 and received the Order of Merit in 1935.

405

RATIONAL CHRISTIANITY

ERNST TROELTSCH (1865–1923). Die Soziallehren der Christlichen Kirchen und Gruppen. *Tübingen: J. C. B. Mohr (Paul Siebeck), 1912*

Ernst Troeltsch was born near Augsburg. The decisive period of his education was spent as a theology student at Göttingen under the famous and formidable protestant theologian Albrecht Ritschl (1822–89), professor there for twenty-five years. Ritschl himself had been a student under Baur (322) at Tübingen, where Harnack (390) was also among his disciples.

Troeltsch's life was spent as an academic theologian and philosopher, but his teaching and writing did not follow the conventional pattern such a career might suggest. His first appointment was as professor of theology at Bonn in 1892, from which he moved two years later to a similar chair at Heidelberg. During this period, he became known as a philosophical theologian, and his teaching followed the traditional Kantian line of demonstrating the existence of God and religion as the necessity of reason. From this, however, he struck out on a line which he made peculiarly his own. From his study of the philosophy of history he concluded that the underlying principles and methods of historical study must be essentially distinct from those governing scientific investigation. The historian, although his work depends on the study of the causal relation of events, must deal less with causes than with their meaning. The 'meaning of history' was to be the problem which occupied Troeltsch for the rest of his life.

The *magnum opus* of his vast erudition was the book here cited: 'The Social Theory of the Christian Churches and Groups'. Like Gierke (360★), but as a theologian and in terms of Christian thought, whereas Gierke thought as a lawyer and constitutionalist, Troeltsch pursued his way through centuries of history, exploring the historic systems of group-life, and the controlling ideas by which they were permeated, from the days of the early church to the days of medieval Catholicism, and thence to Protestantism and the various Protestant sects. Thus he came to see that the meaning of history lies in the growth and dissolution of social groups and movement of thought and culture. Each of these is entitled to be investigated and judged on its own inherent merits, in consideration of which it is unique. This uniqueness inhibits the reduction of each group and its philosophy of existence to its historical antecedents; these are the facts of history, to which a study of causes will not contribute.

In 1915 Troeltsch changed his theology professorship for the chair of philosophy at Berlin, where he remained for the rest of his life. In 1919 as Under-Secretary of State in the Prussian Ministry of Culture and Education he played a decisive role in the modernization of the secondary schools. His last work was a notable series of lectures in 1922 on 'The Ideas of Natural Law and Humanity'. These, like Fichte's (244) lectures a hundred years earlier, did much to restore German morale, though the aim was different. Troeltsch sought, not like Fichte to produce a specifically German political thought, but to relate the absolutist trend which had occupied German thinking since the Romantic Movement with the more liberal Natural Law lines of thought prevalent in the rest of Europe, and thus to produce a catholic European outlook.

406

X-RAY CRYSTALLOGRAPHY

(*a*) MAX VON LAUE (1879–1960). (*a*) Interferenz-Erscheinungen bei Röntgenstrahlen; (*b*) Eine quantitative Prüfung der Theorie für die Interferenz-Erscheinungen bei Röntgenstrahlen. *In*: Sitzungsberichte der Mathematisch-physikalischen Klasse der K. B. Akademie der Wissenschaften. *Munich, 1912*

(*b*) WILLIAM HENRY BRAGG (1862–1942) and WILLIAM LAWRENCE BRAGG (b. 1890). X-rays and Crystal Structure. *London: G. Bell, 1915*

100 ANALYSIS OF CRYSTAL STRUCTURE

other that the sulphurs come in the places we want them, *i.e.* at the centres of the small cubes of the zinc lattice. We get the structure shown in Fig. 30.

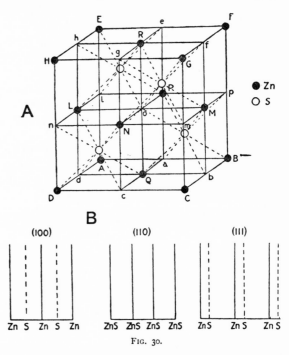

FIG. 30.

The representation of these three-dimensional figures is so complicated that only four sulphur atoms can be shown in the figure, this being all there are inside the unit cube of the structure. If the reader imagines cubes such as this put side by side so as to

Röntgen rays (380) and their uses had become widely familiar long before the exact nature of the waves could be decided. It was suggested that they were akin to some forms of light, but to prove this it was necessary to determine their wavelength. Such wavelengths are calculated by a process far too complicated for description here. Diffraction gratings are used. These are mirrors on which very fine lines are engraved at intervals of about one thousandth of a centimetre. This method could not be used with X-rays because their wavelength was found to be far shorter than any feasible grating intervals.

Laue suggested, in 'Interference Phenomena in Röntgen Rays' (a), that the accepted atomic arrangement of crystals might form a grating sufficiently fine to diffract the X-rays and thus to give their wavelength. He worked out the complicated formula for the operation. In his second paper—'A Quantative Proof of the Theory'—he was assisted by two members of his staff, W. Friedrich and P. Knipping.

The Braggs, father (knighted 1920) and son (knighted 1941), approached this phenomenon from the other end, by concentrating on the knowledge of atomic structure that X-ray shadows could provide. Their earliest experiments in this connexion, with rock salt and diamonds, were highly successful in showing the arrangement of atoms in these substances. Later developments have shown that these experiments of the Braggs have virtually given the science of crystallography a new basis. Thus the fundamentally different qualities of two forms of carbon, graphite and diamond, are seen to be due to differences in the arrangements of the atoms and in the distances between them. This makes it possible in the commercial laboratory to build new substances and materials based on an arrangement of atoms that will ensure certain desired qualities.

In pure chemistry one of the most fruitful sequels was Moseley's (407) reconstruction of the periodic table. The discovery of the chemical basis of life—DNA—by Perutz and others is the most recent of the sensational sequels to the Bragg experiments.

Laue was awarded the Nobel Prize for Physics in 1914, and the Braggs shared it the following year.

407

THE ATOMIC TABLE

HENRY GWYN JEFFREYS MOSELEY (1887–1915). The High-Frequency Spectra of the Elements. *In:* The Philosophical Magazine. *London, 1913–14*

Dalton (261) had set out a list of twenty-one atomic weights, each related to hydrogen, to which he allotted the basic figure of 1. In 1815 and 1816 William Prout contributed two articles to the *Annals of Philosophy* surmising that the remarkable approximation of these figures to whole numbers suggested that hydrogen may be the primordial substance from which all forms of matter are constructed—the *prima materia* of Aristotelian philosophy.

In 1825, in two volumes entitled *An Attempt to Establish the First Principles of Chemistry by Experiment*, Thomas Thomson, who had been the first to print Dalton's hypothesis, disclosed Prout's authorship of these articles and based upon them an attempt to construct an atomic table with each element represented by a whole number. But Berzelius, the great Swedish chemist, showed that Thomson's figures would not bear close analysis.

Much has been made of the 'law of octaves' outlined by J. A. R. Newlands, a good self-publicist, in the *Chemical News*, 18 August 1865, but greater credit is in

fact due to William Odling who, in the *Quarterly Journal of Science*, 1, 642 (1864), produced a superior table much more like Mendeleev's who, in 1869, in the *Journal of the Russian Chemical Society*, not only compiled a periodic table reflecting chemical properties as well as arithmetical relationships between atomic weights, but pointed out that the gaps in it indicated the existence of undiscovered elements. In 1870 J. R. Mayer (in *Annalen der Chemie*) detailed in almost identical terms the table he had constructed in 1868 at Eberswalde. The two men were jointly awarded the Davy Medal of the Royal Society.

In 1888 Sir William Crookes, in his presidential address to the Chemical Society, threw out the provocative suggestion that atomic weights were not necessarily invariable or uniform, since they were arrived at by calculating the average weight of the atoms making up an element. In 1910 F. Soddy demonstrated that certain elements with apparently identical chemical properties and behaviour had different atomic weights (*Chemical Society's Annual Reports*, 1910, 7, 285). Such groups of elements he called isotopes (see 412).

Moseley, working under Rutherford (411) at Manchester, used the method of X-ray spectroscopy devised by the Braggs (406) to calculate variations in the wavelength of the rays emitted by each element. These he was able to arrange in a series according to the nuclear charge of each element. Thus if the nuclear charge of hydrogen is 1, in helium it is 2, in lithium 3, and so on by regular progression to uranium as 92. These figures Moseley called atomic numbers. He pointed out that they also represented a corresponding increase in extranuclear electrons and that it is the number and arrangement of these electrons rather than the atomic weight that determines the properties of an element. It was now possible to base the periodic table on a firm foundation, and to state with confidence that the number of elements up to uranium is limited to 92.

When Moseley's table was completed, six atomic numbers had no corresponding elements; but Moseley himself was able to predict the nature of four of the missing elements. Five of the six have since been discovered by others using Moseley's X-ray spectroscopic method. At least two further elements—93, neptunium and 94, plutonium—emerged as by-products in the chain-reaction experiments of Fermi and his colleagues (422a).

Moseley was killed at Gallipoli in 1915 at the age of twenty-seven.

408

RELATIVITY

ALBERT EINSTEIN (1879–1955). Die Grundlage der allgemeinen Relativitätstheorie. *In:* Annalen der Physik. *Leipzig, 1916*

Reference has been made to the nature and effects of the 'special' theory of relativity expounded in 1905 by Einstein under the entries for Lobatchewsky (293), Lorentz (378) and Minkowski (401).

That theory was in fact principally directed towards resolving inconsistencies arising from the Newtonian system (161). Indeed, Einstein himself did not call it a theory of relativity: his paper was concerned with 'the electro-dynamics of moving bodies'. Its two vitally important, revolutionary conclusions were (1) that 'it is impossible by any experiment to detect uniform motion relative to the ether', (2) that energy and mass are equivalent, expressed in the now famous equation $e = mc^2$.

This attempt to circumvent the impasse created by the negative results of the Michelson–Morley experiment derived from a kind of neo-Berkeleyism, which made it appear that the material nature of real objects changed in relation to the position of the observer.

Thus the logical conclusion of the Lorentz hypothesis is that physical objects change their size, that the duration of any process varies in length according to the observer's position. For example, on any clear night stars are simultaneously visible at various stages in their history according to the time taken by their light to reach the earth. Given the possibility of astronomers on the stars, this earth might be under observation at one and the same moment not only as it now is, but also as it was at the time of the birth of Christ and of the Stone Age and of its earliest existence as a separate body.

Observers would not in fact disagree about the order in which events had happened in the same region; obviously Stonehenge was built before Salisbury Cathedral, though the gap might seem less to some than to others. But events in widely separated parts of space—say in two stars—could not be put in a definitive temporal order. To observers in one part of the universe one might seem to happen first, and to those elsewhere the other. The notion that events in places remote from each other could be said to be contemporaneous turns out to be meaningless, for, as Einstein saw, there is no reason to prefer one observer's account to another's. Eddington, in Space, Time and Gravitation, 1920, has given other striking examples of the confusion arising from the application of 'commonsense' methods to spatial problems.

Thus, while it is not possible for a space traveller to reach his destination before he starts, were he to travel at the speed of light, an adventurer could reach Arcturus one hundred light-years away in an instant. 'So long as he travels at the speed of light he has immortality and eternal youth.' To a space traveller at a lesser speed than ourselves what is for us a square becomes an oblong, and the comparative length of the sides would vary according to the direction in which he is travelling. Clearly, then, length, breadth, depth and even time itself are not inherent properties of spatial objects but variables related to the position and motion of a particular observer. Paradoxes resulted from the assumption that there was a privileged frame of reference, to which all events could be unambiguously referred, a non-empirical hypothesis.

'The General Theory of Relativity' is Einstein's bold attempt to escape from this dilemma. We must give up the idea of taking a God's eye view of the world. Thus, it had been supposed that the earth must be moving through the luminiferous ether, fixed in absolute space; but experiments had not revealed any such motion.

Einstein wrote: 'According to this theory there is no such thing as a "specially favoured" [unique] co-ordinate system to occasion the introduction of the ether-idea, and hence there can be no ether-drift, nor any experiment with which to demonstrate it'. The theory of relativity has transformed astrophysics, and indeed the whole scientific outlook.

For his 'special' theory Einstein was awarded a fellowship (fourth class) of the Kaiser-Wilhelm-Institut in Berlin. In 1921 he was awarded the Nobel Prize. The Committee referred with caution to the relativity theory and cited the greatest physicist of the century for his discovery of the law of the photo-electric effect.

The layman who finds the theory dauntingly incomprehensible may draw some consolation from Sir James Jeans when he says '[There is] a science of everyday life which is still entirely Newtonian; the engineer who is building a ship or a locomotive does precisely what he would have done if Einstein's challenge to Newton had never appeared, and so does the computer who is preparing the Nautical Almanac, and the astronomer who is discussing the general motion of the planets'.

BIBLIOGRAPHY: E. Weil, Albert Einstein, a Bibliography (London, 1960).

409

BLUEPRINT FOR PEACE

WOODROW WILSON (1856–1924). The Fourteen Points. Washington, D.C.: Government Printing Office, 1918

Firm in his belief that the Allies were fighting the 'war to end war' President Woodrow Wilson outlined in his speech before the Congress of the United States on 8 January 1918 the Fourteen Points which were to form the basis of a lasting peace.

A just and not a vindictive peace had been his long proclaimed intention, but a shadow had been cast over the integrity of this position by the events at the end of 1917. The Bolsheviks had overthrown the Czarist Russian government and negotiated a separate treaty with the Germans. As part of their effort to consolidate their position at home they had released the terms of the secret treaties between the Czarist government and the Allied powers, much to the embarrassment of the latter whose ambitions for territorial expansion were thus made public. Both Lloyd George and Wilson saw the necessity of reaffirming their countries' commitment to a just peace. Lloyd George replied first (5 January) and his answer to the Bolshevik charges included all but the first three of the Fourteen Points; but Wilson's statement was much broader and his high idealism caught the public ear, not only in the United States but everywhere.

Briefly summarized from the form in which they were first printed as House Document 765 in the papers of the 65th Congress, the Fourteen Points called for (1) the abolition of secret diplomacy, (2) freedom of the seas in peace and in war, (3) the removal of economic barriers to free trade, (4) the reduction of armaments, (5) the impartial settlement of colonial claims taking into consideration the interests of the inhabitants, (6–13) certain specific territorial adjustments based in a large measure on the principle of self-determination, and (14) the establishment of an international body, 'a general association of nations...for the purpose of affording mutual guarantees of political independence and territorial integrity to great and small states alike'.

The immediate effect of this statement of principles was to undermine morale in the Central Powers and to encourage German moderates to work toward a negotiated peace. However, unilateral declarations of principle are not binding on other parties, as Wilson discovered when the time came to formulate the Treaty of Versailles. Yet if national ambitions and a desire for vengeance prevailed at the conference table, the Fourteen Points may be credited with making the final treaty less vindictive than it might otherwise have been. They set the moral tone, even if they did not provide 'the moral climax' of what Wilson called 'this...final war for human liberty'.

Wilson's passionate interest in the creation of a new world safe for democracy had so preoccupied him since the United States' entry into the war that he had neglected his political fence-mending at home. Nor did he trouble to enlist bipartisan support when he left, a world figure but a solitary one, for the negotiations at Versailles. The Republican Party had already made great inroads into his popular support and in the Congressional election of 1918 won a majority in both House and Senate. It was this Congress which rejected United States participation in the League of Nations. The last and crowning point of the Fourteen was not to be realized in the United States until another great war had been fought.

The tremendous success of the book among the semi-literate, especially in Germany and America, during the period after the First World War, is a politico-sociological phenomenon that has nothing to do with the intrinsic merits or demerits of this 'new outlook on history and the philosophy of destiny', as the author himself described the aim of his book. This popular success was certainly not foreseen by the leading German philosophy publisher (Felix Meiner of Leipzig) who turned down the manuscript offered first to him, nor by the leading Austrian academic publisher who, after the first volume,

DER UNTERGANG DES ABENDLANDES

UMRISSE EINER MORPHOLOGIE DER WELT-GESCHICHTE

VON

OSWALD SPENGLER

ERSTER BAND

GESTALT UND WIRKLICHKEIT

WIEN UND LEIPZIG
WILHELM BRAUMÜLLER
K. K. UNIVERSITÄTS-VERLAGSBUCHHANDLUNG GESELLSCHAFT M. B. H.
1918

410

'THE TWILIGHT OF THE WEST'

OSWALD SPENGLER (1880–1936). Der Untergang des Abendlandes. Vol. I. *Vienna & Leipzig: Wilhelm Braumüller, 1918;* vol. II. *Munich: C. H. Beck, 1922*

Spengler was a mathematics and science teacher who in 1911, on inheriting a small competence, gave up school-mastering and concentrated on the writing of 'The Decline of the West'.

In it he propounded a 'morphology of universal history' which he believed could not only explain the past but would allow us to predict the future. For he contended that all civilizations, like every other living organism, pass through a predetermined 'life cycle' of prime, maturity and decay; and that this trend can be neither halted nor reversed. Spengler distinguished eight civilizations which, independent of one another, have run this course: Egyptian, Babylonian, Indian, Chinese, Greco-Roman, Arabic, Mexican and Western. The outlook for western civilization, to Spengler, is gloomy. The end is at hand. Democracy, the typical product of western civilization, will be wiped out by caesarean autocracy.

transferred his rights to a Munich general publisher. In fact, every responsible historian repudiated Spengler's theory; but it offered a plausible pseudo-scientific basis to the innate propensity of the Germans for ascribing to an inexorable fate what they refused to acknowledge as their own shortcomings and failures; and it confirmed the Americans in their complacent belief that 'the West' (which they equated with the Old World) was in fact 'finished'. For it should be said in parenthesis that the title of the English translation, with its mild suggestion of a gradual loss of vigour, entirely fails to convey Spengler's deliberately emotional implications of a Wagnerian twilight of the gods and the crack of impending doom. Reversing the roles of Elijah and Elisha, it was the major prophet, Toynbee (421), who took up the mantle that fell from the minor prophet, Spengler.

SPLITTING THE ATOM

ERNEST RUTHERFORD (1871–1937). Collision of α Particles with Light Atoms. *In:* The Philosophical Magazine. *London, 1919*

Röntgen's discovery of the X-rays (380) and its sequel in Becquerel's discovery of radio-activity (393) changed the face of modern life. Their consequences have even threatened its survival.

Ingenious experiments by R. J. Strutt, afterwards Lord Rayleigh, proved that the emanations given off by radio-active substances are not homogeneous but are of at least two different kinds, one of which will and another will not pass through tin-foil (Strutt, *The Becquerel Rays and the Properties of Radium*, 1902). Eventually the emanations were classified as of three kinds—the so-called alpha, beta and gamma rays. Rutherford, the Cambridge physicist, in conjunction with his pupil Frederick Soddy, put forward in 1902–3 (*Transactions of the London Chemical Society*, and *Philosophical Magazine*) the revolutionary theory that radio-activity is a by-product of the transmutation of one form of matter into another. Soddy, in conjunction with William Ramsay, demonstrated this fact when they showed that radon, an emanation of radium, disintegrated into helium (*Proceedings of the Royal Society*, 1903). And in 1909 Rutherford in conjunction with Royds showed that alpha particles are in fact atoms of helium (*Philosophical Magazine*).

In 1911, as a result of bombarding goldfoil with alpha particles, Rutherford formulated the hypothesis of the nuclear construction of the atom which is the basis of all subsequent work in atomic physics and chemistry. Most of the alpha particles passed straight through the foil, but some bounced back from it. Rutherford interpreted the bouncing in terms of his theory. Those that went through were simply passing through the planetary systems of electrons, while those that bounced back had hit, or interacted with, a nucleus. Eight years later, as reported in the paper cited, he found that alpha particles in collision with nitrogen atoms liberated from them nuclei of hydrogen atoms. Thus artificial transmutation was induced: in other words the atom had been split.

Uranium 235 is an isotope of natural uranium. The fateful consequences ensuing from the bombardment of this material by neutrons—a constituent of the atom discovered by James Chadwick, another pupil of Rutherford's (*Nature*, 1932)—are elaborated under 422.

Rutherford was awarded the Nobel Chemistry Prize in 1908. He was knighted in 1914 and raised to the peerage in 1931. These were symbolic of the countless honours and distinctions bestowed on this great New Zealander in many parts of the world.

ISOTOPES

FRANCIS WILLIAM ASTON (1877–1945). Isotopes. *London: Arnold, 1922*

In 1911 J. J. Thomson (386) discussed in the *Philosophical Magazine* a new method of analysing positive rays. He passed the rays through a cathode tube and subjected them to electric and magnetic forces which caused their deflexion in such a way that when made to fall upon a photographic plate the particles formed a parabola. The form of the parabola was characteristic of each element. When Thomson used neon as the source material, however, he found that two different parabolas were produced. In 1913 he entrusted to his assistant, F. W. Aston, the task of ascertaining the difference in the atomic weights of these two forms of neon.

Aston's work was interrupted by the First World War. On his return to Cambridge he set himself to improve Thomson's parabola apparatus and devised the mass spectrograph by which the gas traces were induced to focus themselves within a much smaller area. This produced a more concentrated effect which gave greater clarity of identification. He thus found that the atomic weights of the two forms of neon were 20 and 22 respectively, whereas the normal atomic weight of neon was somewhere between the two.

Further experiment with other substances and everincreasing improvements in the mass spectrograph convinced Aston that elements are composed of atoms of varying mass, the atomic weight of an element being the average of those of the atoms comprising it. This was a striking verification of Crookes's prediction in 1888 that an 'absence of absolute homogeneity may possibly yet be traced in many of the "elements"' with the inference that every 'element' is in fact (and in contradiction to its name) comprised of mixed materials. Previous investigators had assumed a mystique of the atomic table by which the atomic weights of the elements would prove to be exact multiples of hydrogen; yet Rydberg, the Swedish chemist, had calculated that the chance of twenty-two atomic weights being so near to whole numbers as was essential to this assumption was less than one in one thousand million.

Soddy (see 407, Moseley) had coined the term *isotopes* for elements that are 'homogeneous in chemical behaviour'. Thus, for example, no process of chemical analysis will differentiate between thorium, one form of uranium, and ionium, although each has a different atomic weight. Aston carried this investigation one very important stage further by demonstrating that similar conditions occur within the elements themselves.

Once Aston had shown that the true atomic weight of an element is arrived at by averaging the mass of its constituent parts, and that there are seven isotopes of mercury and nine of xenon, the possibility that the atomic weights of elements would generally be whole numbers was finally abandoned. The reconstruction of the table of atomic weights by Aston's methods showed that they are only in exceptional cases whole numbers when considered as multiples of the weight of a hydrogen atom. The ultimate consequences of these discrepancies are far-reaching. The ratio between hydrogen and oxygen is not 4:1, as it 'should' be, but rather less; which means that when four atoms of hydrogen are transformed into one helium atom some matter is annihilated. In fact this is an example of the interchangeability between mass and energy which is postulated in Einstein's 'General Theory of Relativity' (408).

Of more general significance in our everyday lives are the experiments of Meitner and others (see 422) with isotopes of uranium, which have resulted in the atomic bomb and the peaceful uses of atomic energy. These experiments suggest very strongly that the assumption of the chemical identity of isotopes is false. Clearly some isotopes of uranium have different potentialities from others, which may necessitate a fundamental redrafting of atomic theory.

413

THE NEW ARCHITECTURE

LE CORBUSIER [i.e. CHARLES ÉDOUARD JEANNERET] (1887–1965). Vers une Architecture. *Paris: G. Crès*, [1923]

Charles Édouard Jeanneret was born at La-Chaux-de-Fonds in Switzerland, and after attending the art school there he worked for short periods under several of the more forward-looking European designers and architects of the time, including Auguste Perret, the master of re-inforced concrete construction, and the great German industrial architect Peter Behrens. During the First World War, and after, Jeanneret, though still mainly known as a painter, turned increasingly to architecture, de-signing plans for post-war rebuilding, with heavy emphasis on mass production, standard designs, etc. He lived in Paris and with Amédée Ozenfant, whom he met there in 1917, he developed a branch of Cubism known as 'Purism'. In 1920 he and Ozenfant began to publish a magazine devoted to a very wide coverage of the arts and called *L'Esprit Nouveau*. In 1923, however, Jeanneret determined to be recognized as an architect and, adopting the pseudonym of 'Le Corbusier', he published *Vers une Architecture* ('Towards Architecture') which consisted of articles originally appearing in *L'Esprit Nouveau*.

Its publication marks a milestone in the development of the modern movement and Le Corbusier's influence has probably been greater than that of any other writer on architecture in this century. The book established Le Corbusier, if only as a prophetic voice; for before 1923 he had built only one or two houses of little interest, and the best of his unexecuted designs, such as the *Domino* houses of 1914 and the *Citrohan* house and the *Ville Contemporaine* of 1922, were not widely known.

Vers une Architecture is a passionate work, written with emotion and rhetoric, and the arguments are neither con-sistently developed nor rationally presented; but it ex-presses, with prophetic fervour, a poetic vision of a new architecture in a new society. The challenge of modern

materials and engineering advances is stressed, but Le Corbusier was no functionalist—construction and the problems of construction are not architecture: architecture is something over and above—'Art enters in'. In spite of the most often quoted and superficially influential remark in the book—'La maison est une machine à habiter'—Le Corbusier was above all else an artist and a romantic. Certainly the aesthetics of the book are those of machine art, but the emphasis is on the art rather than the machine.

Vers une Architecture is more than a defence of the new aesthetic. Le Corbusier recognized sooner than most the vital importance of mass production in the solution of world housing problems, and the book pleads for the standardization of design necessary for efficient produc-tion. This concern for standardization, with a re-exam-ination of the Greek 'Golden section', leads to the germ of the idea that he later developed into the *Modulor*, a proportional system based on the dimensions of the human body. His concern was coupled with a broad vision of the place of architecture in society and especially of a new architecture of the city as a planned and inte-grated whole: he saw clearly that our problem was not only to build a new kind of house, and a new kind of city, but also to change ourselves—to learn to live in a new way.

414

ATONAL MUSIC

ARNOLD SCHÖNBERG (1874–1951). Eine neue Zwölfton-Schrift. *In:* Musikblätter des Anbruch. *Vienna*, 1925

The impact of Schönberg's musical theories, first fully outlined in 'A New Twelve-note Notation' published in the avant-garde journal *Anbruch*, has been slow. Indeed it was for long virtually imperceptible and, where per-ceptible, unsympathetic.

Schönberg's first conscious rejection of the 'tyranny' of the major-minor key system came in 1908 when he published *Drei Klavierstücke* (Op. 11) without a key signature. In the first edition of his *Harmonielehre*, 1910, there is a short reference to the possible development of a chromatic notation based on the twelve-note scale. Alban Berg and Anton Webern were among his earliest pupils and the former's opera *Wozzeck*, begun in 1917 and finished in 1925, was the first notable product of the system by an avowed disciple. Ernst Krenek's opera *Karl V*, 1932, is a later example.

Nevertheless, despite the theoretical writings of Schönberg and others on the subject, the formidable extent of his own compositions, and his appointment to teaching posts in the United States after his dismissal by the Nazis in 1933, it is only within the last two decades that his influence has been widely felt. It would be diffi-cult to improve on the summary of modern opinion of Schönberg given by Mr Humphrey Searle in *Grove's Dictionary of Music* (5th ed., 1954): 'Whatever may be the verdict of history on Schönberg's works', he writes,

248

'there is no doubt that they have revolutionized the whole of twentieth-century music. Without them the free use of all the notes of the chromatic scale, which every composer today accepts as a matter of course, would have been impossible, or at any rate considerably delayed. One has only to add to this Schönberg's innovations in form and instrumentation to see that his historical importance cannot be rated too highly.'

415

THE THIRD REICH

ADOLF HITLER (1899–1945). Mein Kampf. 2 vols. *Munich: Franz Eher, 1925–7*

Political creeds as the basis for new religions have usually spelt danger for humanity. When they are distilled from the half-baked prejudices harboured by the more reactionary section of a nation not particularly noted for political enlightenment, they spell disaster.

Mein Kampf

Eine Abrechnung

von

Adolf Hitler

1. Band

1925

Verlag Franz Eher Nachfolger G.m.b.H. München NO 2

This was not only the origin but also the strength of the National-Socialist programme developed by Hitler on principles drawn up by Anton Drexler and Karl Haner for a small splinter group which they called 'The German Workers' Party' (*Die Deutsche Arbeiterpartei*). Official histories claim that Hitler joined this party on an unspecified date in 1919 as its seventh member. His party-card, with his name misspelled, is dated 1 January 1920 and his party-number is given on it as 555.

Although the name of the party was changed to National-Socialist in August 1920, it was not until July 1921 that Hitler felt strong enough to oust Drexler and to assume the leadership. This may have been due in part to his activities as an army undercover man. In November 1923 came the Nazi Putsch in Munich. This, although abortive, had, in its sequel, much to do with Hitler's rise to national stature. The ill-advised prominence given to his trial, the ineffectiveness with which it was conducted and the dignified nature of his detention in the Fortress of Landsberg transformed his status from that of a seedy local agitator to a potential national saviour.

His detention, moreover, gave him the opportunity to dictate to his associate Rudolf Hess the contents of the first volume of the testament and programme of a political gangster which he called *Mein Kampf*—'My Struggle'. Although it contained much that was shocking to many Germans, its main sentiments were widely shared in central Europe. A pseudo-mystic racial theory, totally unrelated to fact, was made to support pan-Germanism, anti-semitism, militarism and ultra-nationalism, the combination of which was to be implemented by the unrestricted use of power as interpreted through the mentality of a superstitious bully.

This programme, with a detailed account of what it would entail nationally and internationally, is stated with complete frankness in the two volumes of *Mein Kampf*. The brazenness of the declaration was due to naivety and immaturity. Unfortunately Europe was governed by small men at the time and when Hitler came to power in 1933 he found that his wildest claims and most extravagant actions earned but mild and ineffectual rebuke. His enemies accepted the occupation of the Rhineland, the tearing-up of the Versailles and Locarno Treaties, the abandonment of the League of Nations and the seizure of Austria and Czechoslovakia. Hitler had a right to be surprised at their violent reaction to the attack on Poland. It was all in *Mein Kampf*, but they just could not believe it.

416

A NEW THEORY OF GRAVITATION

ALBERT EINSTEIN (1879–1955). Einheitliche Feldtheorie von Gravitation und Elektrizität. *In: Sitzungsberichte der Preussische Akademie der Wissenschaften. Berlin, 1925* (and four further papers)

There is a striking passage in an essay by Jeans on Clerk Maxwell, which reads as follows: 'Most of the symbols used by the mathematical physicist of today convey no physical meaning to his mind: he can explain and predict the whole course of atomic nature in terms of the behaviour of a symbol...but he cannot tell us what [it] means in physics; and I for one doubt if he will ever be able to do so.' Einstein is the prime example of this kind of thinking and he has himself more than once recorded

Unabhängig von diesem affinen Zusammenhang führen wir eine kontravariante Tensordichte $\mathfrak{g}^{\mu\nu}$ ein, deren Symmetrieeigenschaften wir ebenfalls offen lassen. Aus beiden bilden wir die skalare Dichte

$$\mathfrak{H} = \mathfrak{g}^{\mu\nu} R_{\mu\nu} \tag{3}$$

und postulieren, daß sämtliche Variationen des Integrals

$$\mathfrak{J} = \int \mathfrak{H}\, dx_1\, dx_2\, dx_3\, dx_4$$

nach den $\mathfrak{g}^{\mu\nu}$ und $\Gamma^{\alpha}_{\mu\nu}$ als unabhängigen (an den Grenzen nicht varierten) Variabeln verschwinden.

Die Variation nach den $\mathfrak{g}^{\mu\nu}$ liefert die 16 Gleichen

$$R_{\mu\nu} = 0\,, \tag{4}$$

die Variation nach den $\Gamma^{\alpha}_{\mu\nu}$ zunächst die 64 Gleichungen

$$\frac{\partial \mathfrak{g}^{\mu\nu}}{\partial x_\alpha} + \mathfrak{g}^{\beta\nu}\Gamma^{\mu}_{\beta\alpha} + \mathfrak{g}^{\mu\beta}\Gamma^{\nu}_{\alpha\beta} - \delta^{\nu}_{\alpha}\left(\frac{\partial \mathfrak{g}^{\mu\beta}}{\partial x_\beta} + \mathfrak{g}^{\sigma\beta}\Gamma^{\mu}_{\sigma\beta}\right) - \mathfrak{g}^{\mu\nu}\Gamma^{\beta}_{\alpha\beta} = 0\,. \tag{5}$$

Wir wollen nun einige Betrachtungen anstellen, die uns die Gleichungen (5) durch einfachere zu ersetzen gestatten. Verjüngen wir die linke Seite von (5) nach den Indizes ν, α bzw. μ, α, so erhalten wir die Gleichungen

$$3\left(\frac{\partial \mathfrak{g}^{\mu\alpha}}{\partial x_\alpha} + \mathfrak{g}^{\alpha\beta}\Gamma^{\mu}_{\alpha\beta}\right) + \mathfrak{g}^{\mu\alpha}(\Gamma^{\beta}_{\alpha\beta} - \Gamma^{\beta}_{\alpha\beta}) = 0 \tag{6}$$

$$\frac{\partial \mathfrak{g}^{\nu\alpha}}{\partial x_\alpha} - \frac{\partial \mathfrak{g}^{\alpha\nu}}{\partial x_\alpha} = 0\,. \tag{7}$$

Führen wir ferner Größen $g_{\mu\nu}$ ein, welche die normierten Unterdeterminanten zu den $\mathfrak{g}^{\mu\nu}$ sind, also die Gleichungen

$$g_{\mu\alpha}\mathfrak{g}^{\nu\alpha} = g_{\alpha\mu}\mathfrak{g}^{\alpha\nu} = \delta^{\nu}_{\mu}$$

erfüllen, und multiplizieren (5) mit $g_{\mu\nu}$, so erhalten wir eine Gleichung, die wir nach Heraufziehen eines Index wie folgt schreiben können

$$2\mathfrak{g}^{\mu\alpha}\left(\frac{\partial \lg \sqrt{\mathfrak{g}}}{\partial x_\alpha} + \Gamma^{\beta}_{\alpha\beta}\right) + (\Gamma^{\beta}_{\alpha\beta} - \Gamma^{\beta}_{\beta\alpha}) + \delta^{\mu}_{\beta}\left(\frac{\partial \mathfrak{g}^{\beta\alpha}}{\partial x_\alpha} + \mathfrak{g}^{\sigma\beta}\Gamma^{\beta}_{\sigma\beta}\right) = 0\,, \tag{8}$$

wenn man mit $\mathfrak{g}$ die Determinante aus den $g_{\mu\nu}$ bezeichnet. Die Gleichungen (6) und (8) schreiben wir in der Form

$$\mathfrak{f}^{\mu} = \tfrac{1}{3}\mathfrak{g}^{\mu\alpha}(\Gamma^{\beta}_{\alpha\beta} - \Gamma^{\beta}_{\beta\alpha}) = -\left(\frac{\partial \mathfrak{g}^{\mu\alpha}}{\partial x_\alpha} + \mathfrak{g}^{\alpha\beta}\Gamma^{\mu}_{\alpha\beta}\right) = -\mathfrak{g}^{\mu\alpha}\left(\frac{\partial \lg \sqrt{\mathfrak{g}}}{\partial x_\alpha} + \Gamma^{\beta}_{\alpha\beta}\right), \tag{9}$$

wobei $\mathfrak{f}^{\mu}$ eine gewisse Tensordichte bedeutet. Es ist leicht zu beweisen, daß das Gleichungssystem (5) äquivalent ist dem Gleichungssystem

$$\frac{\partial \mathfrak{g}^{\mu\nu}}{\partial x_\alpha} + \mathfrak{g}^{\beta\nu}\Gamma^{\mu}_{\beta\alpha} + \mathfrak{g}^{\mu\beta}\Gamma^{\nu}_{\alpha\beta} - \mathfrak{g}^{\mu\nu}\Gamma^{\beta}_{\alpha\beta} + \delta^{\nu}_{\alpha}\mathfrak{f}^{\mu} = 0 \tag{10}$$

the history of modern physics in terms of getting the equations right.

Newton's great achievement (161) was, in Einstein's words, to discover the concept of the differential co-efficient and the enunciation of the laws of motion in the form of total differential equations: 'perhaps the greatest intellectual stride that it has ever been granted to any man to make'. This left the concept of physical reality as purely mechanical, all change being interpreted in terms of the movement of inertial masses. Maxwell's equations (355) changed all that and introduced the notion of fields of force to replace the former theories of action at a distance. To quote Einstein once more: 'Since Maxwell's time, physical reality has been thought of as represented by continuous fields, governed by partial differential equations'. Maxwell correlated light and electricity, but gravitation could not yet be included in any general correlation of forces.

It had been repeatedly observed that Einstein's general theory of relativity (408) necessitated a pluralistic explanation of the universe. In 1925 he announced that he had resolved this difficulty, but the announcement was premature. In 1928 he attacked the problem once more, only to find that Riemann's conception of space (293 b), on which the general theory was based, would not permit of a common explanation of electromagnetic and gravitational phenomena. In a series of papers devoted to the development of 'A Uniform Theory of Gravitation and Electricity' he outlined a new theory of space with a view to the unification of all forms of activity that fall within the sphere of physics, giving them a common explanation. All that would then remain to complete a scientific unison is the correlation of the organic and the inorganic.

BIBLIOGRAPHY: See no. 408. The five papers cited are Weil nos. 147, 162, 165, 166 and 168.

417

MATTER A FORM OF ENERGY

LOUIS VICTOR, DUC DE BROGLIE (b. 1892). Ondes et Mouvements. *Paris: Gauthier-Villars, 1926*

At the end of the nineteenth century most scientists thought that matter was made up of hard atoms, which were somehow also elastic, and that light was a wave motion in the ether. Tyndall, for example, believed that the existence of the ether was as well established as the reasonableness of his fellow men. And he chided sceptics: 'The chemists who recoil from these notions of atoms and molecules accept, without hesitation, the Undulatory Theory of Light. Like you and me they one and all believe in an ether and its light-producing waves.'

These beliefs were shaken when Einstein (408) applied the quantum theory (see 391) to the photo-electric effect and showed that light there behaves as though it were particulate, made up of 'photons', and not at all as one would expect a wave motion to behave. All sorts of other phenomena could be readily explained by a wave model

(the phenomena that had convinced Tyndall and his audience) and not by a particle one. So there seemed to be two sorts of phenomenon that required two different, and incompatible, theories of light to explain them.

The simple atoms of Dalton (261) had already been modified before 1926 by the discoveries of radio-activity and the splitting of the atom; but now the Duc de Broglie—in 'Waves and Movements'—proposed an even more radical amendment. Light had been shown to behave as though it were waves and also as though it were particles; matter had been always supposed to be made up of particles, but perhaps it shared the duality of light. Perhaps indeed there might be circumstances in which matter might behave as though it were a wave.

This idea was tested and confirmed by Davisson and Germer in 1927. They directed a beam of electrons on to a crystal of metal, and found that instead of bouncing off, as particles would, the beam was diffracted; just as the X-rays had been in the experiments of von Laue and the Braggs (406). Electron diffraction has since become a useful tool for the discovery of structures.

Thus the duality of both light and matter had been established, and physicists had to come to terms with fundamental particles which defied simple theories and demanded two sets of 'complementary' descriptions, each applicable under certain circumstances, but incompatible with one another.

418

WELL-MANNERED ENGLISH

HENRY WATSON FOWLER (1858–1933). A Dictionary of Modern English Usage. *Oxford: at the Clarendon Press, 1926*

With no trace of pedantry, with a constant sense that language is a living growth, and with inimitable wit and humour, Fowler compiled this complete guide to good sense and good taste in the choice of words. It was an entirely new kind of 'dictionary', concerned as it is with the meaning of the words, the analysis of idioms, only as a part of the discipline of their proper use.

Fowler became a professional grammarian and lexicographer after resigning in 1899 as a housemaster at Sedbergh because his conscience would not allow him to prepare boys for confirmation. For some years he contributed essays to various journals, and in 1905 he and his brother, F. G. Fowler, published a translation of Lucian. This was followed in 1906 by *The King's English*, a forerunner to the present work. The brothers also produced the first abridgement of the Oxford Dictionary (371) in 1911 and H.W. alone, after his brother's death in 1918, edited the *Pocket Oxford Dictionary* in 1924.

Fowler contributed several characteristic monographs to the quietly influential series of 'tracts' issued by the Society for Pure English (1919–48); and in no. XLIII, of 1934, G. G. Coulton gave an excellent account of this firmly secluded but immensely percipient expositor of 'English as she is spoke'.

419

THE BETRAYAL OF THE INTELLECT

JULIEN BENDA (1867–1956). La Trahison des Clercs. *Paris: Grasset, 1927*

Julien Benda, philosopher and novelist, was born in Paris. He was educated at the École Centrale, which he left to become a student at the Sorbonne. His early reputation was made in the field of controversy (which he was not to desert for the rest of his life) with a series of articles in the *Revue Blanche* on the Dreyfus affair. He became associated with Charles Péguy, and in all his early works he adopted the standpoint of a complete rationalist contempt for any philosophic system which depended on resort to the emotions, sensation or intuition. This brought him into sharp conflict with Bergson, whose philosophic reputation was then at its height, and in *Le Bergsonisme*, 1912, he gave full vent to his opposition, which he followed up in other works. In 1922 he published *Belphégor*, a study of aestheticism in French society, which remains perhaps his best known book after *La Trahison des Clercs* ('The Treason of the Intelligentsia').

‹ *LES CAHIERS VERTS* ›

PUBLIÉS SOUS LA DIRECTION DE DANIEL HALÉVY

— 6 —

LA TRAHISON

DES

CLERCS

PAR

JULIEN BENDA

PARIS
BERNARD GRASSET
6 1, RUE DES SAINTS-PÈRES
1927

The publication of the latter in 1927 was undoubtedly one of the major events in political thought between the two wars. The 'Clerc' is what Benda conceived the intellectual to be, someone disengaged from the mere contingencies of existence and fighting for ideals which went beyond the demands of a given moment in space and time. In violent and brilliant invective, he attacked

the intellectuals of the nineteenth and twentieth centuries for having fallen short of this ideal by becoming the devoted advocates not of ideals, but of groups or existences, material and transient, such as a nation or a social class. The title of Benda's manifesto became a kind of catch phrase which, by a curious irony of fate, inverted its original sense, and came sometimes to be used as a term of reproach for the intellectuals who shut themselves off from the march of events in an ivory tower.

La Trahison des Clercs achieved a world-wide popularity and was translated and reprinted over and over again. Benda continued to develop his thesis in a series of works before the war. After the war, some of his magic seemed to have departed and the value of his arguments was less apparent. *La France Byzantine* aroused a storm of protest, and his later books, *Exercise d'un Interré Vif*, *Les Cahiers d'un Clerc* and others, seemed to be labouring a long-dead controversy. He died in 1956, but *La Trahison des Clercs* continues to be read; and its invigorating attack on over-involvement deserves not to be forgotten.

420

PENICILLIN

(a) ALEXANDER FLEMING (1881–1955). On the Antibacterial Action of Cultures of a Penicillium. *In:* The British Journal of Experimental Pathology. *London, 1929*
(b) ERNST BORIS CHAIN (b. 1906), HOWARD WALTER FLOREY (b. 1898), and others. Penicillin as a Chemotherapeutic Agent. *In:* The Lancet. *London, 1940*

The knowledge that some moulds, such as those growing on bread and old leather, could promote the rapid healing of wounds, seems to have been traditional in folk-medicine. The first scientific observation of the bactericidal properties of the penicillium moulds was published by John Tyndall in 1876; and Lister (316c) recorded his interest in its possibilities for wound healing. At about the same time some French physiologists coined the term 'antibiosis' to describe the use of living organisms to destroy the microbes harmful to man.

When Alexander Fleming began his work at St Mary's Hospital in London under the leadership of Sir Almroth Wright he was following the Listerian tradition and seeking new and more powerful antiseptics which could be used internally without damaging healthy tissues. It was in the course of this research that Fleming noticed the accidental contamination of a culture plate of staphylococci by a mould which had floated through the window. The colonies of this common pus-forming bacterium adjacent to the mould appeared to be destroyed by it.

The mould was identified as *penicillium notatum* and when cultures of it were developed it was found to produce a brown liquid substance which Fleming named 'penicillin' and which was shown to have a powerful destructive action on a wide range of microbes. It was also found to be a chemically complex and unstable substance which, it seemed, would be impossible to produce and store on a large scale. Many attempts at chemical analysis were fruitless and it might well have become an obscure scientific curiosity but for the work of Chain and Florey.

Chain, a refugee from Nazi oppression, had worked under Hopkins (404★), who discovered vitamins at Cambridge. In 1935 he was invited to Oxford by Florey, an Australian by birth, who was then professor of pathology. In 1938 he and Chain embarked on a systematic survey of bactericidal substances, which led them to Fleming's paper of 1929. They determined that penicillin was by far the most powerful microbe-killer yet discovered—it was found capable of inhibiting some kinds of bacterial growth at a dilution of one part in 50,000,000—and they set themselves the arduous and elusive task of isolating its active principle, elucidating its chemical structure, and producing it in the laboratory. All of this they did, and they also worked out suitable dosages for the treatment of infections susceptible to the action of the drug.

War-time conditions prohibited the manufacture in Britain of penicillin on the vast scale demanded by the emergency. This was taken up by several pharmaceutical houses in America, where the complicated problems of mass manufacture were resolved in astonishingly short order.

Fleming, Chain and Florey shared the Nobel Prize for Medicine in 1945.

421

CYCLICAL HISTORY

ARNOLD TOYNBEE (b. 1889). A Study of History. 10 vols. Oxford University Press, 1934–54

Toynbee, a nephew of the social reformer of the same name, started his academic career as professor of Byzantine history and subsequently became professor of international history and director of Chatham House, the Royal Institute of International Affairs. His extension and modification of the historical theories of Spengler (410) must therefore be acknowledged as the work of a professional, although it has attracted much the same objections and criticisms as that of the German amateur to whom Toynbee is undoubtedly indebted more deeply than he cares to admit.

Toynbee's gigantic study was bought, and left unread, by the same European and American public who, during the previous decade or two, had fallen for Spengler; abridgements, still over one thousand pages long, were necessary to make it more palatable and easier to digest. Toynbee extended the number of civilizations to twenty-one, or including some minor groups, twenty-six. With deeper insight than Spengler possessed he did not view these 'significant units' of history in isolation but in cross-fertilizing 'filiation and apparentation'. Spengler's biological, actually materialistic, standpoint he abandoned. The great universal religions have been assigned their proper place in a world-history which spurns the traditional divisions into nations and periods; and the fact is stressed that religious movements are not tied to the country of their origin.

Whether Toynbee's exposition of the course of history can be transformed from a stimulating theory into a body of accepted data, only later generations of historians will be able to tell.

422

THE ATOM BOMB

(a) ENRICO FERMI and others (Assignors to G. M. Giannini & Co.). Method for increasing the Efficiency of Nuclear Reactions and Products (Patent Application, London)—Process for the Production of Radioactive Substances (Patent Application, Washington), 1935
(b) LISE MEITNER and O. R. FRISCH. Disintegration of Uranium by Neutrons: a new type of Nuclear Reaction. In: Nature. London, 1939
(c) O. R. FRISCH. Physical Evidence for the Division of Heavy Nuclei under Neutron Bombardment. Ibid. 1939
(d) H. VON HALBAN, Jun., F. JOLIOT and L. KOWARSKI. Liberation of Neutrons in the Nuclear Explosion of Uranium. Ibid. 1939
(e) HENRY DE WOLF SMYTH. A General Account of the Development of Methods of using Atomic Energy for Military Purposes. Washington, D.C., 1945

Although Nagaoka outlined a Saturnian atom in 1904 it was Rutherford (411) in 1911 who rounded out the picture and reinforced it experimentally. He concluded that the atom was composed of a positively charged nucleus surrounded by negatively charged electrons rotating in peripheral orbits. In 1904, and more specifically in 1920, he referred to the possibility of an atom containing an uncharged particle.

In 1932 James Chadwick proved the existence of atomic particles carrying no electric charge which, for this reason, he called 'neutrons'.

In 1934 Senator Corbino, head of the physics department at the University of Rome, urged Enrico Fermi and his collaborators, among whom was Bruno Pontecorvo, to patent a process they had perfected for the production of artificial radio-activity by slow neutron bombardment. This process was a by-product of repetitions and enlargements of a discovery by Irène Curie and her husband Frédéric Joliot that the bombardment of certain light elements with alpha particles induced radio-activity.

Further experiments conducted in 1938 at Berlin by Hahn and Strassman were reported to Lise Meitner, an Austrian scientist who had fled to Copenhagen to escape religious persecution. She and her nephew, O. R. Frisch, working in Nils Bohr's laboratory, found the true explanation of these phenomena. The interpolation of a neutron into the nucleus of a uranium atom caused it to divide into two parts and to release energy amounting to about 200,000,000 electron volts. This process bore such a close similarity to the division of a living cell that Frisch suggested the use of the term 'fission' to describe it.

Even before the publication in Nature of the findings of Meitner and Frisch, Bohr had described their work to a session of the American Physical Society in Washington, and the experiments were widely repeated in several countries.

Halban, Joliot and Kowarski established the theoretical possibility of a self-perpetuating reaction chain. Furthermore, in a paper published in the *Physical Review* two days before war broke out, Bohr and his American student J. A. Wheeler published a paper in which the principles governing nuclear fission were clearly defined.

All of this information was therefore in the public domain; but the only practical use suggested for it was implied in the Fermi patent for producing radio-active isotopes, which has been a continued blessing to medical and physiological research.

Fermi's process, however, also isolated as by-products two new elements, heavier than uranium, which by analogy, were called 'neptunium' and 'plutonium'. The latter was later found to be fissionable.

Frisch was on a visit to England when war broke out and joined R. E. Peierls, another refugee, in Birmingham. In 1940, in the *Annual Reports on the Progress of Chemistry*, Frisch wrote to allay fears of the possibility of a super-bomb on the grounds that, if not impossible to produce, its prohibitive cost would be totally disproportionate to its limited effect.

From this point onwards the story is continued in secret and, at the time, unpublished memoranda and reports. The very process of writing his reassuring report caused Frisch to reconsider his conclusions and, still in 1940, in three typed foolscap pages, he and Peierls declared the bomb to be feasible, defined its critical size and worked out the safeguards and the method of detonating it. But, being enemy aliens, they were excluded from the British MAUD Committee when it was formed in 1940 to investigate, and ultimately to declare practicable, the manufacture of an atom bomb.

This thrilling and horrific story is admirably told and documented by Margaret Gowing, the historian and archivist of the Atomic Energy Authority, in *Britain and Atomic Energy*, 1964.

Finally, there was published on 12 August 1945 (only six days after Hiroshima) the remarkably full and candid account of the development work carried out between 1940 and 1945 by the American-directed but internationally recruited team of physicists, under the code name of 'Manhattan District', which culminated in the production of the first atomic bomb. Dalton's chickens had come home to roost with a vengeance.

Compiled by Professor Smyth of Princeton, a consultant to the 'Manhattan District' project at Los Alamos, whose commandant General L. R. Groves provided the foreword, 'the Smyth Report', as it is familiarly known, was published at one dollar by the U.S. Superintendent of Documents. (It was preceded by a preliminary mimeographed version prepared for press use.)

423
MANAGED ECONOMICS

JOHN MAYNARD KEYNES (1883–1946). The General Theory of Employment, Interest and Money. *London: Macmillan, 1936*

Keynes's father was a lecturer in moral science deeply versed in political economy. He grew up under the influence of the Cambridge economists of Alfred Marshall's generation (as well as G. E. Moore's *Principia Ethica*) and although his first love was mathematics—his fellowship dissertation at King's was on the theory of probability—he turned in 1908 to teaching economics at Cambridge. In 1915 he was summoned thence to Whitehall, and he was the principal representative of the British Treasury at the Peace Conference in 1919.

He soon resigned, in protest against the terms imposed on the Central Powers, and rapidly produced *The Economic Consequences of the Peace*, 1919. In 1922 came *A Revision of the Treaty*, in which he expounded the defects of what he described as 'a Peace, which if it is carried into effect, must impair, yet further, when it might have restored, the delicate, complicated organisation...through which the European peoples alone can employ themselves and live'. The violence of the controversy aroused by these two books is now difficult to appreciate. Even while they were being written many of his prophecies came true and, in the light of subsequent history, the foresight of his conclusions would be uncanny did they not proceed so inevitably from his premises.

The world-wide slump after 1929 prompted Keynes to attempt an explanation of, and new methods for controlling, the vagaries of the trade-cycle. First in *A Treatise on Money*, 1930, and later in his *General Theory*, he subjected the definitions and theories of the classical school of economists to a penetrating scrutiny and found them seriously inadequate and inaccurate. By-passing what he termed the 'underworlds' of Marx (359), Gesell and Major Douglas, he propounded a hardly less unorthodox programme for national and international official monetary policies. A national budget, over and above its function of providing a national income, should be used as a major instrument in planning the national economy. The regulation of the trade-cycle—that is to say the control of booms and slumps, the level of employment, the wage-scale and the flow of investment—must be the responsibility of governments. Lost equilibrium in a national economy could and should be restored by official action and not abandoned to *laisser faire*.

In 1936, although Roosevelt's 'New Deal' had utilized Keynesian prescriptions, *The General Theory* ('on which', says *D.N.B.*, 'his fame as the outstanding economist of his generation must rest') threw the economists of the world into two violently opposed camps. Yet eight years later Keynes was to dominate the international conference at Bretton Woods, out of which came the International Monetary Fund and the World Bank; and his influence during the ensuing decades, even on his theoretical opponents, has been such that a highly placed American official recently remarked that 'we are all Keynesians today'.

FINAL

Subject to full freedom of proof correction

VOLUME II BOOK 3

CHAPTER XII

ALONE

July, 1940

424

THE LION'S VOICE

Winston Leonard Spencer Churchill (1874–1965). A Speech in the House of Commons, 20 August 1940. *In*: Parliamentary Debates. *London: His Majesty's Stationery Office, 1940*

If the Gettysburg Address (351) is one of the most moving statements of democracy confronted by tragedy, Churchill's historic exhortations are its equal in their ringing assertion of democracy confronting the seemingly irresistible forces of tyranny. (Lincoln and Churchill were far more than a century apart in temperament, but they shared a genius for language.)

At the time when Great Britain stood alone against the weight of Nazi and Fascist aggression, her allies either prostrate or yet to join her, the gap between destruction and survival seemed a very narrow one. In it stood nothing much but the resolution of the islanders and the indomitable figure of their Prime Minister. When the crunch came, it was the fighter pilots of the Royal Air Force of whom he could justly say, in this speech, that 'never in the field of human conflict was so much owed by so many to so few'. He himself maintained in later years that it was the people of Britain who had the lion's heart; that he was merely privileged to make it roar. His countrymen know better. It was Churchill, by the force of his dauntless personality, by an eloquence that matched the hour, who fired their blood.

This (as Sir Isaiah Berlin has written), was 'a man larger than life, composed of bigger and simpler elements than ordinary men, a gigantic historical figure during his own lifetime, superhumanly bold, strong and imaginative... an orator of prodigious powers, the saviour of his country, a mythical hero who belongs to legend as much as to reality, the largest human being of our time'.

LEFT: from one of the seventy-five copies printed for the author
prior to the publication of *The Second World War*
(by courtesy of Desmond Flower, Esq., M.C.)

INDEX

References are to the *entry numbers*, except for the small roman numerals, which refer to the introductory pagination.

All titles of books or articles mentioned in the text have been included (but not the suffixed bibliographies and other reference books). Where the book is the subject of an entry, the reference is in heavy type. These therefore indicate immediately the main entry (or entries) on the author in question. Actual titles of books are in italics; translated titles, and titles of contributions to periodicals, are in roman within quotes.

Printers and publishers are indexed (and identified as such) only when they are mentioned in the text.